D1242373

Cell Culture and Somatic Variation

Morgan Harris

UNIVERSITY OF CALIFORNIA AT BERKELEY

Cell Culture
and Somatic Variation

HOLT, RINEHART AND WINSTON

New York   Chicago   San Francisco

Toronto   London

146591

Preface

This book deals with the newly emerging field of somatic cell heredity, broadly interpreted to include developmental, genetic, and neoplastic changes in differentiated cells and tissues. It is intended as a synthesis and summary of the research literature bearing on these topics, much of which presently exists in widely scattered form. The discussion has been developed with cell culture, and to a lesser extent, tissue transplantation, as the principal experimental approaches. Through these techniques, isolated cell populations can be created for the analysis of somatic change. Considered in such a framework, somatic variation can be expressed by a series of specific processes—for example, differentiation and dedifferentiation in cell groupings, the evolution of growth forms and chromosome patterns, nutritional shifts, antigenic changes, the development of resistance to drugs or other extrinsic agents, and carcinogenesis *in vitro*. The concepts and patterns that emerge from these studies require for their interpretation a background of more general information. For this reason, the treatment of population dynamics in cell cultures and transplant systems is here preceded by an outline of developmental genetics, tumor biology, and microbial variation.

The present account cuts freely across established disciplines in describing mechanisms that operate in somatic variation at the cellular level. No claim can be made for completeness in this regard, or for adequacy in relating separate approaches. There can be little question, however, that a more unified picture is desirable. Somatic cell heredity, like growth, is still a frontier field. Some of the most significant developments will continue to arise in borderline areas, through links created between focal points of research. The establishment of cross-correlations can be facilitated by increased communication between embryologists, geneticists, pathologists, and other students of cellular change. This book attempts to supply in part the necessary information and to bridge certain gaps that have arisen through parallel rather than complementary studies on somatic cells and their information systems.

In its final form, the volume at hand reflects the generous assistance of friends and associates. I am particularly grateful to Dr. Curt Stern and Dr. Frank Ruddle, both of whom read the entire manuscript and offered many helpful suggestions. Additional criticism and comment were provided by the following individuals, to whom I am indebted for their willingness to review chapters appropriate to their special fields: Dr. E. A. Adelberg, Dr. R. E. Billingham, Dr. R. W. Briggs, Dr. Harry Eagle, Dr. Glenn Fischer, Dr. T. C. Hsu, Dr. George Klein, Dr. Harry Rubin, Dr. K. K. Sanford, and Dr. W. Szybalski. In assembling the illustrations, I have made use of numerous photographs that were provided by individual investigators from original sources. It is a pleasure to acknowledge their generosity, and credit in each case is specified with the corresponding text figure. The line drawings that accompany the text were prepared directly or adapted from published sources by Mrs. Emily Reid, with patience and skill. To Dame Honor B. Fell I wish to express my appreciation for courtesies extended during a sabbatical year at the Strangeways Research Laboratory, Cambridge, England, and to the John Simon Guggenheim Foundation for a fellowship provided during the same period. Lastly, my wife has provided continuous advice and assistance in the preparation of this book. Much of the bibliographic labor as well as the typing of the manuscript became her responsibility, and without this effective collaboration the work would still be far from complete.

M. H.

Berkeley, California
February, 1964

Contents

Three types of
somatic variation

chapter 1 Cellular transformation is a familiar event in multicellular organisms, and assumes many forms. Somatic variation is implicit, for example, in the ordered sequences of embryonic development, and local foci of differentiation persist into later stages. The implementation of these processes is distinctive, for morphogenetic conversions of cellular phenotypes seem to proceed without modification of hereditary determinants. However, genetic changes are by no means excluded at the somatic level, and can be documented on occasion during developmental stages. Isolated mutations or chromosome changes within the cells of embryonic rudiments sometimes occur, and may give rise to patches of cells with a variant phenotype. By inference, similar alterations may take place in the genetic apparatus of differentiated cells, although their detection in this case is more difficult. More spectacular examples of unprogramed variation within somatic cells can be found in the origin and evolution of tumors. The basis for neoplastic conversion is uncertain, and it is not clear whether transformation in this case rests on genetic alteration, an aberrant sequence of development, or some more distinctive process. Biologically, however, tumors represent a unique degree of freedom in multicellular systems. Evidently the autonomy of somatic units is a persistent, if largely potential, property within organized cell groupings. Developmental, genetic, and neoplastic changes thus constitute distinct modalities of somatic variation when viewed at a purely operational level. Their closer identification in terms of basic mechanisms presents an outstanding series of problems.

Conceptually, the partial processes of somatic variation can for convenience be assigned to alternative categories. Those that depend on a recasting of hereditary determinants stand in contrast to shifts

1

which take place against a constant cellular genome. In this respect, a useful distinction can be made between genetic and epigenetic control systems (Nanney, 1958). Truly genetic mechanisms are concerned with the preservation and replication of information in structural form; for example, the molecular configurations of deoxyribonucleic acid or the individuality of self-duplicating cytoplasmic organelles. Epigenetic mechanisms, on the other hand, regulate the expression of genetic information. They serve to translate structural symbols into phenotypic reality. Since control systems at the effector level may be modulated to yield alternative or multiple end products, it follows that epigenetic as well as genetic changes can provide a basis for heritable variation. Accordingly these two patterns form the central themes of somatic cell inheritance. Much effort has been expended, directly or indirectly, to give these distinctions a substantial meaning in experimental terms. The relevant data are to be found in a broad spectrum of studies of embryonic differentiation, developmental genetics, and experimental carcinogenesis, with which the present discussion begins. In brief perspective, this information provides a backdrop for more detailed descriptions of variation in isolated cell systems.

THE ESTABLISHMENT OF CELLULAR SPECIFICITY

The emergence of cell lineages in specific form from more general precursors is one of the hallmarks of embryonic development. These products often display remarkable stability. While the reversibility or irreversibility of differentiation has long been debated, it is obvious that *in situ* each cell type perpetuates a characteristic pattern. The constancy of end products is seen with particular clarity in those instances where differentiation is not accompanied by the cessation of cell division. In embryonic cartilage, for example, the chondrocytes can fix inorganic sulfate and elaborate extracellular matrix, and these potentials are transmitted in stable fashion to mitotic derivatives. Aside from their predictability and occurrence in organized patterns, developmental changes may thus on occasion simulate genetic change. Nevertheless, it is clear that cellular specificity in embryonic differentiation originates largely, if not entirely, by epigenetic means. Evidence for this well-known generalization has been accumulating for many years, and some of the critical proofs are classics in the biological literature.

Types of Developmental Patterns   The early history of experimental embryology has as one of its most colorful concepts the "germ plasm" theory of August Weismann (1892). This explanation sought to explain the facts of heredity as well as the basic mechanisms of development. According to Weismann, the chromosomes of the zygote contain a large number of determinants, which correspond to the parts of the embryo ultimately to be formed. These were assumed to persist as an intact array within the line giving rise to the germ cells, a concept still preserved in the phrase "continuity of the germ plasm." A very different fate, however, was depicted for the developing somatic cells. At each division of these units, a segregation of determinants was thought to occur. Finally, only one kind of determinant remained, in accordance with which the end products of differentiation emerged.

Weismann's idea of "unpacking" the nucleus was an attractive mechanism to explain the multiplicity of cell types as races of cells in developing embryos. It did not, however, stand up to experimental tests. One of the earliest of these was based on a separation of the embryo into parts. Driesch (1891), in a historic paper, described the results of dissociating sea urchin embryos at the two-cell stage by means of shaking. The isolated blastomeres were allowed to develop further, but did not differentiate into part embryos as expected. Instead, both formed complete and normally proportioned individuals. Thus, in the two-cell stage at least, the sea urchin nuclei are equivalent and totipotent; that is, each nucleus in the presence of competent cytoplasmic systems can give rise to a complete embryo. Many experiments have confirmed these results and have shown that isolated blastomeres from the early stages of a number of other embryos retain a full range of formative potentialities. Somatic cells, however, do not remain equipotential indefinitely. With continuing development, there is a progressive restriction in capability. In the sea urchin, for example, occasional cells at the 8-cell stage may form complete individuals, but cells isolated from the animal or vegetal regions of later cleavage stages give rise to partial larvae only (Hörstadius, 1939).

Evidence that the nuclei are undifferentiated during early development can also be found in other types of experiments. Among these are a number of investigations performed by pioneer workers to test the effect of pressure on cleavage. If the eggs of sea urchins (Driesch, 1892) or of frogs (Hertwig, 1893) are placed between two glass plates under pressure, cleavage continues to occur. A unidimensional aggregate of cells arises under these conditions, since all cleavage planes are oriented perpendicular to the glass surfaces. If the pressure is then relieved, however, the eggs regulate to form normal embryos. This result is obtained despite the fact that the topographic relations of individual nuclei are quite different from what would be the case in an intact

embryo. The interchangeability of nuclei in early stages is further documented by the studies of Seidel (1932), made on embryos of the dragon-
fly *Platycnemius pennipes*. In the eggs of insects, the cleavage nuclei
multiply initially in an undivided cytoplasmic mass and migrate only
later to various positions in the elongate embryo, where cell boundaries
are established and further development occurs. Seidel showed that
there is no regional specialization of the nuclei during this process. If
one of the first two cleavage nuclei is destroyed by local application of
ultraviolet light, descendants of the other proceed to nucleate the entire
egg, and differentiation occurs normally. An equally typical pattern of
development is observed if the migration of nuclei into the posterior
part of the embryo is delayed, so that this region is provided with the
products of the eighth rather than the fourth cleavage.

Perhaps the most striking demonstration of nuclear equivalence in
early stages is to be seen in Spemann's "noose" experiment (Spemann,
1928, 1938). Using a fine loop of hair, Spemann constricted the egg of
the European newt, *Triturus* (*Triton*), shortly after fertilization had
taken place (see Figure 1.1). Initially the noose was passed around
animal and vegetal poles and was oriented so as to bisect symmetrically
the gray crescent. This structure, a region of cytoplasmic specialization,
appears as a pale area on one side of the amphibian zygote. The embryo
constricted in this way becomes dumbbell-shaped, with the egg nucleus
on one side of the noose. The constriction in Spemann's experiment was
left incomplete, however, so that an open cytoplasmic bridge remained
between the two halves of the original egg. Under these conditions,
cleavage occurs normally on the nucleated side, but the other half of
the original egg remains unsegmented. Spemann noted, however, that
occasionally a cleavage nucleus at the 16- or 32-cell stage might pass
across through the persisting cytoplasmic bridge to the adjoining blasto-
mere. When this took place, cleavage was initiated in the previously
undivided cytoplasm. The noose could then be tightened so as to separate
the two original halves of the egg completely, and under these conditions, both halves continue to develop. In such cases, twin larvae are
eventually produced. These experiments show unmistakably that even
as late as the 16- or 32-cell stage, nuclei of the newt embryo are still
totipotent and can initiate the full range of embryonic differentiation.

Information of many kinds thus demonstrates that the establishment
of specificity in the developing embryo depends on cytoplasmic differentiation, rather than on the progressive segregation of nuclear determinants
as Weismann had supposed. It is equally obvious, however, that development is closely determined by nuclear factors and must be viewed as
a function of gene actions, ordered in time and space. Nucleocytoplasmic

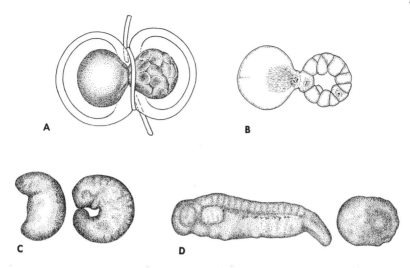

FIG. 1.1. Spemann's noose experiment. (A) Egg of European newt, *Triturus*, constricted soon after fertilization by a loop of hair in the median plane. Cleavage has occurred on one side only. (B) Diagram of a similar embryo in section, showing eventual passage of a cleavage nucleus across the persistent cytoplasmic bridge. (C) Later stage, showing the formation of twins. Embryo at left is normal in appearance, but retarded in development, owing to delayed nucleation of egg cytoplasm. (D) Two embryos resulting from a frontal constriction of the fertilized egg. The dorsal half forms a normally proportioned embryo, whether provided initially or later with a nucleus. The ventral half, lacking gray crescent material, forms only a rounded mass without external differentiation. (Redrawn from Fankhauser, 1930, and Spemann, 1938.)

interactions thus hold the key to morphogenetic change, a conclusion reached by experimental embryologists well before the turn of the century. Among others, Driesch (1894), Morgan (1934), and Waddington (1956) have pointed out that the sequential activation of genes in development can be visualized as a feedback relationship between nucleus and cytoplasm. Within the fertilized egg, or early embryo, a differential distribution of cytoplasmic substances occurs, and elicits a complementary pattern of gene action in the cells concerned. The cytoplasmic systems are further modified in different directions, calling forth a new individuation in operation at the genic level. This process may be mediated by activators and repressors for specific genetic loci, which come into being, disappear, or undergo modification as the developmental prospectus unfolds. "Operator" genes may turn on or turn off particular sequences of gene action in accordance with the constellation of factors present at the cytoplasmic level (see Chapter 2). Conceptually, at least, it is thus possible to visualize the processes of cytoplasmic localization and specialization taking place against the background of a constant genotype.

Regardless of the exact mechanism of cytoplasmic specialization, there are wide differences in the extent and timing of this process among different embryos. A substantial part of the embryological literature during the early part of the present century was devoted to the analysis of these differences. The classic studies of E. B. Wilson, Conklin, and others showed that a precocious localization of morphogenetic substances occurs in the eggs of a number of invertebrate groups such as the ctenophores, annelids, molluscs, and tunicates. In these embryos, regional specialization is pronounced even at the time of fertilization and early cleavage. Such germinal localizations, as they were called, can be illustrated by the investigations of Conklin (1905, 1931) on the ascidian tunicate, *Cynthia* (*Styela*). In this embryo, as in a number of others, visible differences exist in the various regions. These can be described in terms of granules, mitochondria, or other inclusions of different color and appearance. Thus, in *Cynthia*, four cytoplasmic regions are evident in an egg that has completed the first cleavage (Conklin, 1905). The animal hemisphere consists of a colorless cytoplasm, whereas in the region of the vegetal pole, the cytoplasm is a contrasting gray. In addition, a light-gray crescentic area appears on one side of the egg and a yellow crescent on the opposite side. Because these cellular inclusions can be distinguished for some time in development, it is possible to show that the nervous system and notochord originate from the gray crescent and mesoderm from the yellow crescent. Ectoderm is derived from the clear cytoplasm of the animal hemisphere and the gray vegetal region produces endoderm. The colored granules or mitochondria are thus useful "markers" for the prospective developmental fates of specific regions, although the inclusions as such seem to have little significance. Conklin (1931) showed that the relative position of these particles can be altered by centrifuging eggs of *Cynthia* without seriously deranging development. However, he felt that the underlying ground substance of the cytoplasm did possess regional specializations, for if part of the early embryo was injured or removed, the remainder formed only those parts corresponding to its normal developmental fate. Complete individuals are not ordinarily obtained from isolated blastomeres. The egg of *Cynthia* thus seemed to represent a patchwork of morphogenetic substances, distributed during cleavage in orderly fashion to give rise to various parts of the future embryo. A similar picture emerged from the studies of E. B. Wilson (1904) on the mollusc *Dentalium* and from the work of various investigators on a number of other eggs.

As a result of a number of such studies, the concepts of mosaic and regulatory eggs came into being. The latter category is typified by the sea urchin embryo, in which differential distribution of cytoplasmic components does not occur in early cleavage stages, or is easily reversible. By contrast, mosaic eggs such as *Cynthia* or *Dentalium* can be pictured in terms of an early segregation of morphogenetic substances into specific cytoplasmic regions, which are thereby correspondingly limited in developmental potentialities. This apparent dualism in organization of the egg was intriguing to early investigators, and discussions of the difference dominated morphogenesis for a number of years. On the basis of more recent studies, however, it does not appear that any qualitative distinction can be made between the patterns of mosaic and regulatory eggs (Grobstein, 1959; Brachet, 1960). It is now known that twinning or other examples of regulation can be observed in some mosaic eggs by variation of the techniques used earlier. On the other hand, even the blastomeres of the sea urchin assume a mosaic character after the first few cleavages (Hörstadius, 1939). Cytoplasmic localization is thus a universal feature of differentiation. Although the time relationships of this process may vary among different embryos, it seems doubtful that these distinctions are of any fundamental significance.

Cytoplasmic localization and the segregation of morphogenetic substances by cleavage were the first mechanisms of embryonic differentiation to be demonstrated in clear-cut fashion by experimental means. These were soon followed by the discovery that developmental patterns can also be established by a more dynamic process, involving the interaction of embryonic rudiments. This phenomenon, termed embryonic induction, is associated particularly with the name of Spemann, although many investigators have joined in establishing its broad validity as a developmental principle. The nature of inductive processes became known largely as a result of studies by Spemann and others on the formation of the eye in amphibian embryos (see Spemann, 1938). In amphibia, as in other vertebrates, differentiation of the lens of the eye is a sequential process, involving outgrowth of the optic vesicle from the embryonic brain and contact with the overlying ectoderm. The question posed initially was whether the association of optic cup and lens-forming ectoderm is fortuitous or represents a causal relationship. In some embryos the lens proved to be self-differentiating, but the more typical finding was a correlative relationship with the optic cup. In *Rana fusca* or *R. palustris*, for example, removal of the optic vesicle prevents formation of the lens, whereas if the optic cup is implanted beneath the trunk ectoderm, a lens is elicited from ectodermal cells that would not otherwise form such a structure (Lewis, 1904; Spemann,

1912). Other induction systems were subsequently discovered in the embryos of amphibia and other types of animals. It was not until later, however, that the fundamental role of organizers in development was perceived. The basic discovery that opened up this new vista was the induction of secondary embryos in amphibia by the implantation of embryonic rudiments from the early gastrula stage (Spemann and Mangold, 1924; Spemann, 1938). In these experiments a piece of chordamesoderm was excised from the dorsal lip of the blastopore in an egg at the early gastrula stage. This block of cells was then grafted to the lateral marginal zone of another embryo and became covered over with host ectoderm. In this location, a new system of embryonic organization subsequently developed, complete with nervous system, notochord, somites, and other axial structures (see Figure 1.2). By making use of two species of newts whose cells differ in degree of pigmentation, Spemann and Mangold were able to distinguish the cells of host and graft. Rather than merely undergoing transformation, the implant had served as an organizer to implement a far-reaching reorganization within adjacent host tissues. Some parts of the secondary embryo, such as the nervous system, were derived entirely from host cells; other structures were composite in nature, derived partly from the graft and partly from the host.

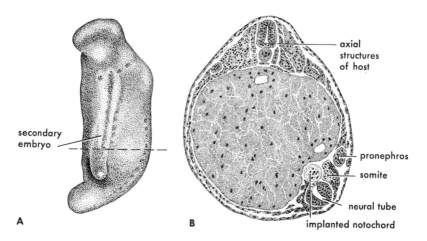

A   **B**

FIG. 1.2.   Induction of a secondary embryo in *Triturus* by means of grafted chordamesoderm. (A) Host embryo bearing an accessory set of axial structures on the left side. Note two rows of somites, and ear vesicles at anterior end of neural tube. (B) Cross-section along plane indicated by dotted line in (A). Differences in pigmentation of cells show that secondary embryo is derived from tissues of both graft and host. (Redrawn from Spemann and Mangold, 1924.)

This spectacular result ushered in a new era of research in experimental embryology, characterized by a search for the mechanisms of induction and an extension of the organizer principle to numerous embryonic systems. In spite of a vast amount of work, however, the exact nature of inductive processes has proved to be singularly elusive (Oppenheimer, 1959; Balinsky, 1960). The difficulty, a familiar one from experimental study of such processes as parthenogenesis and carcinogenesis, is the multiplicity of agents that can bring about inductions. Sterols, fatty acids, proteins, nucleic acids, and many other specific factors have all been championed at one time or another as specific organizers. The complexity of induction can be illustrated by considering the conditions under which nervous tissue may arise experimentally from neutral amphibian ectoderm. These include the addition of extracts from a wide variety of tissues and organs, as well as various pure chemical substances, and even simple treatments in some cases such as the alteration of pH, the use of distilled water instead of salt solution, or the withdrawal of calcium from the external medium. Findings of this type have led to a change in emphasis in the study of induction. It appears more profitable to characterize reacting systems in chemical and physical terms rather than to continue the search for master molecules that may direct specific pathways of differentiation (Holtfreter, 1951).

Viewed from the cellular standpoint, therefore, the establishment of specificity as development proceeds begins with cytoplasmic localizations at an early stage, and may be conditioned in some cases by primary inductions that impose a regional pattern, channeling the further individuation of populations. The mechanisms associated with the terminal specification of cell types are less clear. These final phases of cellular differentiation have usually been assumed to be under the control of extrinsic factors. Such views find expression in the gradient-field theory of Huxley and De Beer (1934) or the concept of morphogenetic fields as developed by Weiss (1939). The validity of these interpretations has been brought into question, however, by the results of studies made with dissociated populations of embryonic cells (Chapter 3). The conflict that arises is put into striking perspective by the recent experiments of Weiss and Taylor (1960). In these studies, skin, liver, and kidney were removed from 8- to 14-day chick embryos, at which time these organs are already at an advanced stage of differentiation. By means of tryptic digestion, the excised fragments were dissociated into the form of single cell suspensions and deposited as random aggregates on the chorioallantoic membrane of host embryos for cultivation. Surprisingly, these scrambled aggregates do not give rise to chaotic mixtures, but are re-formed instead into whole organs remarkably normal in histogenetic and morphogenetic detail. In the absence of external gradients or fields, the information for this complex series of processes must clearly be derived from the cells themselves. Whether these morphogenetic capabilities develop progressively within aggregates or are conferred by previous inductions that merely persist through the reassortment process, is yet to be determined. Thus the mechanisms of terminal individuation are still an open question.

Nuclear Transplantation and Differentiation The classical approaches to cellular differentiation, which have been outlined in the preceding discussion, are based primarily on the assumption of an unaltered background of nuclear competence. Explicitly or implicitly, the equivalence of nuclei in early cleavage stages has been generalized to imply that somatic nuclei remain undifferentiated throughout life. Until recently, there has been little or no information that could challenge such an assertion or provide a basis for re-examination. The development of techniques for nuclear transplantation removes this limitation and opens up a new series of problems for investigation. Although special conditions are required for successful transfer, the results that have been obtained are of fundamental significance.

Methods for nuclear transplantation were first described by Comandon and De Fonbrune (1939) in the course of studies on amoebae. Working with *Amoeba sphaeronucleus*, they found that if two individuals are placed in close apposition, the nucleus of one can be pushed with a blunt glass probe into the cytoplasm of the other. Although transfers initiated in this way have proved useful for genetic studies with protozoa (Chapter 2), other techniques are required for the more delicate cells and nuclei of higher organisms. An effective solution has been to employ enucleated eggs as recipients for single nuclei released experimentally from other cells. This new departure was devised by Briggs and King (1952) for amphibian embryos, with the object of determining whether differentiation involves qualitative changes in the nucleus as well as in the cytoplasm. A schematic picture of the procedure employed is given by Figure 1.3. *Rana pipiens* offers convenient material, since the egg nucleus in this form is situated just beneath the animal pole at the time of ovulation. The unfertilized egg can be activated by pricking, after which the egg nucleus is easily removed with a fine glass needle (Porter, 1939). Nuclei for implantation are obtained from single embryonic cells, which are disrupted in a micropipette of appropriate size. The crushing of peripheral structures does not damage the nucleus as long as contact with saline solution or other artificial media is avoided. For protection, it is necessary to sur-

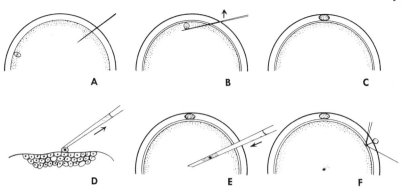

FIG. 1.3. Technique devised by Briggs and King for nuclear transplantation in *Rana pipiens*. (A–C) Steps in removal of the egg nucleus. The unfertilized egg is activated by pricking, and rotates, bringing the nucleus upper-
most. Enucleation is accomplished with a glass needle. (D–F) Transfer of a
donor nucleus into the enucleated egg. A loosened cell from another embryo
is drawn up into a fine pipette, of diameter small enough to crush the cell
surface without injuring the nucleus. The broken cell is then injected into the
recipient cytoplasm, and the canal of entry severed with glass needles.
(Redrawn from Briggs and King, 1955. Copyright, Princeton University Press.)

round the nucleus with its own cytoplasmic remnants during injection
into the recipient egg. The latter, it should be emphasized, does not
undergo cleavage unless a competent nucleus is introduced. Thus the
enucleated egg provides an assay system in which the degree and kind
of development reveal the potentialities of individual nuclei.

With these techniques, the question of whether developmental
equivalence of nuclei extends beyond the cleavage period can be approached experimentally. In their initial studies, Briggs and King (1952,
1953) selected cells from the animal hemisphere of late blastulae or
early gastrulae as donors. Normal cleavage took place in approximately
one-third of the eggs receiving nuclei; of these, approximately two-thirds
continued to develop, with the formation of normal or nearly normal
tadpoles. With improvements in method, the number of eggs with
blastula nuclei that undergo complete cleavage rises to over half, and
85 percent or more develop into normal larvae (King and Briggs, 1955;
Briggs and King, 1959). Even in the late blastula or the early gastrula
stage, therefore, many at least of the somatic nuclei are still capable
of initiating the full sequence of developmental processes if placed in
a competent egg. A different picture emerges when donor cells are taken
from older embryos. If, for example, nuclei are transplanted from cells
of the chordamesoderm or presumptive medullary plate of the late
gastrula, development of the recipient eggs is much more restricted

(King and Briggs, 1954, 1955). In both cases, cleavage occurs in only a minority of implanted eggs, and the further differentiation of such embryos is even more abnormal. About half cease to develop as blastulae or gastrulae; the majority of others undergo developmental arrest at neurula or postneurula stages. Technical considerations in the transplantation procedure do not account for this declining capability. It appears rather that nuclei become specialized as development proceeds, and lose progressively their ability to promote the full range of developmental processes.

These conclusions have been strengthened by studies directed more specifically toward the changing properties of endodermal nuclei as differentiation proceeds (Briggs and King, 1957, 1960). If endoderm nuclei from the vegetal pole of early gastrulae are used, the degree of successful development obtained is only slightly less than that with blastula nuclei. About half of the transplant-embryos are indistinguishable from controls, even when reared through metamorphosis, but when nuclei from the midgut at the end of gastrulation are tested, the majority give rise to embryos with prominent defects (see Figure 1.4). To some extent these deficiencies appear to reflect the developmental fate of the

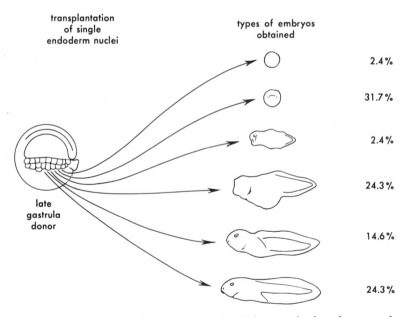

FIG. 1.4. Developmental potentialities of endoderm nuclei from late gastrula of *R. pipiens*. Single nuclei from these cells, when transferred to enucleated eggs, are for the most part incapable of promoting normal differentiation. (After King and Briggs, 1956.)

donor cells. Thus, most of the transplant-embryos with nuclei from gastrula midgut are deficient in ectodermal derivatives, although structures formed from endoderm are normal, and both notochord and somites appear. The developmental potential of endoderm nuclei appears to be even more drastically curtailed at later stages. When nuclei are taken from midgut cells of tailbud embryos, only a small minority of implanted eggs undergo cleavage, and of these, almost all are arrested as blastulae or early gastrulae.

The provocative studies done by Briggs and King on R. *pipiens* have led to similar investigations on the eggs and embryos of other amphibians. Although the large cells of urodeles would appear to offer the material of choice for nuclear transfers, early attempts to secure development with transplanted nuclei were unpromising (Waddington and Pantelouris, 1953; Lehman, 1955). These difficulties may be technical in nature rather than a reflection of differences in timing or degree of nuclear differentiation in urodeles. It is now clear, for example, that nuclear transplantations may be carried out efficiently in eggs of the Mexican axolotl (*Siredon*), provided enucleation and activation of the recipient egg are accomplished by new methods appropriate to this material (Signoret, Briggs, and Humphrey, 1962). The necessary conditions include the use of heat treatment for activation, ultraviolet irradiation for enucleation, and a delay of 2 to 4 hours after heat shock before implantation of donor nuclei. When these requirements are met, the implantation of blastula nuclei into axolotl eggs leads to cleavage in nearly every instance. More than half of these transplant-embryos develop into postneurula stages and some form larvae as well. The prospective usefulness of urodele as well as anuran materials for the study of nuclear differentiation seems established by these studies, although the exact patterns of change in the axolotl and other species remain to be worked out.

The chief extension of the work done by Briggs and King on R. *pipiens*, however, lies in the extensive experiments performed by Gurdon and his collaborators on the eggs and cells of the African clawed toad, *Xenopus laevis* (Gurdon, 1963). The procedure for nuclear transfer in this species follows closely that described for R. *pipiens*, but several special features may be noted (Elsdale, Gurdon, and Fischberg, 1960). In *Xenopus*, it is difficult to remove the egg nucleus mechanically, and in general it has been left in place during nuclear transplantation. To prevent participation in development, the egg pronucleus is inactivated with a small dose of ultraviolet light before nuclear transfers are performed (Gurdon, 1960a). This procedure leads to disintegration of the egg pronucleus without interfering with subsequent development, although the possibility that nuclear breakdown products may affect differentiation has not been excluded directly. That the egg pronucleus is eliminated as a functional unit, however, is clear from experiments in which donor nuclei carry a cytological marker. The latter are conveniently available through the existence of a special mutant strain of *X. laevis* in which the cells have a reduced number of nucleoli (Elsdale, Fischberg, and Smith, 1958; Fischberg and Wallace, 1960). Heterozygous individuals with this mutation develop normally, but exhibit only one nucleolus rather than the two normally present in body cells. Through the use of this marker, it can be demonstrated that the egg pronucleus after irradiation does not persist as such; all nuclei within transplant-embryos are of the donor type.

In *Xenopus*, as in *Rana*, normal development may be elicited by embryonic nuclei from a variety of sources (Fischberg, Gurdon, and Elsdale, 1958a, 1958b). Many of the transplant-embryos have been raised to the adult stage, and when mated with normal animals, give rise to typical offspring (Gurdon, Elsdale, and Fischberg, 1958; Gurdon, 1962a). The latter result is particularly interesting because it indicates that the developmental potentialities of single nuclei in somatic tissues may include the formation of new germ cells. In agreement with experiments of Briggs and King, the ability of transfer nuclei in *Xenopus* to promote normal differentiation declines progressively with donor age. But a number of normal embryos have been obtained with nuclei from remarkably advanced stages. These positive results include the formation of typical larvae by the implantation of nuclei from endoderm and mesoderm of neural fold, tailbud, and even muscular response stages. In one instance, complete development resulted from a nucleus taken from somite material only 9 hours before the commencement of muscular contraction.

These findings present an interesting contrast to the early specialization of nuclei in *R. pipiens*, and suggest that in *Xenopus*, at least some nuclei may remain totipotent well beyond the time when differentiation is evident in morphological terms. The trends observed are documented particularly well in the study by Gurdon (1960c) on changes in endoderm nuclei. For practical purposes, the chief interest in this material lies in the analysis of postgastrula embryos. Evidence is available that beyond the time of gastrulation, variations in development are independent of the original transplantation procedure (Gurdon, 1960b). On such a base line, no decline in developmental potential of endoderm nuclei can be observed in blastulae or gastrulae, but beyond this point, the proportion of normal larvae decreases regularly with donors of advancing age. However, Gurdon (1962c) did obtain some normal tadpoles with endodermal nuclei of *Xenopus* at all stages tested, which ranged up into swimming larvae with beginning torsion of the gut. From these results, it appears that although progressive differentiation of nuclei is a common feature of embryonic cells in both *Xenopus* and *Rana*, there are distinctive differences in the extent and timing of this process (see Figure 1.5). In *Xenopus*, at least, the restriction of nuclear potentialities proceeds in a pattern that coincides with differentiation at the cellular rather than tissue or organ level (Gurdon, 1960c).

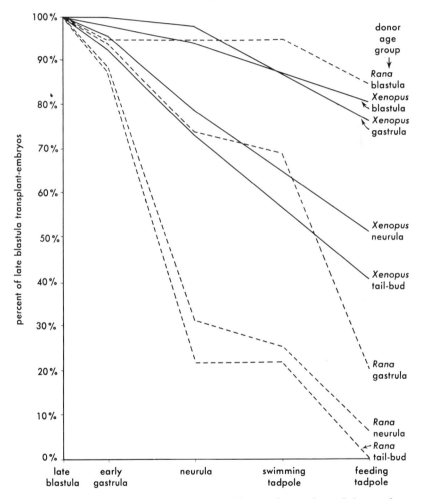

FIG. 1.5. Comparative survival of transplant embryos derived by nuclear transfers in *Rana* and *Xenopus*, respectively. Survival in each case is expressed as a function of the total embryos estimated to reach the blastula stage. (From Gurdon, 1960c.)

Whatever the time of onset and exact sequence of nuclear specialization in embryos, the changes concerned seem to be relatively stable and perhaps even irreversible. This conclusion emerges from studies in which nuclei have been transferred serially through a number of transplant-embryo generations. The relevant data can be illustrated by the experiments of King and Briggs (1956), in which development was initiated in a series of *R. pipiens* eggs by implanting nuclei from late gastrula endoderm. When the experimental embryos reached the gastrula stage, one or more were sacrificed, and nuclei from the undetermined cells of the animal hemisphere were implanted in a new group of recipient eggs. In such an experiment, all nuclei in a given blastula derive from one original nuclear implant, and thus each of the groups of eggs in the second transplant generation can be considered as a nuclear clone. On analyzing a number of these clones, King and Briggs found that the embryos of any single clone develop much more uniformly than do groups of eggs implanted with nuclei taken directly from separate cells of the late gastrula endoderm. Marked differences can be found, however, when the developmental patterns of a series of clones are compared. In a few of these, nearly all the embryos develop into normal tadpoles, whereas in other clones, development is arrested uniformly at the gastrula stage. Still other clones are characterized by abnormal differentiation in later stages, especially of the ectodermal derivatives. The consistency of these differences can be further examined by transplanting blastula nuclei to establish third, fourth, or fifth generations of embryos for any given nuclear clone. The developmental pattern for each clone, whatever its character, tends to remain unchanged or to become increasingly abnormal in the course of these serial transfers. King and Briggs observed no sign of reversion to normal development in clones that had shown deficient differentiation. This general picture described for serial transplantation of *R. pipiens* nuclei has been confirmed with *Xenopus* in all essential details (Fischberg, Gurdon, and Elsdale, 1958b; Gurdon, 1960c).

Central to all these discussions is the nature of the restrictions that appear in the developmental potential of somatic nuclei as differentiation of the embryo proceeds. Are these based on changes in the genetic apparatus or on epigenetic alterations in the nuclei that affect the expression of genetic capabilities? An answer is complicated by the fact that the developmental potential of nuclei may decline from nonspecific changes as well as from those that may reflect morphogenetic specialization of particular cell types. A model for the first process can be found in the behavior of nuclear implants in hybrid combinations between two species (Moore, 1958, 1962). If, for example, a nucleus from a blastula of R. *pipiens* is transferred to the enucleated egg of R. *sylvatica,* cleavage takes place, but development is blocked at the late blastula stage. The nuclei of such cells are still capable of growth and multiplication, for if reimplanted into native (R. *pipiens*) cytoplasm, they bring about normal cleavage. Yet differentiation only rarely proceeds beyond this stage and is consistently abnormal; this restriction remains even though the nuclei in question are passed through four or five back transfers in R. *pipiens* eggs for possible recovery (Moore, 1960). Evidently, replication for a limited period in foreign cytoplasm somehow alters the developmental potential of the donor nuclei. Such a result appears to be typical in general for nuclear exchanges between two remotely related species (Gurdon, 1962b).

To account for this loss in morphogenetic capabilities, Moore has suggested that the replication of DNA from foreign substrates in the host cytoplasm can lead to structural alterations, which are expressed by a change in genetic information in the donor nuclei. With a further "scrambling" in prospect on return to native cytoplasm, these nuclei may become incapable of transmitting instructions for normal development. Although this ingenious hypothesis is not necessarily to be ruled out, a more direct explanation can now be invoked. From the experiments reported by Hennen (1961) and Briggs (1962), it appears that most if not all nuclei that undergo a restriction of morphogenetic potential as a result of replication in foreign cytoplasm also exhibit chromosomal abnormalities. The supporting material consists of back transfers in R. *pipiens* eggs, initiated by *pipiens* nuclei that had been previously passed for 10 to 12 divisions in eggs of R. *sylvatica*. Most of the back-transfer embryos were blocked in early stages. Cytologically, all showed abnormalities in chromosome number as well as multiple aberrations in morphology; for example, shortened or ring chromosomes, minutes, and acentric fragments. Some of the back-transfer embryos did develop to the late tailbud stage or beyond; in such cases, karyotypic changes, although present, were less marked. From these observations it seems reasonable to attribute the deleterious effect of interspecific transfer on nuclei to chromosomal damage, although the mechanism of this effect remains to be determined.

One implication of these findings is the possibility that even for nuclear transplantations made within a single species, some of the losses in morphogenetic potential may be due to chromosomal aberrations or other nonspecific causes. That this view is essentially correct is shown by the investigations of Briggs, King, and Di Berardino (1960). In these experiments, a series of transplant-embryos were initiated in R. *pipiens* with nuclei derived from late gastrula endoderm. As previously indicated, a minority of these develop into normal larvae, and the remainder differentiate abnormally or are arrested at various developmental stages. By examining the chromosomal pattern of each embryo from a small piece taken at the gastrula stage, a significant correlation can be observed. Embryos that are blocked at early stages, or which continue further but show no consistent pattern of defects, all exhibit aberrations in chromosome number or morphology. The remaining embryos, with normal chromosome patterns at least to the time of gastrulation, fall into two groups: Either development proceeds normally, or the characteristic syndrome of changes associated specifically with older endoderm nuclei appears (that is, malformation of ectodermal derivatives). These observations clearly support the concept of selective nuclear differentiation in development, although it remains to be shown that a similar segregation of morphogenetic potential can be associated with the nuclei of other cell types. Just how such specific restrictions in nuclear capability may arise is still an open question. Although genetic specialization might be assumed, a stable shift in functional properties of the nucleus seems more plausible (Gurdon, 1963); alternatively, the loss of some closely associated perinuclear organelle in the cytoplasm cannot be conclusively ruled out (Briggs and King, 1959). The resolution of these uncertainties will require innovations in technique and experimental designs.

Aside from questions of morphogenetic specialization, the transfer of nuclei provides a means for inspecting the control of specific characters by nuclear and cytoplasmic factors, respectively. Useful information can be obtained by exchanges between subspecies with contrasting genetic markers. Fortunately, the developmental blocks described for interspecific combinations do not appear in this case. In such an investigation, Sambuichi (1957) transplanted blastula nuclei from *Rana nigromaculata brevipoda* to enucleated eggs of *Rana nigromaculata nigromaculata*. These two forms differ in pigment pattern, and in at least one animal which metamorphosed, the *brevipoda* character was clearly apparent. Similarly, McKinnell (1960) has carried out exchanges of nuclei between stock lines of *R. pipiens* and a substrain (*kandiyohi*), which carries a dominant mutant gene conferring a mottled color pattern. In every instance the transplantation of *kandiyohi* nuclei into stock *R. pipiens* eggs results in expression of the mutant phenotype (see Figure 1.6). The extensive studies of Gurdon (1961) serve to project these findings into a more general format. Using nuclear transplant-embryos between two subspecies of *Xenopus laevis*, Gurdon has followed a number of diagnostic features that separate the forms in question. All these heterotypic animals display the characteristics of the nuclear rather than the cytoplasmic donor, and if carried to the adult stage,

FIG. 1.6. Expression of a mutant character in leopard frogs derived by nuclear transplantation. (A) Normal juvenile, Vermont *R. pipiens* (control). (B) Juvenile frog produced by transplanting Wisconsin *kandiyohi* nucleus into Vermont *R. pipiens* cytoplasm. Note mottled color pattern, which is typical of the *kandiyohi* mutant type. (From McKinnell, 1960.)

give rise to offspring that are again of the original nuclear type. In such subspecific combinations, there is no evidence that nuclei are affected by replication in foreign cytoplasm. Even after numerous serial transfers in eggs of opposite type, the nuclei, when transplanted to native cytoplasm, give rise to typical normal larvae of unchanged character. These important findings indicate that within a given species, nuclear markers exhibit conspicuous stability in a contrasting cytoplasmic milieu. From such base lines, model systems may conceivably be constructed for the analysis of somatic mutation and clonal variation at the nuclear level.

GENETIC CHANGES IN DEVELOPMENT

Embryos and their parts are a subtle blend of genetic and epigenetic mechanisms. The workings of the latter are conspicuous in morphogenesis: the establishment of patterns by localization or induction; and the individuation of cell types by specialization of cytoplasmic systems or perhaps even by nuclear differentiation. Yet the effector mechanisms of development operate within a genetic framework that defines in precise fashion the cells, tissues, and organs of each new individual. From this standpoint, the relevant problems of embryology are the mechanics of coding in genetic structures, the mechanisms for transfer of information to cytoplasmic systems, and the basis for differential response in the peripheral centers, which give rise to the final products of differentiation. The information system thus envisioned operates on the basis of choice from an intact genotype rather than by segregation. From a possible hierarchy of gene actions, only those appropriate to a given developmental pattern are called forth at a particular time. The exact sequence that appears may be a resultant of sequential relations to other processes in development, as well as the local milieu prevailing in specific cells, and the positional relationships of these cells in larger patterns (Stern, 1954).

Considering the complexity of development, it is not surprising that deviations occur at many levels in the differentiation process. Some of these may represent hereditary predispositions; others are clearly epigenetic in origin. The close relationship between the two mechanisms is illustrated in graphic form by the production of phenocopies (see Goldschmidt, 1955). This term is used to characterize nonhereditary variations that mimic closely the results of genetic change. In *Drosophila*, for example, it is possible to duplicate the phenotypes of a large number of standard mutants merely by imposing temperature treatments on wild-type larvae at specific stages in development. Apparently there are sensitive phases in the morphogenesis of specific somatic structures, and during these critical periods, environmental stimuli may alter a key sequence of gene action. The phenocopies that arise by this process illustrate shifting expressions of a basically constant genome, for the acquired characteristic is not transmitted to succeeding generations.

Not all developmental anomalies, however, can be accounted for as epigenetic accidents or as expressions of mutant genes inherited from parent stocks. Some, at least, stem from genetic changes taking place directly within isolated cells of the emerging embryonic rudiments. Where the end products of differentiation are affected, such changes can often be detected and may be referred to as somatic mutations. For animal cells, however, this designation is ordinarily an inferential one. It is not possible to determine the exact basis for phenotypic alteration in such cases by the conventional procedures of crossing over and recombination. In practice, therefore, the term somatic mutation does not have a precise genetic meaning. It can connote merely a stable change perpetuated in a given cell and its descendants, without specification of any underlying mechanism (Luria, 1960).

Mosaics in Somatic Tissues The principal indications of genetic change within developing cell populations are to be found in the appearance of mosaics within somatic tissues. These are seen as sectors or islands of nonconforming cells within a background of otherwise predictable pattern. Such variations may arise, for example, as isolated irregularities in color or texture of the hair in laboratory mammals. In *Drosophila* unpigmented ommatidia may be formed, in contrast to the red pigment present in the rest of the eye field. Many other instances of mosaicism can be observed among both plants and animals, characterized in each case by the occurrence of patches of cells that differ from surrounding tissues of the same type.

Variegation in somatic tissues as such does not necessarily imply the occurrence of mutations or other heritable changes in the cells concerned. Geneticists have long known, for example, that color patterns in the fur of mammals are controlled by an interacting complex of genes. By selective breeding, it is possible to obtain strains of rats that possess black hoods or show other specific variegations in coat color. Local differences in this case reflect the action of modifier genes rather than genetic alterations in the cells concerned, and are reproducible in animals of appropriate genotype. In some instances, localized changes within a uniform somatic field may result from the action of extrinsic or environmental factors. The classic example of this process is found in the pigmentation of hair in Himalayan rabbits. Given animals of appropriate genotype, the development of pigment in the fur of these animals can be made a function of temperature. In a warm environment no pigment is produced and all offspring are white, whereas if the external temperature is low, the fur is black. At an intermediate point, only the tip of the ears, paws, and nose show pigmentation, a fact that reflects the lower temperature of these peripheral parts.

The majority of mosaic conditions, however, are to be explained by genetic change rather than by the modifying action of accessory genes or environmental factors. Direct proof can be obtained in plants, at least, by propagating cuttings or seeds that have originated from cells within a variant sector and which continue to show the variation in question. Among animals, evidence is more difficult to obtain that cells in mosaic regions differ genetically from cells of the same type, and reliance must be placed on similarity to characteristics known to have arisen in other individuals by germinal mutations. A dominant marker, for example, may emerge locally within a population of somatic cells known to be homozygous recessive for the gene in question, as has been observed for at least one coat color mosaic in mice (Bhat, 1949). More commonly, recessive characters appear as mosaics within heterozygous individuals or in sex-linked combination. The underlying genetic change may be assumed to occur in random fashion at any stage of development. The timing of this event will therefore be shown roughly by the size of the mosaic that arises by further proliferation of the altered cells. Early genetic changes will give rise to a large sector of variant tissue, whereas alterations at a late stage in development may be evident only as tiny patches. Obviously, mosaic conditions that arise within somatic tissues as such will not be transmitted to subsequent generations. If, however, genetic changes occur very early in development, before germinal and somatic cell lineages are separated, it is possible for mosaics to arise that include all or part of a gonad as well as an adjacent sector of somatic tissue. In this rare circumstance it may be possible to detect a given change both as a somatic variation and as a germinal mutation (Dunn, 1934).

The induction of mosaics in *Drosophila* by X irradiation provided an early experimental approach to genetic aspects of somatic cell variation. Patterson (1929a, 1929b) showed that if larvae are exposed to appropriate doses of radiation, eye-color mosaics and other localized changes may be produced in appreciable numbers. The induction of mosaics within the eye field is particularly convenient for the study of somatic mutations, since the unpigmented areas that arise from X irradiation contrast sharply with the pigmented surroundings. Mosaics varying in extent from an entire eye to a single ommatidium may be readily distinguished. Localized changes can also be observed in other external characters, such as the color and shape of the bristles that cover the body surface in *Drosophila*. Patterson found mosaics arise regularly in wild-type males following X irradiation. The newly emerging markers within these mosaics closely resemble features known to have arisen in stock strains by germinal mutation; for example, white eye, yellow body, or singed bristles. All these features are controlled by recessive genes with loci in the X chromosome. By implication, mosaics in question had originated by similar mutations from the dominant wild-type allele in an early embryonic cell. Patterson found, however, that mosaics could be produced even more frequently in female than in male *Drosophila*, provided these individuals were heterozygous for the corresponding recessive gene. No mosaics appeared in homozygous females. In this case, the expression of recessive markers in mosaics seems to depend on chromosome aberrations produced by X irradiation and which eliminate the accompanying dominant allele. Mosaics thus may arise from chromosomal changes as well as from point mutations.

The relationship between germinal and somatic mutations was explored more directly by Demerec (1941) in a study of the so-called miniature alleles in *Drosophila*, a series that is characterized by a relatively high rate of mutability. The genes in question act to produce characteristic modifications in wing structure. It is possible to distinguish miniature variations even at the cellular level, since the cell walls persist in mutant wings instead of being absorbed, as they are in wild-type flies. Demerec observed that flies of miniature genotype commonly exhibit mosaic spots of wild-type tissue within the miniature wing field. These mosaic areas may involve part of or all the wing structure; by performing breeding experiments, Demerec was able to determine the stage at which mutation to the dominant wild-type allele had occurred. Some miniature genes showed high mutability only in the germ cells, others only in somatic cells, and still others were capable of a high rate of mutation in either the somatic or germ line. Alterations were also observed in which an allele previously giving rise to frequent changes in both germ cells and somatic cells became restricted in its variability to the germ line alone, or vice versa. From these transitions it is clear that for the system in question, germinal and somatic mutations do not differ in any qualitative sense.

Among mammals, somatic mosaics are found occasionally as spontaneous local variations in coat color. They have also been induced systematically in mice by X irradiation (Russell and Major, 1957). For this purpose, embryos of 10.25 days of age were irradiated, using stocks of animals heterozygous for four different recessive genes affecting coat color. Numerous mosaic patches appeared in the fur of the irradiated animals, indicating the expression of one or another of the recessive coat color genes. Such changes did not take place in animals homozygous for the corresponding wild-type alleles. The low incidence of variations in a control series of heterozygous animals maintained without irradiation indicated that these mosaics are not to be explained by the abnormal differentiation of pigment cells or other nongenetic alterations. The most probable explanation seems to be the production of gene mutations or small deficiencies in the loci under study.

Estimates of the frequency of somatic mutation can be made by determining the approximate number of cells in precursor tissues at the time of X irradiation. Thus Lefevre (1950), in a study of eye-color mosaics in *Drosophila* males, calculated a mutation constant for $w^+ \rightarrow w$ of 14×10^{-8} for somatic cells as compared with a value of 12×10^{-8} for germinal cells. Similarly, Russell and Major (1957) estimated a mutation rate of $7.0 \times 10^{-7}/r/$ locus for pigment cells in X-irradiated mice, while the comparable figure in mouse spermatogonia has been reported as $2.4 \times 10^{-7}/r/$ locus (Russell, 1951). Although there is no good reason to expect that mutation rates in somatic and germ cells will coincide ordinarily, a similar order of magnitude is apparent in these results.

It is now clear that a variety of chromosomal changes may contribute to the origin of somatic mosaics. At least one of these has been known for many years, through the study of gynandromorphs in insects. Such individuals, often called gynanders, are striking mosaics of male and female structures in varying combination, a circumstance made possible in insects by the absence of circulating sex hormones. Pioneer studies on gynanders in *Drosophila* showed that an X chromosome may be occasionally lost by elimination or nondisjunction in one of the early cell divisions of a female embryo, thus giving rise to an island of male cells. The variable character of these gynanders is partly a function of the time at which chromosome loss occurs during development and partly the result of differential growth of tissues and organs in succeeding stages (Stern, 1954). Parenthetically, it should be noted that gynanders are not always the result of chromosome loss. In silkworms and bees, gynanders may originate from binucleate eggs in which the two nuclei after fertilization are male and female, respectively (see Figure 1.7).

The process of chromosome elimination was originally considered as a generalized mechanism for local cellular variation, but it is doubtful that mosaics arise commonly by this process in somatic tissues. The effects of X irradiation in unmasking recessive genes, for example, are more likely to be exerted by localized deletions rather than by the

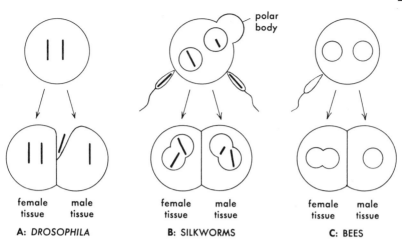

female   male   female   male   female   male
tissue   tissue   tissue   tissue   tissue   tissue

A: DROSOPHILA   **B: SILKWORMS**   **C: BEES**

FIG. 1.7. Types of gynanders arising during embryonic development. (A) Loss of an X chromosome during an early cell division in *Drosophila* ♀ results in mosaic of female (XX) and male (XO) cells. (B) Silkworm eggs occasionally retain a polar body, thus becoming binucleate. If such an egg is fertilized by two spermatozoa, nuclei give rise to cells that are XX (male in silkworms) and XY (female), respectively. (C) Occasional eggs in bees are binucleate. If fertilized by a single sperm, cells arise from the two nuclei and are haploid (male) and diploid (female), respectively. (Redrawn from Altenburg, 1957. Copyright, Holt, Rinehart and Winston, Inc.)

elimination of whole chromosomes as such (Patterson, 1929b; Russell and Major, 1957). It is worth pointing out, however, that in at least one group of organisms, chromosome elimination does take place regularly as a basis for mosaicism. Within the mold *Aspergillus nidulans,* mosaic haploid sectors may arise from nominally diploid colonies by the loss of an entire genome (Pontecorvo, 1958). Commonly, this seems to occur by the repeated loss of one or a few chromosomes at a time (Pontecorvo and Käfer, 1958). Although the possibility of haploidization in the somatic cell populations of higher organisms is generally discounted, the reports of Gläss (1957) on genome separation in rat liver may bear closer investigation (Stern, 1958).

At least in *Drosophila,* mosaics may also arise by somatic crossing over rather than by mutation or a process of deletion of accompanying alleles. Crossing over was first demonstrated in germ cells; as one of the strategic means for recombination, it has been the subject of intensive study for many years. Until Stern's classic study (1936), however, this process was thought to be confined to meiosis. The discovery of its occurrence in somatic cells was the result of an investigation of mosaics in *Drosophila,* first believed to be caused by chromosome elimination.

Such mosaics can be found in numbers within certain strains because of the presence of certain mutant genes (minute factors), which greatly increase the frequency of somatic variations. Among such flies, Stern examined two characters, both affecting bristles on the surface of the body. In the normal wild-type flies, the bristles are straight and black, but mutants exist in which the bristles are yellow (y), instead of black, or show a curled condition referred to as singed (sn) (see Figure 1.8). The genes for both markers are located in the X chromosome. A cross between stocks homozygous for yellow, straight and black, singed would therefore give rise to females of the type $y +/+ sn$. Ordinarily,

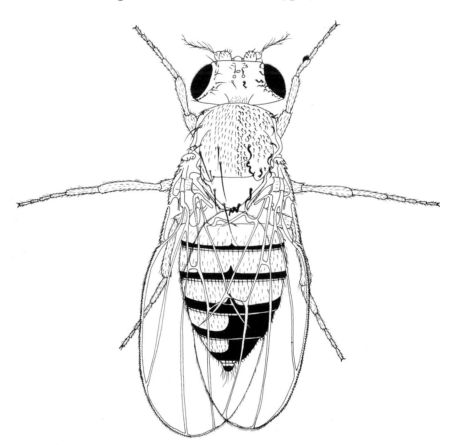

FIG. 1.8. A gynandromorph of *Drosophila*, represented in semidiagrammatic fashion. The female parts of the body are recognized by the possession of straight bristles and the male parts by singed bristles. Note the male foreleg (*right*) with its "sex comb" and the dark coloration of the male tip of the abdomen (*right*). (From Stern, 1954.)

the bristles of these flies should be black and straight, since a dominant wild-type allele occurs for each gene pair. If elimination of one chromosome occasionally took place during development, one or the other of the two recessive genes would be left free to express the corresponding phenotype. When Stern performed crosses of this type, however, he obtained unexpected results. A typical finding in females was the occasional occurrence of a twin mosaic against a general background of bristles with wild-type characters. In one of these mosaic spots, the bristles were yellow but not singed; in the adjoining area, they were singed but not yellow. More rarely, yellow spots were observed alone, and isolated areas with singed bristles alone were still less frequent. The twin mosaics are particularly illuminating because the regular association of variant spots on the basis of probability cannot be explained by simultaneous mutation or by coincidental elimination of different chromosomes in adjacent cells. Stern showed, however, that the results obtained can be accounted for by assuming that crossing over occurs occasionally between two homologous chromosomes at some mitotic division in development. The mechanism of this process is illustrated schematically in Figure 1.9. If an exchange takes place between two chromatids from homologous chromosomes, it is possible for one daughter cell at a mitotic division to receive chromosomes represented as $y +/y +$, and those distributed to the other cell may be represented as $+ sn/+ sn$. In this event, twin mosaics will eventually arise by subsequent multiplication and differentiation of the populations of cells derived from these two variant precursors. Failure of twin spots to appear, however, does not preclude the occurrence of somatic crossing over. If one mosaic region falls within an area of the body surface where bristles are not formed, the variant character is merely not expressed. Single mosaics can also result from differences in the point at which crossing-over occurs. If, for example, crossing over takes place between y and s instead of between these loci and the centromere, single yellow spots can arise. On the other hand, simultaneous crossovers at both sites can give rise to single mosaics with singed bristles only. These findings exemplify a process that occurs more broadly in *Drosophila*. Stern has shown that somatic crossing over can be documented for gene pairs in the autosomes as well as X chromosomes, and that it occurs in both males and females.

Somatic crossing over has not yet been demonstrated with certainty in mammals or any other higher organisms, although the evidence is strong that a phenomenon of this type occurs in tumors and perhaps in other cells as well (see Chapter 8). It is not known whether somatic pairing has any necessary relation to mitotic interchanges between homologous chromosomes, although such pairing is a regular event in

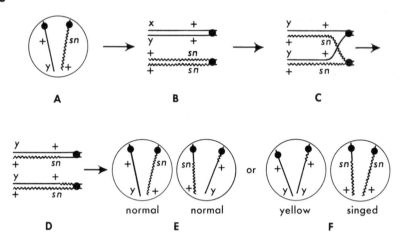

FIG. 1.9. Somatic crossing over in *Drosophila*. (A) Schematic diagram of two homologous chromosomes in a mitotic cell. Note mutant loci *sn* (singed) and *y* (yellow) as markers, and centromeres. (B–D) Sister chromatids form from each chromosome as division proceeds. Crossing over occurs between centromere and *sn* locus, leading to a two-strand exchange of corresponding segments. (E–F) Daughter cells, showing alternative distribution of markers, depending on random orientation and distribution of chromosomes at metaphase. If *sn* and *y* markers are brought together as shown in *F*, the resulting daughter cells establish variant lineages. These will be recognizable in the adult as adjacent spots of tissue with singed bristles and yellow bristles, respectively. (Data from Stern, 1936.)

dipteran cells during mitosis as well as meiosis (Stern, 1958). Some degree of somatic pairing does occur in a variety of other organisms (Boss, 1955), but this process may be misleading as an indication of possible crossing over. Among microorganisms, crossing over has been demonstrated frequently in diploid yeast cells (Roman, 1956) and is especially common in *Aspergillus*. Pontecorvo and his associates have in fact utilized this phenomenon for detailed genetic studies in molds. Detailed chromosome maps can be constructed for *Aspergillus* by the analysis of mitotic recombination (Pontecorvo and Käfer, 1956, 1958). From all indications, therefore, crossing over may be a process of considerable significance for somatic cell variation, although the supporting information does not as yet have a very broad base.

Variegation and Position Effects   The most speculative explanations for somatic variegation are those that postulate the occurrence of position effects. This concept arose a number of years ago as a result of Sturtevant's well-known study (1925) on bar eye in *Drosophila*. The mutation concerned causes a decrease in the number of ommatidia in the eye structure, and depends on the presence of a duplication of the bar locus. Owing to the occurrence of unequal crossing over in meiosis, gametes may be formed with chromosomes containing one, two, or three bar loci. Sturtevant's basic finding was that individuals of genotype *BBB/B* show a more extreme phenotypic expression of bar eye than do those of *BB/BB* constitution. Thus an altered pattern of gene action is obtained, without further mutation, merely by changing the topographic relationships of the four loci concerned.

Although bar eye proved to be a special case, the continuing study of position effects has led to other processes of more general interest. Of these, the V-type position effect is of particular significance for somatic variegation (Lewis, 1950; Hannah, 1951; Schultz, 1936, 1959; Russell and Bangham, 1960; Russell, 1962). This phenomenon arises from an altered relationship between two components of chromosomes, which have been called euchromatin and heterochromatin, respectively. In *Drosophila,* for example, cytological distinctions may be made between the two on the basis of affinity for stains, and there are genetic differences as well. For the most part, genes in the usual sense are confined to euchromatin. Heterochromatin occurs in *Drosophila* near centromeres and in certain other localized regions, which vary in number and extent among individual chromosomes. It is possible, by chromosomal rearrangements, to alter the usual topographic relationships that exist between euchromatin and heterochromatin. Through X irradiation, for example, crossing over, translocation, or other changes may occur that bring specific genes into close proximity to heterochromatic regions. Under these conditions, a number of genes have been found to show a more variable pattern of expression. A typical example is the condition of white-mottled eye in *Drosophila,* which superficially resembles the eye mosaics produced by mutation. In this case, however, local variation within the eye field seems not to be caused by genetic changes at the white locus as such. Rather, mottling results from genic instability of the normal allele for eye color, operating from a heterochromatic region of the chromosome.

A similar variability in expression can be seen for genes affecting such characters as body color, bristle pattern, and wing morphology, where the genetic determinants in question are transposed near or into heterochromatin (Hannah, 1951). The decisive influence of this association is seen in the fact that the V-type position effects are readily reversible. If crossing over or other chromosomal rearrangements that occur return such genes to euchromatic regions, variegation is lost and a uniform wild-type pattern is reasserted. Mutation in the conventional sense is thus not to be invoked as an explanation. In fact, the immunochemical studies of Fuscaldo and Fox (1962) suggest that for the white locus in *Drosophila,* mutation and heterochromatic rearrangements produce characteristically different phenotypic effects. In this system, a protein, W-1, can be identified as a probable product of the white segment in the X chromosome. Chromosomal arrangements that lead to white-mottled eye are accompanied by immunochemical alterations in the properties of W-1. Similarly, point mutations at several sites within the white segment cause modifications in W-1, but in a different direction. The two groups of variants can be separated effectively on an immunochemical basis.

An explanation for the influence of heterochromatin is not yet available, despite much study. The reality of position effects, however, emphasizes that gene action can be modulated by physical relationship of parts within the chromosome as a whole, a view long championed by Goldschmidt (1951). This thesis has found its most general form in experiments on somatic mutation in plants. Indian corn (*Zea mays*) is especially favorable for such studies because mutations occur frequently in the seed structure and can be analyzed by cytogenetic methods. Working with this material, McClintock (1956) proposed a series of new concepts, which may be of very general interest not only for maize but for other cell systems as well. In essence, her observations suggest the existence of so-called controlling elements as a new type of genetic unit within the chromosomal structure as a whole. Physically, such agents may conceivably represent fragments of heterochromatin (Swanson, 1957; Sonneborn, 1960). They are known through two unique aspects of cytogenetic behavior. It is assumed that controlling elements (1) occur as discrete units at particular sites within chromosomes, but can apparently be transposed to other locations; and (2), if present at a given site, tend to modulate the action of nearby genes, including the capacity of the latter to undergo mutation. These are indeed distinctive properties, for if the scheme proposed is one of general validity, heritable variations could result from a shift in the location of controlling elements as well as from structural changes at genetic loci.

The principal evidence for the existence of controlling elements comes from an analysis of variation within individual kernels in ears of corn. Normally, these kernels are purple, owing to the production of pigment in the fleshy endosperm cells under the influence of a dominant gene for color (*C*). Stable recessive alleles (*c*) are also known which give rise to uniformly white kernels. McClintock discovered, however, that unstable whites may be obtained in which there are frequent localized reversions to the normal production of pigment. Such plants exhibit kernels with a mottled appearance, caused by the development of numerous purple spots against the continuous white background. The question therefore arises whether this mosaic condition is the result of mutations from $c{\to}C$ or whether it is caused by a variable pattern of expression of the normal color gene, C. Cytogenetic evidence favors the latter view. Specifically, chromosome rearrangements, which are especially common in maize (McClintock, 1941, 1951), may bring a heterochromatic locus, called dissociation (Ds), into occasional association with C, the purple color gene. Under these conditions, the normal production of pigment appears to be suppressed, and in plants of this genotype, the endosperm cells are ordinarily white. The dissociation element (Ds) is so named because it seems to initiate chromosome breaks frequently; actually it was first discovered at its normal location by this means. When in association with the color gene, Ds continues to induce such breaks, some of which may cause the loss of Ds as such from the chromosome. In these cells and their descendants, production of pigment is then resumed under the influence of the normal color gene, C, giving rise to a mosaic purple spot in the developing kernel.

In order for any of these changes to take place, a second type of controlling element, known as activator (Ac), must be present within the chromosomal complement. In stocks that lack Ac, chromosome breaks and the characteristic modifications in pigmentation cannot be detected. Ac need not occur in close proximity to Ds, but serves to modulate action by the latter. The timing of Ds-induced chromosome breaks, for example, depends on the dosage of Ac. In stocks that contain one, two, and three Ac elements, respectively, the purple mosaic sectors that appear within a white endosperm field are progressively reduced in size, as if the loss of Ds had occurred at successively later stages of development. McClintock has observed that the expression of a number of other genes in maize can be affected by the Ac-Ds system (McClintock, 1956, 1961). In each case where transpositions appear to bring Ds into close association with the allele in question, there is a suppression of normal phenotype in favor of a recessive condition, reversible by loss of Ds from the vicinity of the gene concerned. The Ac-Ds combination in this form does not seem to be unique. Several other systems of controlling elements have been described in maize (McClintock, 1956, 1961; Brink, 1958; Peterson, 1960). None of these can be identified with genes in the conventional sense; they occur in association with loci that are unstable or frequently mutable, and may be responsible for this characteristic.

The disorganized variation that results from position effects in maize may well represent a special case, not applicable as a model to more stable systems. However, the dual organization of chromosomal components is a concept that in more general form may be useful for an understanding of somatic differentiation (Brink, 1960, 1962). According to this thesis, chromosomes consist of orthochromatin, made up of genes, and in addition an accessory array of self-perpetuating materials, which may be called parachromatin. Conceivably, the latter may be similar to or even identical with heterochromatin, but it is assumed to pervade chromosomes generally rather than being restricted to isolated regions. Brink suggests that parachromatin, which affects the expression of genes, may undergo an orderly series of changes as somatic differentiation proceeds. These alterations can be termed paramutations, and they are thought to take place as a directed response to the changing cellular milieu. Paramutations cause shifts in gene action; these changes are relatively stable and mitotically transmissible.

The principal evidence for the reality of paramutation comes from experiments on maize (see Brink, 1960). A number of alleles occur at the R locus, which modulates the pigmentation of individual kernels. R^r, for example, produces darkly mottled kernels, and R^{st} causes stippling. A test-cross between the heterozygote $R^r R^{st}$ and $r^g r^g$ should thus produce a population with equal numbers of darkly mottled and stippled kernels. Actually, however, only the stippled kernels appear as expected; the darkly mottled class is completely replaced by a new phenotype, in which the kernels are only lightly pigmented. Surprisingly, the altered characteristic is genetically transmissible; in further crosses using the modified kernels, the original R^r allele cannot be recovered as such.

Provisionally, a paramutation of R^r can be assumed to be induced uniformly in the heterozygote by R^{st}, which appears to be paramutagenic. Using the same methods, Brink and his collaborators have described a number of other instances in which the pattern of action for particular alleles undergoes heritable change as a result of passage through heterozygotes. There are also indications that paramutation in this sense may occur in other organisms as well (see Brink, 1960). Admittedly, the modification of gene action in such systems is an exceptional event, but it may be indicative of changes that on a programed basis are characteristic of normal differentiation.

Models for somatic cell variation can accordingly be built on a number of speculations concerning the existence of regulators as well as genetic determinants within the chromosomal complement. New approaches will be needed, however, to test the usefulness of these hypotheses, especially in organisms less favorable than maize for cytogenetic analysis. In animals there is as yet no evidence that controllers as defined by McClintock actually exist, although the possibility has been frequently raised (Schultz, 1959; Sonneborn, 1960). Similarly, paramutation offers a potential explanation for nuclear differentiation in development, but techniques that would permit an experimental test are not yet forthcoming. Nevertheless, the possibility that epigenetic control systems may operate even from within chromosomes is an intriguing concept. As such, it may repay intensive study.

NEOPLASTIC VARIATION AND PROGRESSION

The enigma of carcinogenesis is one of the outstanding mysteries of present-day biology. By what means do tumors emerge as autonomous variants within somatic cell populations? The compelling significance of this question in human terms tends to obscure its broader biological implications. More than any other phenomenon, the natural history of tumors illustrates the potential for variation that may be latent in somatic cells. The manifestations of these changes are the subject of an enormous and ever-increasing literature (see Greenstein, 1954; Cowdry, 1955; Huxley, 1958; Homburger, 1959; Graffi and Bielka, 1959; Hieger, 1961; Busch, 1962, 1963; Bauer, 1963). Within various tumors, these alterations cover almost every known aspect of cell structure and function. Even for a single type of neoplasm [as, for example, the well-known mammary carcinomas of the mouse (Dunn, 1959)], the range of variation is kaleidoscopic. Yet, mere divergence from expected patterns does not provide a key to the underlying neoplastic transformation. Despite intensive studies carried on for decades, no diagnostic differences that will consistently separate tumors from their normal counterparts have been discovered. In structural features (Oberling and Bernhard, 1961) as well as in physiological and biochemical mechanisms (Winzler, 1959; LeBreton and Moulé, 1961), tumors and normal cell types clearly overlap. These findings imply that for the most part, at least, the cellular variations observed are an accompaniment rather than a direct cause of neoplastic change.

Tumors tend to proliferate in individualized forms, and differences in architectural design form the basis for various schemes of descriptive classification. But an essential feature of neoplastic systems is the potential for continuing evolution at the cellular level. Whatever the nature of the initiating change in carcinogenesis, it seems to facilitate an increased variation that finds no organized expression within the framework of normal developmental patterns. In some cases, however, the cellular alterations that appear may have selective value in a steadily proliferating system; for example, increased growth rate, ability to proliferate at reduced oxygen tensions, without the stimulus of specific hormones, or in freedom from normal stromal and vascular patterns. There is thus a tendency for sequential remodeling with tumor cell populations, the degree and tempo varying widely among individual neoplasms but leading ordinarily in the direction of increasing autonomy from the controlling mechanisms of the host. Accordingly, two types of processes are posed by the study of variation in tumor cell systems: (1) the steps leading to the initial onset of neoplastic properties, and (2) the further evolution of cell characteristics within established tumors. Whether the events concerned in both can be explained in terms of a common pattern remains to be determined.

Experimental Production of Tumors   The analysis of carcinogenesis would scarcely be possible without some means of initiating neoplastic changes in experimental animals. Over a period of years, many different model systems have been developed for this purpose, and a wide variety of agents have been implicated as specific carcinogens. That environmental factors may precipitate the development of tumors was first shown by Percival Pott (1775) in a classic study on the occurrence of scrotal cancer among chimney sweeps. It was not until much later, however, that the experimental induction of cancer was achieved with specific chemical agents. The strategic lead was again a circumstantial correlation: Workers in the coal tar industry during the early part of the present century showed an unusual predisposition to develop skin cancer. Accordingly, many efforts were made to produce tumors in laboratory animals by the application of coal tar, and two Japanese investigators, Yamagiwa and Ichikawa (1918), finally succeeded. By patiently treating the ears of rabbits with coal tar over a period of two or three months, they obtained benign growths and ultimately malignant tumors.

The discovery of Yamagiwa and Ichikawa served to launch an intensive era of research on the induction of tumors by carcinogenic substances (see Greenstein, 1954; Hieger, 1961). By a combination of analytical and synthetic approaches centering on coal tar, the first chemically pure carcinogens were finally isolated (Kennaway and Hieger, 1930; Cook, Hewitt, and Hieger, 1933). These substances, such as 1,2,5,6-dibenzanthracene, 3,4-benzpyrene, and 20-methylcholanthrene (which may be referred to also as 3-methylcholanthrene), are related structurally as polycyclic hydrocarbons (see Figure 1.10). Thus, for a time it seemed possible that carcinogenesis might be associated with disturbances in steroid metabolism or the intervention of similar products as extrinsic agents. This hope proved fruitless, however, as a widening array of polycyclic hydrocarbons was subjected to test. Many of these were indeed carcinogenic, but others were not. It

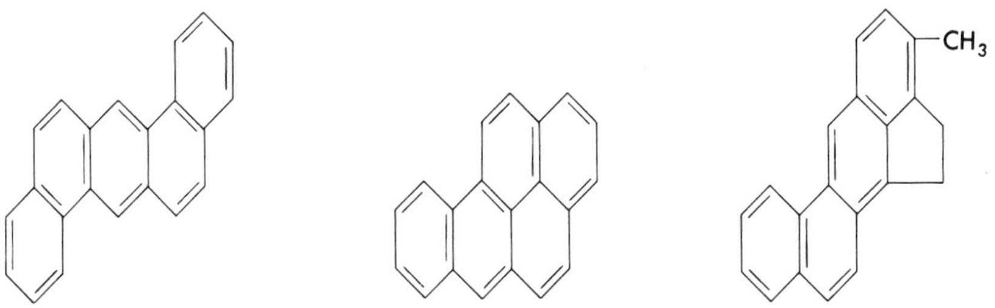

1,2,5,6-dibenzanthracene   3,4-benzpyrene   20-methylcholanthrene

FIG. 1.10. Polycyclic hydrocarbons with carcinogenic properties.

did not prove possible to associate the degree or kind of tumor-producing activity with any specific configuration in the hydrocarbon molecule.

As the scope of investigation extended into other fields, it gradually became clear that tumors can be induced by many types of compounds quite unrelated to the polycyclic hydrocarbons. Among these, for example, are the azo dyes (see Figure 1.11). In 1934 Yoshida showed that o-aminoazotoluene has no local effects if injected subcutaneously into rats or mice or if fed with certain diets, but hepatomas characteristically appear in the liver after months of treatment. Similarly, Kinosita (1937) found that 4-dimethylaminoazobenzene incorporated in the diet produces hepatomas in rats, although not in mice. Later, a wide range of carcinogenicity was demonstrated for substances of the azo dye group, and extensive investigations were made on the

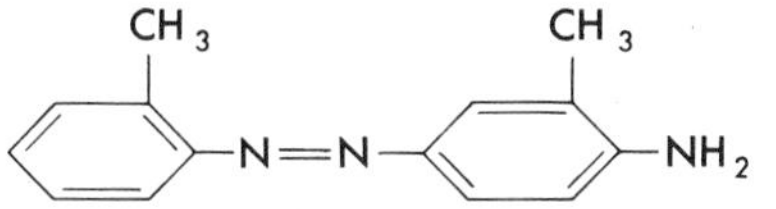

o-aminoazotoluene

4-dimethylaminoazobenzene

FIG. 1.11. Carcinogenic azo dyes.

effects of substitution or modification of active compounds (Greenstein, 1954). In this way, new classes of potent carcinogens, such as the benzocarbazoles and aminostilbenes, were discovered (Haddow, 1959).

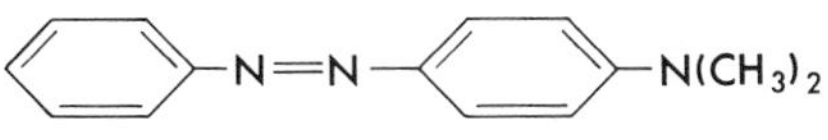

To the azo dyes and polycyclic hydrocarbons investigated at an early stage may be added numerous other types of organic compounds that are carcinogenic under appropriate conditions. Certain of the aromatic amines, for example, were implicated through studies on the high incidence of bladder cancer, which formerly occurred among workers in the aniline dye industry. Aniline as such is noncarcinogenic, but the manufacture and handling of the substance 2-naphthylamine proved to be a critical factor (see Cowdry, 1955). This substance and certain other aromatic amines will produce bladder tumors and other neoplasms in experimental animals (Bonser, Clayson, and Jull, 1958). Another group of carcinogens that has received much attention in recent years includes the nitrogen mustards and related compounds (Haddow, 1959). These substances came to be investigated through experiments on the biological effects of mustard gas and its derivatives, which revealed extensive nuclear abnormalities in dividing cells. In a study of related compounds, Boyland and Horning (1949) administered nitrogen mustards to mice over longer periods of time and obtained a variety of neoplasms. These results have been extensively confirmed by inoculation or feeding of nitrogen mustards in several species of laboratory animals (Haddow, 1958). Paradoxically, however, the principal interest in nitrogen mustards has been in the field of cancer chemotherapy rather than experimental carcinogenesis (see Chapter 6). For this purpose a number of other compounds have been investigated that are (like the nitrogen mustards) cytotoxic and appear to act chemically by alkylation of cellular constituents. At least some of these, such as the ethyleneimines and diepoxides, are also carcinogenic (Haddow, 1959).

Particular interest may attach to the appearance of tumors following the implantation of plastics and polymers, since the substances used are widely regarded as innocuous or even inert from a chemical standpoint. Work in this field begins with the studies of Turner (1941), who noted that sarcomas can be produced by implanting bakelite discs into rats for long periods. Later, Oppenheimer, Oppenheimer, and Stout (1948) observed the incidental appearance of sarcomas during an experiment in which the kidneys of rats were wrapped with cellophane to produce disturbances in blood pressure. Subsequently, they found that a similar result can be obtained by implanting cellophane sheets subcutaneously. Following this lead, sarcomas were also induced by implantation of nylon, dacron, polyethylene, and silicone films. More surprisingly, sarcomas can be made to appear even after the insertion of chemically cleaned glass coverslips (Oppenheimer, Oppenheimer, and Stout, 1952; Oppenheimer, Oppenheimer, Danishefsky, Stout, and Eirich, 1955; see also Merwin and Redmon, 1963). The latter finding suggests that carcinogenesis by plastics is implemented by some change that does not necessitate direct chemical action by an extrinsic agent. This view is supported even more strongly by studies in which it has been shown that plastics or glass produce tumors only if introduced as films; powdered preparations of these materials are noncarcinogenic (Oppenheimer, Willhite, Danishefsky, and Stout, 1961). It is perhaps significant that a dense pocket of connective tissue forms around glass or plastic films, for if this capsule is removed, tumor formation is inhibited. A similar pocket does not develop around the same materials in powdered form.

These findings may conceivably also illuminate the puzzling induction of tumors by a variety of metallic substances. Experimentally, tumors may be produced in laboratory animals by such means as the implantation of finely divided nickel or cobalt, and selenium and beryllium have also been shown to be carcinogenic (Hueper, 1952; Heath, 1956). The causal relationship of arsenic to cancer in man is recognized as an industrial hazard, and similar associations with other metals in varying form are suspected. There is no reason to assume that carcinogenesis by metals and by their compounds are necessarily mediated by a common mechanism. In at least some cases, a direct chemical action can be inferred; for example, the induction of bone tumors in rabbits by the intravenous injection of beryllium compounds (Haddow, 1958).

Radiations of varying character constitute another broad class of carcinogenic agents, and tumors are known to arise in man as well as in experimental animals following critical exposures. The latent period is characteristically a long one, as with chemically induced neoplasms. Chronologically, ionizing radiations were the first extrinsic agents to be specifically associated with cancer. This realization came as a by-product of tragic episodes which marred the early investigations of X rays and radium. Tumors developed in individuals who through lack of shielding had received massive exposures. In animals, the first induction of malignancy by irradiation appears to be that of Clunet (1910). He exposed rats to repeated X irradiation, and after many months observed the formation of sarcomas. Tumors of many types have now been produced in experimental animals by the effective administration of radioactive compounds as well as by direct application of ionizing radiations from an external source. Alpha and beta particles, neutrons, and both gamma and X rays are carcinogenic under appropriate conditions (Lacassagne, 1945; Brues, 1951; Law, 1960; Upton, 1962; Harris, 1963). Ultraviolet light may also produce tumors under appropriate conditions. In man, indications of this relationship are seen in the high incidence of skin cancer among farmers, sailors, and others routinely exposed for long periods to sunlight. The causal association was made more explicit by Findlay (1928), who showed that skin cancer in mice follows laboratory exposure to ultraviolet irradiation. A number of quantitative studies have been made subsequently on ultraviolet carcinogenesis in rodents (see Blum, 1959).

The multiplicity of extrinsic agents that may precipitate a neoplastic change is reminiscent of embryonic induction, in which the characteristics of the reacting system seem more important than the particular chemical or physical stimulus used to elicit a response. That a similar emphasis may be appropriate in carcinogenesis is indicated by the network of factors that condition the appearance of tumors, both spontaneous and induced. Thus, in carcinogenesis with polycyclic hydrocarbons, for example, the appearance of tumors is affected by such factors as the solvent vehicle used for administration, the method and site of application, anticarcinogenic or cocarcinogenic action of substances given simultaneously, the nutritional state of the animal, and species as well as strain and organ differences in susceptibility to the particular agent used (see Greenstein 1954; Berenblum, 1954).

Endocrine relationships within the host organism may on occasion also play a key role in carcinogenesis. A leading observation in this field was that of Lathrop and Loeb (1916), who showed that castration of female mice at an early age prevents the subsequent formation of mammary tumors. Later, it was found that administration of estrogens to male mice leads to the appearance of mammary carcinoma, where otherwise none would occur (Lacassagne, 1932). The complex of endocrine influences that operate in normal development and tumorigenesis within the mouse mammary gland offers a particularly interesting model system, and as such has received intensive study (see Bern and Nandi, 1961). Other examples of the modulative action of hormones in carcinogenesis are to be seen in ovarian tumors, which may arise from various disturbances of the pituitary-ovarian relationship in mice, by the neoplasms that may be initiated in the testes of rodents by estrogen administration, or by the tumors that may develop in the adrenal cortex of certain strains of mice and rats following gonadectomy (see Hertz, 1957; Bielschowsky and Horning, 1958; Clifton, 1959).

The most important modifying factors in carcinogenesis, however, appear to be hereditary in character. There is strong evidence that susceptibility or resistance to the development of particular types of tumors is genetically determined (see Strong, 1958). Most of this information comes from experimental studies on inbred strains of mice. By systematic brother-sister mating and selection for variants, a wide variety of genetically different lines have been produced (Strong, 1942; Little, 1947; Jay, 1963). Among the hereditary characteristics that can be selected for are differences in the incidence of particular types of spontaneous tumors or the tendency for specific neoplasms to appear after treatment with a given carcinogen. Strain C57 *Black*, for example, shows few mammary or pulmonary tumors, whereas in strains *A* and *DBA* nearly all breeding females develop neoplasms of the mammary gland. Strain *C* is characterized by a high incidence of pulmonary tumors and of lymphatic leukemia as well. Susceptibility to individual carcinogens also varies between strains, but in general the relative incidence of spontaneous and induced tumors of a given type do not run in parallel. No strains of mice or other animals are found with a uniformly high or low incidence of all tumors, and it thus seems clear that the influence of genetic factors on carcinogenesis is wielded separately for each type of tumor.

The genetic mechanisms underlying susceptibility and resistance have been revealed most clearly for chemically induced tumors (Heston, 1944, 1948, 1963; Law, 1954). Crosses between strains of mice differing in incidence of lung tumors suggest that a pattern of multiple factors is involved. The genes concerned appear to segregate in Mendelian fashion in the F_2 generation and in backcrosses to the original parental lines. It has been possible to associate a high incidence of such lung tumors with known genetic markers such as shaker, flexed tail, and yellow (Heston, 1948). The influence of hereditary factors is shown with particular clarity by the experiments of Heston and Dunn (1951). In this investigation, L-strain mice, which are resistant to the development of lung tumors, were crossed with individuals of the susceptible A strain. Some of the F_1 hybrids were implanted with lung tissue from A mice; others received transplants of L-strain lung. All these animals were then given 1,2,5,6-dibenzanthracene intravenously to induce lung tumors. Within the hybrid hosts, only 3 percent of the L-strain implants developed tumors, but 39 percent of the A-strain grafts showed neoplastic change. Since the host background in this case was identical, it is clear that the competence for neoplastic change in lung cells is determined by cellular rather than by systemic factors.

One other major category, the tumor-producing viruses, must be added to the plethora of agents now known to initiate or modulate neoplastic change. In the minds of some investigators, viruses are unique as carcinogens and must be assigned a central role in the mechanisms of tumor production. The existence of such agents was first demonstrated by Peyton Rous in 1911, when he showed that sarcomas could be induced in chickens by cell-free filtrates from a tumor of the same type. The Rous virus has been the subject of many studies in the intervening years, and particular interest has focused on its effects on cells in tissue culture. These studies will be described in detail in Chapter 7. A striking feature of carcinogenesis with the Rous virus, as with most other tumor viruses, is the rapidity with which tumors appear following inoculation. Young chickens infected with the Rous agent may develop sarcomas at the site of injection within as little as 5 to 6 days. The long latent period of weeks or months, characteristic of tumor induction with radiation or chemical agents, is essentially lacking. That the Rous virus is a foreign infectious agent is shown by the appearance of antibodies to its presence, both in chickens and in other species (for example, ducks and turkeys) in which the virus can be propagated. Interestingly, although sarcomas of a specific type are characteristically produced in pullets or adult chickens, the Rous agent, if injected into chick embryos, causes merely hemorrhagic nonneoplastic lesions. After cultivation in guinea pigs or ducks, altered strains of Rous virus may elicit new types of tumors, such as periosteal neoplasms, if reinoculated into chickens (Duran-Reynals, 1959).

Although painstaking investigation over many years has failed to reveal the presence of viruses in most other tumors, a number have been discovered in which viruses or viruslike agents do occur (see Oberling, 1952; Andervont, 1959; Graffi and Bielka, 1959; Gross, 1961b). Such neoplasms are distributed broadly among animal groups. In birds, several other viruses besides the Rous agent have been shown to produce malignant tumors, and a complex array of avian leukoses appears to be associated with filterable factors (see Gross, 1961b). Among amphibia, evidence for an oncogenic virus can be found in the occurrence of kidney tumors in wild populations of R. pipiens (Lucké, 1938, 1952; see also Chapter 7). The most extensive information on tumorigenic viruses, however, comes from mammalian systems, beginning with the pioneer investigations of Shope (1932). Working with wild cottontail rabbits, Shope noted the occurrence of horny benign growths in the integument, and found that cell-free extracts of these papillomas could induce similar tumors when administered to other cottontail rabbits. The Shope virus, as it has been designated, can also elicit papillomas on injection into domestic rabbits. In this case, however, the filterable agent as such disappears, and can only rarely be recovered. Later, these tumors may undergo a further conversion to squamous cell carcinomas, a process that occurs much less frequently in cottontails. The relation, if any, of the Shope agent to this secondary transition remains to be clarified.

In mice, the most conspicuous indication of tumor viruses until recent years has been the so-called mammary tumor agent, or milk factor. The discovery of this viruslike agent stemmed from earlier observations that transmission of the tendency to develop mammary tumors followed a maternal pattern of inheritance. Seeking an explanation for this phenomenon, Bittner (1936) found that a factor conditioning the development of mouse mammary cancer can be transferred from mother to offspring through nursing. Thus, if mice from a high mammary cancer strain such as A or DBA are removed at birth and foster-nursed by a female from a low cancer strain such as *C57BL*, the subsequent incidence of mammary tumors is greatly reduced. Conversely, foster nursing in the reverse direction leads to an increase in mammary tumor frequency. The agent present in the milk of mice from such strains as *A* or *DBA* is commonly referred to as the mouse mammary tumor virus. A great number of studies have been performed on this factor (see DeOme, 1962). The milk agent can be extracted from the tissues and organs of males or females as well as from milk per se; it can be transmitted experimentally by various means, including subcutaneous and intraperitoneal injection, but only rarely by cage contact. Unlike the Rous or Shope viruses, if introduced locally, the milk factor has no effect at the site of inoculation. Tumors arise in the mammary gland as a selective target organ and only after a long latent period measured in months. The milk factor thus becomes an additional strand in the web of intrinsic and extrinsic factors that condition the appearance of mouse mammary cancer. Whether it has an indispensable role is debatable. Transmission of the milk agent does not occur *in utero*. Thus, mice removed by Caesarian section and foster-nursed by a female lacking the milk factor can be used to establish an agent-free strain. Characteristically the incidence of mammary tumors in these strains is low, but it can be restored to a high level at any time by reintroduction of the mammary tumor virus. Even without such treatment, however, the incidence of mammary cancer can be elevated by changing the hormonal status of these mice appropriately. Mammary tumors in agent-free animals may also be induced with chemical carcinogens. With the aid of the electron microscope, conspicuous viruslike particles can be visualized in tumors or preneoplastic lesions in the mammary gland of mice. Interestingly, however, inclusions are to be found in the tissues of agent-free animals as well as those from mice bearing the milk factor. The particles are identical in appearance and relative number in the two groups. The functional relation of these visible elements to the mouse mammary virus as such is accordingly uncertain (Pitelka, DeOme, and Bern, 1960). New methods for bioassay of the tumor agent (Nandi, 1963) may aid in resolving this problem.

Two additional discoveries in mice have opened up broadly the topic of tumorigenic viruses. One of these is the demonstration that certain types of murine leukemia can be transmitted by cell-free agents. The initial findings of Gross (1951) on this point were greeted with some skepticism, but a number of investigators have confirmed that induction of leukemia with appropriate cell-free filtrates is indeed possible (see Graffi and Bielka, 1959; Moloney, 1960, 1962; Miller, 1961; Gross, 1961a, 1961b). The number and kind of tumorigenic agents represented by these observations is as yet uncertain, and their mechanism of action remains to be determined. But in the course of searching for leukemogenic viruses, Stewart (1955) discovered incidentally an even more interesting factor. Inoculating mice with extracts from leukemic animals, she observed in one inbred strain that the typical response was not the induction of leukemia. Instead, tumors appeared in the parotid glands and often in the adrenals as well. This discrepancy led eventually to the characterization of a new transmissible factor, which has been termed polyoma virus. Fortunately, the agent in question can readily be propagated in cell culture (Stewart, Eddy, Gochenour, Borgese, and Grubbs, 1957), particularly if the cultures are prepared from mouse embryonic cells (Stewart, Eddy, and Borgese, 1958).

Spectacular results are obtained by inoculating mice with polyoma virus grown in an embryonic mouse cell system. As many as 20 different types of tumors have been observed, covering a broad span of histological types. A number of animals display neoplasms at different sites (see Figure 1.12). Polyoma also produces a more limited array of tumors in other species, including hamsters, rats, and rabbits. It would be misleading to regard polyoma virus as a universal carcinogen (Dawe, 1960), but the broad spectrum of effectiveness seen here, combined with immediacy of action, is certainly unparalleled by any other agent. The multiple effects obtained seem to stem from a single factor, which displays other properties typical of an infectious virus; for example, marked antigenicity in mice as well as in other species, production of cytopathic changes in cell cultures, and hemagglutination of erythrocytes (Stewart, Eddy, and Stanton, 1960). As a model for cell-virus relationships, therefore, the polyoma system has received intensive study (see Chapter 7).

The efforts of many investigators have thus provided an extensive fabric of background information concerning the factors that initiate or modulate neoplastic transformations. It cannot be said, however, that substantial light has yet been shed on the important questions of where and how these manifold influences operate within somatic cells, although there has been no lack of speculation. There is, of course, no logical necessity for a unitary concept in the origin of tumors. The transition of normal to neoplastic cells has often been pictured as a complex of parallel and perhaps unrelated processes, and cancer may conceivably be a family of diseases rather than a single entity. Yet, for most investigators, it has been difficult to escape the view that common elements do in fact exist in neoplastic transformations. Upon this premise, the somatic mutation and virus theories have frequently been raised as rival explanations. The idea that tumors represent genetic variants is

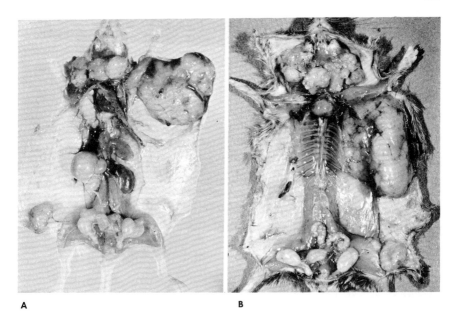

A B

FIG. 1.12. Production of multiple tumors in mice with polyoma virus. (A) Neoplasms arising in a young male animal inoculated with cell-free fluids from cultures of mouse embryo tissues containing the tumor agent. Prominent mammary tumors have appeared; also parotid gland tumors, and a large renal sarcoma. (B) Tumors appearing in another male mouse, similarly inoculated: mammary adenocarcinoma can be seen in left axilla and left inguinal area. Animal also has bilateral tumors of parotid and sublingual glands, and an epithelial thymoma. (From Stewart, Eddy, and Borgese, 1958.)

an attractive one, and has been advocated by many different workers (see Boveri, 1912; Fardon, 1953; Burdette, 1955; Graffi and Bielka, 1959; Bryan, 1960; Hieger, 1961). According to this concept, the neoplastic state arises from a mutation or a series of mutations that releases the corresponding cells from growth-controlling mechanisms and permit autonomous multiplication (Burnet, 1959). This process might depend on point mutation or chromosomal changes, or even on the alteration of some self-replicating system in the cytoplasm. From this standpoint, the multiplicity of carcinogenic agents is understandable, since an equally diverse array of factors affects the rate of mutation in more conventional systems.

Other investigators have preferred to assert the primacy of viral factors as a conceptual background (Oberling, 1952; Duran-Reynals, 1959; Gross, 1961b). According to this view, cancer is essentially an infective process, arising from the entry of tumor viruses into susceptible cells or by the activation of viral agents previously present in latent form. This concept draws strong support from the fact that viruses appear to have the most direct and immediate action of any known carcinogenic agents. The apparent absence of viruses from the majority of tumors is attributed to the occurrence of viral factors in an inactive or nontransmissible form. From this point of view, the activation of viral agents is the final common path in carcinogenesis, whatever the nature of the initial stimulus. Chemical carcinogens, radiations, and other extrinsic factors are assumed to act indirectly in the genesis of tumors. The long latent period characteristically observed with these agents is interpreted to mean that a secondary activation of tumor virus must take place before neoplastic conversion finally occurs.

It does not seem profitable to recapitulate the detailed arguments that have been presented in support of one or another of these theories, since the resulting polemics have often been based on the mistaken assumption that mutational and viral concepts for the origin of tumors are mutually exclusive. With the rise of bacterial and viral genetics (Chapter 2), it has become abundantly clear that no hard and fast line can be drawn between infection and heredity. In some cases, viruses may be directly incorporated into the bacterial genome, and this finding has led to suggestions that tumor viruses may be similarly integrated into the genetic apparatus of host cells as a basis for neoplastic change. Experimental models can be constructed for the examination of this hypothesis as well as for alternative explanations; for example, that tumor viruses bring about the directed conversion of epigenetic control systems (see Chapter 7). Thus, genetic, epigenetic, and viral concepts can be considered together in a broader view of carcinogenesis (Luria, 1960). Their relative importance may perhaps best be assessed from a free construction of inductive explanations rather than by continuing attempts to fit observation and experiment into preconceived theories.

Evolution of Tumor Patterns The obscurity that surrounds the onset of neoplasia is due in part to the difficulty in separating what may be strategic initial changes from others that are clearly sequelae within established tumors. Many of the latter are secondary alterations, quite unrelated to the initial acquisition of malignant properties. Drug resistance may develop within a clone of sensitive tumor cells, for example, or changes in antigenicity may arise during serial transplantation. There is, however, no reason to conclude that the basic mechanisms of variation are necessarily different for the origin and remodeling of tumor cell populations respectively. The development of neoplastic properties appears to be a multistage process in which the overt manifestations of malignancy are an indication but not an end point of cellular change.

The plasticity of tumor cell populations is supported by a wide array of observations and experiments. From the earliest histological studies, for example, it has been obvious that tumors tend to diverge from the morphological configurations of normal structures and that sequential changes in this respect may occur within single neoplasms. This tendency is referred to as anaplasia and as a rule leads in the direction of less specialized patterns. The degree of anaplastic change is widely variable between different tumors and even in various parts of a single neoplasm (see Willis, 1953). Thus, some benign tumors may closely resemble their normal counterparts, differing from them only in an unrestricted course of growth. Even among malignant tumors, occasional neoplasms are comparatively well-differentiated and continue to form specialized products corresponding to a specific cell type; for example, connective-tissue fibers, keratin, pigment, or hormones. More anaplastic tumors may be recognizable only as carcinomas or sarcomas of a particular organ on the basis of epithelial or mesenchymal characteristics. In such cases, the degree of differentiation is inadequate to reveal the exact precursor cells. In extremely anaplastic tumors, the population sometimes consists of a chaotic jumble of cells with a variable or pleomorphic character, in which it may be difficult to establish any origins with certainty.

Dedifferentiation in tumors thus implies a tendency for the architectural designs and specialized structures of normal tissues to undergo modification or replacement by simplified or variant growth forms. Whether this is accomplished by genetic or epigenetic means is not clear. Once established, however, each tumor tends to grow according to a characteristic structural pattern. But further alterations may arise during continued proliferation. Such changes appear to be random and irreversible, leading almost invariably toward more anaplastic patterns of organization. The combination of increased growth and decreased differentiation has sometimes occasioned interpretations of anaplasia as a reversion to more pluripotent states of development. On closer inspection, however, there can be no question of regarding the loss of specialized structure within tumors as a simple regression along embryonic pathways (Huxley, 1958). The structural configurations of tumors are not those of embryonic rudiments, but are instead frequently characterized by novel and atypical elements of histiotypic design. Neoplasms of the mammary gland in mice, for example, may display a wide variety of unit patterns based on cystic, papillary or solid cellular growths, and marked fluctuations may be found between the relative development of parenchyma, stroma, and extracellular materials (Dunn, 1959). Some examples of this disparity are shown in

Figure 1.13. At the cellular level, the distinguishing features of anaplasia are an increasing disorganization and pleomorphism that bears little or no resemblance to the generalized cell groupings of the early embryo.

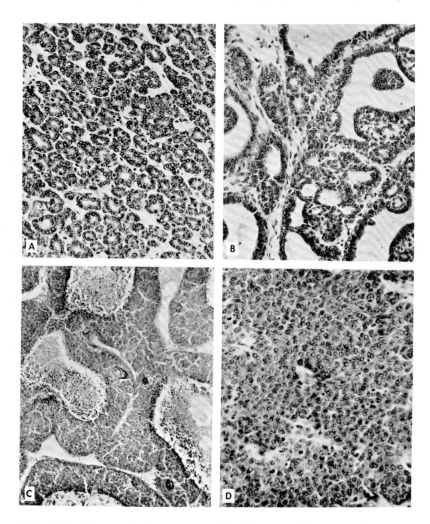

FIG. 1.13. Tumors of the mammary gland in mice, illustrating diversity in structural pattern. (A) Adenocarcinoma with fine uniform acinar structure. (B) Adenocarcinoma, which shows cyst formation and papillary ingrowth. Small glandular structures are present in the more cellular areas. (C) Adenocarcinoma with macroglandular pattern. Necrotic material is found between broad bands of epithelial cells. Small masses of squamous cells are seen in the center. (D) Adenocarcinoma showing solid cellular formation with no apparent glandular structure. (From Dunn, 1959.)

As a concept, anaplasia was originally framed in morphological terms. Within recent years, however, striking indications have been obtained of similar regressions at the biochemical level. This tendency has been most sharply defined through the extensive studies of Greenstein and his associates on enzyme activities in normal and neoplastic tissues (Greenstein, 1954; Weinhouse, 1960). A comparison between the two is not easily made, for the characterization of enzymes in tumors is fraught with numerous practical difficulties and potential artifacts. Of necessity, determinations are based usually on extracts from neoplastic tissue, and thus can depict merely the potential rather than the effective levels of enzyme activity within living cells. A more serious problem arises from the difficulty of separating neoplasms from the surrounding or enclosed normal tissues for purposes of analysis. Particularly for primary tumors in early stages, the resulting bias may obscure small but strategic focal changes. Transplanted tumors are much more satisfactory as uniform sources of material, but these are obviously the end result of secondary changes as well as those that may be associated with the initial conversion to malignancy.

Despite these qualifications, the work of Greenstein illustrates in striking fashion the evolution of enzyme patterns within tumor cell populations. Over a period of years he and his associates assembled a broad array of data for normal tissues as well as for transplanted neoplasms in several species, notably the mouse and rat. From this vantage point, a number of basic trends can be discerned, and have been expressed in the form of generalizations (Greenstein, 1954). Normal tissues, it appears, are characterized by well-differentiated profiles of enzymatic activities, and these differences in biochemical texture are as distinctive as elements in morphological design (see Figure 1.14). Although occasional enzymes may be unique to particular tissues (for example, pepsin in gastric mucosa), the differences observed are mainly quantitative in nature. Mouse liver, for example, exhibits high arginase and catalase activities, with a low level of alkaline phosphatase. Intestinal mucosa, on the other hand, is characterized by a very high level of alkaline phosphatase, moderate arginase, and a low catalase activity. A similar individuality in enzyme spectrum can be found in other normal tissues.

In contrast, the enzymatic patterns of tumors are much less differentiated. No enzymes unique to neoplastic tissues have been found, and there is a tendency for regression of those enzymes presumably associated with specialized functions in the tissue of origin. Thus distinctive individual enzymes, such as cystine desulfurase, may disappear. Others that show high levels of activity in normal homologues may decline in

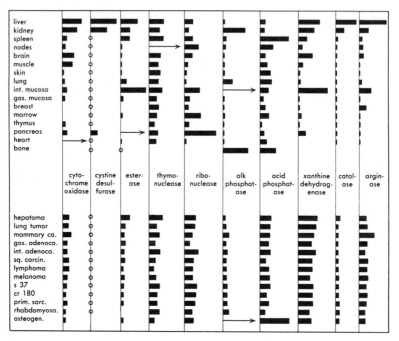

FIG. 1.14. Levels of various enzymes in normal and cancerous tissues of mice. Relative activities are denoted by length of horizontal bars. (After Greenstein, 1956. Copyright, University of Chicago Press.)

a relative sense within tumors, although there is no over-all reduction of enzymatic activity as such. Obvious exceptions can be found to this pattern; for example, alkaline phosphatase may be retained at high levels in osteogenic sarcoma, and the degree of change in enzyme spectrum is usually less for benign than for malignant neoplasms. But on the whole, the range of activities for any given enzyme is less among tumors than for a corresponding group of tissues. This is especially true for long-established neoplasms maintained by serial transplantation. Expressed differently, tumors come to resemble one another more closely in terms of enzymes than do the normal tissues of origin.

Greenstein interpreted these findings to mean that tumors tend to converge toward common metabolic patterns. This generalization has received increasing support from studies on other functional components in normal and neoplastic cells (Winzler, 1959). The patterns of B-complex vitamins, soluble cytoplasmic proteins, and free amino acids all become more uniform within tumors than in normal tissues. Anaplasia in tumors is thus a process that can be examined at molecular as well as morphological levels. The intermediate stages in the evolution of biochemical patterns among tumors have not as yet been studied in detail. There are a number of observations, however, that show that occasional enzymatic changes may occur even within transplanted tumors, and that these stepwise alterations are often associated with changes in invasiveness or histological appearance (Greenstein, 1954).

The evolution of tumor patterns has been formulated in a more comprehensive fashion by Foulds (1954, 1958) under the concept of tumor progression. Starting from the assumption that tumors arise and continue to develop by stepwise changes, Foulds has outlined a number of principles that appear to govern the course of this process. Certain of these may be expressed by the following generalizations:

(1) *Progression takes place separately for different tumors in a common environment.* Where neoplasms arise from multicentric origins, as in the mouse mammary gland, only one or a few tumors undergo progressive development at any given time, and these develop according to individualized patterns. Similarly, within a prepared field such as an area of skin treated with chemical carcinogens, the tumors that arise are heterogeneous and focal. Their origin cannot be regarded as a uniform response by a competent substrate.

(2) *Individual characteristics within a given tumor progress independently.* The evolution of skin cancers induced by chemical carcinogens in mice, for example, may involve changes in growth rate, invasiveness, and histiotypic pattern. Experimental observations show that each of these can vary without an accompanying shift in the other two characteristics (Shubik, Baserga, and Ritchie, 1953). The variety and pleomorphism of tumors may thus be an expression of the unlimited permutations and combinations that result from independent progression of unit characters.

(3) *Tumor progression appears to be potentially unlimited, without any well-defined end points.* Among different neoplasms the evolution of new patterns is capricious with respect to extent and timing. Frequently the degree of tumor progression is limited within the primary host. But by prolonging the existence of the tumor indefinitely in serial transplantation, a much more extensive pattern of variation is usually observed. There appears to be no stage at which further variations cannot take place within tumor cell populations. Even in neoplasms maintained for many years by serial propagation, alterations continue to occur spontaneously or can be induced experimentally.

The progression of unit characters within neoplastic populations can be illustrated by the acquisition of independence from growth stimulation or inhibition within the host environment. A specific example is the evolution of autonomy within those tumors that at early stages are hormone-dependent (Furth, 1953; Bielschowsky and Horning, 1958; Furth, Kim, and Clifton, 1960). Ordinarily, fluctuations in hormonal level do not produce tumors, but several cases are known in which neoplasms arise in target organs following excessive and long-continued endocrine stimulation. Thus tumors appear regularly if ovarian transplants are placed within the spleens of castrated mice. In this position, the estrogen produced by the graft is inactivated in the liver. Consequently, it does not reach the pituitary as a normal feedback mechanism to check the production of gonadotropic hormones, which impinge on the ovarian transplant continuously. Similarly, if the production of thyroid hormone is blocked by thiouracil, neoplasms of the thyroid appear in mice, whereas the administration of high levels of estrogen to males may result in Leydig cell tumors of the testes. Tumors may also arise from hormonal deficiencies if this condition leads to compensatory processes in endocrine organs. For example, chronic deficiency of thyroid hormone in mice or rats may cause the appearance of tumors in the pituitary which secrete thyrotropic hormones, and removal of the gonads may give rise to neoplasms of the adrenal cortex as an accessory source of sex hormones.

Characteristically, tumors arising from endocrine imbalance of either type are at first hormone-dependent. Thus Leydig cell tumors of the testes in mice require the continued presence of estrogen, and thyrotropic neoplasms of the pituitary grow as transplants only in thyroidectomized animals. In some cases, tumors that are conditioned by specific hormones may arise from the action of extrinsic carcinogens rather than from functional changes within. In the rat, for example, hormone-responsive tumors of the mammary gland may be produced by administration of 3-methylcholanthrene or by exposure to ionizing radiation (Furth, Kim, and Clifton, 1960). But regardless of the exact mechanism by which hormone-dependent tumors are initially derived, the response to endocrine stimulation is not usually a stable condition. Sooner or later in most, if not all, of these neoplasms, hormone-independent variants arise. These proliferate in an autonomous manner, unresponsive to stimulation or inhibition by the host. The onset of this change is variable and random in character, often occurring only in serial transplantation rather than in the primary tumor. The acquisition of hormone independence may coincide, although not necessarily, with anaplastic changes in tumor morphology or a reduction in the secretion of particular endocrine factors (Klein and Klein, 1957).

The mechanisms of tumor progression can be explored in a number of different systems, and for this purpose the so-called ascites growth form is particularly useful. Ascites tumors are defined as neoplastic populations capable of growth in free suspension within the body fluids, typically in the peritoneal cavity. They may originate from a variety of different solid tumors or leukemias; characteristically, the proliferation of well-isolated single cells occurs, or small aggregates form without supporting stroma or direct vascular supply. The simplicity of growth pattern renders these tumors particularly suitable for studies in population dynamics. Most ascitic neoplasms when initiated with inocula of appropriate size grow at first in unrestricted fashion in the peritoneal cavity. There is a well-defined logarithmic growth phase at this point, and population doubling times of 16 to 24 hours have been measured with various ascites tumors of mice (Klein, 1956; Patt and Straube, 1956). Later, the growth rate declines, and the number of cells in suspension may reach a limiting value or rise slowly until death occurs. Such populations can be easily maintained by serial inoculation in animals of similar genetic constitution. In favorable instances, they offer nearly pure cultures of neoplastic cells without substantial admixture of host elements, and are particularly valuable for biochemical and cytogenetic studies. Consequently, ascites tumors, particularly those of mice, have come into broad use in experimental oncology (see Hauschka, 1956).

The mechanisms that underlie conversion of solid tumors into the ascites form have been the subject of a number of studies, principally those of George and Eva Klein. The stage was set for these investigations by the discovery that tumors can be classified into three groups according to their tendency to undergo ascites transformation under experimental conditions (Klein, 1951, 1953). If a broad spectrum of mouse tumors is examined, a few prove to be immediately convertible, that is, ascites populations can be established directly by inoculating minced tissue from a solid neoplasm into the peritoneal cavity of a compatible host. The suspensions thus obtained include a variable percentage of blood cells and exudate elements, but consist predominantly of tumor elements. Figure 1.15 provides a typical picture of such populations. Once established, these tumors can be continued indefinitely in the ascites form by serial transfer.

Other tumors are only gradually convertible, a phenomenon first encountered in an ascites variant from the Ehrlich mouse carcinoma (Klein and Klein, 1951). In such cases, intraperitoneal inoculation of a tumor mash gives rise merely to solid neoplasms initially, although a fluid exudate accumulates within the body cavity. This fluid as a rule contains at first few or no detectable tumor cells. Presumably a few cells are contributed, however, by desquamation of the adjacent solid tumors. Their presence can be inferred by transferring the neoplasms serially with fluid exudate alone. After a variable number of such fluid

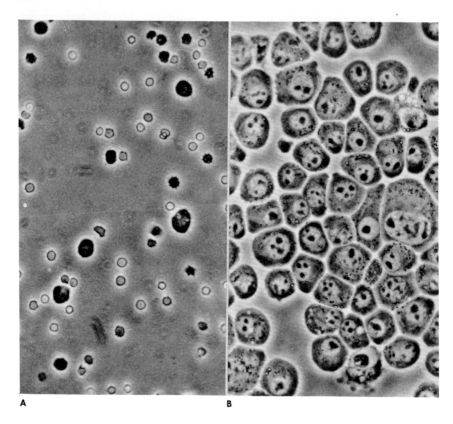

FIG. 1.15. Growth of mouse cells as ascites tumors. (A) Peritoneal exudate from a C_3H mouse 10 days after inoculation with 10^6 *MCIM* sarcoma cells from solid tumor (M_{SS} line). No tumor cells are visible. The field contains erythrocytes and a few nontumorous nucleated cells. Phase contrast. (B) Ascites from a C_3H mouse, 10 days after inoculation of 10^6 *MCIM* sarcoma cells in ascites form (line M_{AA}). The population represents nearly a pure culture of free tumor cells. Phase contrast. (From Ringertz, Klein, and Klein, 1957.)

transfer generations, the number of tumor cells in free suspension rises to a high value and the resulting populations can be propagated indefinitely in a typical ascites form (see Figure 1.16).

Still other tumors appear to be inconvertible to the ascites form under the range of conditions that have thus far been explored. In the study mentioned above (Klein, 1953), this group accounted for 30 out of 42 of the mouse neoplasms examined. The convertible and inconvertible tumors did not differ distinctively in histogenetic features, although all those capable of ascites transformation were rapidly growing and anaplastic. Six tumors proved to be gradually convertible; these included both carcinomas and sarcomas. In the immediately convertible group, one tumor was a transplantable sarcoma and five were lymphomas. The latter appear to be preadapted for multiplication in the peritoneal fluid. All that have been tested so far grow readily in the ascites form (Klein, 1956).

In considering the inability of a majority of tumors to grow directly or at all in the ascites form, one reasonable explanation might be that these neoplasms fail to elicit an adequate exudate as the milieu essential for proliferation of a free cell population. This possibility has been systematically explored in mice by implanting cell suspensions from solid tumors into exudates pre-established in the peritoneal cavity (Klein and Klein, 1954). It is difficult to produce and maintain a large volume of sterile ascitic fluid by nonspecific agents, but known "carrier" ascites tumors can be employed instead for the purpose. Although intermingling of carrier and test cells under these conditions is inevitable, an ingenious experimental design may be used to discriminate between the two cell types. For this purpose, carrier tumors are chosen that have originated from a line of mice other than those from which the test tumors are

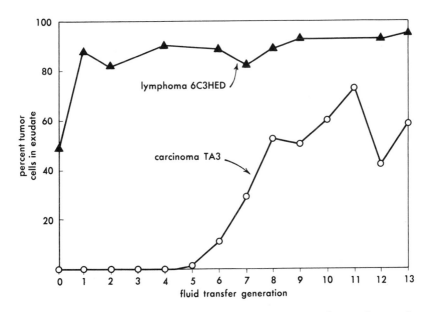

FIG. 1.16. Conversion of solid tumors into ascites populations by serial transfers in the peritoneal cavity of mice. Upper curve shows an example of immediate conversion to the ascites form. Lower curve illustrates gradual conversion. (After Klein, 1956; and Klein and Klein, 1956.)

derived. If these carrier tumors are strictly strain-specific, they will grow progressively only in the strain of origin, or in F_1 hybrid mice obtained by crosses with other lines. Thus it is possible to grow the carrier and test tumor cells as mixed populations in F_1 hybrids between the two respective strains. Eventually the carrier component can be eliminated selectively by inoculating such mixtures into mice of the test-tumor line.

In the experiments mentioned above, F_1 hybrid mice of appropriate genetic constitution were prepared and inoculated first with a carrier tumor. After a conspicuous exudate had accumulated in the peritoneal cavity, cells from the neoplasm to be tested for ascites growth were added to the carrier population. Following two days of further propagation, the mixtures were assayed by inoculating mice of the test-tumor strain and carrier strain, respectively. When the test neoplasm was one previously shown to be convertible either immediately or gradually to the ascites form, the Kleins found that most, if not all, of the mice in both assay groups developed tumors and eventually died. A quite different result was obtained with tumors that had been inconvertible by serial transfer of exudates. In this case, the assay populations gave rise uniformly to tumors in mice of the carrier strain, but few if any of the mice from the test-tumor strain developed progressively growing neoplasms.

The inability of certain tumors to undergo ascites transformation thus seems to be correlated directly with the failure to survive even for short periods as suspensions in the peritoneal fluid. This characteristic, rather than differences in ability to promote an exudate, appears to be the chief limiting factor. On the other hand, survival within exudates is a permissive but not sufficient condition as such for ascites growth. The Kleins could demonstrate no differences in survival of tumor elements within exudates, whether the cells in question were derived from a gradually convertible neoplasm already established in ascites form or from one that was not. The cellular adjustments that facilitate survival in free suspension, therefore, are not identical with the changes required to implement progressive growth and proliferation under the same conditions. A sequential progression appears to underlie the conversion process as a whole.

From the standpoint of mechanisms that enter into ascites conversions, the most important question is whether this phenomenon is to be construed as a physiological adaptation or as the result of random variation and selection (Klein and Klein, 1955, 1956). The latter alternative is supported by a variety of evidence, obtained for the most part by a closer analysis of the events that underlie gradual conversion. It can be shown, for example, that the eventual population shift is a relatively permanent change, not readily reversible by an alteration of environmental conditions (Klein, 1954; Ringertz, Klein, and Klein, 1957). Tumors that have been gradually converted from the solid (SS) to the ascites (AA) form can be easily re-established as solid neoplasms (AS) by subcutaneous inoculation. The solid AS sublines, however, differ distinctively from the original SS tumors in that they are immediately convertible to ascites populations, even after many serial transfers in the solid form.

More direct confirmation of the variation-selection hypothesis can be obtained from the study of ascites transformation in sublines established with small numbers of cells from a gradually convertible tumor. In one investigation of this type, a number of subpopulations (FC) were derived as solid tumors by inoculating an average of four cells into the peritoneal cavity of mice (Klein, 1955a, 1955b). The ability of these FC sublines to undergo ascites conversion was compared to that of the original mass SS population, using a technique in which intraperitoneal and subcutaneous transfers were alternated. Presumably by increasing the number of tumor cells available at the alternating fluid transfers, this procedure lowered the number of transfer generations required for conversion of the mass SS population from 23 to 13. Under the same conditions, seven out of eight FC sublines remained inconvertible after 21 to 29 transfers. One gave rise to an ascites population, but only after 24 transfers.

These results clearly suggest that gradually convertible tumors consist initially of a small proportion of AA cells in populations predominantly of the SS type. Most sublines derived from a few cells are thus presumably lacking at the outset in the AA component, which must be selected out if ascites growth is to occur. This explanation is reinforced by model experiments in which cells of the original solid (SS) and derivative ascites (AA) sublines have been mixed in known proportions (Klein and Klein, 1955, 1956). When the resulting populations are assayed for ascites growth by the usual transfer of fluid exudates, immediate conversion occurs only if 5 percent or more AA cells are included in the initial mixture. Below this level, gradual conversion takes place with a linear correlation between the logarithmic proportion of AA cells and the number of fluid-transfer generations required. By extrapolating this relationship to ten transfers, the number usually required for the neoplasm in question, the Kleins estimated the frequency of AA variants in the solid tumor at one in 2.4×10^6 cells (see Figure 1.17).

The mechanisms of ascites transformation thus provide an interesting model for the analysis of unit variation in tumor cell populations.

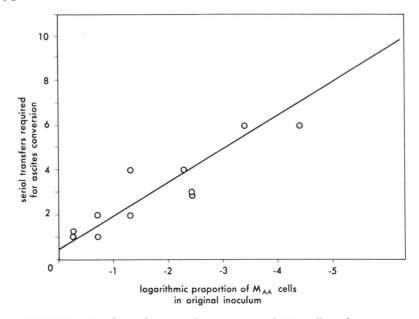

FIG. 1.17. Correlation between the proportion of M_{AA} cells in known mixtures with solid tumor (M_{SS}) cells, and the number of serial transfers required to convert the population as a whole into the ascites form. The regression line has been calculated by the method of least squares. (After Klein, 1956.)

The conditions that apply to this particular system may be specialized, but the trends observed are general ones. Parallel progressions can be followed for other characteristics of neoplasms, such as variation in chromosome pattern, the development of resistance to drugs or other extrinsic agents, and the acquisition of transplantability in hosts of differing genetic constitution. These phenomena will be explored more extensively in later chapters. They depict established tumors as diverse assemblages of variant cell types and as mosaics in continuous evolution. In this sense, the sequential changes that take place constitute a series of problems in population dynamics. As such, they can be investigated with experimental systems *in vitro* as well as in the intact organism.

■ References

ALTENBURG, E. 1957. Genetics. Revised edition. New York: Holt, Rinehart and Winston, Inc. 496 pp.

ANDERVONT, H. B. 1959. Problems concerning the tumor viruses. *In: The Viruses*, Vol. 3, pp. 307–368. F. M. Burnet and W. M. Stanley, eds. New York: Academic Press, Inc.

BALINSKY, B. I. 1960. An introduction to embryology. Philadelphia: W. B. Saunders Company. 562 pp.

BAUER, K. H. 1963. Das Krebsproblem. Second edition. Berlin: Springer-Verlag. 1099 pp.

BERENBLUM, I. 1954. A speculative review: the probable nature of promoting action and its significance in the understanding of the mechanism of carcinogenesis. Cancer Res., **14**: 471–477.

BERN, H. A., and NANDI, S. 1961. Recent studies of the hormonal influence in mouse mammary carcinogenesis. Progr. Exp. Tumor Res., **2**: 90–144.

BHAT, N. R. 1949. A dominant mutant mosaic house mouse. Heredity, **3**: 243–248.

BIELSCHOWSKY, F., and HORNING, E. S. 1958. Aspects of endocrine carcinogenesis. Brit. Med. Bull., **14**: 106–115.

BITTNER, J. J. 1936. Some possible effects of nursing on the mammary gland tumor incidence in mice. Science, **84**: 162.

BLUM, H. F. 1959. Carcinogenesis by ultraviolet light. Princeton, N.J.: Princeton University Press, 340 pp.

BONSER, G. M., CLAYSON, D. B., and JULL, J. W. 1958. Some aspects of the experimental induction of tumours of the bladder. Brit. Med. Bull., **14**: 146–152.

BOSS, J. M. N. 1955. The pairing of somatic chromosomes: a survey. Texas Repts. Biol. Med., **13**: 213–221.

BOVERI, T. 1912. Zur Frage der Entwicklung maligner Tumoren. Jena. English translation, *The Origin of Malignant Tumors*, by M. Boveri, 1929. Baltimore: The Williams and Wilkins Company. 119 pp.

BOYLAND, E., and HORNING, E. S. 1949. The induction of tumours with nitrogen mustards. Brit. J. Cancer, **3**: 118–123.

BRACHET, J. 1960. The biochemistry of development. London: Pergamon Press, Inc. 320 pp.

BRIGGS, R. 1962. Comments following paper by J. A. Moore. J. Cellular Comp. Physiol., **60**(Suppl. 1): 32–33.

BRIGGS, R., and KING, T. J. 1952. Transplantation of living nuclei from blastula cells into enucleated frogs' eggs. Proc. Natl. Acad. Sci., **38**: 455–463.

BRIGGS, R., and KING, T. J. 1953. Factors affecting the transplantability of nuclei of frog embryonic cells. J. Exptl. Zool., **122**: 485–506.

BRIGGS, R., and KING, T. J. 1955. Specificity of nuclear function in embryonic development. *In: Biological Specificity and Growth*, pp. 207–228. E. G. Butler, ed. Princeton, N.J.: Princeton University Press.

BRIGGS, R., and KING, T. J. 1957. Changes in the nuclei of differentiating endoderm cells as revealed by nuclear transplantation. J. Morphol., **100:** 269–312.

BRIGGS, R., and KING, T. J. 1959. Nucleocytoplasmic interactions in eggs and embryos. *In: The Cell. Biochemistry, Physiology, Morphology,* Vol. 1, pp. 537–618. J. Brachet and A. E. Mirsky, eds. New York: Academic Press, Inc.

BRIGGS, R., and KING, T. J. 1960. Nuclear transplantation studies on the early gastrula *(Rana pipiens).* I. Nuclei of presumptive endoderm. Develop. Biol., **2:** 252–270.

BRIGGS, R., KING, T. J., and DI BERARDINO, M. A. 1960. Development of nuclear-transplant embryos of known chromosome complement following parabiosis with normal embryos. *In: Symposium on the Germ Cells and Earliest Stages of Development,* pp. 441–447. S. Ranzi, ed. Milan: Fondazione A. Baselli.

BRINK, R. A. 1958. Mutable loci and development of the organism. J. Cellular Comp. Physiol., **52**(Suppl. 1): 169–195.

BRINK, R. A. 1960. Paramutation and chromosome organization. Quart. Rev. Biol., **35:** 120–137.

BRINK, R. A. 1962. Phase change in higher plants and somatic cell heredity. Quart. Rev. Biol., **37:** 1–22.

BRUES, A. M. 1951. Carcinogenic effects of radiation. Advan. Biol. Med. Phys., **2:** 171–191.

BRYAN, W. R. 1960. A reconsideration of the nature of the neoplastic reaction in the light of recent advances in cancer research. J. Natl. Cancer Inst., **24:** 221–251.

BURDETTE, W. J. 1955. The significance of mutation in relation to the origin of tumors: A review. Cancer Res., **15:** 201–226.

BURNET, F. M. 1959. The clonal selection theory of acquired immunity. Nashville: Vanderbilt University Press. 209 pp.

BUSCH, H. 1962. An introduction to the biochemistry of the cancer cell. New York: Academic Press, Inc. 424 pp.

BUSCH, H. 1963. Biochemistry of cancer. *In: Biochemical Frontiers in Medicine,* pp. 210–244. H. Busch, ed. Boston: Little, Brown, and Co.

CLIFTON, K. H. 1959. Problems in experimental tumorigenesis of the pituitary gland, gonads, adrenal cortices, and mammary glands: A review. Cancer Res., **19:** 2–22.

CLUNET, J. 1910 Recherches expérimentales sur les tumeurs malignes. Paris: Steinheil. 336 pp.

COMANDON, J., and DE FONBRUNE, P. 1939. Greffe nucléaire totale, simple ou multiple, chez une Amibe. Compt. Rend. Soc. Biol., **130:** 744–748.

CONKLIN, E. G. 1905. Organ-forming substances in the eggs of ascidians. Biol. Bull., **8:** 205–230.

CONKLIN, E. G. 1931. The development of centrifuged eggs of ascidians. J. Exptl. Zool., **60:** 1–119.

COOK, J. W., HEWITT, C. L., and HIEGER, I. 1933. I. The isolation of a cancer-producing hydrocarbon from coal tar. Parts I, II, and III. J. Chem. Soc., 1933: 395–405.

COWDRY, E. V. 1955. Cancer cells. Philadelphia: W. B. Saunders Company. 677 pp.

DAWE, C. J. 1960. Cell sensitivity and specificity of response to polyoma virus. Natl. Cancer Inst. Monogr., 4: 67–128.

DEMEREC, M. 1941. Unstable genes in Drosophila. Cold Spring Harbor Symp. Quant. Biol., 9: 145–150.

DEOME, K. B. 1962. The mouse mammary tumor virus. Federation Proc., 21: 15–18.

DRIESCH, H. 1891. Entwicklungsmechanische Studien. I. Der Werth der beiden ersten Furchungszellen in der Echinodermenentwicklung. Experimentelle Erzeugung von Theil—und Doppelbildungen. II. Über die Beziehungen des Lichtes zur ersten Etappe der thierische Formbildung. Z. f. wiss. Zool., 53: 160–184.

DRIESCH, H. 1892. Entwicklungsmechanische Studien. IV. Experimentelle Veränderung des Typus der Furchung und ihre Folgen (Wirkungen von Wärmezufuhr und von Druck). Z. wiss. Zool., 55: 10–29.

DRIESCH, H. 1894. Analytische Theorie der Organischen Entwicklung. Leipzig: W. Engelmann. 184 pp.

DUNN, L. C. 1934. Analysis of a case of mosaicism in the house mouse. J. Genet., 29: 317–326.

DUNN, T. B. 1959. Morphology of mammary tumors in mice. *In: The Physiopathology of Cancer*, second edition, pp. 38–84, F. Homburger, ed. New York: Hoeber-Harper Inc.

DURAN-REYNALS, F. 1959. Virus-induced tumors and the virus theory of cancer. *In: The Physiopathology of Cancer*, second edition, pp. 238–292. F. Homburger, ed. New York: Hoeber-Harper Inc.

ELSDALE, T. R., FISCHBERG, M., and SMITH, S. 1958. A mutation that reduces nucleolar number in *Xenopus laevis*. Exptl. Cell Res., 14: 642–643.

ELSDALE, T. R., GURDON, J. B., and FISCHBERG, M. 1960. A description of the technique for nuclear transplantation in *Xenopus laevis*. J. Embryol. Exp. Morphol., 8: 437–444.

FANKHAUSER, G. 1930. Zytologische Untersuchungen an geschnürten Triton-Eiern. I. Die verzögerte Kernvorsorgung einer Halfte nach hantelförmiger Einschnürung des Eies. Arch. f. Ent.-mech., 112: 117–139.

FARDON, J. 1953. A reconsideration of the somatic mutation theory of cancer in the light of some recent developments. Science, 117: 441–445.

FINDLAY, G. M. 1928. Ultra-violet light and skin cancer. Lancet, 215: 1070–1073.

FISCHBERG, M., GURDON, J. B., and ELSDALE, T. R. 1958a. Nuclear transplantation in *Xenopus laevis*. Nature, 181: 424.

FISCHBERG, M., GURDON, J. B., and ELSDALE, T. R. 1958b. Nuclear transfer in amphibia and the problem of the potentialities of the nuclei of differentiating tissues. Exptl. Cell Res., Suppl. 6: 161–178.

FISCHBERG, M., and WALLACE, H. 1960. A mutation which reduces nucleolar number in *Xenopus laevis*. *In: The Cell Nucleus*, pp. 30–34. J. S. Mitchell, ed. London: Butterworth and Co., Ltd. 269 pp.

FOULDS, L. 1954. The experimental study of tumor progression: A review. Cancer Res., **14**: 327–339.

FOULDS, L. 1958. The natural history of cancer. J. Chronic Diseases, **8**: 2–37.

FURTH, J. 1953. Conditioned and autonomous neoplasms. Cancer Res., **13**: 477–492.

FURTH, J., KIM, U., and CLIFTON, K. H. 1960. On evolution of the neoplastic state; progression from dependence to autonomy. Natl. Cancer Inst. Monogr., **2**: 149–171.

FUSCALDO, K. E., and FOX, A. S. 1962. Immunochemical analysis of the effects of heterochromatic-euchromatic rearrangements on a protein in *Drosophila melanogaster*. Genetics, **47**: 999–1015.

GLÄSS, E. 1957. Das Problem der Genomsonderung in den Mitosen unbehandelter Rattenleber. Chromosoma, **8**: 468–492.

GOLDSCHMIDT, R. B. 1951. Chromosomes and genes. Cold Spring Harbor Symp. Quant. Biol., **16**: 1–12.

GOLDSCHMIDT, R. B. 1955. Theoretical genetics. Berkeley: University of California Press. 563 pp.

GRAFFI, A., and BIELKA, H. 1959. Probleme der experimentellen Krebsforschung. Leipzig: Akademische Verlagsgesellschaft. Geest and Portig K.-G. 560 pp.

GREENSTEIN, J. P. 1954. Biochemistry of cancer. Second edition. New York: Academic Press Inc. 653 pp.

GREENSTEIN, J. P. 1956. Some biochemical characteristics of morphologically separable cancers. Cancer Res., **16**: 641–653.

GROBSTEIN, C. 1959. Differentiation of vertebrate cells. *In: The Cell. Biochemistry, Physiology, Morphology*, Vol. 1, pp. 437–496. J. Brachet and A. E. Mirsky, eds. New York: Academic Press, Inc.

GROSS, L. 1951. "Spontaneous" leukemia developing in C_3H mice following inoculation in infancy with AK-leukemic extracts or AK-embryos. Proc. Soc. Exptl. Biol. and Med., **76**: 27–32.

GROSS, L. 1961a. Viral etiology of mouse leukemia. Advan. Cancer Res., **6**: 149–180.

GROSS, L. 1961b. Oncogenic viruses. New York: Pergamon Press. 393 pp.

GURDON, J. B. 1960a. The effects of ultraviolet irradiation on uncleaved eggs of *Xenopus laevis*. Quart. J. Microscop. Sci., **101**: 299–311.

GURDON, J. B. 1960b. Factors responsible for the abnormal development of embryos obtained by nuclear transplantation in *Xenopus laevis*. J. Embryol. Exptl. Morphol., **8**: 327–340.

GURDON, J. B. 1960c. The developmental capacity of nuclei taken from the differentiating endoderm cells of *Xenopus laevis*. J. Embryol. Exptl. Morphol., **8**: 505–526.

GURDON, J. B. 1961. The transplantation of nuclei between two subspecies of *Xenopus laevis*. Heredity, **16**: 305–315.

GURDON, J. B. 1962a. Adult frogs derived from the nuclei of single somatic cells. Develop. Biol., **4:** 256–273.

GURDON, J. B. 1962b. The transplantation of nuclei between two species of Xenopus. Develop. Biol., **5:** 68–83.

GURDON, J. B. 1962c. The developmental capacity of nuclei taken from intestinal epithelium cells of feeding tadpoles. J. Embryol. Exptl. Morphol., **10:** 622–640.

GURDON, J. B. 1963. Nuclear transplantation in amphibia and the importance of stable nuclear changes in promoting cellular differentiation. Quart. Rev. Biol., **38:** 54–78.

GURDON, J. B., ELSDALE, T. R., and FISCHBERG, M. 1958. Sexually mature individuals of Xenopus laevis from the transplantation of single somatic nuclei. Nature, **182:** 64–65.

HADDOW, A. 1958. Chemical carcinogens and their modes of action. Brit. Med. Bull., **14:** 79–92.

HADDOW, A. 1959. The chemical and genetic mechanisms of carcinogenesis. I. Nature and mode of action. II. Biologic alkylating agents. In: The Physiopathology of Cancer, second edition, pp. 565–685. F. Homburger, ed. New York: Hoeber-Harper Inc.

HANNAH, A. 1951. Localization and function of heterochromatin in Drosophila melanogaster. Advan. Genet., **4:** 87–125.

HARRIS, R. J. C., ed. 1963. Cellular basis and aetiology of late somatic effects of ionizing radiation. New York: Academic Press, Inc. 359 pp.

HAUSCHKA, T. S., ed. 1956. Ascites tumors as tools in quantitative oncology. Ann. N. Y. Acad. Sci., **63:** 637–1030.

HEATH, J. C. 1956. The production of malignant tumours by cobalt in the rat. Brit. J. Cancer, **10:** 668–673.

HENNEN, S. 1961. On the capacity of Rana pipiens nuclei to promote development in their own cytoplasm after replicating in Rana sylvatica cytoplasm. Genetics, **46:** 869–870.

HERTWIG, O. 1893. Über den Wert der ersten Furchungszellen für die Organbildung des Embryo. Arch. mikroskop. Anat., **42:** 662–806.

HERTZ, R. 1957. An appraisal of the concepts of endocrine influence on the etiology, pathogenesis, and control of abnormal and neoplastic growth. Cancer Res., **17:** 423–431.

HESTON, W. E. 1944. Role of heredity in tumor development. J. Natl. Cancer Inst., **5:** 161–172.

HESTON, W. E. 1948. Genetics of cancer. Advan. Genet., **2:** 99–126.

HESTON, W. E. 1963. Genetics of neoplasia. In: Methodology in Mammalian Genetics, pp. 247–268. W. J. Burdette, ed. San Francisco: Holden-Day, Inc.

HESTON, W. E., and DUNN, T. B. 1951. Tumor development in susceptible strain A and resistant strain L lung transplants in LA F_1 hosts. J. Natl. Cancer Inst., **11:** 1057–1072.

HIEGER, I. 1961. Carcinogenesis. New York: Academic Press Inc. 138 pp.

HOLTFRETER, J. 1951. Some aspects of embryonic induction. Growth, 15(Suppl.): 117–152.

HOMBURGER, F. 1959. The physiopathology of cancer. Second edition. New York: Hoeber-Harper Inc. 1180 pp.

HÖRSTADIUS, S. 1939. The mechanics of sea urchin development studied by operative methods. Biol. Revs., 14: 132–179.

HUEPER, W. C. 1952. Experimental studies in metal cancerigenesis. I. Nickel cancers in rats. Texas Repts. Biol. Med., 10: 167–186.

HUXLEY, J. 1958. Biological aspects of cancer. New York: Harcourt, Brace and World. 156 pp.

HUXLEY, J. S., and DE BEER, G. R. 1934. The elements of experimental embryology. Cambridge: The University Press. 514 pp.

JAY, G. E., Jr. 1963. Genetic strains and stocks. In: Methodology in Mammalian Genetics, pp. 83–123. W. J. Burdette, ed. San Francisco: Holden-Day, Inc.

KENNAWAY, E. L., and HIEGER, I. 1930. Carcinogenic substances and their fluorescence spectra. Brit. Med. J., 1: 1044–1046.

KING, T. J., and BRIGGS, R. 1954. Transplantation of living nuclei of late gastrulae into enucleated eggs of Rana pipiens. J. Embryol. Exptl. Morph., 2: 73–80.

KING, T. J., and BRIGGS, R. 1955. Changes in the nuclei of differentiating gastrula cells, as demonstrated by nuclear transplantation. Proc. Natl. Acad. Sci., 41: 321–325.

KING, T. J., and BRIGGS, R. 1956. Serial transplantation of embryonic nuclei. Cold Spring Harbor Symp. Quant. Biol., 21: 271–290.

KINOSITA, R. 1937. Studies on the cancerogenic chemical substances. Trans. Soc. Pathol. Japan, 27: 665–725.

KLEIN, E. 1954. Gradual transformation of solid into ascites tumors. Permanent difference between the original and the transformed sublines. Cancer Res., 14: 482–485.

KLEIN, E. 1955a. Gradual transformation of solid into ascites tumors. Evidence favoring a mutation-selection theory. Exptl. Cell Res., 8: 188–212.

KLEIN, E. 1955b. Transformation of solid into ascites tumors. Uppsala: Almqvist and Wiksells Boktryckeri. 40 pp. New York: Academic Press, Inc.

KLEIN, E., and KLEIN, G. 1954. Differential survival of solid tumor cells after inoculation into established ascites tumors. Cancer Res., 14: 139–144.

KLEIN, G. 1951. Comparative studies of mouse tumors with respect to their capacity for growth as "ascites tumors" and their average nucleic acid content per cell. Exptl. Cell Res., 2: 518–573.

KLEIN, G. 1953. Conversion of solid into ascites tumors. Nature, 171: 398–399.

KLEIN, G. 1956. Some recent studies on the production and growth characteristics of ascites tumors. A review. Z. Krebsforsch., 61: 99–119.

KLEIN, G., and KLEIN, E. 1951. The transformation of a solid transplantable mouse carcinoma into an "ascites tumor." Cancer Res., 11: 466–469.

KLEIN, G., and KLEIN, E. 1955. Variation in cell populations of transplanted tumors as indicated by studies on the ascites transformation. Exptl. Cell Res., Suppl. 3: 218–229.

KLEIN, G., and KLEIN, E. 1956. Conversion of solid neoplasms into ascites tumors. Ann N. Y. Acad Sci., **63**: 640–665.

KLEIN, G., and KLEIN, E. 1957. The evolution of independence from specific growth stimulation and inhibition in mammalian tumour-cell populations. Symp. Soc. Exptl. Biol., **11**: 305–328.

LACASSAGNE, A. 1932. Apparition de cancers de la mamelle chez la souris mâle, soumise à des injections de folliculine. Compt. Rend. Acad. Sci., **195**: 630–632.

LACASSAGNE, A. 1945. Les cancers produits par les rayonnements électromagnétiques. Paris: Hermann et Cie. 137 pp.

LATHROP, A. E. C., and LOEB, L. 1916. Further investigations on the origin of tumors in mice. J. Cancer Res., **1**: 1–19.

LAW, L. W. 1954. Genetic studies in experimental cancer. Advan. Cancer Res., **2**: 281–352.

LAW, L. W. 1960. Radiation carcinogenesis. Advan. Biol. Med. Phys., **7**: 295–342.

LEBRETON, E., and MOULÉ, Y. 1961. Biochemistry and physiology of the cancer cell. In: The Cell. Biochemistry, Physiology, Morphology, Vol. 5, pp. 497–544. J. Brachet and A. E. Mirsky, eds. New York: Academic Press Inc.

LEFEVRE, G., JR. 1950. X-ray induced genetic effects in germinal and somatic tissue of Drosophila melanogaster. Am. Naturalist, **84**: 341–365.

LEHMAN, H. E. 1955. On the development of enucleated Triton eggs with an injected blastula nucleus. Biol. Bull., **108**: 138–150.

LEWIS, E. B. 1950. The phenomenon of position effect. Advan. Genet., **3**: 73–115.

LEWIS, W. H. 1904. Experimental studies on the development of the eye in amphibia. I. On the origin of the lens. Rana palustris. Am. J. Anat., **3**: 505–536.

LITTLE, C. C. 1947. The genetics of cancer in mice. Biol. Revs., **22**: 315–343.

LUCKÉ, B. 1938. Carcinoma in the leopard frog. Its probable causation by a virus. J. Exptl. Med., **68**: 457–468.

LUCKÉ, B. 1952. Kidney carcinoma in the leopard frog: a virus tumor. Ann. N. Y. Acad. Sci., **54**: 1093–1109.

LURIA, S. E. 1960. Viruses, cancer cells, and the genetic concept of virus infection. Cancer Res., **20**: 677–688.

McCLINTOCK, B. 1941. Spontaneous alterations in chromosome size and form in Zea mays. Cold Spring Harbor Symp. Quant. Biol., **9**: 72–81.

McCLINTOCK, B. 1951. Chromosome organization and genic expression. Cold Spring Harbor Symp. Quant. Biol., **16**: 13–47.

McCLINTOCK, B. 1956. Controlling elements and the gene. Cold Spring Harbor Symp. Quant. Biol., **21**: 197–216.

McCLINTOCK, B. 1961. Some parallels between gene control systems in maize and in bacteria. Am. Naturalist, **95**: 265–277.

McKINNELL, R. G. 1960. Transplantation of Rana pipiens (kandiyohi dominant mutant) nuclei to R. pipiens cytoplasm. Am. Naturalist, **94**: 187–188.

MERWIN, R. M., and REDMON, L. W. 1963. Induction of plasma cell tumors and sarcomas in mice by diffusion chambers placed in the peritoneal cavity. J. Natl. Cancer Inst., 31: 997–1017.

MILLER, J. F. A. P. 1961. Etiology and pathogenesis of mouse leukemia. Advan. Cancer Res., 6: 291–368.

MOLONEY, J. B. 1960. Properties of a leukemia virus. Natl. Cancer Inst. Monogr., 4: 7–38.

MOLONEY, J. B. 1962. The murine leukemias. Federation Proc., 21: 19–31.

MOORE, J. A. 1958. Transplantation of nuclei between Rana pipiens and Rana sylvatica. Exptl. Cell. Res., 14: 532–540.

MOORE, J. A. 1960. Serial back-transfers of nuclei in experiments involving two species of frogs. Dev. Biol., 2: 535–550.

MOORE, J. A. 1962. Nuclear transplantation and problems of specificity in developing embryos. J. Cellular Comp. Physiol., 60(Suppl. 1): 19–34.

MORGAN, T. H. 1934. Embryology and genetics. New York: Columbia University Press. 258 pp.

NANDI, S. 1963. New method for detection of mouse mammary virus. I. Influence of foster nursing on incidence of hyperplastic mammary nodules in BALB/cCrgl mice. J. Natl. Cancer Inst., 31: 57–73.

NANNEY, D. L. 1958. Epigenetic control systems. Proc. Natl. Acad. Sci., 44: 712–717.

OBERLING, C. 1952. The riddle of cancer. Revised edition. New Haven: Yale University Press. 238 pp.

OBERLING, C., and BERNHARD, W. 1961. The morphology of the cancer cells. In: The Cell. Biochemistry, Physiology, Morphology, Vol. 5, pp. 405–496. J. Brachet and A. E. Mirsky, eds. New York: Academic Press Inc.

OPPENHEIMER, B. S., OPPENHEIMER, E. T., DANISHEFSKY, I., STOUT, A. P., and EIRICH, F. R. 1955. Further studies of polymers as carcinogenic agents in animals. Cancer Res., 15: 333–340.

OPPENHEIMER, B. S., OPPENHEIMER, E. T., and STOUT, A. P. 1948. Sarcomas induced in rats by implanting cellophane. Proc. Soc. Exptl. Biol. Med., 67: 33–34.

OPPENHEIMER, B. S., OPPENHEIMER, E. T., and STOUT, A. P. 1952. Sarcomas induced in rodents by imbedding various plastic films. Proc. Soc. Exptl. Biol. Med., 79: 366–369.

OPPENHEIMER, E. T., WILLHITE, M., DANISHEFSKY, I., and STOUT, A. P. 1961. Observations on the effects of powdered polymer in the carcinogenic process. Cancer Res., 21: 132–134.

OPPENHEIMER, J. 1959. Intercellular activities in vertebrate development. Science, 130: 686–692.

PATT, H. M., and STRAUBE, R. L. 1956. Measurement and nature of ascites tumor growth. Ann. N. Y. Acad. Sci., 63: 728–737.

PATTERSON, J. T. 1929a. The production of mutations in somatic cells of Drosophila melanogaster by means of x-rays. J. Exptl. Zool., 53: 327–372.

PATTERSON, J. T. 1929b. X-rays and somatic mutations. J. Heredity, 20: 260–267.

PETERSON, P. A. 1960. The pale green mutable system in maize. Genetics, **45:** 115–133.

PITELKA, D. R., DeOME, K. B., and BERN, H. A. 1960. Viruslike particles in precancerous hyperplastic mammary tissues of C_3H and C_3Hf mice. J. Natl. Cancer Inst., **25:** 753–777.

PONTECORVO, G. 1958. Trends in genetic analysis. New York: Columbia University Press. 145 pp.

PONTECORVO, G., and KÄFER, E. 1956. Mapping the chromosomes by means of mitotic recombination. Proc. Roy. Phys. Soc. Edinburgh, **25:** 16–20.

PONTECORVO, G., and KÄFER, E. 1958. Genetic analysis based on mitotic recombinations. Advan. Genet., **9:** 71–104.

PORTER, K. R. 1939. Androgenetic development of the egg of Rana pipiens. Biol. Bull., **77:** 233–257.

POTT, P. 1775. Chirurgical observations relative to the cataract, the polypus of the nose, the cancer of the scrotum, the different kinds of ruptures and the mortification of the toes and feet. London: Hawes, Clarke, and Collins. 208 pp.

RINGERTZ, N., KLEIN, E., and KLEIN, G. 1957. Histopathologic studies of peritoneal implantation and lung metastasis at different stages of the gradual transformation of the MCIM mouse sarcoma into ascites form. J. Nat. Cancer Inst., **18:** 173–199.

ROMAN, H. 1956. A system selective for mutations affecting the synthesis of adenine in yeast. Compt. Rend. Trav. Lab. Carlsberg, Sér. Physiol., **26:** 299–314.

ROUS, P. 1911. Transmission of a malignant new growth by means of a cell-free filtrate. J. Am. Med. Assoc., **56:** 198.

RUSSELL, L. B. 1962. Chromosome aberrations in experimental animals. Progr. Med. Genet., **2:** 230–294.

RUSSELL, L. B., and BANGHAM, J. W. 1960. Variegated-type position effects in the mouse. Genetics, **46:** 509–525.

RUSSELL, L. B., and MAJOR, M. H. 1957. Radiation-induced presumed somatic mutations in the house mouse. Genetics, **42:** 161–175.

RUSSELL, W. L. 1951. X-ray-induced mutations in mice. Cold Spring Harbor Symp. Quant. Biol., **16:** 327–336.

SAMBUICHI, H. 1957. The roles of the nucleus and the cytoplasm in development. I. An intersubspecific hybrid frog, developed from a combination of Rana nigromaculata nigromaculata cytoplasm and a diploid nucleus of Rana nigromaculata brevipoda. J. Sci. Hiroshima Univ., Sec. B., Div. 1, **17:** 33–41.

SCHULTZ, J. 1936. Variegation in Drosophila and the inert chromosome regions. Proc. Natl. Acad. Sci., **22:** 27–33.

SCHULTZ, J. 1959. The role of somatic mutation in neoplastic growth. In: Genetics and Cancer, pp. 25–42. Austin: University of Texas Press.

SEIDEL, F. 1932. Die Potenzen der Furchungskerne im Libellenei und ihre Rolle bei der Aktivierung des Bildungszentrums. Arch. f. Entw.-mech., **126:** 213–276.

Shope, R. E. 1932. A transmissible tumor-like condition in rabbits. J. Exptl. Med., **56**: 793–802.

Shubik, P., Baserga, R., and Ritchie, A. C. 1953. The life and progression of induced skin tumors in mice. Brit. J. Cancer, **7**: 342–351.

Signoret, J., Briggs, R., and Humphrey, R. R. 1962. Nuclear transplantation in the axolotl. Dev. Biol., **4**: 134–164.

Sonneborn, T. M. 1960. The gene and cell differentiation. Proc. Natl. Acad. Sci., **46**: 149–165.

Spemann, H. 1912. Zur Entwicklung des Wirbeltierauges. Zool. Jahrb. Abt. f. allg. Zool. Physiol., **32**: 1–98.

Spemann, H. 1928. Die Entwicklung seitlicher und dorso-ventraler Keimhälften bei verzögerter Kernversorgung. Z. wiss. Zool., **132**: 105–134.

Spemann, H. 1938. Embryonic development and induction. New Haven: Yale University Press. 401 pp.

Spemann, H., and Mangold, H. 1924. Über Induktion von Embryonalenanlagen durch Implantation artfremder Organizatoren. Arch. f. Entw.-mech., **100**: 599–638.

Stern, C. 1936. Somatic crossing over and segregation in *Drosophila melanogaster*. Genetics, **21**: 625–730.

Stern, C. 1954. Two or three bristles. Am. Scientist, **42**: 213–247.

Stern, C. 1958. The nucleus and somatic cell variation. J. Cellular Comp. Physiol., **52**(Suppl. 1): 1–34.

Stewart, S. E. 1955. Neoplasms in mice inoculated with cell-free extracts or filtrates of leukemic mouse tissues. I. Neoplasms of the parotid and adrenal glands. J. Natl. Cancer Inst., **15**: 1391–1415.

Stewart, S. E., Eddy, B. E., and Borgese, N. 1958. Neoplasms in mice inoculated with a tumor agent carried in tissue culture. J. Natl. Cancer Inst., **20**: 1223–1243.

Stewart, S. E., Eddy, B. E., Gochenour, A. M., Borgese, N. G., and Grubbs, G. E. 1957. The induction of neoplasms with a substance released from mouse tumors by tissue culture. Virology, **3**: 380–400.

Stewart, S. E., Eddy, B. E., and Stanton, M. F. 1960. Progress in virus research—the polyoma problem. Exptl. Tumor Res., **1**: 67–85.

Strong, L. C. 1942. The origin of some inbred mice. Cancer Res., **2**: 531–539.

Strong, L. C., ed. 1958. Genetic concept for the origin of cancer. Ann. N. Y. Acad. Sci., **71**: 807–1241.

Sturtevant, A. H. 1925. The effects of unequal crossing over at the *Bar* locus in *Drosophila*. Genetics, **10**: 117–147.

Swanson, C. P. 1957. Cytology and cytogenetics. Englewood Cliffs, N.J.: Prentice-Hall, Inc. 596 pp.

Turner, F. C. 1941. Sarcomas at sites of subcutaneously implanted bakelite disks in rats. J. Natl. Cancer Inst., **2**: 81–83.

Upton, A. C. 1962. The dose-response relation in radiation-induced cancer. Cancer Res., **21**: 717–729.

Waddington, C. H. 1956. Principles of embryology. London: George Allen and Unwin, Ltd. 510 pp.

WADDINGTON, C. H., and PANTELOURIS, E. M. 1953. Transplantation of nuclei in newt's eggs. Nature, 172: 1050–1051.

WEINHOUSE, S. 1960. Enzyme activities and tumor progression. In: Amino Acids, Proteins, and Cancer Biochemistry, pp. 109–119. J. T. Edsall, ed. New York: Academic Press Inc.

WEISMANN, A. 1892. Das Keimplasma. Jena: G. Fischer; English translation, The Germ-Plasm, 1893, by W. N. Parker and H. Rönnefelt. London: Walter Scott, Ltd. 447 pp.

WEISS, P. 1939. Principles of development. New York: Holt, Rinehart and Winston. 601 pp.

WEISS, P., and TAYLOR, A. C. 1960. Reconstitution of complete organs from single-cell suspensions of chick embryos in advanced stages of differentiation. Proc. Natl. Acad. Sci., 46: 1177–1185.

WILLIS, R. A. 1953. Pathology of tumors. Second edition. London: Butterworth and Co. 997 pp.

WILSON, E. B. 1904. Experimental studies on germinal localization. J. Exptl. Zool., 1: 1–72.

WINZLER, R. J. 1959. The chemistry of cancer tissue. In: The Physiopathology of Cancer, second edition, pp. 686-706. F. Homburger, ed. New York: Hoeber-Harper Inc.

YAMAGIWA, K., and ICHIKAWA, K. 1918. Experimental study of the pathogenesis of carcinoma. J. Cancer Res., 3: 1–29.

YOSHIDA, T. 1934. Studien über die Entwicklung des experimentellen Hepatoms durch o-Amidoazotoluol, besonders die stufenweise Verfolgung der Leberveränderung bis zur Carcinomentstehung. Trans. Soc. Pathol. Japan, 24: 523–530.

Microorganisms
as model systems

chapter

2

Somatic variation, in whatever context of study, leads ultimately to analysis in terms of cellular mechanisms. The outcome, however, depends on the experimental tools available. Cell culture, tissue transplantation, and other novel materials offer promising designs, but the dynamics of these isolated cell systems are only beginning to emerge clearly. Their effective use in the study of the mechanisms of cellular heredity will require an expanding series of new approaches. Here, the most significant developments may be methodological. Operational advances, such as the discovery of crossing over or the successful transplantation of nuclei, have frequently opened up new insights into biological phenomena. In the field of somatic heredity the need for such innovation is particularly pressing. There is a fundamental roadblock in the lack of techniques for genetic recombination within somatic units or for the possible transfer of determinants from cell to cell. If some means can be found for a solution of this strategic problem, the way would be open for a systematic exploration of inheritance in cellular terms.

In this light, it is useful to turn to microorganisms for models that may aid in understanding the alterations that occur in isolated somatic populations. Some microbial types (for example, protozoans, yeasts, and molds) display sexual or quasi-sexual cycles that can provide a basis for Mendelian analysis. But until recent years, bacteria as a group seemed much less promising for genetic studies. Obviously, one cannot examine bacterial cells within a population directly for individual variation. Further, the multiplication of bacteria by means of binary fission would seem to preclude the occurrence of genetic recombination. Despite these handicaps, a number of ingenious procedures have been devised for the recognition and isolation of bacterial variants and for the systematic

68

analysis of genetic information within individual cells. As a result, the field of bacterial genetics has mushroomed within a few years to become one of the most active and fertile areas of general biology. The highlights of this development are of particular interest as perspectives for the study of somatic variation. Obviously, the analogy to be made is one of concept and approach rather than the direct comparison of specific mechanisms. In a more general sense, the unfolding picture of bacterial inheritance illustrates the value of bold and unorthodox explorations in a new field.

ADAPTATION AND BACTERIAL VARIATION

Bacteria in nature are conspicuous for their highly adaptive patterns of growth and metabolic activities. The emergence of variants resistant to penicillin or other antibiotics, for example, is a commonplace practical problem, and bacteria can acquire the ability to grow progressively in the presence of various deleterious factors. Many years ago, too, investigators learned that microorganisms can be "trained" to utilize inert sugars and other substrates not ordinarily attacked. The mechanism of these adaptive variations involves a basic ambiguity which was the starting point for genetic studies in bacterial systems. For in microbial cells, as in higher organisms, variations can be imposed from without by the action of environmental factors or from within by genetic change. In either case an altered phenotype may arise that confers improved fitness in a given environment, that is, adaptation. Adaptive variations thus do not in themselves indicate the nature of the underlying change.

Selection enters as a complicating factor when adaptation is considered in terms of populations, whether these consist of cells or of organisms. If the characteristics of a population undergo an adaptive shift, the change observed may result (1) from phenotypic changes in all members of the population, taking place in response to extrinsic stimuli without alteration in genotype; or (2) by mutation or recombination as a random process, giving rise to occasional variants that selectively multiply to eliminate the pre-existing population. The distinction between these two mechanisms offers little difficulty in higher plants and animals, where individual organisms may be examined in detail and tested by breeding experiments for the occurrence of genetic changes. It is much more difficult to determine the nature of adaptive variation in bacterial populations. Many bacteria divide remarkably fast. The doubling time for these populations is measured in hours and, in many cases, in minutes. Selective overgrowth of variants may occur so rapidly that the process simulates a direct phenotypic adaptation. Since this difficulty is coupled with the absence of an easily observed nucleus, it is perhaps not surprising that microbiologists for many years believed that bacterial variation, or "dissociation" as it was called, had a different basis from the Mendelian mechanisms of higher organisms. Such beliefs were not dispelled until experimental means were finally devised to discriminate between spontaneous random changes, as contrasted to variations imposed directly by environmental factors. This turn of events made possible a search for genetic mechanisms and the emergence of new principles for bacterial inheritance.

Development of Genetic Concepts In 1943 Luria and Delbrück published a paper that represents a cornerstone in the field of bacterial genetics. By a statistical procedure, the so-called fluctuation test, they were able to show for the first time that adaptation can occur as a result of random change within individual cells, the environment serving only to select the favorable variants. For this work human colon bacillus, *Escherichia coli*, was used, as in many other studies in microbiology. Populations of *E. coli*, like many other bacteria, are ordinarily susceptible to infection with bacterial viruses (bacteriophage, or simply phage). In normally sensitive strains, the propagation of phage causes massive destruction, or lysis, of all but a small proportion of bacteria. A few cells survive, however, and proliferate to form a new resistant population, unaffected by phage.

It was to this question of phage resistance that Luria and Delbrück directed their investigation. Do a few cells of the original population acquire resistance as a result of exposure to bacteriophage, or does phage merely select for pre-existing resistant cells? To reach an experimental decision on this point, a small broth culture of *E. coli* was split into two equal parts (see Figure 2.1). One of these was further divided into a series of separate tubes while the other half was maintained as a single culture. After incubation and growth had occurred, both the undivided culture and the separate sublines were tested for resistance to bacteriophage. This was accomplished by transferring samples to petri dishes containing nutrient agar on which phage had previously been spread, and counting the number of resistant colonies that subsequently appeared. From the undivided culture, an appropriate number of replicate plates were made, to match the test plates obtained from each of the sublines grown separately. The petri dishes with replicate inocula all showed approximately the same number of resistant colonies. In contrast, test plates from the series of sublines incubated separately showed great variability. Samples from some sublines contained many

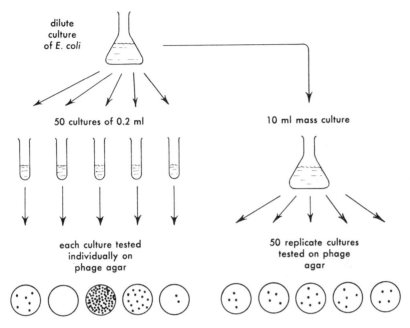

FIG. 2.1 Schematic representation of the Luria-Delbrück fluctuation test. Resistance to bacteriophage is shown as the assay character. The assay is based on random variation in replicate samples from a single culture, as compared to variation observed among samples from strains cultivated in parallel. Total variance is greater in the latter case.

resistant colonies, while in others none were found. Still other sublines exhibited various intermediate conditions.

In these experiments, all cultures were grown in the absence of bacteriophage, and the greater variability of the separate sublines in contrast to the undivided culture thus could not be explained as differences in adaptation to phage. On a statistical basis, however, the increased variation in separate sublines might be accounted for by assuming that mutations from sensitivity to resistance had occurred, and that these were random and spontaneous events, taking place at different times in the growth of the various isolated subpopulations. For example, if mutation to resistance occurred early in the growth period of a given subline, the variant cells should pile up as the population continued to increase in number, and would give rise to many resistant colonies when the subline was assayed with phage. But if a mutation occurred somewhat later or at the end of the initial growth period, the number of resistant cells that had accumulated at assay ought to be correspondingly less. By contrasting the variability of isolated subpopulations with the uniformity of samples from an undivided population, Luria and Delbrück presented in this way strong circumstantial evidence that mutations occur in bacteria as in other types of organisms. The fluctuation test as defined here proved to be of general validity in bacterial systems. Investigators working with resistance to antibiotics or with the development of nutritional variants were able to obtain results similar to those of Luria and Delbrück, and the explanation proposed became widely accepted (Oakberg and Luria, 1947; Ryan and Schneider, 1949; Newcombe and Hawirko, 1949).

More direct proofs for spontaneous variation in bacteria were also forthcoming. The most elegant and convincing of these is the replica-plating technique devised by Lederberg and Lederberg (1952). By this procedure, bacterial mutants can be isolated without ever coming in contact with the corresponding selective agent, such as streptomycin or phage. The basic technique is a simple one. A cylindrical block is covered with sterile velvet and pressed against an agar plate on which a normal population of bacteria are growing. Some of these organisms adhere to the velvet surface, which can then be used to "stamp" one or more fresh petri dishes with a replica of the original pattern. In a typical experiment, the Lederbergs prepared a number of replicate cultures from a petri dish containing a dense confluent film of sensitive *E. coli* cells on nutrient agar. These duplicates, but not the original master plate, were then exposed to phage and incubated. A few colonies subsequently appeared, and these were demonstrably phage resistant. For the most part, these variant growths arose at corresponding locations in the phage-agar cultures. This suggested the presence of resistant cells at congruent sites on the untreated master plate. Accordingly, a few cells were secured from appropriate areas of the latter, and were inoculated into broth cultures so that a larger population could be obtained. Dilutions from these secondary cultures were then spread on nutrient agar, replicate cultures prepared by the velvet stamp technique, and the whole process repeated. This time, the frequency of phage-resistant colonies was higher in the assay populations. Several cycles of enrichment were carried through in this fashion, each time a higher dilution of the stock culture being plated. Finally, it was possible to pick single colonies from nutrient agar plates, on the basis of correspondence in position to resistant colonies on phage agar, and to show that such cells were completely resistant. The definitive refractory populations were thus selected indirectly for phage resistance without exposure to phage at any time. By further experiments, the Lederbergs showed that streptomycin-resistant cells may be obtained in a similar manner, and the phenomenon appears to be a general one.

Replica plating provides graphic proof that adaptive variants in bacteria can arise spontaneously, but it does not necessarily follow that all of the variants isolated with a given selective agent are of random origin. The number of pre-existing variants might conceivably be augmented by the direct induction of others during the selection process. Indeed, some investigators have felt that despite the occurrence of mutations, environmentally induced variants are predominant in drug resistance and other adaptive changes. A full discussion of this topic is deferred to Chapter 6, but in general, the assumption of directed mutation in bacteria, as in other organisms, does not find experimental support. The evidence presented by Cavalli-Sforza and Lederberg (1956) is particularly convincing. While searching for a means of indirect selection more quantitative than replica plating, they devised the technique of sib selection. This is a procedure for serial enrichment, based on the systematic identification and selection of individual samples that, within a series, prove at random to contain a higher number of variant cells. In practice, this end is achieved most readily by dividing stock cultures into a number of small aliquots, each calculated to contain a variant cell only occasionally. Part of each sample is incubated subsequently with a selective agent; for example, streptomycin. From such assays, the rare aliquot containing resistant cells is identified. The corresponding reference culture in nutrient medium can then be used to initiate a new series of assays. At each step in this process, the percentage of variants increases despite the fact that the stock cultures used for serial transfer do not as such come into contact with the drug. The degree of enrichment that should be obtained by sequential selection can be calculated by appropriate means. These theoretical estimates may then be compared with the proportion of mutants actually observed in assay populations. If a significant number of variants do arise from direct exposure to the selective agent, an appreciable disparity in the two values should be found. Such was not the case, however, for the populations of E. coli studied by Cavalli-Sforza and Lederberg. In sib selection experiments with streptomycin and chloramphenicol, the number of mutants observed in assays corresponded closely to the predicted frequencies. Adaptive variation in this system, therefore, cannot be attributed to directed shifts in response to an environmental factor.

As a result of these and other studies, it gradually became clear that most, if not all, stable variations in bacterial populations are the result of random genetic change. Heritable alterations were observed in cell morphology, colonial characteristics, antigenic structure, acquisition or loss of specific biosynthetic mechanisms, resistance to inhibitors, virulence for particular hosts, and other specific characters (see Braun,

1953). From the first experiments of Luria and Delbrück it was apparent that many of these changes could be described as mutations in the classical sense, although the exact genetic mechanism was at first unknown. With the passage of time, the validity of this assumption was increasingly evident. The similarities between bacterial variations and the mutations of higher organisms were pointed out (Tatum and Perkins, 1950). The frequency of mutation in bacteria accords well with mutation rates as observed in plants and animals (J. Lederberg, 1951). Such estimates, for the most part, have been based on the original analysis of Luria and Delbrück (1943) or modifications thereof (Newcombe, 1948; Lea and Coulson, 1949). The frequency of spontaneous mutations as determined by any of these methods varies widely, depending on the characters chosen and species of bacteria. Values of 10^{-6} to 10^{-8} (one mutation in 10^6 to 10^8 cells per generation) are common, however, and compare favorably with known rates for spontaneous mutations in more conventional systems.

Strong support for the mutation hypothesis in bacteria also arose from studies on induced mutation. In agreement with the findings obtained in classic genetic systems, X rays and ultraviolet light proved to be effective mutagenic agents (Demerec and Latarjet, 1946). The types of mutants that arise in this way are similar to those appearing spontaneously within bacterial populations, but the frequency of variation is greatly increased (see Figure 2.2). It is also possible to cause a general increase in mutation rates by application of chemical agents. Among the first of these compounds to be studied were formaldehyde and the various nitrogen mustards (Auerbach and Robson, 1946). With the rapid expansion of studies in this field, the list of chemical mutagens has become quite extensive (Westergaard, 1957; Strauss, 1960). In bacteria, as well as in *Drosophila,* mutation rates may be enhanced with such diverse agents as peroxides, acridine dyes, purine or pyrimidine analogues, nitrous acid, and ferrous or manganous ions. Little is known concerning the exact mode of action for most of these mutagenic compounds, but the end results are similar to the products of irradiation treatment or of spontaneous mutational change.

Some discrepancies in early studies on mutation in bacteria, whether spontaneous or induced, are now known to reflect differences in the phenotypic expression of variant characters. Where the new genetic marker represents a positive gain (for example, the synthesis of a nutritional factor previously required), variation becomes evident soon after mutation has occurred. A different result may be obtained, however, if the mutation depends for its expression on the disappearance of structural or functional elements normally present in precursor cells.

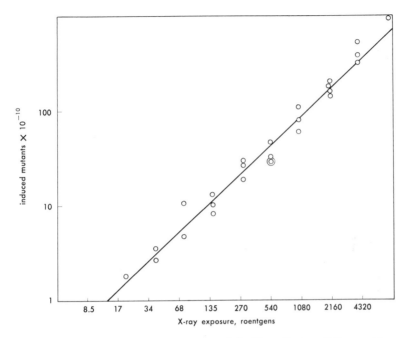

FIG. 2.2. Induction of mutations in *E. coli* by X irradiation. Cells requiring methionine for growth were exposed to graded doses of irradiation and scored on minimal medium for mutations to methionine independence. (After Demerec and Sams, 1960.)

Such may be the case, for example, in cells acquiring resistance to a specific drug by the deletion of an enzyme that otherwise converts the compound into a toxic form. Here, one or more cell divisions may be necessary to dilute out the supply of pre-existing enzyme during cell growth before resistance can actually become manifest. A delay of this type in the expression of resistance is referred to as "phenotypic lag," and complications of a similar sort are encountered in a number of experimental systems.

The occurrence of mutations continuously and at random within bacterial populations leads to predictable consequences in terms of population dynamics. If selection does not discriminate in a given system between variant and parental cell types, the percentage of mutant cells can be expected to increase linearly with time. Under ideal conditions, the forward progress of mutants within a population structure is opposed by the tendency for back mutation, or reversion. Thus, an equilibrium in principle may be reached, with the two opposing types of genetic change in substantial balance. Actual shifts in the composition of bacterial populations are rarely simple, although Stocker (1949) has described one case in which mutational equilibrium was attained in the manner indicated (see Figure 2.3). As a rule, however, long-term changes in population structure are complicated by a process that has been variously described as "periodic selection," or "orthoselection" (Atwood, Schneider, and Ryan, 1951; Sager and Ryan, 1961). Using a strain of *E. coli* unable to synthesize histidine, Atwood and his collaborators showed that histidine-independent mutants appear, but do not accumulate indefinitely, in spite of the uninterrupted production of such variants. Instead, the population structure fluctuates, with occasional periods when histidine-independent variants are absent or present only in negligible numbers. The explanation for this finding apparently lies in the periodic emergence of a new class of variants in which dependence on histidine for growth is unaltered. These mutants, however, are characterized by more efficient mechanisms for growth, so that both the precursor parental cells and their histidine-independent sublines are gradually eliminated from the population structure. New histidine-independent mutants then arise from the improved parental type, and both may in turn disappear in a further cycle of selective change (see

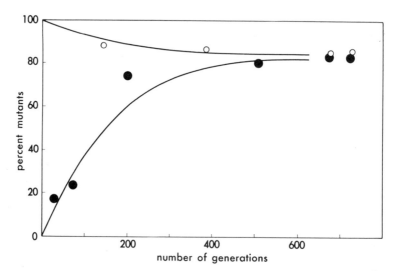

FIG. 2.3. Approach to mutational equilibrium in a population of bacterial cells. Lower curve shows accumulation of antigenic mutants within a strain of *Salmonella* where the mutation rate is relatively high. Back mutation or reversion (upper curve) lowers the increase of variants until a balance point is reached. (After Stocker, 1949. Copyright, Cambridge University Press.)

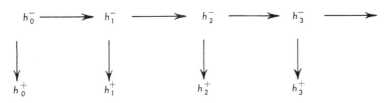

FIG. 2.4. Orthoselection in a bacterial population. A histidine-requiring strain (h_0^-) throws off histidine-independent mutants (h_0^+). Indefinite accumulation of the h_0^+ variants does not occur because another mutant (h_1^-) with a selective growth advantage arises from the parental cell type and replaces both h_0^- and h_0^+. Periodic repetition of this process prevents the establishment of a mutational equilibrium, and the proportion of histidine-independent variants remains relatively low. (From Atwood, Schneider, and Ryan, 1951.)

Figure 2.4). By these "adaptive leaps," cell strains thus tend to achieve a greater genetic stability than would obtain in the absence of ortho-selection.

The mutation process, and the natural history of mutants in bacterial populations, are thus seen to follow closely the analogous events within higher organisms, despite differences in the organization of hereditary materials. This convergence of observations and concepts has been capped finally by direct proof that recombination of genetic determinants occurs in microorganisms as in other biological systems. Such findings will be discussed in more detail in a later section, and they serve to emphasize the basic character of studies in microbial inheritance. As this field continues to expand, it is abundantly clear that, far from representing systems of specialized interest, bacteria are actually indispensable tools for the analysis of fundamental genetic mechanisms (see Sager and Ryan, 1961).

Induced Biosynthesis of Enzymes Adaptive variations in bacteria, as in other organisms, are not always mediated by mutation and selection. Some obviously represent functional adjustments in competent cells, occurring as a response to specific factors in the cellular environment. Many instances could be cited of such nongenetic or phenotypic adaptations. Typhoid bacilli, for example, are characteristically covered with flagella. These structures disappear in presence of phenol, but are re-formed if the corresponding populations are returned to normal medium (J. Lederberg, 1951). In this and other reversible processes of a similar character, several common features can be recognized: (1) Adaptation occurs directly in response to an extrinsic stimulus, rather than as a spontaneous, random event; (2) variation takes place as a mass shift by all cells in the population; and (3) reversion to the original state tends to occur relatively rapidly as soon as the specific stimulus is removed. Even without formal evidence from fluctuation tests or other experiments, it is apparent that these adaptations represent transient alterations in phenotype, taking place against a constant genotypic background.

The best-known processes of phenotypic adaptation involve the synthesis of specific enzymes in response to particular substances in the external medium. Such phenomena occur widely among microorganisms and have been the subject of intensive study (see Monod and Cohn, 1952; Hogness, 1959; Halvorson, 1960). Bacteria can often be adapted directly to a new carbon or nitrogen source, for example, and this process coincides with the rapid synthesis of an enzyme previously present only in trace form. Early workers, in fact, interpreted this phenomenon as *de novo* synthesis of enzyme in response to the corresponding substrate. More recent studies have shown, however, that inducible enzymes are always present in small amounts within competent cells (Pollock and Mandelstam, 1958). Induction must thus be viewed as a rate-controlling process within established enzyme-forming systems, a release of biosynthetic mechanisms normally held in check. For this purpose, a minute stimulus sometimes suffices. In *B. cereus*, for example, small quantities of penicillin are irreversibly absorbed by cells exposed to antibiotics for a brief period, and this leads to a maximum production of penicillinase (Pollock, 1950). A typical experiment of this kind is shown in Figure 2.5. Using penicillin S^{35}, Pollock later found that as little as 200 molecules are sufficient for the inductive process (Pollock, 1959). Surprisingly, even the immediate substrate is dispensable as such. Studies with structural analogues have shown that some compounds are efficient inducers even though they cannot be metabolized by the enzyme system that appears (Monod and Cohn, 1952; Halvorson, 1960). Findings of this type make clear that inductors do not operate by bringing about changes in enzyme-substrate equilibria. Their action is directed instead toward factors regulating biosynthetic pathways. Induction, it seems, takes place in competent cells by the neutralization of repressors, which otherwise serve to block formation of the enzyme in question. Such interpretations have been especially fruitful in unifying the phenomena of induction with repressor mechanisms that operate for the adjustment of enzymatic activity in general (see Vogel, 1961; Monod, Jacob, and Gros, 1962; Moyed and Umbarger, 1962).

These considerations can be made more explicit by examining the formation of β-galactosidase in *E. coli*, a system that has furnished much of the basic information on enzyme induction (Monod and Cohn, 1952;

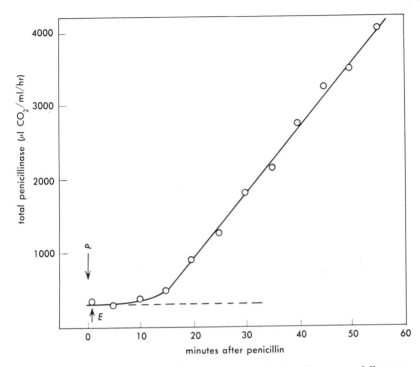

FIG. 2.5. Induction of penicillinase production in *Bacillus cereus* following exposure to penicillin. One unit/ml penicillin (*P*) is added to a logarithmically growing culture, and free penicillin is destroyed after a brief interval by adding an active preparation of penicillinase (*E*). (Redrawn from Pollock, 1953. Copyright, Cambridge University Press.)

Cohn, 1957). The enzyme in question is so named because it acts on a class of compounds known as β-galactosides. Lactose, for example, is hydrolyzed to form galactose and glucose. Cells of *E. coli*, grown on glucose as an energy source, ordinarily contain only traces of β-galactosidase. If these bacteria are incubated in a lactose medium, there is an initial lag in growth, but β-galactosidase is synthesized rapidly during this time. After about 30 minutes, the bacteria are fully adapted and grow at a normal rate. Enzyme continues to be formed as long as lactose is present. If the cells are put back on a glucose medium or changed to another energy source, however, synthesis of β-galactosidase stops and the residual enzyme is rapidly diluted out in continuing growth.

A number of substances related to lactose can induce the formation of β-galactosidase. Among these structural analogues the thiogalactosides are particularly interesting (Monod and Cohn, 1952). Thiomethyl-β-D-galactoside (TMG), for example, causes rapid synthesis of β-galactosidase, but is not hydrolyzed by the enzyme. Since TMG is inert metabolically, it is possible to measure the rate of appearance of β-galactosidase in nonadapted cells, uncomplicated by utilization of the substrate. If, for example, E. coli cells are grown on succinate as an energy source in the presence of fairly high concentrations of TMG, there is from the start a linear increase in enzyme protein per unit bacterial protein (Cohn, 1957). But if nonsaturating concentrations of inducer are used (for example, $1 \times 10^{-5}M$) a lag phase is observed in which the rate of formation of β-galactosidase gradually increases up to a constant limiting value. An accelerating synthesis of this type, it should be emphasized, is characteristic only of a population. At the level of individual cells, the induction process appears to be an all-or-none phenomenon (Novick and Weiner, 1957). These investigators showed that with very low concentrations of TMG, induction is slow and does not occur in all cells at the same time. But if induction does occur in a given bacterium, it accelerates rapidly to completion. With the passage of time, more and more cells within the population are brought to this state. Thus the rising tempo of enzyme synthesis within the culture as a whole reflects the increasing number of bacteria that have undergone induction, and hence it does not give a true picture of enzyme formation within individual cells.

The kinetics of enzyme induction are further complicated by permeability factors. The uptake of inducing agents by bacteria appears to facilitate the further entry of molecules of the same kind. In the β-galactosidase system, for example, cells that have been grown in the presence of a galactoside acquire a marked ability to concentrate TMG (Monod, 1956). If such bacteria are washed and exposed to TMG labeled with S^{35}, this compound is accumulated to levels of 100-fold over the concentration in the surrounding medium. Such phenomena require energy, are stereochemically specific, and necessitate the occurrence of protein synthesis. Monod and his collaborators, therefore, have postulated that the penetration of inducer is itself conditioned by the activation of a special enzyme for this purpose, which can be termed galactoside-permease (Rickenberg, Cohen, Buttin, and Monod, 1956). Whether or not permeases actually exist as specific chemical entities is still uncertain, since it has not been possible to isolate enzymes of this type so far (Halvorson, 1960). But a variety of evidence has been amassed that indicates that inducible systems specifically concerned with the permeation of substrates do exist within the bacterial cell (Cohen and Monod, 1957). There are, for example, variants such as the "cryptic" mutants in E. coli, which show specific defects in facilitated transport (Cohn, 1958). These cells cannot be adapted to grow on lactose, but this deficiency does not stem from any inability to form β-galactosidase. Prominent induction of enzyme occurs when cryptic cells grown on succinate are exposed to TMG, and cell-free preparations then hydrolyze lactose quite effectively. Thus the cryptic mutants seem merely to lack a permease system. This is borne out by the fact that although TMG may enter the cryptic cells, there is no accelerated uptake of further inducer. In such populations the synthesis of β-galactosidase remains linear with time at all concentrations of inducer capable of initiating the process.

The fact that, ordinarily, the uptake of inductors is facilitated in fully induced *E. coli* cells makes it possible to construct some interesting population models. One of these has been described by Novick and Weiner (1957) in the course of the experiments mentioned above. It has been pointed out that with low concentrations of TMG, only a fraction of the cell population undergoes induction during a short period of time. If a culture is exposed for a brief interval to such a concentration of TMG and then transferred to a still lower level of inducer, no further induction takes place. But TMG enters more efficiently into cells that have already been induced, and thus "maintenance" concentrations of this type do preserve the synthesis of β-galactosidase at a stable elevated rate if it has been established previously. Noninduced cells in the population, however, grow more rapidly than induced bacteria. At maintenance levels of inducer, therefore, the latter would eventually be eliminated by selection. But, by choosing a slightly greater concentration of TMG in continuous culture, it is possible to establish an equilibrium in which the appearance of newly induced cells is just balanced by the differential in growth rate. The population then exhibits a constant proportion of adapted and nonadapted cells. Individual bacteria may be removed from such a culture and used to establish clonal sublines. If these sublines of single cell origin are propagated uniformly in the presence of TMG at *maintenance* levels, they fall into two sharply contrasting classes. One of these forms β-galactosidase at the maximum rate, while the other shows no induced synthesis of enzyme at all. This phenomenon bears a superficial resemblance to mutation, although clearly the propagated differences between sublines are the result of physiological adaptation. A useful comparison might also be drawn between the model of Novick and Weiner and the process of differentiation in multicellular systems. In both cases, cell types of contrasting phenotypic pattern emerge against a constant genetic background. Although the analogy can hardly be more than a general one, it is instructive to observe how stable differences between cells can arise from a variable balance in steady-state systems.

Although the *E. coli* β-galactosidase system is particularly interesting as an example of how biosynthesis may be regulated by external factors, it should be emphasized that each step of induction and adaptation is under genetic control. These patterns have been unraveled with conspicuous success in recent years, and provide the most explicit illustrations yet seen of gene action at the molecular level (Pardee, Jacob, and Monod, 1959; Jacob and Monod, 1961a, 1961b; Jacob and Wollman, 1961). A general discussion of this work lies beyond the scope of the present volume, but it may be useful to summarize briefly the genetic outlines that have emerged. The studies of Lederberg (1947) and others showed at an early stage that mutants affecting the formation of β-galactosidase may be obtained. Among the variants that cannot utilize galactosides, several types of cells may be distinguished (Rickenberg, Cohen, Buttin, and Monod, 1956; E. Lederberg, 1960; Jacob and Wollman, 1961). One of these represents a failure to synthesize the β-galactosidase molecule as such. Mutants of a second category, as previously noted, are incapable of forming inducible permease systems, although such cells can synthesize β-galactosidase when higher than usual concentrations of inducer are employed. Still other mutants are characterized by a shift from inducible to constitutive states; that is, β-galactosidase is formed freely in the absence of external inducers. The last-named category is particularly significant, since observations of this type show clearly that repression as well as enzyme synthesis is regulated by hereditary factors.

All these functions are governed by determinants that reside within a relatively short sector of the bacterial chromosome, known as the *lac* region (Lederberg, 1947). Mapping experiments, by techniques to be discussed later, now show that this locus is actually a complex one, with three distinct subregions in its fine structure (Pardee, Jacob, and Monod, 1959). Of these, the z region contains information concerning the composition and assembly of the β-galactosidase molecule. A second site, the y region, defines the specific characteristics of the permease system. Lastly, the i region appears to stimulate production of a cytoplasmic repressor. Normally inducible cells are thus $i^+ z^+ y^+$; and constitutive mutants, in which the repressor is not formed, are $i^- z^+ y^+$. In a similar fashion, cryptic mutants, which cannot utilize galactosides but can form enzyme inductively, are designated $i^+ z^+ y^-$. Still a further class, the "constitutive cryptics," are $i^- z^+ y^-$. The latter form β-galactosidase regularly without inducers, but are unable to utilize external substrate as intact cells. The reality of this picture has been demonstrated by a broad array of genetic studies, including the isolation of i, z, and y mutants in all possible combinations (Jacob and Wollman, 1961).

One important question left unresolved in this explanation of the β-galactosidase system concerns the mechanism and site of action of the cytoplasmic repressor. In an outstanding paper, Jacob, Perrin, Sanchez, and Monod (1960) filled this gap and added thereby a new concept, that of the "operon." Briefly, an operon can be regarded as a functional unit consisting of a so-called "operator" locus in tandem with a group of closely associated structural genes. The latter specify the nature of the product to be formed (for example, enzyme protein), and the operator serves merely to "turn on" or "turn off" these action patterns. Operator genes may also be targets for products emanating from one or more modifier genes, which are thus able to govern functional activity by the operon as a whole. These concepts find extensive support in a variety of studies with *E. coli* (Jacob and Wollman, 1961). The operator, or *o* locus, for the β-galactosidase system has been identified within the *lac* region and lies between the *i* and *z* loci. Within this site, mutations occur that can be designated $o^+ \rightarrow o^0$. Such variants are characterized by a complete loss of the capacity to synthesize permease and β-galactosidase; the y^+ and z^+ factors, although present, are inactive. In wild-type cells, action by the o^+ locus is normally held in check by the cytoplasmic repressor, which is formed by the i^+ locus as a regulator gene. But if inducers neutralize the repressor, or if an $i^+ \rightarrow i^-$ mutation occurs, the operator locus is released to "switch on" activity in the *y* and *z* regions. The o^+ locus may also become active by a mutation that reduces the normal sensitivity of this gene to repressor. Mutations of this type can be designated $o^+ \rightarrow o^c$, and are manifest as a special class of variants that form β-galactosidase constitutively.

The operator-regulator mechanism thus provides an attractive explanation for the control of enzyme biosynthesis, and may be of very general validity for patterns of gene action. Whether comparable systems exist in organisms other than bacteria is not yet known with certainty. Perhaps the closest analogy is to be found in the controlling elements of maize, which have been discussed previously (see Chapter 1). McClintock (1961), in a thoughtful paper, has pointed out a number of parallels between these two types of gene control systems. It will be recalled that in maize, several two-unit mechanisms are known for the adjustment of gene action; of these, the dissociation-activator (*Ds-Ac*) combination has received most attention. The *Ds* element may be comparable to an operator locus, since it functions only when present in direct association with structural genes and can elicit from them the patterns of activity that would not otherwise appear. The *Ac* element regulates action by *Ds*, and thus ultimately controls the expression of structural genes. It need not be in direct proximity to *Ds*, although whether a chemical mediator exists for interaction is unknown. In principle, the *Ds-Ac* grouping thus seems to represent an operator-regulator system. Other analogies have been raised, however, based on the remarkable mobility of controlling elements within the maize genome (see Chapter 1). These comparisons will be elaborated in more detail in a later section.

RECOMBINATION AND GENE TRANSFER IN BACTERIA

Genetic variations, considered broadly, fall under two principal headings: mutation and recombination. Changes that take place through mutation are often more striking, but it is the analysis of recombination that provides the greatest insight into workings of the genetic apparatus. This has long been apparent in studies with higher organisms, where sexual reproduction affords opportunities for segregation, independent assortment, and crossing over. The latter process has been particularly fruitful in shaping a picture of hereditary units in spatial and functional terms. In bacteria, the prospects for a similar analysis seemed at first remote. Several well-defined mechanisms for reassortment and gene transfer, however, are now known to exist in bacterial cells. These discoveries are among the outstanding achievements of modern biology, and have had a far-reaching influence in such basic fields as biochemistry, virology, and pathology.

Transformation and Transduction The first indication of genetic recombination in bacteria arose from a study by Griffith (1928). Using various strains of pneumococci (*Streptococcus pneumoniae*), he described a unique conversion of one form into another. On agar plates, this organism forms either smooth (*S*) or rough (*R*) colonies, distinguished superficially by differences in external contour. Bacteria in rough colonies lack an external capsule and do not ordinarily produce an infection in experimental animals. Pneumococci from smooth colonies are surrounded by a characteristic capsule composed of polysaccharide, which protects the organisms from phagocytosis and thus is necessary for growth in an appropriate host. The nature of this polysaccharide is genetically determined, and differs among various strains of pneumococci. A number of specific types can be differentiated by serological procedures. In his original work, Griffith attempted to convert *R* cells into *S* cells by inoculating the avirulent *R* cells into mice along with a heat-killed suspension of *S* cells. Mice treated in this fashion subsequently died, and from the blood of these animals Griffith obtained cultures of typical S cells. Even more significantly, the R → S transformation turned out to be type-specific. If heat-killed cells with Type I capsular polysaccharide were used, this compound could be demonstrated in the capsules of pneumococci that had been converted to a virulent form. Similarly, if the conversion was initiated with killed cells of Type II or III, the corresponding capsular polysaccharide appeared uniformly in the final population.

These experiments led to an intensive search for the transforming agents that were responsible for such remarkable shifts in heritable characteristics of the pneumococcal cells. Through appropriate modifications in technique, conversions were produced by mixing heat-killed S cells with R cells in culture; later, these were produced even by means of cell-free extracts from S cells. As a culmination of this work, transforming principle was finally isolated by Avery, MacLeod, and McCarty (1944) in the form of pure deoxyribonucleic acid (DNA). A minute amount of purified DNA from a given S strain is sufficient to convert competent R cells to S bacteria of the donor type. From cultures of converted cells, DNA for similar transformations can be isolated in large quantities, indicating that extensive replication of the original material has occurred. It is difficult to overestimate the importance of this demonstration, which focused attention for the first time on DNA as the ultimate bearer of hereditary properties, and away from proteins, which had been previously regarded as the principal or sole repository of genetic information within cells.

Although the original studies on transformation were confined to capsular types, additional investigations have shown that resistance to penicillin or streptomycin, ability to form adaptive enzymes, and other characters may be similarly transferred from cell to cell (Hotchkiss, 1955a, 1955b; Ephrussi-Taylor, 1955). It is also clear that transformation is not a process peculiar to the pneumococci in which it was originally discovered. Transformations with purified DNA have been obtained in *Hemophilus influenzae* (Alexander and Leidy, 1951), in *Bacillus subtilis* (Spizizen, 1958), and in a number of other bacteria (Ravin, 1961).

Apparently the DNA sequence that participates effectively in transformation is relatively small. Ordinarily only one property at a time is conferred by transforming DNA on recipient cells. In pneumococci, for example, transfer of capsular type is not accompanied by a simultaneous shift of penicillin or streptomycin resistance from the donor strain, although the latter may be transferred independently (Hotchkiss, 1951). Linkage has been clearly demonstrated in some cases, however. Two such characters in pneumococci are streptomycin resistance and the ability to synthesize the adaptive enzyme mannitol dehydrogenase

(Hotchkiss and Marmur, 1954). If DNA from a strain with both markers is used to treat bacteria that lack the characters in question, most of the transformed cells, if isolated, will show one or the other property. But approximately 10 percent of the transformants exhibit both markers, which is clearly too high a proportion to be attributed to chance coincidence of separate processes.

Although transformation at one time was regarded as an example of directed mutation, this concept has long since been abandoned. Transforming DNA is best looked upon as a molecular derivative from the chromosomes of donor cells, carrying information from this source into the genome of a competent recipient (J. Lederberg, 1951). Two mechanisms may be visualized to explain how incorporation occurs. The actual process might, for example, involve an alignment of donor and host DNA strands, followed by breakage and reunion between localized regions; that is, crossing over. Alternatively, a more indirect method has been proposed, which can be termed "copy-choice" replication (see Lederberg, 1955). Under this hypothesis, the DNA fragment that enters the cell is not inserted as such into the host chromosome. Instead, it serves merely as an alternative template. When new DNA is formed, the pre-existing host DNA specifies the pattern to be formed, except for a localized region in which part of the donor fragment is copied instead. Of these alternatives, the first seems clearly to be favored by recent studies that point to the inclusion of donor DNA per se into the chromosomal strand of the host cell (see Ephrussi-Taylor, 1960; Ravin, 1961; Fox, 1962; Lacks, 1962).

Transformation by purified DNA is closely related to another process, which at first sight seems quite different in character. This is the transfer of genetic information between cells by means of viruses, a phenomenon that has been labeled transduction (Zinder and Lederberg, 1952; Lederberg, 1956a). The discovery of transduction emerged from studies on mutant strains of Salmonella typhimurium, which require specific nutritional factors. Such variants, termed auxotrophs, grow only in the presence of the corresponding compound and can be contrasted with prototrophs, which proliferate without special supplements to the culture medium. Using materials of this type, Zinder and Lederberg found that prototrophs emerged far more frequently when two auxotrophs were mixed than when each of the nutritionally deficient strains was maintained separately. These results might be explained by a recombination of genetic factors between the two bacterial types, a process that would compensate for deficiencies at different loci. Direct contact between individual cells did not prove to be necessary, however. This was demonstrated by growing two different strains in opposite arms of a U tube, with a filter at the bottom of the tube to prevent passage of bacteria from one side to the other (see Figure 2.6). Under these conditions, if the culture was maintained in minimal medium without supplements, prototrophs could be recovered in numbers from one arm of the U tube but not from the other. The filterable agent was identified eventually as a bacteriophage, designated *P22*, acting as a vector to pass through the filter and transfer part of the bacterial genome from cell to cell. Phage-mediated transductions have subsequently been demonstrated by various workers in a number of different bacteria (Lennox, 1955; Morse, 1959), and the phenomenon must be regarded as a general one (Hartman, 1957; Jacob and Wollman, 1961).

Transductions have been particularly valuable as a means of revealing genetic structure and mechanisms through recombination of markers (Demerec, 1956; Demerec and Demerec, 1956). Usually the bacteria of a donor strain are infected with phage under conditions that result in lysis or destruction of cells, giving large quantities of phage in the resulting lysate. The cell-free lysate is then used to infect bacteria of a second, genetically different strain. A few of the recipient cells are phage-resistant and will survive. Among the survivors, a small proportion (about one cell in 10^4 or 10^5) shows characteristics of the original donor strain, and these can be isolated for study by selective methods. Initially, only one character was observed to be conferred on recipient bacteria at one time. With continuing study, however, enough closely

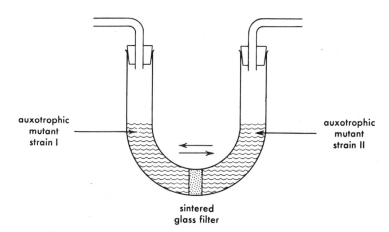

FIG. 2.6. U-tube apparatus used to test whether cell contact is required for recombination in bacteria. Two strains with contrasting genetic markers are cultivated in the sidearms, separated by a porous filter which prevents passage of bacteria. The medium is flushed repeatedly between the two compartments by alternating air pressure.

linked markers have been found to make linked transductions relatively common (Gross and Englesberg, 1959). The variant characters that may be transduced in this way cover a wide range. In their initial experiments, Zinder and Lederberg were able to transfer requirements for amino acids, ability to utilize sugars, resistance to antibiotics, and antigenic specificity of flagella. It has since become clear that, in appropriate systems, almost any mutant marker can be carried by phage lysates (Hartman, 1957). Such a broad spectrum of transfers has been termed generalized, or common, transduction (Clowes, 1960).

There is another pattern of phage-mediated gene transfer that is, however, much more specific. In this case, only a localized region of the bacterial chromosome is affected, and the phenomenon has accordingly been termed *special*, or restricted, transduction. This process was discovered by Morse (1954) in a study performed with the bacteriophage λ of *E. coli*. Anticipating the discussion to be presented subsequently, it can be pointed out that λ is a so-called "temperate" phage, which under appropriate conditions can replicate in close association with the chromosome of the bacterial cell without destroying its host. The point of attachment is the *gal* region, a series of loci that controls the fermentation of galactose. Interestingly, it is only these genetic determinants of the bacterial cell that can be transferred by λ to a competent recipient. Searching for an explanation, Morse, Lederberg, and Lederberg (1956) found that *gal* genes under certain circumstances are associated with practically every λ particle of a transducing lysate. These results have been interpreted to indicate that a partial replacement of genes in the phage genome takes place by a genetic interchange with the *gal* region of the bacterial chromosome (Luria, Fraser, Adams, and Burrous, 1958; Luria, 1959). It might then be expected that the transducing particles would in many cases be defective as phages, since a portion of the phage genome is lost. The experiments of Arber, Kellenberger, and Weigle (1957) show that such defects do indeed occur. Transducing λ particles are unable to multiply in bacterial cells if introduced alone, but can do so if an active bacteriophage (containing phage genes for the missing functions) is present as well. Thus, far from being a model of restricted interest, the λ *gal* system and others like it afford an insight into the probable mechanism for all transductions; that is, a genetic exchange between phage and bacterial host. The random transfer of characters that takes place in common transduction seems to be explained by the fact that phage vectors which operate in this pattern have no fixed point of association with the bacterial chromosome (Jacob and Wollman, 1958b). Accordingly, markers throughout the genome are transduced at random, although with a correspondingly reduced probability at any given locus.

On the whole, transduction and transformation thus represent variations on a common theme. Both processes deal with the transfer of genetic information in fragmentary form. The mode of delivery, however, does seem quite different. In transducing systems, the message is integrated with the genome of a viral vector, from which it must be extracted in recipient cells. By contrast, the process of transformation offers the ultimate in simplicity, with the introduction of purified nucleic acid free with any accompanying agent. But despite this disparity at the transfer phase, there is no evidence to indicate that the final incorporation of donor DNA is accomplished by different methods in transformation and transduction, respectively. Copy-choice replication can be invoked in both cases as an implementing mechanism (Jacob and Wollman, 1961), but the evidence cited earlier (see p. 86) makes it increasingly likely that the common element is in fact a process of direct integration.

Conjugation in Bacteria   While gene transfer in bacteria can take a variety of forms, the most striking and unexpected mechanism is that of direct conjugation between individual cells. The discovery of a mating process in *E. coli* by Lederberg and Tatum (Tatum and Lederberg, 1947; Lederberg, 1947) can be regarded as a true milestone, for until that time, no manifestations of sexuality in bacteria were known. Stimulated by the occurrence of transformation, these investigators began a search for recombination of genetic determinants between intact bacterial cells. The experimental design for this work is familiar, for it is the one previously described for the study of transduction; that is, two auxotrophic strains of bacteria were mixed and a search made for prototrophs arising as recombinants. It should be emphasized however, that transduction actually was not discovered until some years after conjugation was well known, and was recognized first in the analysis of an experiment that gave exceptional results. In the original studies of Lederberg and Tatum, work was initiated with two doubly mutant strains, obtained by irradiation. One of these required biotin and methionine for growth; the other, leucine and threonine. Consequently, neither population could proliferate alone on a minimal agar medium, but if 10^8 cells from each strain were mixed, a few prototrophs appeared. These proliferated as wild-type colonies without additional growth factors (see Figure 2.7). In this case (and in contrast to the transduction process), recombination was shown by a variety of experiments to take place only under conditions that permitted direct contact between bacteria of the two different types. An especially clear-cut

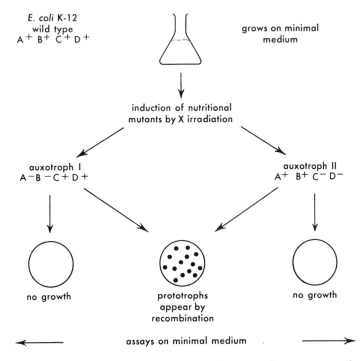

FIG. 2.7. Schematic diagram to show the original experiments of Lederberg and Tatum on genetic recombination in *E. coli.*

demonstration was provided by Davis (1950) in the first use of a U tube apparatus for this purpose. The data thus clearly pointed to a process of gene transfer between individual cells. But because conjugation was at first believed to be a rare event, the cytological mechanisms were not immediately looked for. Ultimately, however, side-by-side pairing of bacteria was observed directly (Lederberg, 1956b), and electron micrographs showed definite protoplasmic connections between conjugating cells (see Figure 2.8, taken from the paper of Anderson, Wollman, and Jacob, 1957).

A number of unique features of the conjugation process soon became apparent. The transfer of genes was demonstrated to occur as a "one-way" process rather than an exchange of hereditary materials between the two cells undergoing fusion (Hayes, 1952; 1953b; Lederberg, Cavalli, and Lederberg, 1952). Strains of bacteria proved to be differentiated to serve as donor or recipient, and crosses between two recipient strains were always sterile. Later, this difference was found to depend on the presence of a fertility factor, termed *F*, present in donor strains (F^+) and absent in recipient strains (F^-) (Hayes, 1953a; Cavalli, Lederberg, and Lederberg, 1953). In an $F^+ \times F^-$ cross, recipient cells are converted to the F^+ type in high efficiency by transmission of the F factor; other genetic markers from the donor strain show no linkage to F and are transferred much less frequently. But occasional variants appear within F^+ strains with greatly increased rates of recombination in crosses with F^- cells; these have been designated "high frequency" or Hfr strains (Hayes, 1953b). The discovery of these Hfr strains greatly facilitated the analysis of gene transfer, for the rate of recombination for many markers rose from one in 10^5 or less, to one per 2 to 10 cells. Significantly, however, Hfr cells could no longer transfer the independent F factor to recipient cells, which remained F^- even after transmission of other markers had occurred.

A comprehensive picture of these and other events of the conjugation process has been provided through the outstanding investigations of Jacob and Wollman (Wollman and Jacob, 1955; Wollman, Jacob, and Hayes, 1956; Jacob and Wollman, 1958b, 1961; see also Clark and Adelberg, 1962). It has become clear that recombination of markers in recipient cells is based on oriented transfer of a chromosomal segment

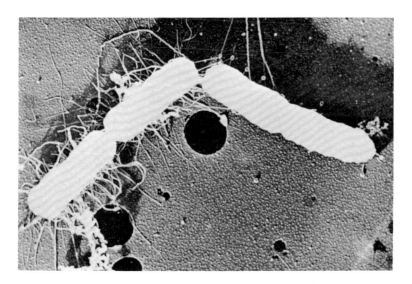

FIG. 2.8. Electron micrograph of conjugation in *E. coli*. Two bacteria shown are undergoing division. They are paired end to end and are connected by a bridge. The cell at the right (*Hfr*) has numerous particles of bacteriophage λ attached to the surface. These are attached by the tail and show heads emptied of DNA. The bacterium at left (*F⁻*) is recognizable because of its many fimbriae. (From Anderson, Wollman, and Jacob, 1957.)

of varying length from the donor bacterium. This conclusion stems from a simple but ingenious approach to the kinetics of the mating process. Conjugation is established between *Hfr* and *F⁻* cells in broth cultures, and at progressive intervals thereafter the pairing is disrupted by strong agitation in a Waring blendor. Diluted samples are then plated to test for the transmission of markers by the appearance of recombination in recipient cells. The results show that each of a series of markers is transferred at a specific time in the mating process; interruption of conjugation prior to this time prevents the appearance of the marker in recipient cells. Wollman and Jacob found, for example, that if bacterial pairs were separated at less than 8 minutes after mixing, no donor characteristics could be found in cultures from recipient cells. Separation at successively later intervals was followed by the appearance of more and more markers from the donor cells until, at 30 minutes, the mating process was essentially complete (see Figure 2.9). The order of entry of individual markers in any given cross is always the same, and the total number transferred depends on the time allowed for conjugation.

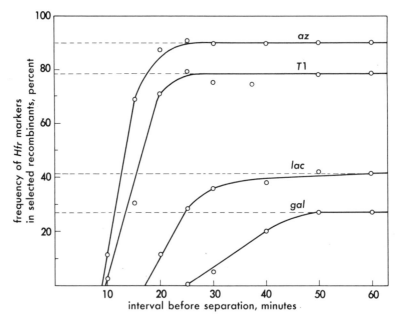

FIG. 2.9. Sequential transfer of genetic markers during conjugation in *E. coli*. The order of penetration of individual genes during a cross between *Hfr* and *F⁻* bacteria is determined by separating the conjugating pairs at graded intervals and plating in a selective medium. (Redrawn from Wollman and Jacob, 1958c.)

But even when the pairs were disrupted at a late stage, a systematic decrease could be observed in the probability of transmission for particular characteristics within the series studied.

The results obtained in blendor experiments might be considered in one sense as artifacts, were it not for the fact that even in undisturbed matings, there is a gradient of gene transfer frequency. Thus, if conjugation is not interrupted artificially, the total number of markers transmitted still varies from one pair to another. Apparently the bacterial chromosome breaks spontaneously during the transfer process, with a constant probability per unit length. It follows that the linear segment actually injected is variable in size. The frequency of transfer and seriation in transmission for particular markers as determined in this way correlates directly with the order of entry as observed in blendor experiments. From these results, it can be inferred that the markers in question are arrayed within a common linkage group; this confirms the conclusions reached earlier by more conventional methods (Lederberg, 1947). The actual transfer process may be visualized as the directed injection of a chromosomal element from *Hfr* to *F⁻* cells. Owing to spontaneous or induced breaks during transmission, however, the donor segment is incomplete.

By analyzing gene transfer to recipient cells as mediated by a series of different *Hfr* strains, Jacob and Wollman were finally able to devise a working picture of the bacterial chromosome as a whole. Each *Hfr* strain transfers a series of markers in predictable order, but different groups of characteristics are transmitted by the various strains. Some of these groups overlap, indicating that different segments of chromosome are transferred by the respective *Hfr* strains. When many such results were assembled, it finally became apparent that there are no breaks in continuity corresponding to the ends of linear chromosomes; there is instead a continuous serial linkage. This novel situation therefore seems to depict the genetic apparatus in these strains of *E. coli* as an endless array with the configuration of a circular chromosome (Hayes, 1960).

If the genetic markers are actually disposed in a circular pattern, how can the injection of chromosomal segments occur during conjugation? A suggestive clue lies in the fact that most, if not all, recombination seems to occur via *Hfr* cells as donors. In actual experiments, fluctuation tests showed that even the rare occurrence of gene transfer in ordinary $F^+ \times F^-$ crosses took place from donors formed by an $F^+ \rightarrow Hfr$ mutation in the F^+ strain. On the other hand, *Hfr* strains, whatever their origin, are distinguished by an inability to transmit the *F* factor alone to *F⁻* cells. The *Hfr* character itself is transferred only in low frequency and always at the end of any series of markers. A synthesis of these observations was made by Jacob and Wollman, who proposed that the F factor in F^+ cells is a genetic agent that replicates independently from linked markers in the bacterial chromosome. It can be transmitted directly to F^- cells as an isolated unit without the simultaneous passage of any chromosomal determinants. The $F^+ \rightarrow Hfr$ mutation may be explained as a direct integration of the F factor into the bacterial linkage group, with a break in the circular pattern at the point of insertion. This would give rise to a linear chromosome with the F factor at one end as a prerequisite for the gene transfer characteristic of Hfr strains (see Figure 2.10). If incorporation of F can take place at various loci in a circular chromosome, Hfr mutants would be expected to differ (as they do) in the particular sequence of markers transferred by any given strain. As a corollary to this thesis, mutations from $Hfr \rightarrow F^+$ could also be predicted by reversion of the linear to a circular linkage group, and such variants have been found.

Conjugation thus provides a direct method for viewing the genetic apparatus of bacterial cells. Whether processes of a similar nature occur generally among bacteria is not yet known. Mating and recombination do take place, however, in *Pseudomonas aeruginosa* (Holloway, 1955; Holloway and Fargie, 1960), an organism widely separated in its evolutionary affinities from *E. coli*. Within the coliform group, Luria and Burrous (1957) observed that conjugation occurs in *Shigella*, and they found that hybridization may occur between *Shigella* and *E. coli*. Similarly, Baron, Carey, and Spilman (1959) discovered an *Hfr* strain in *Salmonella typhosa*, which is capable of mating not only with other cells of this species but also with all *Salmonella*, *Shigella*, and *Escherichia* strains tested. It seems probable, therefore, that cell-to-cell transfer of

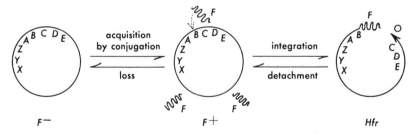

FIG. 2.10. Diagrammatic representation of sexual types in *E. coli*. An F^- recipient has a closed chromosome but no sex factor. An F^+ donor has a closed chromosome and contains several sex factors that are not integrated with the chromosome. An Hfr has a linear chromosome with an integrated sex factor. (Redrawn from Jacob and Wollman, 1961.)

genetic material can take place between any two members of the coliform group of bacteria. Such an assemblage conforms to the classical concept of a single species, in the sense of a potentially interbreeding population.

Apart from its usefulness in characterizing the genome, conjugation also serves as a means for the selective study of gene action. A special advantage of this approach is the fact that individual factors may be transferred at will to cells lacking the determinants in question. The β-galactosidase system provides one readily accessible model in which these variables can be manipulated. On the basis of information now available, it is possible to design experiments that highlight the action of a single gene, such as the z locus containing information required for the specific structure of the enzyme molecule. This can be illustrated by the results of crosses between strains of *E. coli* that are *Hfr i⁺ z⁺* and *F⁻ i⁻ z⁻*, respectively (Pardee and Prestidge, 1959; Riley, Pardee, Jacob, and Monod, 1960). Under these conditions, the z^+ gene is transferred to a recipient cell, which is competent in all other respects for the immediate production of enzyme. Within 2 minutes after gene transfer, the synthesis of β-galactosidase is at its maximal rate, with no further increase in a 30-minute period. Techniques involving this degree of selectivity in the expression of genes have hitherto been unknown, and offer great promise in broader studies.

Lysogeny and Episomic Agents   Infection and heredity in general would seem to have little in common, even at the cellular level. Yet, in microbiology, these two fields have converged increasingly in terms of virus-host relationships. By a generalization of studies from bacterial recombination on the one hand and phage infections on the other, Jacob and Wollman (1958a) have postulated a new class of hereditary determinants called episomes, which may be added to or subtracted from the genetic apparatus of competent cells. The nature of episomic agents can be made clear by considering a special aspect of phage infections known as lysogeny (Lwoff, 1953; Jacob and Wollman, 1959a). Ordinarily, bacteriophage may be regarded as a foreign infectious agent that multiplies rapidly on entry into susceptible bacteria and is then in turn released by the rapid destruction and lysis of host cells. But infection in some cases may proceed differently. In many types of bacteria, temperate phages occur, of which λ in *E. coli* is an example. These do not usually cause destruction when introduced into the host. The temperate phage passes instead into a latent form. In this state, infectious phage particles cannot ordinarily be recovered by physical disruption of the bacterial cells. Such bacteria are termed lysogenic because a phage precursor (termed prophage) is still present, and if activated can cause typical lysis of the host or other sensitive cells. Activation occurs spontaneously in a small proportion of the bacteria in a lysogenic strain, with destruction of the affected cells and release of typical phage particles in quantity. The remainder of the population is immune to damage by these phage particles, but their presence can be demonstrated by adding lysogenic bacteria to a so-called indicator strain. The indicator cells, of normal sensitivity, undergo lysis, showing that phage particles have been released. In some cases, the lysogenic state can also be revealed more directly by treating a lysogenic population with ultraviolet light or various other agents, which induce phage production in a high percentage of the affected cells.

The nature of lysogeny remained obscure for many years. Since the inactive precursor, or prophage, can persist indefinitely in lysogenic cells, there was a strong implication that the phage genome somehow replicated in accordance with that of the host. When the techniques of genetic recombination were used to dissect the lysogenic state, the host-virus relationship finally became clear. In this work, the λ *gal* system provided a strategic breakthrough. The phage λ was first discovered by E. Lederberg (1951) among strains of *E. coli* employed for conjugation. Lysogeny can readily be produced by λ in these materials, and from such populations, nonlysogenic mutants may be obtained. It was by matings between lysogenic and nonlysogenic strains that an association of λ with the *gal* region was finally recognized. The λ prophage thus behaves as an extrinsic unit attached to a specific site on the bacterial chromosome. It may be released from this relationship by induction with ultraviolet light or other extrinsic factors, and in this case, infective bacteriophage particles are formed through vegetative multiplication. A number of other temperate phages have been examined experimentally, and all conform to the λ model (Jacob and Wollman, 1959b, 1961). In each case, a prophage appears and passes into direct association with the bacterial chromosome at a different but characteristic locus. Some of these lysogenic systems, as in the case of λ, can give rise to infective particles when exposed to ultraviolet or other agents; the remainder are noninducible by all experimental treatments that have thus far been tried.

The mechanism of phage induction poses a fundamental problem, since it brings into focus the control system that determines whether temperate phages are to exist as prophage or as fully infective particles, respectively. The phenomenon of zygotic induction (Jacob and Wollman, 1954, 1956) can be mentioned in this connection, since it has provided a series of key observations. This term was coined to describe the active production of infective bacteriophage that sometimes occurs when a

lysogenic bacterium conjugates with a nonlysogenic cell. Zygotic induction takes place, for example, if an *Hfr* strain bearing prophage mates
with an F^- strain that is nonlysogenic for the same factor. Under these
circumstances, vegetative multiplication of phage particles occurs, and
the recipient bacteria are lysed. Zygotic induction does not take place
in the reverse combination, however; that is, following the union of a
nonlysogenic *Hfr* bacterium with an F^- cell carrying prophage. Such
observations clearly suggest the existence of a cytoplasmic repressor
that prevents the development of vegetative bacteriophage in bacteria
that have been lysogenized. This explanation is also consistent with the
fact that lysogenic bacteria are ordinarily immune to superinfection by
a phage of the same kind. A number of genetic experiments indicate
that the repressor is formed under the influence of prophage attached
to the bacterial chromosome and that it acts to prevent the synthesis
of viral protein, which is necessary for the formation of vegetative particles (Jacob and Campbell, 1959; Jacob, 1960; Jacob and Wollman,
1961).

Two opposing tendencies may therefore be visualized whenever a
temperate bacteriophage infects a competent recipient; (1) the propagation of vegetative phage particles, and (2) attachment to the bacterial
chromosome in prophage form. If the former process gains ascendancy,
the host cell is promptly lysed. But, if the latter is predominant and
takes place first, repressor is formed and a lysogenic state is established.
In this case, only when production of repressor is interfered with (for
example, by exposure to ultraviolet light or by unknown spontaneous
events) does replication of vegetative bacteriophage take place. The
devices that govern the phenomenon of lysogeny thus offer a singular
parallel to those determining the synthesis of inducible enzymes. The
formation of vegetative virus, like the synthesis of enzyme protein, can
be initiated by external agents, and the implementing mechanism appears to be the same (that is, neutralization of repressor). Although an
operator locus within the phage genome has not been specifically
identified as a target for repressors, the pattern of gene action that
has been observed clearly fits this concept. Likewise, mutations from
inducible to constitutive formation of enzymes find an analogy in the
continuous production of vegetative bacteriophage by variants within
lysogenic strains. Over-all, the similarity in these repressor-regulator
control systems is striking.

As a class of genetic determinants, temperate bacteriophages present a twofold aspect. Such agents may exist in an integrated form,
associated with the bacterial genome and replicating in accordance with
it. Alternatively, they may operate as autonomous particles in the cyto-

plasm, multiplying more rapidly than the host bacterium and giving rise to infectious units that may pass from cell to cell. This dual pattern of genetic behavior is not confined to the bacteriophage system. Jacob and Wollman have pointed out that the sex factor of *E. coli* presents a close parallel. Thus the *F* factor appears to occur as an autonomous unit in *F*⁺ cells, replicating independently from the bacterial chromosome. It is transmitted with high efficiency by contact between *F*⁺ and *F*⁻ cells, even under circumstances that preclude the transfer of chromosomal markers from the donor cell. Although this process cannot be termed infection and occurs only as a result of conjugation, the significant point is the passage of *F* as an independent unit from cell to cell. In *Hfr* bacteria, on the other hand, the *F* factor is integrated with the bacterial chromosome, as is prophage in the lysogenic state. It may be released from this association in *Hfr* → *F*⁺ mutations, and interestingly, the autonomous *F* factor may then carry with it occasional markers from former adjacent regions in the bacterial chromosome. These markers are transmitted when the *F* factor alone passes from *F*⁺ to *F*⁻ cells, a process that can be termed *F*-mediated transduction, or alternatively, "sexduction" (Jacob and Adelberg, 1959; Jacob and Wollman, 1961).

The genetic properties of the sex factor in *E. coli* are thus seen to be remarkably similar in principle to those of temperate bacteriophage. How many other systems there may be in bacteria that conform to this pattern is unknown, but at least one additional example has been described (see Jacob and Wollman, 1961). This concerns the production of so-called colicins by certain sublines of *E. coli*. The factors in question are specific proteins that, if formed, are toxic agents which can kill other bacteria in the same group (Fredericq, 1957). The potential for synthesis and release of colicins is genetically determined. It seems to depend on a genetic factor that can be passed readily by conjugation to noncolicinogenic strains. In *F*⁺ × *F*⁻ crosses, the determinant for colicinogeny passes with high efficiency from donor to recipient, and without any necessary transfer of other genetic markers. When *Hfr* bacteria are used as donors, however, the colicinogenic factor is found in direct association with the bacterial chromosome at a site that can be experimentally identified (Alfoldi, Jacob, Wollman, and Mazé, 1958).

To all such particulate elements, the term episome can be appropriately applied (Jacob and Wollman, 1958a; Wollman and Jacob, 1959; Jacob, Schaeffer, and Wollman, 1960; see also Campbell, 1962). Episomes have in common a flexibility in genetic behavior that is the distinguishing feature. Here are agents that can combine with or dissociate from the chromosomal system of genetic determinants, or even be dispensed with entirely (see Figure 2.11). Such a concept implies a significant departure from the classical integrity of the chromosome as a self-contained genetic unit and opens up new vistas. It remains to be seen what the generality of the episome model may be for other types of cells. Episomes have been compared to controlling elements in maize, partly on the basis that the sex factor at least has no fixed position within the bacterial chromosome (Jacob, 1960; Jacob, Schaeffer, and Wollman, 1960). Perhaps more significant is the fact that prophages, like controlling elements, appear to affect the expression of genes in their immediate neighborhood (Buttin, Jacob, and Monod, 1960; Yarmolinsky and Wiesmeyer, 1960). The behavior of episomes thus resembles to a degree the unique chromosomal components described by McClintock (1956). However, controllers and conventional genes can also be compared to regulator-operator systems (see p. 83; also Jacob and Monod, 1963). These somewhat different suggestions are not mutually exclusive.

In another context, Jacob, Schaeffer, and Wollman (1960) suggest that episomic concepts are potentially useful for an understanding of morphogenesis. On a purely speculative basis, the participation of episomic agents might lead to a modification of developmental potentialities within the emerging cell types of a given organism. The integration or loss of episomes, for example, could conceivably provide an explanation by the differentiation of somatic nuclei. Whether analogies of this type have more than a formal validity, however, can be determined only by further study.

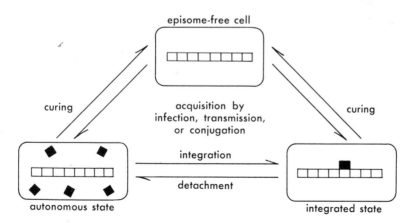

FIG. 2.11. Diagrammatic representation of episomic behavior. (Redrawn from Wollman and Jacob, 1959. Copyright, M. D. Anderson Hospital and University of Texas Press.)

SOME MECHANISMS OF
CYTOPLASMIC INHERITANCE

In all but the simplest cells, there is a clear distinction between nucleus and cytoplasm. Given this pattern, a first assumption might be that the expression and maintenance of cellular characteristics are a function of structural information found in the genes and chromosomes of the nucleus. But are additional control systems located in the cytoplasm? This question has been a difficult one to resolve. Cytoplasmic controls, in all probability, are concerned more with the stable perpetuation of cell differentiation than with the transmission of genetic information in coded form. In this case, the methods of classical genetics could be expected to yield relatively little information. How might the regulation of cell characters be achieved at the cytoplasmic level? In principle, at least two types of mechanisms can be entertained. The first of these assumes the presence of self-duplicating particles in the cytoplasm, carrying genetic information directly or in relay form from the nucleus (Ephrussi, 1953, 1958). A second and rather different view would attribute the stabilizing action of peripheral control systems to an intrinsic property of cytoplasmic organization, namely, the existence of "steady states" (Delbrück, 1949; Beale, 1954; Nanney, 1957).

There has been no lack of speculation concerning the possible existence and nature of genetic particulates at the cytoplasmic level. Wright (1941), Darlington (1949, 1958, 1959), and other investigators have suggested that plasmagenes may exist within the cytoplasm, but this hypothesis has remained in schematic form without appreciable support from experimental data. More conventional structures, such as the mitochondria, have also frequently been postulated to act as genetic agents. At one time or another, in fact, practically all recognized cytoplasmic particulates have been endowed with genetic attributes. Actual evidence for hereditary functions in these organelles, however, is in general slight or lacking (Lederberg, 1952). Viruses and microorganisms may also on occasion exist as intracellular symbionts, but their role in the heredity of animal cells is problematical. The line between infectious agents and cellular components, difficult to draw in bacteria, is equally ill-defined for such well-known constituents as the kappa factor of *Paramecium* (Preer and Stark, 1953; Beale, 1954; Sonneborn, 1959). To cover all these extrachromosomal particles that may conceivably act as hereditary determinants, Lederberg (1952) has proposed the term plasmid. It is obvious that the characterization and study of plasmids has not yet advanced beyond a preliminary stage.

The alternative notion of "steady states," referred to above, is even less adequately established as an implementing mechanism for the regulation of cell characters. Nevertheless, an attractive picture can be formulated in purely conceptual terms. According to the views of Delbrück, among others, cytoplasmic patterns may be self-perpetuating because of homeostatic mechanisms that tend to preserve constancy of type at the molecular level. The stability of characteristics within cell lineages would thus be identified with an innate property of metabolic sequences that carry out specific patterns of gene action. But stability in this sense can include the possibility of alternative "steady states." Within a given metabolic system, shifts may occur to other levels of organization, which are likewise perpetuated as dynamic equilibria. If such stepwise transformations are induced by extrinsic factors or can occur as spontaneous alterations, the steady-state concept would provide a mechanism for cellular variation that does not require any change in genotype.

There is no inherent conflict between these two types of cytoplasmic control systems or in their relation to the action of nuclear determinants. Conceivably, both may occur in varying combination within particular cells. At present, the principal problem is that of amassing enough information so that discussion of cytoplasmic inheritance can be carried out on a less speculative basis. As yet, little is known of the possibilities for variation at this level within somatic cell populations, but several examples in microorganisms have been analyzed in detail. The genetic implications of these systems form the subject matter of the following sections.

Formation of Respiratory Enzymes in Yeast The control of cell characters by cytoplasmic particulates is perhaps most clearly suggested by the work of Ephrussi and his collaborators on growth and respiration in yeast (see Ephrussi, 1953). These investigations take their origin from the analysis of variant dwarf colonies termed "petites." If, for example, an ordinary culture of baker's yeast (*Saccharomyces cerevisiae*) is plated on nutrient agar, about 1 to 2 percent of the resulting colonies are distinctly smaller than the rest. These variants may be designated "vegetative petites." They can be isolated and are stable in serial subculture; reversion to the normal colonial pattern does not take place. On the other hand, the normal large colonies, or even clonal populations from single cells of a large colony, give rise to vegetative petites with the same frequency as observed in stock cultures. The essential difference between variant and normal cells was established early by physiological studies. Fermentation occurs in both cell types, but when respiratory quotients are examined, it is clear that the respiration of petites has been practically abolished (Slonimski, 1949). This in turn reflects the loss of a whole series of respiratory enzymes, notably succinic dehydrogenase and cytochrome oxidase (Slonimski, 1953).

Such observations suggest that vegetative petites are derived from normal cells by a gene mutation resulting in an inability to synthesize respiratory enzymes, but a number of observations are difficult to fit into this picture. The high rate of appearance of vegetative petites in normal populations (about two variants per thousand cells per division) is not easy to reconcile with the relative rarity of most gene mutations, both in yeast and in other systems. Moreover, normal populations can be converted completely into vegetative petites by the application of euflavine or other acridine dyes (Ephrussi and Hottinguer, 1951). This process is not due to selection, for if single normal cells are isolated with a micromanipulator and allowed to multiply in a suitable concentration of euflavine, all resulting buds give rise to petites. In essence, a directed shift occurs here, which is quite unlike the random changes ordinarily obtained with mutagenic agents.

Fortunately, vegetative proliferation in yeast alternates with a sexual phase, so that mutant characters can be examined by Mendelian analysis. The diploid cells produced by vegetative growth may undergo two meiotic divisions, to produce a group of four haploid ascospores. When these ascospores are allowed to germinate, fusion takes place in pairs to re-establish the diploid state. In certain yeasts this fusion occurs only between cells of opposite mating type, so that if individual ascospores are dissected out and caused to generate in isolation, the resulting populations multiply as haploids. Fusion can be induced at will, however, by mixing two haploid strains of opposite mating type. In this way, normal cells and vegetative petites can be crossed to give a hybrid strain. Such hybrids in some cases are entirely normal with respect to growth and respiration (Ephrussi, Hottinguer, and Tavlitski, 1949). When sporulation is induced and the resulting ascospores are analyzed, all give rise to haploid strains with normal respiration: The mutant character has disappeared. In this case, the precursor petite strain is said to be neutral (see Figure 2.12). More commonly, vegetative petites are found to be suppressive; that is, they prevent to some extent the expression of normal phenotype in the progeny from a cross with normal cells (Ephrussi, de Margerie-Hottinguer, and Roman, 1955). In this case, a fraction of the hybrids will give rise to cells that are respiration-deficient. The degree of suppressiveness varies widely among different vegetative petites and is a relatively stable feature of each strain as populations are carried on through serial propagation. An explanation for the suppression phenomenon is not yet available, but apparently it

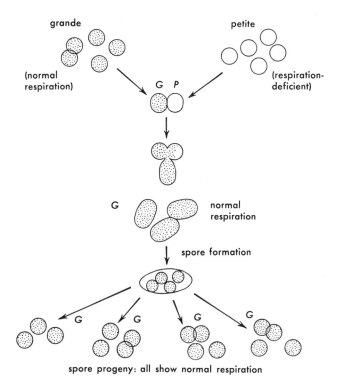

FIG. 2.12. Genetic behavior of a cytoplasmic mutation in yeast. Diagram shows the results of crossing a normal strain, or *grande*, with a so-called *neutral petite* (respiration-deficient). The mutant character disappears in hybrids formed by cell fusion and does not reappear by segregation when haploid spores are produced. (Redrawn from Ephrussi, 1953).

does not stem from the loss of respiration per se (Sherman and Ephrussi, 1962).

More important than the detailed differences between neutral and suppressive variants, however, is the fact that in neither case does the mutant character segregate in Mendelian fashion during crosses with normal cells. This behavior is particularly striking when additional markers, derived by known gene mutations, are included in the same crosses. The latter characters do segregate in expected patterns when ascospores are isolated and subjected to tetrad analysis. The appearance of vegetative petites thus seems to represent a cytoplasmic change rather than a nuclear mutation. In explanation, Ephrussi has postulated that self-duplicating particles exist within the cytoplasm of yeast cells and are essential for the synthesis of respiratory enzymes. Vegetative petites, either neutral or suppressive, are thought to arise through loss or inactivation of the cytoplasmic determinants. This interpretation has been sustained by James and Spencer (1958), who conclude that in yeast a mechanism for determining the precise distribution of essential cytoplasmic particles at cell division does not exist. Occasional buds could thus arise with few, or none, of the particulates in question; these may constitute the vegetative petites that appear spontaneously in normal populations. By an extension of this reasoning, the direct induction of petites by acridine dyes can be viewed as a selective elimination or repression by the hypothetical particles required for enzyme synthesis (Ephrussi, 1953). This hypothesis is a reasonable one, since in a number of other systems specific plasmids can be deleted by experimental means. For example, chloroplasts may be removed permanently from *Euglena* by treatment with streptomycin (Provasoli, Hutner, and Pintner, 1951; de Deken-Grenson and Messin, 1958), and by heat (Pringsheim and Pringsheim, 1952). In *Paramecium*, "disinfection" of kappa particles can be achieved by exposure to chloramphenicol, and plants may be freed from latent viruses by heat treatment (Lederberg, 1957). In this connection it is worth noting that heat treatments greatly increase the formation of vegetative petites in yeast (Sherman, 1959) and even exposure to metallic salts can induce respiratory deficiency (Lindegren, Nagai, and Nagai, 1958). A variety of evidence thus supports the concept that vegetative petites originate through changes that affect cytoplasmic determinants for respiratory enzymes, and this common end result can apparently be brought about by a number of diverse factors.

The ultimate control for biosynthesis of respiratory enzymes in yeast, however, resides within the nucleus. This was demonstrated clearly through the discovery of a very different class of respiratory mutants (Chen, Ephrussi, and Hottinguer, 1950). Such variants, termed "segregational petites," are indistinguishable phenotypically from vegetative petites, but give contrasting results in crosses with normal strains. Typically, the hybrid cells show a normal respiration, but if induced to sporulate, they give rise to haploid spores of two types. When these are germinated individually, progeny populations arise that are either normal or respiratory deficient, in equal numbers. This result suggests a simple Mendelian explanation: The respiratory deficiency of the segregational petite originates by mutation of a normal dominant gene to a recessive allele. The latter is unable to promote synthesis of the corresponding enzymes.

The relation of segregational to vegetative petites poses an interesting problem, which can be approached by examining the fusion products from crosses between strains of these two different types. If a neutral vegetative petite is employed in combination with a segregational petite, the hybrids in most cases are uniformly normal in respiration. When the ascospores produced by these hybrids are analyzed, the progeny are observed to be normal or petite, in a 2:2 ratio. Such results can be explained by making two assumptions (Ephrussi, 1953). These are (1) that segregational petites carry the cytoplasmic particles required for the synthesis of respiratory enzymes, but in the absence of the dominant wild-type nuclear gene, these potentialities are not expressed; and (2) that vegetative petites possess a normal gene for the production of respiratory enzymes, but lack the essential cytoplasmic determinants. In the diploid hybrids that arise between strains of these different types, there is a mutual compensation of deficiencies, giving a normal pattern of respiration. But since these hybrids are heterozygous for the nuclear gene pair, segregation takes place during sporulation and the mutant character reappears in 50 percent of the haploid progeny populations. Segregational petites may give rise to "double" mutants by additional loss of the cytoplasmic factor, and some strains consist largely or entirely of such cells (Sherman, 1963).

That vegetative and segregational petites represent variation at different levels within the yeast cell has become further evident through a study of mitochondrial patterns (Yotsuyanagi, 1962a, 1962b). In this analysis, the modulation that mitochondria exhibit in normal cells during an aerobic growth cycle provides an essential base line. While exponential multiplication is occurring, supported through fermentation, the mitochondria of normal yeast cells are few in number and relatively simple in structure. But as the stationary phase sets in, the rate of respiration rises conspicuously. At the same time, the mitochondria become much more numerous and exhibit well-differentiated cristae. Such a change-over does not occur in the cells of segregational petites. Here, the mitochondrial picture in the stationary phase, interestingly enough, is identical with that of normal cells in logarithmic growth. Neither of these patterns applies to vegetative petites, in which the mitochondria prove to be aberrant at all stages of the growth cycle. In such cells, the mito-chondria are less abundant, more poorly developed, and polymorphic in appearance. These abnormalities cannot be attributed to the absence of respiration or to the failure of particular enzymes to become active, for changes of this type are not found in the cells of segregational petites. Rather, it is the inverse relationship that needs to be considered further; that is, the possibility that changes in mitochondrial pattern may prevent the expression of respiratory function. Conceivably, both operational and genetic units at the cytoplasmic level may be represented by mitochondria as such, but proof for the identity of these two factors is still lacking.

To complete the picture of controlling mechanisms in yeast respiration, it can be pointed out that under anaerobic conditions, the respiratory enzymes become inducible rather than constitutive components of the yeast cell (Ephrussi and Slonimski, 1950; Slonimski, 1953). Spectroscopically, for example, normal cells that are maintained anaerobically can be shown to lack cytochromes a, b, and c. They are not, however, deficient in the ability to form these factors. If oxygen is readmitted to the system, a rapid resynthesis of respiratory enzymes occurs. The biosynthesis of respiratory enzymes in yeast thus provides another meeting point for concepts of variation based on phenotypic adaptation and genetic change, respectively.

Serotypes and Mating Types in *Paramecium* The ciliate protozoa, despite their apparent specialization, have yielded a wealth of information in recent years on nucleocytoplasmic mechanisms in inheritance. This development has come about through a better understanding of conjugation in these organisms, so that the resulting nuclear exchange can be used effectively as a tool for genetic analysis. In 1937 Sonneborn discovered that individuals of *Paramecium* fall into mating types of opposite sign, which interact during the conjugation process. Subsequent studies have shown that in *Paramecium aurelia*, the species most intensively studied, nine groups or varieties can be identified, each with a distinctive pair of opposite mating types. Conjugation takes place only between the two mating types corresponding to a given variety. The nine varieties thus correspond functionally to separate taxonomic units (Sonneborn, 1947; Beale, 1954). Within a given variety, conjugation can be obtained at will by mixing populations of complementary mating types. By using stocks with different markers for such crosses, Sonneborn found that conjugation brings about an equalization in genotype between the exconjugants, and consequently in their descendants, which are derived by binary fission. This result is understandable in the light of classic cytological studies that show that the macronuclei disappear in conjugation, whereas the micronuclei multiply and participate in a process of exchange and fusion between the two partners. It appears that meiosis occurs during this preliminary multiplication, with Mendelian segregation and reassortment of genes as haploid micronuclei are formed. Accordingly, Sonneborn (1939), with appropriate markers, was able to backcross a doubly heterozygous stock, and by examining the offspring of a large number of conjugating pairs, to recover the four expected types in equal numbers. For any single conjugating pair, however, exconjugants and offspring were identical in genotype.

Although conventional Mendelian patterns can in this way be recognized in *P. aurelia,* a number of novel nucleocytoplasmic relations have been uncovered. One of the most interesting concerns the inheritance and expression of surface antigens (Sonneborn, 1950; Beale, 1954, 1957). These are to be found as a series of substances covering the cilia and pellicle of paramecia generally. Although referred to earlier as ciliary antigens, it is now recognized that they do not form structural elements of the cilia and are not confined to these organelles (Preer, 1959; Beale and Wilkinson, 1961; Beale and Mott, 1962). The term immobilization antigen is more appropriate, since the factors in question can be demonstrated selectively with immune sera. These are obtained by injecting experimental animals with paramecia of the corresponding type. Individual animals are immobilized in the presence of specific immune serum, but are unaffected by sera for which they lack the complementary antigen. By this means, it can be shown that individuals of any given genotype have the potential for producing a series of alternative surface antigens, but only one of these appears at a particular time. This characteristic is a relatively stable one. If the descendants derived from a single cell by fission are maintained under constant conditions, all display the same immobilization antigen.

The ability to form other antigens is latent, however, and can be activated by various types of environmental shocks. If, for example, a homogeneous population of paramecia is given a sublethal exposure to the corresponding antiserum, all the animals are temporarily immobilized, but recover eventually when returned to a normal environment. After a variable period of growth, there is a massive population shift to a new antigenic type in which many, or sometimes essentially all of the cells undergo transformation (Sonneborn and LeSuer, 1948). These animals can no longer be inhibited by the original antiserum, but are readily immobilized by a serum corresponding to the new antigenic type. This process can be repeated indefinitely; when grown asexually under constant conditions, the paramecia tend to preserve a stable serotype, but following limited exposure to the corresponding antiserum, shifts to another pattern may occur. The number of potential alternative antigens is not unlimited, however. For any one strain, only a specified series of antigens may appear, and the number and kind of antigens within this series varies from strain to strain, depending on the genotype.

Transformations of serotype, as noted above, take place even when all individuals of a given population are immobilized with antiserum and recovery occurs without significant mortality. Thus the changes concerned are induced by exposure to antiserum and do not result from the selection of resistant individuals pre-existing in small numbers in the original population. It is clear also that immobilization with antiserum does not alter the existing antigens as such, but merely brings about a change in biosynthetic mechanism. After a period of further growth, this shift is expressed in the production of a new antigen in place of the old. But the presence of a specific antiserum as such is not essential for the transformation of antigenic types. Similar conversions can be induced by a number of other extrinsic stimuli, including changes in temperature, X rays, ultraviolet light, and treatment with trypsin (Beale, 1954).

The alterations between the antigens of a given series appear to depend on cytoplasmic changes rather than on mutations in genotype. This can be seen clearly in the results of conjugation between two individuals of different antigenic type (Sonneborn and LeSuer, 1948). Ordinarily, only nuclear exchange occurs between conjugating individuals, without passage of cytoplasm across the interconnecting bridge. Under these conditions, the nuclear constitution of the exconjugants becomes identical; yet they and their respective descendants retain the separate, original antigenic characters. A quite different result is observed, however, in occasional conjugating pairs where extensive interchange of cytoplasm occurs. In this case, a common antigen is produced by the exconjugants and their offspring. The factor that appears may correspond to one or the other original partner in various individual pairs.

The expression of serotypes in *P. aurelia* is thus only indirectly controlled by nuclear genes. These serve merely to set the limits for an array of phenotypic alternatives. Which pattern actually emerges appears to depend more on the metabolic state of cytoplasmic systems that affect the biosynthesis of antigens and that can exist in mutually exclusive forms. Very little information exists as yet to show how this cytoplasmic effect is mediated (Beale, 1957, 1958). The concept of differential gene action does provide a formal explanation for the selective production of alternative antigens, since by an internal "switch" mechanism only one of a series of gene pairs may be active under a given set of conditions. In this case, "steady states" in the cytoplasm may be identified with the production or presence of specific suppressors for the products of individual genes. That phenotypic expression can be determined by specific repressors has been demonstrated by the studies described earlier on the formation of β-galactosidase in *E. coli*. It should be pointed out, however, that the production of suppressor it itself a gene-controlled process, a function of the i^+ region in the bacterial chromosome. Conceivably, the production of suppressors for individual genes or their products may be also controlled by cytoplasmic systems, although as yet there is no proof that this occurs in *Paramecium*.

The influence of cytoplasmic factors in *Paramecium* is not confined to the specification of surface antigens. Other studies (Sonneborn, 1947; Beale, 1954; Nanney, 1957) show that the inheritance of mating types in *P. aurelia* is likewise influenced by nucleocytoplasmic interactions. Within this organism, individuals of any given genotype differentiate alternatively into one of the two mating types specified for the variety in question. The parallel in genetic mechanism to the serotype model is thus clear: The potential range of mating types is under gene control, but the specific type that appears is determined by extrinsic factors. The actual picture is more complex, however, because the mechanism for expression of mating type is not uniform within *P. aurelia*, but varies from one variety to another. These varieties fall into two groups, A and B. In group A, mating types are directly determined by random differentiation of the macronucleus during the period that immediately follows conjugation. In each exconjugant the macronuclei form from the fusion nucleus, which is established following the nuclear exchange between partners. The fusion nucleus subsequently divides twice, and two of the resulting nuclei differentiate as macronuclei. By a cytoplasmic division without further nuclear division, each macronucleus is distributed to a separate cell. Together with their descendants, each of the resulting individuals constitutes a caryonide, or group of animals containing macronuclei derived from a single macronucleus. In animals of group A in *P. aurelia*, all animals of a given caryonide have the same mating type, but the two caryonides derived from a single exconjugant may vary: Both may correspond in mating type to the original parent or both to the opposite type, or one of each mating type may be represented. Thus the expression of mating type in group A is essentially independent from cytoplasmic factors and depends instead on the specific ·macronucleus present in a given cell.

In group B of *P. aurelia*, the inheritance and expression of mating types follows a different course, and at first sight, this pattern seems to parallel the cytoplasmic control observed with serotypes. In this case, if cytoplasmic exchange does not occur during conjugation, each exconjugant as well as all its descendants preserve the original mating type. In pairs with appreciable cytoplasmic transfer, both exconjugants assume one or the other mating type. Even within this system, however, effective control in the determination of mating type resides within the macronucleus. This was demonstrated by Sonneborn (1954) in an ingenious experiment. Animals of group B were allowed to conjugate, and pairs were selected that showed extensive interchange of cytoplasm. In animals of group B, such interchange, as just noted, converts both partners and their caryonides to a common mating type. These pairs were exposed to high temperatures, which partially suppressed the development of new macronuclei, so that occasional caryonides were obtained in which the old macronucleus regenerated instead to form a functional structure. In these exceptional caryonides the mating type of the original parent was preserved, even when the other three caryonides from a given pair, with newly formed macronuclei, were of opposite mating type. This finding can be explained by assuming that in group B animals, the macronucleus differentiates in accordance with the existing cytoplasmic state, but once differentiation has occurred, the process is irreversible, even in regeneration. It thus appears that the macronucleus is the immediate source of information for the expression of mating types in *P. aurelia*. The demonstrable effect of the cytoplasm in group B may merely reflect the release into the cytoplasm of an inhibitor that is retained within the macronucleus in animals of group A (Nanney, 1957).

Nucleocytoplasmic Hybrids in Amoeba Where nuclear transfers can be made between cells, the location and kind of control systems for cell characters can be investigated more directly. As previously described, this technique has been employed extensively for the analysis of embryonic development. The methods of Briggs and King, however, necessitate the use of whole eggs as recipients in nuclear transfers. Individual cell characters can thus be studied only as part of a developmental ensemble, and the progressive differentiation of both nucleus and cytoplasm limits the examination of their mutual effects. These objections can be obviated in part by the choice of protozoan cells as test material. In *Amoeba*, for example, nuclei can be transferred directly between animals of the same type or even between individuals of two different strains. In this way, the influence of nucleus and cytoplasm on specific characteristics may be explored in reciprocal combination. The restricted spectrum of cellular characteristics available for study in these organisms is compensated for by the continuity of organization and stabilized pattern of differentiation within single cells.

Studies of inheritance in *Amoeba* have been carried on chiefly by Danielli and his colleagues, using the organisms *A. proteus* and *A. discoides*. Lorch and Danielli (1950, 1953b) found that amoebae of either type can be readily enucleated and supplied with a nucleus from a different cell. Homotransfers between individuals within the same strain are ordinarily successful, and give rise to clones that proliferate indefinitely. Heterotransfers of nuclei between *proteus* and *discoides* yield less favorable results. The foreign nuclei can reactivate enucleated animals, but as a rule, they are compatible for limited periods only. Cell division occurs less frequently in these heterotransfers, and although the animals survive for considerable periods, they do not in general produce mass cultures. In rare instances, however, hybrid amoebae can give rise to a stable population that proliferates indefinitely in logarithmic fashion. Such heterotransfer clones have been a prime source of information on the patterns of control for specific cell characters. A shorthand method for describing these animals has been useful. Thus, $P_n D_c$, for example, represents a *proteus* nucleus in *discoides* cytoplasm. In more detail, $[_T D_n, _{T_1} P_c]$ refers to a *discoides* nucleus from strain T in *proteus* cytoplasm of strain T_1.

Despite the simplicity of body plan in amoebae, a number of distinctive differences have been found between *A. proteus* and *A. discoides* (Lorch and Danielli, 1953a; Danielli, 1960). It is questionable that these two forms can be regarded as valid species (Danielli, 1959), but there is no doubt that the particular strains that have been used do show a consistent differential in heritable characteristics. The average nuclear size of *discoides*, for example, is 38μ under standard laboratory conditions, whereas for *proteus*, a figure of 44μ is obtained. When frequency distributions of nuclear size are prepared, the curve for *proteus* shows three peaks whereas that of *discoides* has a single peak only. There are also characteristic differences in shape during locomotion or in the presence of specific antisera. The distinctions between *proteus* and *discoides* are moreover not confined to morphological characteristics. The two types can also be separated on the basis of growth rates, antigenic structure, pattern of free amino acids, and sensitivity to streptomycin.

This background of differences can be used to weigh the relative effects of nucleus and cytoplasm on the expression of cell characters in hybrid amoebae. The most significant observations have been made on stable heterotransfer clones, in which unique patterns are established and remain constant over a period of years (Danielli, Lorch, Ord, and Wilson, 1955; Danielli, 1958, 1959, 1960). In these it might be expected that heritable characteristics would ultimately, if not at the outset, conform to the nuclear type. This prediction has not been borne out, however, with the possible exception of antigen production and the determination of free amino acid patterns. The details of experiments involving the latter are not yet available (Danielli, 1960). For other cellular characters the evidence clearly indicates a joint control by nucleus and cytoplasm; in some cases, the cytoplasmic influence is predominant.

These generalizations can be illustrated more specifically with a few representative data. In transfers between *A. discoides* (strain T) and *A. proteus* (strain T_1), nuclear size is almost entirely determined by the cytoplasm. Thus *discoides* nuclei in $[_T D_n, _{T_1} P_c]$ hybrids increase in average size within a few days, whereas *proteus* nuclei in $[_{T_1} P_n, _T D_c]$

combinations diminish in mean diameter. These size adjustments are stable and persist without change for many years in established hybrid clones. There is, however, a slight but detectable influence on nuclear size by the nucleus itself, recognizable as a minor departure from the cytoplasmic type when large numbers of nuclei are measured in these hybrids. For other strains, the influence of the nucleus on nuclear size may be much greater. In heterotransfers with strains T_4 and Z of A. proteus, the effects of nucleus and cytoplasm on nuclear size are nearly equal.

The shape of hybrid amoebae in long-term cultures is also clearly influenced by both nucleus and cytoplasm. During locomotion the typical proteus individual is relatively compact, with a few smooth pseudopodia, whereas discoides is usually more sheetlike, with several jagged pseudopodia. Both D_nP_c and P_nD_c hybrids are intermediate between these extremes and preserve this external configuration in stable fashion. In the same way, the external form of heterotransfers in the presence of antiserum falls between the round discoides type and the lobose proteus form.

Of further interest are the patterns of sensitivity to streptomycin, which emerge from nuclear transfer combinations (Cole and Danielli, 1963). Here, the results depend on whether nuclear exchanges are made on an intraspecific basis, between sublines of A. proteus, or as reciprocal transfers between A. proteus and A. discoides. Substrains within A. proteus show thresholds for growth inhibition by streptomycin that vary from 0.06 to 0.36 μg/ml, but all absorb the same amount of drug per individual. Interestingly, all the nucleocytoplasmic hybrids between these lines display a streptomycin sensitivity corresponding to the most sensitive parent, regardless of the direction in which nuclear transfer is made. A quite different result, however, is obtained in proteus-discoides combinations, which may reflect the fact that A. discoides not only has a high threshold for growth inhibition by streptomycin, but also absorbs only half as much drug per individual as A. proteus. If heterotransfers are established between A. discoides and a sensitive subline of A. proteus, the hybrids are intermediate between the parents in response to streptomycin, both in D_nP_c and P_nD_c combinations. Joint control of streptomycin sensitivity by nuclear and cytoplasmic factors seems indicated by these observations, with the latter replicating independently. Even more interesting is that the control systems in the cytoplasm can apparently be transferred directly from cell to cell (Hawkins, Cole, and Danielli, 1962). If discoides cytoplasm is injected into A. proteus, the threshold of response to streptomycin can be elevated in stable fashion, but a lowering follows the introduction of proteus cytoplasm into individuals of *A. discoides*. Changes induced in this manner persist for at least 50 generations and evidently represent a change in cytoplasmic pattern, since otherwise the original inoculum in the host cell would have undergone a dilution of 2^{50}.

Significantly, there are indications that the nucleus and cytoplasm of amoebae undergo mutual modification in heterotransfers (Danielli, 1959). Evidence for this view comes from experiments with a P_nD_c clone that had been growing as a stable line for five years. At the end of this time, the hybrid nuclei were transferred back into homologous *proteus* cytoplasm, and fresh *discoides* nuclei were used to renucleate the original hybrids. Only about 1 percent of these back-transfers in either direction were successful, although control transplants with normal nuclei in fresh P_nP_c or D_nD_c combinations showed the usual high viability. Superficially, at least, these changes resemble the differentiation of somatic nuclei observed by Briggs and King or, perhaps more closely, the restriction of nuclear potentialities observed for *R. pipiens* nuclei grown in eggs of *R. sylvatica* to the blastula stage (Moore, 1958).

In evaluating the results obtained by nuclear transplantation in *Amoeba*, Danielli has stressed the possibility that synthesis of macromolecules may be directly determined by the nucleus, while the organization of these and other units into more complex structures is a function of the cytoplasm as well. The evidence for the first assumption is not very strong in *Amoeba* as yet, but the participation of the cytoplasm in the expression of complex cell characters such as body shape has been clearly demonstrated. The mechanism by which this cytoplasmic effect is exerted is still unknown. Certainly, in hybrid clones that have been established for years, there is no vestige of the original cytoplasmic constituents. It must be assumed, therefore, that certain intrinsic properties of the original cytoplasmic organization are self-perpetuating even in the presence of a foreign nucleus. The composite control of cell characters by nucleus and cytoplasm poses a novel problem for which no comparable models exist as yet in conventional genetic systems.

■ References

ALEXANDER, H. E., and LEIDY, G. 1951. Determination of inherited traits of *H. influenzae* by desoxyribonucleic acid fractions isolated from type-specific cells. J. Exptl. Med., **93:** 345–359.

ALFOLDI, L., JACOB, F., WOLLMAN, E. L., and MAZÉ, R. 1958. Sur le déterminisme génétique de la colicinogenie. Compt. Rend. Acad. Sci., **246:** 3531–3533.

ANDERSON, T. F., WOLLMAN, E. L., and JACOB, F. 1957. Sur les processus de conjugaison et de recombinaison chez *Escherichia coli:* III. Aspects morphologiques en microscopie électronique. Ann. Inst. Pasteur, **93:** 450–455.

ARBER, W., KELLENBERGER, G., and WEIGLE, J. 1957. La défectuosité du phage lambda transducteur. Schweiz. Z. allgem. Pathol. Bakteriol., **20:** 659–665.

ATWOOD, K. C., SCHNEIDER, L. K., and RYAN, F. J. 1951. Selective mechanisms in bacteria. Cold Spring Harbor Symp. Quant. Biol., **16:** 345–355.

AUERBACH, C., and ROBSON, J. M. 1946. Chemical production of mutations. Nature, **157:** 302.

AVERY, O. T., MacLEOD, C. M., and McCARTY, M. 1944. Studies on the chemical nature of the substance inducing transformation of pneumococcal types. J. Exptl. Med., **79:** 137–158.

BARON, L. S., CAREY, W. F., and SPILMAN, W. M. 1959. Characteristics of a high frequency of recombination (Hfr) strain of *Salmonella typhosa* compatible with *Salmonella, Shigella,* and *Escherichia* species. Proc. Natl. Acad. Sci., **45:** 1752–1757.

BEALE, G. H. 1954. The genetics of *Paramecium aurelia.* Cambridge: The University Press. 179 pp.

BEALE, G. H. 1957. The antigen system of *Paramecium aurelia.* Intern. Rev. Cytol., **6:** 1–25.

BEALE, G. H. 1958. The role of the cytoplasm in antigen determination. Proc. Roy. Soc. (London) Ser. B., **148:** 308–314.

BEALE, G. H., and MOTT, M. R. 1962. Further studies on the antigens of *Paramecium aurelia* with the aid of fluorescent antibodies. J. Gen. Microbiol., **28:** 617–623.

BEALE, G. H., and WILKINSON, J. F. 1961. Antigenic variation in unicellular organisms. Ann. Rev. Microbiol., **15:** 263–296.

BRAUN, W. 1953. Bacterial genetics. Philadelphia: W. B. Saunders Company, 238 pp.

BUTTIN, G., JACOB, F., and MONOD, J. 1960. Synthèse constitutive de galactokinase consécutive au développement des bactériophage λ chez *Escherichia coli* K 12. Compt. Rend. Acad. Sci., **250:** 2471–2473.

CAMPBELL, A. M. 1962. Episomes. Advan. Genet., **11:** 101–145.

CAVALLI, L. L., LEDERBERG, J., and LEDERBERG, E. M. 1953. An infective factor controlling sex compatibility in *Bacterium coli.* J. Gen. Microbiol., **8:** 89–103.

CAVALLI-SFORZA, L. L., and LEDERBERG, J. 1956. Isolation of pre-adaptive mutants in bacteria by sib selection. Genetics, **41:** 367–381.

CHEN, S. Y., EPHRUSSI, B., and HOTTINGUER, H. 1950. Nature génétique des mutants à déficience respiratoire de la souche B-11 de la levure de boulangerie. Heredity, **4:** 337–351.

CLARK, A. J., and ADELBERG, E. A. 1962. Bacterial conjugation. Ann. Rev. Microbiol., **16:** 289–319.

CLOWES, R. C. 1960. Fine genetic structure as revealed by transduction. *In: Microbial Genetics,* pp. 92–114. H. Hayes and R. C. Clowes, eds. Cambridge: The University Press.

COHEN, G. N., and MONOD, J. 1957. Bacterial permeases. Bacteriol. Revs., **21:** 169–194.

COHN, M. 1957. Contributions of studies on the β-galactosidase of *Escherichia coli* to our understanding of enzyme synthesis. Bacteriol. Revs., **21:** 140–168.

COHN, M. 1958. On the differentiation of a population of *Escherichia coli* with respect to β-galactosidase formation. *In: A Symposium on the Chemical Basis of Development,* pp. 458–468. W. D. McElroy and B. Glass, eds. Baltimore: The Johns Hopkins Press.

COLE, R. J., and DANIELLI, J. F. 1963. Nuclear-cytoplasmic interactions in the responses of *Amoeba proteus* and *Amoeba discoides* to streptomycin. Exptl. Cell Res., **29:** 199–206.

DANIELLI, J. F. 1958. Studies of inheritance in amoebae by the technique of nuclear transfer. Proc. Roy. Soc. (London) Ser. B., **148:** 321–331.

DANIELLI, J. F. 1959. The cell-to-cell transfer of nuclei in amoebae and a comprehensive cell theory. Ann. N. Y. Acad. Sci., **78:** 675–687.

DANIELLI, J. F. 1960. Inheritance in amoebae, studied by nuclear transfer. *In: Microbial Genetics,* pp. 294–300. W. Hayes and R. C. Clowes, eds. Cambridge: The University Press.

DANIELLI, J. F., LORCH, I. J., ORD, M. J., and WILSON, E. G. 1955. Nucleus and cytoplasm in cellular inheritance. Nature, **176:** 1114–1115.

DARLINGTON, C. D. 1949. Genetic particles. Endeavour, **8:** 51–61.

DARLINGTON, C. D. 1958. The evolution of genetic systems. Second edition. New York: Basic Books, Inc. 265 pp.

DARLINGTON, C. D. 1959. Plasmagene theory and cancer genesis. *In: Genetics and Cancer,* pp. 9–24. Austin: University of Texas Press.

DAVIS, B. D. 1950. Nonfiltrability of the agents of genetic recombination in *Escherichia coli.* J. Bacteriol., **60:** 507–508.

DE DEKEN-GRENSON, M., and MESSIN, S. 1958. La continuité génétique des chloroplastes chez les Euglènes. I. Méchanisme de L'apparition des lignées blanches dans les cultures traitées par la streptomycine. Biochim. et Biophys. Acta, **27:** 145–155.

DELBRÜCK, M. 1949. Comments on a paper by T. M. Sonneborn and G. H. Beale. *In: Unités Biologiques Douées de Continuité Génétique,* pp. 33–35. Paris: Colloq. Intern. Centre Natl. Recherche Sci.

DEMEREC, M. 1956. A comparative study of certain gene loci in *Salmonella.* Cold Spring Harbor Symp. Quant. Biol., **21:** 113–121.

DEMEREC, M., and DEMEREC, Z. E. 1956. Analysis of linkage relationships in *Salmonella* by transduction techniques. Brookhaven Symp. Biol., **8:** 75–87.

DEMEREC, M., and LATARJET, R. 1946. Mutations in bacteria induced by radiations. Cold Spring Harbor Symp. Quant. Biol., **11:** 38–50.

DEMEREC, M., and SAMS, J. 1960. Induction of mutations in individual genes of *Escherichia coli* by low X-radiation. *In: Immediate and Low Level Effects of Ionizing Radiations,* pp. 283–293. A. A. Buzzati-Traverso, ed. London: Taylor and Francis, Ltd.

EPHRUSSI, B. 1953. Nucleo-cytoplasmic relations in micro-organisms. Oxford: Clarendon Press. 127 pp.

EPHRUSSI, B. 1958. The cytoplasm and somatic cell variation. J. Cellular Comp. Physiol., 52(Suppl. 1): 35–53.

EPHRUSSI, B., DE MARGERIE-HOTTINGUER, H., and ROMAN, H. 1955. Suppressiveness: a new factor in the genetic determinism of the synthesis of respiratory enzymes in yeast. Proc. Natl. Acad. Sci., 41: 1065–1071.

EPHRUSSI, B., and HOTTINGUER, H. 1951. On an unstable state in yeast. Cold Spring Harbor Symp. Quant. Biol., 16: 75–85.

EPHRUSSI, B., HOTTINGUER, H., and TAVLITSKI, J. 1949. Action de l'acriflavine sur les levures. II. Étude génétique du mutant "petite colonie." Ann. Inst. Pasteur, 76: 419–442.

EPHRUSSI, B., and SLONIMSKI, P. P. 1950. La synthèse adaptative des cytochromes chez la levure de boulangerie. Biochim. et Biophys. Acta, 6: 256–267.

EPHRUSSI-TAYLOR, H. 1955. Current status of bacterial transformations. Advan. Virus Res., 3: 275–307.

EPHRUSSI-TAYLOR, H. 1960. On the biological functions of deoxyribonucleic acid. In: Microbial Genetics, pp. 132–154. W. Hayes and R. C. Clowes, eds. Cambridge: The University Press.

FOX, M. S. 1962. The fate of transforming deoxyribonucleate following fixation by transformable bacteria, III. Proc. Natl. Acad. Sci., 48: 1043–1048.

FREDERICQ, P. 1957. Colicins. Ann. Rev. Microbiol., 11: 7–22.

GRIFFITH, F. 1928. The significance of pneumococcal types. J. Hyg., 27: 113–159.

GROSS, J., and ENGLESBERG, E. 1959. Determination of the order of mutational sites governing L-arabinose utilization in Escherichia coli B/r by transduction with phage Plbt. Virology, 9: 314–331.

HALVORSON, H. O. 1960. The induced synthesis of proteins. Advan. Enzymol., 22: 99–156.

HARTMAN, P. E. 1957. Transduction: a comparative review. In: A Symposium on the Chemical Basis of Heredity, pp. 408–467. W. D. McElroy and B. Glass, eds. Baltimore: The Johns Hopkins Press.

HAWKINS, S. E., COLE, R. J., and DANIELLI, J. F. 1962. Preliminary studies on the basis of cytoplasmic inheritance in amoebae. Nature, 196: 396.

HAYES, W. 1952. Recombination in Bact. coli K-12; unidirectional transfer of genetic material. Nature, 169: 118–119.

HAYES, W. 1953a. Observations on a transmissible agent determining sexual differentiation in Bacterium coli. J. Gen. Microbiol., 8: 72–88.

HAYES, W. 1953b. The mechanism of genetic recombination in Escherichia coli. Cold Spring Harbor Symp. Quant. Biol., 18: 75–93.

HAYES, W. 1960. The bacterial chromosome. In: Microbial Genetics, pp. 12–38. W. Hayes and R. C. Clowes, eds. Cambridge: The University Press.

HOGNESS, D. S. 1959. Induced enzyme synthesis. In: Biophysical Science—A Study Program, pp. 256–268. J. L. Oncley, ed. New York: John Wiley & Sons, Inc.

HOLLOWAY, B. W. 1955. Genetic recombination in *Pseudomonas aeruginosa*. J. Gen. Microbiol., **13**: 572–581.

HOLLOWAY, B. W., and FARGIE, B. 1960. Fertility factors and genetic linkage in *Pseudomonas aeruginosa*. J. Bacteriol., **80**: 362–368.

HOTCHKISS, R. D. 1951. Transfer of penicillin resistance in pneumococci by the desoxyribonucleate derived from resistant cultures. Cold Spring Harbor Symp. Quant. Biol., **16**: 457–461.

HOTCHKISS, R. D. 1955a. The genetic chemistry of the pneumococcal transformations. Harvey Lectures, **49**: 124–144. New York: Academic Press Inc.

HOTCHKISS, R. D. 1955b. Bacterial transformation. J. Cellular Comp. Physiol., **45**(Suppl. 2): 1–22.

HOTCHKISS, R. D., and MARMUR, J. 1954. Double marker transformations as evidence of linked factors in desoxyribonucleate transforming agents. Proc. Natl. Acad. Sci., **40**: 55–60.

JACOB, F. 1960. Genetic control of viral functions. Harvey Lectures, **54**: 1–39. New York: Academic Press Inc.

JACOB, F., and ADELBERG, E. A. 1959. Transfert de caractères génétiques par incorporation au facteur sexuel d'*Escherichia coli*. Compt. Rend. Acad. Sci., **249**: 189–191.

JACOB, F., and CAMPBELL, A. 1959. Sur le système de répression assurant l'immunité chez les bactéries lysogènes. Compt. Rend. Acad. Sci., **248**: 3219–3221.

JACOB, F., and MONOD, J. 1961a. On the regulation of gene activity. Cold Spring Harbor Symp. Quant. Biol., **26**: 193–211.

JACOB, F., and MONOD, J. 1961b. Genetic regulatory mechanisms in the synthesis of proteins. J. Mol. Biol., **3**: 318–356.

JACOB, F., and MONOD, J. 1963. Genetic repression, allosteric inhibition, and cellular differentiation. In: *Cytodifferentiation and Macromolecular Synthesis*, pp. 30–64. M. Locke, ed. New York: Academic Press, Inc.

JACOB, F., PERRIN, D., SANCHEZ, C., and MONOD, J. 1960. L'opéron: groupe de gènes à expression coordonnée par un opérateur. Compt. Rend. Acad. Sci., **250**: 1727–1729.

JACOB, F., SCHAEFFER, P., and WOLLMAN, E. L. 1960. Episomic elements in bacteria. In: *Microbial Genetics*, pp. 67–91. W. Hayes and R. C. Clowes, eds. Cambridge: The University Press.

JACOB, F., and WOLLMAN, E. L. 1954. Induction spontanée du développement du bactériophage λ au cours de la recombinaison génétique chez *E. coli* K-12. Compt. Rend. Acad. Sci., **239**: 317–319.

JACOB, F., and WOLLMAN, E. L. 1956. Sur les processus de conjugaison et de recombinaison chez *Escherichia coli*. I. L'induction par conjugaison ou induction zygotique. Ann. Inst. Pasteur, **91**: 486–510.

JACOB, F., and WOLLMAN, E. L. 1958a. Les épisomes éléments génétiques ajoutés. Compt. Rend. Acad. Sci., **247**: 154–156.

JACOB, F., and WOLLMAN, E. L. 1958b. Genetic and physical determinations of chromosomal segments in *Escherichia coli*. Symp. Soc. Exptl. Biol., **12**: 75–92.

JACOB, F., and WOLLMAN, E. L. 1959a. Lysogeny. *In: The Viruses,* Vol. 2, pp. 319–351. F. M. Burnet and W. M. Stanley, eds. New York: Academic Press Inc.

JACOB, F., and WOLLMAN, E. L. 1959b. The relationship between the prophage and the bacterial chromosome in lysogenic bacteria. *In: Recent Progress in Microbiology,* pp. 15–30. G. Tunevall, ed. Oxford: Blackwell Scientific Publications.

JACOB, F., and WOLLMAN, E. L. 1961. Sexuality and the genetics of bacteria. New York: Academic Press Inc. 374 pp.

JAMES, A. P., and SPENCER, P. E. 1958. The process of spontaneous extra-nuclear mutation in yeast. Genetics, 43: 317–331.

LACKS, S. 1962. Molecular fate of DNA in genetic transformation of *Pneumococcus.* J. Mol. Biol., **5:** 119–131.

LEA, D. E., and COULSON, C. A. 1949. The distribution of the numbers of mutants in bacterial populations. J. Genet., 49: 264–285.

LEDERBERG, E. M. 1951. Lysogenicity in *E. coli* K-12. Genetics, **36:** 560.

LEDERBERG, E. M. 1960. Genetic and functional aspects of galactose metabolism in *Escherichia coli* K-12. *In: Microbial Genetics,* pp. 115–131. W. Hayes and R. C. Clowes, eds. Cambridge: The University Press.

LEDERBERG, J. 1947. Gene recombination and linked segregations in *Escherichia coli.* Genetics, **32:** 505–525.

LEDERBERG, J. 1951. Inheritance, variation and adaptation. *In: Bacterial Physiology,* pp. 67–100. C. H. Werkman and P. W. Wilson, eds. New York: Academic Press Inc.

LEDERBERG, J. 1952. Cell genetics and hereditary symbiosis. Physiol. Revs., **32:** 403–430.

LEDERBERG, J. 1955. Recombination mechanisms in bacteria. J. Cellular Comp. Physiol., 45(Suppl. 2): 75–107.

LEDERBERG, J. 1956a. Genetic transduction. Am. Scientist, **44:** 264–280.

LEDERBERG, J. 1956b. Conjugal pairing in *Escherichia coli.* J. Bacteriol., **71:** 497–498.

LEDERBERG, J. 1957. Viruses, genes, and cells. Bacteriol. Revs., **21:** 133–139.

LEDERBERG, J., and LEDERBERG, E. M. 1952. Replica plating and indirect selection of bacterial mutants. J. Bacteriol., **63:** 399–406.

LEDERBERG, J., CAVALLI, L. L., and LEDERBERG, E. M. 1952. Sex compatibility in *Escherichia coli.* Genetics, **37:** 720–730.

LENNOX, E. S. 1955. Transduction of linked genetic characters of the host by bacteriophage P1. Virology, **1:** 190–206.

LINDEGREN, C. C., NAGAI, S., and NAGAI, H. 1958. Induction of respiratory deficiency in yeast by manganese, copper, cobalt, and nickel. Nature, **182:** 446–448.

LORCH, I. J., and DANIELLI, J. F. 1950. Transplantation of nuclei from cell to cell. Nature, **166:** 329-330.

LORCH, I. J., and DANIELLI, J. F. 1953a. Nuclear transplantation in amoebae. I. Some species characters of *Amoeba proteus* and *Amoeba discoides.* Quart. J. Microscop. Sci., **94:** 445–460.

LORCH, I. J., and DANIELLI, J. F. 1953b. Nuclear transplantation in amoebae. II. The immediate results of transfer of nuclei between *Amoeba proteus* and *Amoeba discoides.* Quart. J. Microscop. Sci., **94:** 461–480.

LURIA, S. E. 1959. Genetic transfers by viruses. Brookhaven Symp. Biol., **12:** 95–102.

LURIA, S. E., and BURROUS, J. W. 1957. Hybridization between *Escherichia coli* and *Shigella.* J. Bacteriol., **74:** 461–476.

LURIA, S. E., and DELBRÜCK, M. 1943. Mutations of bacteria from virus sensitivity to virus resistance. Genetics, **28:** 491–511.

LURIA, S. E., FRASER, D. K., ADAMS, J. N., and BURROUS, J. W. 1958. Lysogenization, transduction, and genetic recombination in bacteria. Cold Spring Harbor Symp. Quant. Biol., **23:** 71–82.

LWOFF, A. 1953. Lysogeny. Bacteriol. Revs., **17:** 269–337.

McCLINTOCK, B. 1956. Controlling elements and the gene. Cold Spring Harbor Symp. Quant. Biol., **21:** 197–216.

McCLINTOCK, B. 1961. Some parallels between gene control systems in maize and in bacteria. Am. Naturalist, **95:** 265–277.

MONOD, J. 1956. Remarks on the mechanism of enzyme induction. *In: Enzymes: Units of Biological Structure and Function,* pp. 7–28. O. H. Gaebler, ed. New York: Academic Press Inc.

MONOD, J., and COHN, M. 1952. La biosynthèse induite des enzymes (adaptation enzymatique). Advan. Enzymol., **13:** 67–119.

MONOD, J., JACOB, F., and GROS, F. 1962. Structural and rate-determining factors in the biosynthesis of adaptive enzymes. Biochem. Soc. Symposia (Cambridge, England), **21:** 104–132.

MOORE, J. A. 1958. Transplantation of nuclei between *Rana pipiens* and *Rana sylvatica.* Exptl. Cell Res., **14:** 532–540.

MORSE, M. L. 1954. Transduction of certain loci in *Escherichia coli* K-12. Genetics, **39:** 984–985.

MORSE, M. L. 1959. Transduction by staphylococcal bacteriophage. Proc. Natl. Acad. Sci., **45:** 722–727.

MORSE, M. L., LEDERBERG, E. M., and LEDERBERG, J. 1956. Transductional heterogenotes in *Escherichia coli.* Genetics, **41:** 758–779.

MOYED, H. S., and UMBARGER, H. E. 1962. Regulation of biosynthetic pathways. Physiol. Revs., **42:** 444–466.

NANNEY, D. L. 1957. The role of the cytoplasm in heredity. *In: A Symposium on the Chemical Basis of Heredity,* pp. 134–166. W. D. McElroy and B. Glass, eds. Baltimore: The Johns Hopkins Press.

NEWCOMBE, H. B. 1948. Delayed phenotypic expression of spontaneous mutations in *Escherichia coli.* Genetics, **33:** 447–476.

NEWCOMBE, H. B., and HAWIRKO, R. 1949. Spontaneous mutation to streptomycin resistance and dependence in *Escherichia coli.* J. Bacteriol., **57:** 565–572.

NOVICK, A., and WEINER, M. 1957. Enzyme induction as an all-or-none phenomenon. Proc. Natl. Acad. Sci., **43:** 553–566.

OAKBERG, E. F., and LURIA, S. E. 1947. Mutations to sulfonamide resistance in *Staphylococcus aureus*. Genetics, **32**: 249–261.

PARDEE, A. B., and PRESTIDGE, L. S. 1959. On the nature of the repressor of β-galactosidase synthesis in *Escherichia coli*. Biochim. et Biophys. Acta, **36**: 545–547.

PARDEE, A. B., JACOB, F., and MONOD, J. 1959. The genetic control and cytoplasmic expression of "inducibility" in the synthesis of β-galactosidase by *E. coli*. J. Mol. Biol., **1**: 165–178.

POLLOCK, M. R. 1950. Penicillinase adaptation in *B. cereus:* adaptive enzyme formation in the absence of free substrate. Brit. J. Exptl. Pathol., **31**: 739–753.

POLLOCK, M. R. 1953. Stages in enzyme adaptation. *In: Adaptation in Microorganisms*, pp. 150–183. R. Davies and E. F. Gale, eds. Cambridge: The University Press.

POLLOCK, M. R. 1959. Induced formation of enzymes. *In: The Enzymes*, Vol. 1, second edition revised, pp. 619–680. P. D. Boyer, H. Lardy, and K. Myrbäck, eds. New York: Academic Press Inc.

POLLOCK, M. R., and MANDELSTAM, J. 1958. Possible mechanisms by which information is conveyed to the cell in enzyme induction. Symp. Soc. Exptl. Biol., **12**: 195–204.

PREER, J. R., Jr. 1959. Nuclear and cytoplasmic differentiation in the protozoa. *In: Developmental Cytology*, pp. 3–20. D. Rudnick, ed. New York: The Ronald Press Company.

PREER, J. R., Jr., and STARK, P. 1953. Cytological observations on the cytoplasmic factor "kappa" in *Paramecium aurelia*. Exptl. Cell Res., **5**: 478–499.

PRINGSHEIM, E. G., and PRINGSHEIM, O. 1952. Experimental elimination of chromatophores and eye spot in *Euglena gracilis*. New Phytologist, **51**: 65–76.

PROVASOLI, L., HUTNER, S. H., and PINTNER, I. J. 1951. Destruction of chloroplasts by streptomycin. Cold Spring Harbor Symp. Quant. Biol., **16**: 113–120.

RAVIN, A. W. 1961. The genetics of transformation. Advan. Genet., **10**: 61–163.

RICKENBERG, H. V., COHEN, G. N., BUTTIN, G., and MONOD, J. 1956. La galactoside permease d'*Escherichia coli*. Ann. Inst. Pasteur, **91**: 829–857.

RILEY, M., PARDEE, A. B., JACOB, F., and MONOD, J. 1960. On the expression of a structural gene. J. Mol. Biol., **2**: 216–225.

RYAN, F. J., and SCHNEIDER, L. K. 1949. Mutations during the growth of biochemical mutants of *Escherichia coli*. Genetics, **34**: 72–91.

SAGER, R., and RYAN, F. J. 1961. Cell heredity. New York: John Wiley & Sons, Inc. 411 pp.

SHERMAN, F. 1959. The effects of elevated temperatures on yeast. II. Induction of respiratory-deficient mutants. J. Cellular Comp. Physiol., **54**: 37–52.

SHERMAN, F. 1963. Respiration-deficient mutants of yeast. I. Genetics. Genetics, **48**: 375–385.

SHERMAN, F., and EPHRUSSI, B. 1962. The relationship between respiratory deficiency and suppressiveness in yeast as determined with segregational mutants. Genetics, **47**: 695–700.

SLONIMSKI, P. 1949. Action de l'acriflavine sur les levures. IV. Mode d'utilization du glucose par les mutants "petite colonie." Ann. Inst. Pasteur, **77**: 510–530.

SLONIMSKI, P. 1953. Recherches sur la formation des enzymes respiratoires chez la levure. Thesis, Faculté des Sciences, Paris. 203 pp.

SONNEBORN, T. M. 1937. Sex, sex inheritance and sex determination in *Paramecium aurelia*. Proc. Natl. Acad. Sci., **23**: 378–395.

SONNEBORN, T. M. 1939. *Paramecium aurelia:* mating types and groups; lethal interactions: determination and inheritance. Am. Naturalist, **73**: 390–413.

SONNEBORN, T. M. 1947. Recent advances in the genetics of *Paramecium* and *Euplotes*. Advan. Genet., **1**: 263–358.

SONNEBORN, T. M. 1950. The cytoplasm in heredity. Heredity, **4**: 11–36.

SONNEBORN, T. M. 1954. Patterns of nucleocytoplasmic integration in *Paramecium*. Proc. Ninth Intern. Congr. Genetics. Caryologia, **6**(Suppl. 1): 307–325.

SONNEBORN, T. M. 1959. Kappa and related particles in *Paramecium*. Advan. Virus Res., **6**: 229–356.

SONNEBORN, T. M., and LeSUER, A. 1948. Antigenic characters in *Paramecium aurelia* (variety 4): determination, inheritance, and induced mutations. Am. Naturalist, **82**: 69–78.

SPIZIZEN, J. 1958. Transformation of biochemically deficient strains of *Bacillus subtilis* by deoxyribonucleate. Proc. Natl. Acad. Sci., **44**: 1072–1078.

STOCKER, B.A.D. 1949. Measurements of rate of mutation of flagellar antigenic phase in *Salmonella typhi-murium*. J. Hyg., **47**: 398–413.

STRAUSS, B. S. 1960. An outline of chemical genetics. Philadelphia: W. B. Saunders Company. 188 pp.

TATUM, E. L., and LEDERBERG, J. 1947. Gene recombination in the bacterium *Escherichia coli*. J. Bacteriol., **53**: 673–684.

TATUM, E. L., and PERKINS, D. D. 1950. Genetics of microorganisms. Ann. Rev. Microbiol., **4**: 129–150.

VOGEL, H. J. 1961. Control by repression. *In: Control Mechanisms in Cellular Processes*, pp. 23–65. D. M. Bonner, ed. New York: The Ronald Press Company.

WESTERGAARD, M. 1957. Chemical mutagenesis in relation to the concept of the gene. Experientia, **13**: 224–234.

WOLLMAN, E. L., and JACOB, F. 1955. Sur le mécanisme du transfert de matériel génétique au cours de la recombinaison chez *Escherichia coli* K-12. Compt. Rend. Acad. Sci., **240**: 2449–2451.

WOLLMAN, E. L., and JACOB, F. 1958c. Sur les processus de conjugaison et de recombinaison chez *Escherichia coli*. V. Le mécanisme du transfert de matériel génétique. Ann. Inst. Past., **95**: 641–666.

WOLLMAN, E. L., and JACOB, F. 1959. Lysogeny, transduction and cancer genesis. *In: Genetics and Cancer*, pp. 43–59. Austin: University of Texas Press.

Wollman, E. L., Jacob, F., and Hayes, W. 1956. Conjugation and genetic recombination in *Escherichia coli* K-12. Cold Spring Harbor Symp. Quant. Biol., **21**: 141–162.

Wright, S. 1941. The physiology of the gene. Physiol. Revs., **21**: 487–527.

Yarmolinsky, M. B., and Wiesmeyer, H. 1960. Regulation of coliphage *lambda* of the expression of the capacity to synthesize a sequence of host enzymes. Proc. Natl. Acad. Sci., **46**: 1626–1645.

Yotsuyanagi, Y. 1962a. Études sur le chondriome de la levure. I. Variation de l'ultrastructure du chondriome au cours du cycle de la croissance aérobie. J. Ultrastruct. Res., **7**: 121–140.

Yotsuyanagi, Y. 1962b. Études sur le chondriome de la levure. II. Chrondriomes des mutants à déficience respiratoire. J. Ultrastruct. Res., **7**: 141–158.

Zinder, N. D., and Lederberg, J. 1952. Genetic exchange in *Salmonella*. J. Bacteriol., **64**: 679–699.

The culture of
somatic cells

chapter **3** Culture methods in microbiology have long been a cornerstone for analysis, but in multicellular systems the application of similar techniques proceeded more slowly. As an experimental procedure, tissue culture emerged in 1907, when Ross Harrison first demonstrated the outgrowth of nerve fibers from explanted fragments of frog embryonic spinal cord. This result served to highlight the usefulness of isolation techniques, but a considerable period elapsed before cell and tissue culture were applied broadly in experimental biology. In the early part of this interval, a series of guidelines were laid down by Carrel and his associates (see Carrel, 1912, 1924). Seeking the basis for a dynamic cytology, they devised methods for the maintenance and serial propagation of vertebrate cells, using plasma clots, serum, and tissue extracts. These procedures, as extensions and refinements of Harrison's original techniques, formed the basis for a broad array of investigations by many investigators over several decades (see Fischer, 1930, 1946; Murray and Kopech, 1953; Willmer, 1958, 1960). During this era of pioneer investigation, nearly all major cell types were cultivated for varying periods, and much descriptive information accumulated on the characteristics of cells and tissues as isolated populations *in vitro*. However, the methods at hand were too laborious for routine use, and the necessity for a complex, undefined medium prevented the application of analytical techniques. Owing to such limitations, cell culture had for many years relatively little general impact, and was regarded more as an art than as a basic research tool in biology and medicine.

This evaluation has changed in recent years as a result of discoveries that make clear the potential of isolated cell systems for the analysis of problems in experimental morphogenesis, cytogenetic varia-

123

tion, cell-virus relationships, and many other types of investigations. A rapid evolution in technology has occurred, which greatly enhances the usefulness of cell cultures in experimental research designs. New and simpler media have been devised, which in some cases are even chemically defined (Chapter 5); methods have become available for the dissociation of intact tissues or other cell groupings to yield suspensions that can be manipulated easily; propagation of isolated strains or primary cultures may be carried out in three-dimensional matrices, as monolayers, or in free suspension; and techniques have emerged for quantitative growth measurement, clonal isolations from single cells, and the preservation of cell populations in the frozen state. Since 1950 the expansion of these and other methods for cell culture has been particularly conspicuous. The details are outlined in a series of reviews (see Murray, 1959; Puck, 1959; Parshley, 1959; Madin, 1959; Swim, 1959; Moser, 1960; Moscona, 1960; Levintow and Eagle, 1961; Salzman, 1961; Ross, Treadwell, and Syverton, 1962). At one extreme, these newer methods now permit the propagation and handling of somatic cells in much the same way as a culture of microorganisms. At the opposite pole may be found techniques for the dissociation and reassembly of cell aggregates in normal histiotypic and organotypic patterns.

AN OUTLINE OF GENERAL METHODS

A full description and critique of procedures for cell culture lies beyond the scope of this book, but a brief orientation is necessary as a basis for discussions to follow. In practice, these methods serve to define in important respects the properties of isolated cell populations. An appreciation of this frame of reference is thus essential in order to compare the properties of cell systems *in vivo* and *in vitro* or to evaluate the evolution of cell strains in long-term culture. For more complete discussions, several books are available that deal specifically with the methods of cell and tissue culture (Paul, 1960; Merchant, Kahn, and Murphy, 1960; Parker, 1961; White, 1963; Penso and Balducci, 1963). Reference may be made to these sources for appropriate details.

Characteristics of Cell Cultures Several techniques have been employed for the primary isolation of cells and tissues *in vitro* and for the serial propagation of cell strains. The first of these, now largely outmoded, features the cultivation of explants in a solid substrate according to the classic procedures devised many years ago by Carrel, Fischer, and other pioneer investigators. Typically, the explanted fragment, derived either from freshly excised tissues or from a pre-existing culture, is embedded in blood plasma and a clot is produced by the addition of embryo juice or other tissue extracts. This system as a hanging drop within a depression slide may suffice for short-time microscopic observations. For longer periods of culture, various types of culture flasks may be used, with a supernatant fluid over a solid coagulum containing serum, saline, tissue extracts, synthetic nutrients, or a variety of other additives. Soon after explantation, an extensive migration of cells occurs from the central fragment into the surrounding meshwork of the plasma clot. This displacement is accompanied by cellular multiplication, which is markedly stimulated by embryonic extract and other nutritional factors. As a result of these processes, an outgrowth zone of variable size is established, with which the central fragment gradually merges and loses its separate identity (see Figure 3.1).

Within the outgrowth zone thus formed, there is a marked tendency for morphological simplification, with the assumption of less complex growth forms within the dispersed cell population. Specialized features such as glandular tubules and intercellular materials tend to disappear, and even the distinctions between related cell types may become difficult to make. After one or more subcultures of cells derived from the outgrowth zone, it is seldom possible to recognize more than three

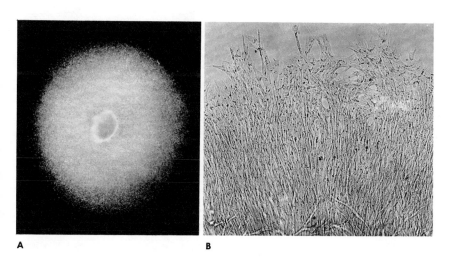

A   B

FIG. 3.1. Colonial pattern in outgrowths from primary explants of chick tissues. Unstained preparations in plasma culture. (A) Low power view of 10-day outgrowth surrounding fragment of chick heart. (From Kutsky, 1953.) (B) Appearance of cells in marginal area of outgrowth from chick skeletal muscle; 4-day culture. (From Kutsky and Harris, 1957.)

generalized categories. These have been designated mechanocytes, epitheliocytes, and amoebocytes by Willmer (1958, 1960), to avoid confusion with specific cell types within the organism. In more common usage, the same cell groupings are referred to simply as fibroblasts, epithelium, and wandering cells (or leucocytes).

Fibroblasts are recognizable as stellate or spindle-shaped cells that grow in a loose meshwork in clot cultures, with little if any affinity for surfaces or ability to form membranes (see Figure 3.2). Cells of this character arise from diverse sources; for example, connective tissue, cartilage, muscle, linings of blood vessels, nerve sheaths, and the stroma of all organs. The term fibroblast in the corresponding context is thus a purely descriptive designation and does not necessarily connote fiber-forming cells as such. Epithelium *in vitro* can be identified by a tendency to form closely adherent mosaics of polygonal cells, usually in the form of simple "pavement" membranes at interfaces in the culture medium. Such outgrowths, interspersed with fibroblasts, develop from fragments of kidney, liver, skin pancreas, thyroid, and other organs

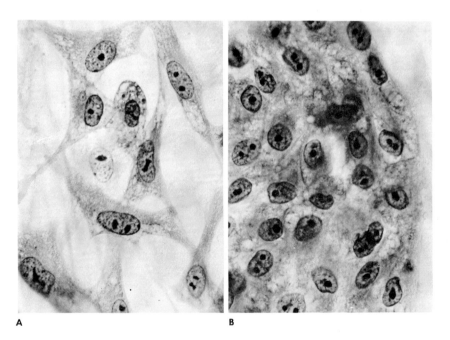

A   B

FIG. 3.2. Cells from chick embryonic tissues in plasma culture. Haematoxylin stain. (A) Heart fibroblasts in outgrowth zone, 4-day culture. (B) Margin of epithelial sheet in 4-day culture of chick kidney. (From Harris, 1948. Copyright, Wistar Institute Press.)

(Figure 3.2). In practically all freshly isolated preparations, leucocytes (or wandering cells) occur and can be regarded as a third principal category of cells. For the most part, these originate from tissue macrophages, but in cultures of blood, spleen, and bone marrow, diverse elements appear in the outgrowth zone, most of which are short-lived.

Growth in simplified, unorganized patterns as a rule characterizes the proliferation of cell populations derived by outwandering into a plasma clot or other three-dimensional matrix. It should not be assumed, however, that disorganization is an inevitable process *in vitro*. If suitable measures are taken to prevent cellular dispersion and to preserve instead the architectural integrity of the initial explant, a quite different result may be obtained. This was first shown some years ago through the development of techniques now commonly referred to as organ culture (Strangeways and Fell, 1926a; Fell, 1951; Borghese, 1958). In essence, these procedures involve the cultivation of embryonic rudiments or fragments of larger organs on the surface of a plasma clot, with frequent transfers to minimize the occurrence of outgrowth from the central explant. Alternatively, the dispersal of cells can be inhibited by culturing solid fragments on an agar substrate (Wolff and Haffen, 1952) or by placing explants on a "raft" of lens paper or cellulose acetate fabric that is floated on the surface of a liquid medium (Chen, 1954; Shaffer, 1956). Embryonic rudiments maintained in this manner as intact explants undergo progressive differentiation, in contrast to the unorganized growth of the same cell populations if permitted to disperse in the form of an outgrowth zone. Skeletal primordia, for example, may acquire not only the normal histiotypic pattern of fully differentiated bone but also the external configuration and individualized morphology of the part in question (Fell and Robison, 1929; Fell, 1956). Figure 3.3 illustrates the degree of self-differentiation that may be achieved. In other cases, histiotypic differentiation alone may occur, as in the formation of rods and cones in cultures of embryonic chick eyes, where organotypic development is rudimentary or lacking (Strangeways and Fell, 1926b).

Cultivation of intact cell complexes as isolated systems continues to provide useful information in experimental morphology and physiology, but the surge of interest in recent years has centered on dissociated cell populations rather than on explanted tissue fragments. An important factor in this development was the innovation of quantitative techniques by Earle and his associates for the serial propagation of mouse cells. Dissatisfied with the plasma clot as an unknown parameter of the culture system, these workers turned to the investigation of other possible substrates. By placing a series of explants beneath perforated cellophane,

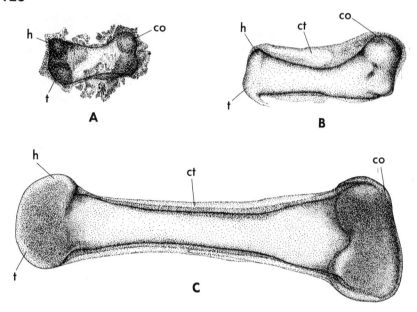

FIG. 3.3. Development of isolated bone rudiments in organ culture. (A) Normal 5½-day chick embryonic femur as dissected for explantation (whole mount). Small processes representing the condyles (co), head (h), and trochanter (t) are present. (B) Similar preparation after 3 days' cultivation *in vitro* (whole mount). The condyles, head, and trochanter are more distinct. A peripheral outgrowth of connective tissue (ct) has appeared and will be trimmed off in subculture. (C) Femur from 5½-day embryo after 21 days in culture. Note the remarkable degree of self-differentiation. (After Fell and Robison, 1929. Copyright, Cambridge University Press.)

they were able to obtain a flourishing continuum of cells. These could be scraped free, dispersed in the form of a suspension, and used to inoculate fresh cultures of the same kind (Evans and Earle, 1947). With increasing experience, the cellophane sheets proved dispensable, and methods progressively evolved for the serial cultivation of cell strains that adhered directly to a glass substrate (Evans, Earle, Sanford, Shannon, and Waltz, 1951). Preparations of this type are now commonly termed monolayer cultures (see Figure 3.4). Strictly speaking, however, this designation is appropriate only in the early phases of a growth cycle. Palisading and the development of multiple layers occur commonly in crowded cultures (see, however, discussion of contact inhibition within monolayers, Chapter 7).

The development of monolayer cultures made possible for the first time accurate determination of cell numbers in growing populations (Sanford, Earle, Evans, Waltz, and Shannon, 1951), and permitted

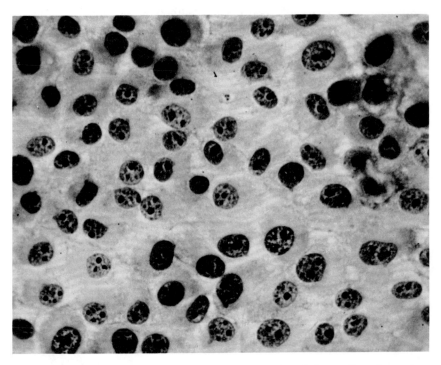

FIG. 3.4. Monolayer formed by a permanent strain of pig kidney cells, cultivated on a glass substrate. The population grows as a mosaic of closely contiguous cells. Haematoxylin stain. (From Ruddle, 1962.)

replicate procedures for quantitative studies. The usefulness of this technique was further enhanced by the discovery that primary cultures could be established directly on glass, using cell suspensions prepared by digesting fresh tissue with trypsin (Dulbecco, 1952; Moscona, 1952). The liberation of cells by tryptic digestion had actually been described many years before by Rous and Jones (1916), but was not employed at that time to establish cell cultures. Enzymatic dissociation was later adapted by Scherer, Syverton, and Gey (1953) to the routine subcultivation of cell strains, and has since been used extensively for this purpose. Besides trypsin, several other enzymes have proved valuable for the dispersal of cells, notably collagenase and elastase. The chelating agent versene, or ethylenediamine tetraacetic acid, has also come into general use (Rinaldini, 1958; Paul, 1960). Through these developments the monolayer technique has become the predominant method for the preparation of cell cultures from fresh tissue, as well as for the maintenance of strains in serial propagation. Within this system, morphological dedifferentiation is usually conspicuous, although occasional exceptions can be noted; for example, the formation of myotubes by freshly isolated chick skeletal muscle cells (see Konigsberg, 1963). But in general, the growth patterns of monolayers seem to represent the multiplication of dissociated units, stripped to a large degree of histiotypic and organotypic individuations. The increase in cell number is characteristically rapid and tends to follow a simple and diagrammatic course, as in a population of microorganisms (see Figure 3.5). Owing to these features, monolayer cultures are particularly useful for studies in cell nutrition (Chapter 5).

The cultivation of cell strains in freely suspended form can be regarded as a three-dimensional variant of the monolayer technique, in which the dissociation of individual cells has been brought to a maximal point. Owens, Gey, and Gey (1954) were the first to report success with this method, using a special "tumble-tube" to maintain malignant mouse lymphoblasts in uniform suspension within a fluid culture medium. Subsequently, Earle and his colleagues developed methods for cultivating dispersions of fixed tissue cells in rotating tubes or shaker flasks (Earle, Bryant, Schilling, and Evans, 1956), and somewhat similar pro-

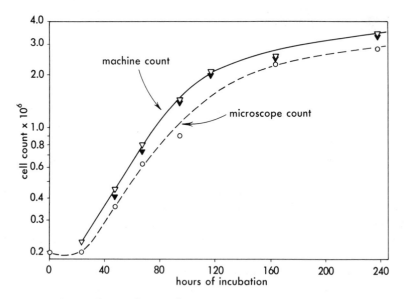

FIG. 3.5. Population changes during a growth cycle of pig kidney cells in monolayer culture. For growth measurements, individual flasks are trypsinized in groups, and cell numbers are determined by hemocytometer or an electronic cell counter. (After Harris, 1959. Copyright, University of Chicago Press.)

cedures have been devised by a number of other workers (see Merchant, Kuchler, and Munyon, 1960). Perhaps the most ingenious and practical method for suspension cultures involves use of the "spinner flask" (Mc-Limans, Davis, Glover, and Rake, 1957). In this procedure, cell populations are kept in uniform distribution by a magnetic stirrer, which activates a plastic-coated bar mounted on a swivel within the culture vessel. By adding devices for the removal of cells and replenishment of medium, simplified chemostats can be constructed for continuous propagation of cell lines (Cohen and Eagle, 1961).

Not all cell strains, however, will proliferate successfully in free suspension, and the cellular adjustments required for progressive growth in suspension form are not yet known. Conceivably, the transition may be mediated by processes of variation and selection, as in ascites transformation of tumors (see Chapter 1). Among cell strains that are capable of proliferation in suspension, the pattern of growth is an individual one. Depending on genetic characteristics, the composition of the medium, presence of surface-active agents, and other variables, a given cell type may proliferate as a monodisperse system or in the form of cell aggregates. At least some lines, however, do grow regularly as single cells, and here the parallel with microbial populations becomes a very close one (see Figures 3.6 and 3.7).

Although methods are thus available for the establishment of somatic units in a variety of isolated systems, obviously the characteristics of cells in explants, monolayers, and free suspensions will not coincide in all respects. More important than these differences, however, are certain changes that may transform cell populations during serial cultivation by any of the techniques described. As a result of such alterations, the original (or primary) cell population can be converted to a permanent cell strain. Cell lines arising in this way are capable of indefinite serial multiplication *in vitro*, and they can be regarded as variant cell types. As subsequent discussions will make clear, such populations exhibit characteristic chromosomal aberrations, differences in morphology, and other deviant cell characteristics arising during long sojourn in isolated systems. By contrast, primary cell populations can be usefully defined as those produced directly by the initial explantation of tissue fragments or dissociated cells, as well as their immediate derivatives in serial passage. Primary cell lines cannot be propagated as such indefinitely, but during serial cultivation they retain a normal diploid karyotype and do not exhibit the variant features characteristically associated with permanent strains. The origin, nature, and significance of these differences between cell strains are important topics. They will be considered in detail in later sections.

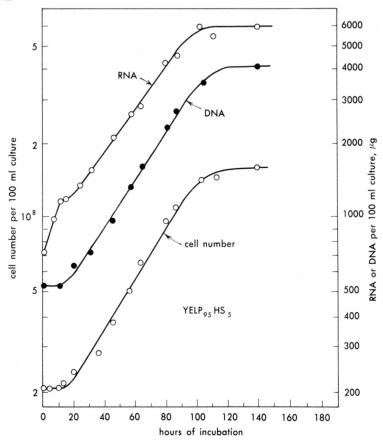

FIG. 3.6. Relationship between cell number and the amount of DNA and RNA in suspension cultures of strain *L* mouse cells. DNA rises in direct parallel with cell number; there is an initial rapid synthesis of RNA during the lag phase. (After Merchant, Kuchler, and Munyon, 1960. Copyright, John Wiley & Sons, Inc.)

Techniques for Clonal Isolation   For the systematic study of variation in isolated populations, a significant development in recent years has been the elaboration of methods for isolating clones from single somatic cells. This objective is not easily attained within the limitations imposed by explant techniques; consequently, early attempts to secure the progressive multiplication of single cells were unsuccessful (Fischer, 1946). A practical solution emerged in 1948 when Sanford, Earle, and Likely established a clonal strain of mouse cells for the first time (see Figure 3.8). The procedure used involves the isolation of single cells within capillary tubes, which are then broken into segments and trans-

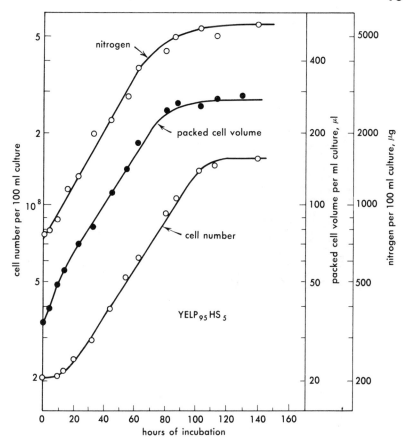

FIG. 3.7. Relative changes in nitrogen content and packed cell volume, as compared to cell number, in suspension cultures of strain L mouse cells. Increases in nitrogen are linear from the outset, and the lag phase is seen to be a period of cell growth without accompanying cell division. (After Merchant, Kuchler, and Munyon, 1960. Copyright, John Wiley & Sons, Inc.)

ferred to suitable vessels for cultivation. Cells within the tubes proliferate more readily than in open culture flasks, apparently because a local conditioning of the medium occurs within this restricted microenvironment. A number of clone strains have been obtained by the same technique (Likely, Sanford, and Earle, 1952). The efficiency of cloning with the capillary tube method was originally very low, but recent improvements, including the use of more optimal culture media, now make this procedure more convenient and effective (Sanford, Covalesky, Dupree, and Earle, 1961). For genetic studies, the technique in question has the important advantage of assuring single-cell origin for any given

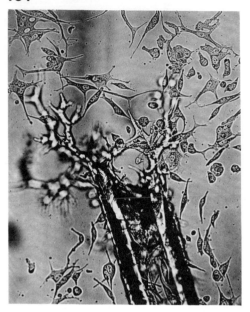

FIG. 3.8. Origin of clone 929 as a subline from strain *L* mouse cells. Photograph shows the clonal population emerging into a plasma coagulum 28 days after a single cell had been isolated in a capillary tube. (From Sanford, Earle, and Likely, 1948.)

line. A somewhat similar method of clonal isolation has also been devised, which involves the pipetting of single cells into droplets of culture medium immersed in layers of paraffin oil (Lwoff, Dulbecco, Vogt, and Lwoff, 1955; Wildy and Stoker, 1958).

For many types of studies, however, a simpler cloning technique, one that permits mass separation of discrete populations under uniform conditions, is desirable. The plating procedures of microbiology meet these requirements, and were actually applied many years ago to the clonal isolation of animal cells (Moen, 1935). In the experiments mentioned, an exudate of mononuclear cells was first elicited in guinea pigs, and the resulting suspension was diluted appropriately in a plasma clot. Some of the dispersed single cells proved capable of proliferating to give clonal colonies of fibroblasts. But despite the success of this application, plating procedures for cloning did not come into general use until methods were available for enzymatic dissociation of fixed tissue cells and for their propagation in more adequate culture media. In this context, Puck and his associates made an important contribution by defining the necessary conditions for clonal isolation of somatic cells as a routine operation (Puck and Marcus, 1955; Puck, Marcus, and Cieciura, 1956; Marcus, Cieciura, and Puck, 1956; Puck, Cieciura, and Fisher, 1957; Puck, 1958, 1959). Initially, these methods were based on conditioning the medium by means of a nonproliferating "feeder layer." Such a feeder population can easily be prepared by X irradiation of monolayer cultures in petri dishes, after which unirradiated test cells are added in small numbers. These form well-isolated clonal colonies after a few days of incubation, and the underlying layer of irradiated cells gradually disintegrates (see Figure 3.9).

The use of feeder layers as a general procedure proved to be super-fluous for cell types now categorized as permanent strains. In these populations a variable but usually substantial proportion of single cells will proliferate without special stimulus. The plating efficiency of one such line employed by Puck approached 100 percent under optimal con-ditions; that is, essentially all cells in a dilute inoculum developed into discrete clonal colonies. The multiplication of cells within individual colonies was found to proceed logarithmically, with mean generation time of less than 24 hours (see Figure 3.10). The isolation of clonal subpopulations from such cultures can be accomplished readily. A stainless steel ring, sealed to the glass substrate by silicone grease, can be used to create a chamber within which the cells can be conveniently dissociated with trypsin and removed for subcultivation. In this way, sublines of single cell origin may be easily obtained in large numbers from a given strain, and routine sampling of the population structure within isolated strains becomes possible. Along with these advantages, plating procedures have some obvious limitations. One of these is the

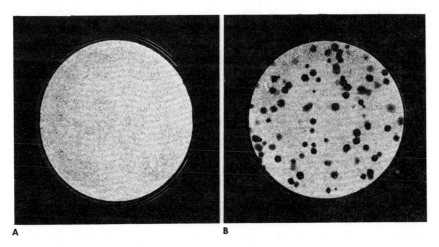

A   B

FIG. 3.9. Use of a "feeder layer" technique to facilitate the growth of isolated cells in culture. (A) Plate with X-irradiated *HeLa* cells 8 days after receiving 4000 r. The granular background consists of debris from these cells. (B) An identical culture, but which received in addition an aliquot of 100 normal *HeLa* cells following irradiation. The colony count in this experiment shows a total of 97. (From Puck, Marcus, and Cieciura, 1956.)

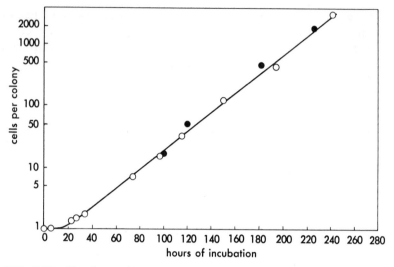

FIG. 3.10. Clonal growth in a population of HeLa S_3 cells. The number of cells within individual colonies in a petri dish culture was determined at successive intervals to give the curve shown. Each point represents the mean value for 6 to 43 colonies examined; solid and open circles denote two separate experiments. The population doubling time is approximately 20 hours. (Redrawn from Puck, Marcus, and Cieciura, 1956.)

fact that clones so isolated have only a statistical purity. There is no guarantee that a given colony originates in fact from a single cell or that it has not become contaminated with cells detached or migrating from adjacent clones. These shortcomings, however, are more than compensated for by the simplicity of method and its ready adaptation to the many different quantitative techniques available from microbiology.

The cloning procedures that have been described are most effective with populations that proliferate indefinitely *in vitro* (that is, permanent cell strains). It is much more difficult to obtain clonal isolates in high yield from cell suspensions derived by dissociation of intact tissues or from the resulting strains in the early phases of serial culture. Such primary cell populations may proliferate well as mass cultures, but characteristically they show a very low plating efficiency from dilute inocula (Puck, 1958). From their work without a feeder system, Sato and his collaborators report that the proportion of clones obtained from cells derived by mechanical dissociation of tissues from day-old rats varies from 2×10^{-4}, for liver and kidney, to 1×10^{-6}, for bone marrow (Sato, Zaroff, and Mills, 1960; Zaroff, Sato, and Mills, 1961). On this basis they have suggested that the majority of cells in populations derived from intact tissues are incapable of proliferation *in vitro*, and that even in mass cultures, the resulting populations originate from a minority nonparenchymal cell type. This interpretation, however, is a debatable one. Differences in viability of individual cell types do exist, particularly in such systems as explanted liver, but there is ample evidence that parenchymal cells of many kinds can in fact proliferate under optimal conditions *in vitro* (Willmer, 1960). The more obvious explanation for the generally low cloning efficiency of freshly isolated cells is that damage or trauma occurs incident to isolation procedures, particularly where mechanical methods are employed, as in Sato's experiments. Leaching of metabolites is facilitated by cell injury, a process that is now known to be limiting for the growth of cell populations from dilute inocula (see Chapter 5). It follows that feeder systems should improve the cloning efficiency of freshly isolated cells, and this is indeed the case.

The mechanisms of feeder action in dilute cell populations are not yet clear in detail, but the careful analysis of Rothfels, Kupelwieser, and Parker (1963) has contributed much useful information. The assay system used by these workers consists of trypsinized cells derived from mouse embryos or primary cell strains laid down as sparse populations in petri dishes, with or without a feeder layer. With inocula below a limiting population density (approximately 3×10^3 cells per dish under the conditions used), no growth takes place unless a feeder system is supplied (ordinarily in the form of X-irradiated mouse cells in a previously established monolayer). The effect of the latter can be measured conveniently in terms of the frequency of mitosis at 24 hours or, in some cases, by the mean generation times determined at daily intervals.

Using the assay described, Rothfels and his collaborators examined a number of variables affecting the action of feeder systems. For example, mouse embryonic cells that have been subcultured several times appear to function as efficiently in feeder layers as those freshly isolated from the organism. Changes of media have in general very little effect on feeder action. Genetic specificity is not a prerequisite, for normal and neoplastic mouse cells of genotype unrelated to the test cells can act as feeders, even where these populations have been maintained *in vitro* for long periods as permanent cell strains. Heterologous feeder systems also stimulate mouse cells in some cases, but this aspect needs further study. Particularly interesting is the fact that unirradiated cells as well as those exposed to X rays can serve as feeder layers; apparently either can function effectively as long as a minimum cell density is maintained in the feeder population. Ultraviolet treatment, as an alternative to X irradiation, may be used to obtain nonproliferating feeder cells, but other treatments abolish the feeder effect. These include air-drying of monolayers, heat treatment at 70° C for 30 minutes, fixation with ethanol, and freeze-thawing. It is evident from these results that feeder activity does not stem primarily from the release of materials by dead or injured cells. An actively metabolizing cell population is required, with the output of substances whose formation or extrusion is not affected by moderate levels of irradiation. Rothfels and his associates have presented evidence that the loss of CO_2 is one such strategic factor in sparse cultures of primary mouse-embryo cells. Provision of oxaloacetate plus optimal CO_2 levels serve to duplicate, at least in part, the feeder effects obtained. Since a multiplicity of metabolites, including cellular protein, may escape from cells into the external medium (see Chapter 5), the limiting variables may differ for particular feeder systems. A practical solution to the problem of cloning primary populations may thus depend on more adequate information concerning the nutritional requirements of individual cell types as a function of population density.

Preservation of Cells by Freezing The experimental usefulness of isolated cell populations has been expanded by the development of practical methods for their preservation and long-term storage at low temperatures. Procedures of this type are well established in microbiology for the maintenance of stock strains or other reference materials in an unchanged state. Until recently, however, the impression prevailed that animal cells could not in general withstand the lethal effects of freezing and thawing. This is true for most cells and tissues frozen without special pretreatment, although survival in varying degree occur with some materials, notably spermatozoa (Parkes, 1945), skin (Billingham and Medawar, 1952), and a number of different tumors (Breedis and Furth, 1938; Breedis, 1942). As a result, the application of freeze-storage techniques for animal cells and tissues lagged behind their uses in microbiology.

The breakthrough that opened up the field of low-temperature studies was the discovery that glycerol exerts a marked protective effect on cells during the freezing process (Polge, Smith, and Parkes, 1949). Although the original observations were made on preparations of fowl spermatozoa, it soon became clear that glycerol pretreatment facilitates the survival of cells in general during freezing, including blood, cell suspensions, and tissue masses. This remarkable effect stems indirectly from a reduction of the tendency for ice formation. Glycerol has a considerable affinity for water, which can be regarded as bound by this procedure (that is, it does not appear in crystalline form during freezing). As a result, less dehydration occurs by the withdrawal of water into ice crystals, and the concentration of intracellular electrolytes in the fluid phase that remains does not rise to so high a level (Lovelock,

1953). A number of additives may be used in place of glycerol to confer
protection during the freezing process (Moline, 1962). Dimethyl sulfoxide
is particularly useful, since this compound diffuses rapidly into or out
of cells and is relatively nontoxic.

Several investigations have defined in practical terms the optimal
conditions for preserving cultures of normal and neoplastic cells at low
temperatures (Scherer and Hoogasian, 1954; Swim, Haff, and Parker,
1958; Stulberg, Soule, and Berman, 1958; Hauschka, Mitchell, and
Niederpruem, 1959; Parker, 1961). Slow freezing and rapid thawing
have in general been found to give most favorable results, and schedules
based on an average drop of 1° C per minute yield satisfactory recoveries.
The concentration of glycerol and pretreatment time required for equi-
libration varies among cell types; high levels of glycerol may be toxic.
For at least some cell strains, dimethyl sulfoxide gives protection superior
to that provided by glycerol (Porterfield and Ashwood-Smith, 1962;
Dougherty, 1962).

Frozen cell populations can be stored for years without substantial
loss of viability, provided the temperature is maintained at a level low
enough to minimize biochemical changes or other alterations occurring
progressively during the storage period. Dry-ice refrigerators at −79° C
seem to be satisfactory for the preservation of many cell types over
considerable intervals, although the same populations do not survive
even briefly at ordinary deep-freeze temperatures (−20° C). However,
there is evidence that slow deterioration may occur in specimens maintained at −65° C to −79° C, and in the opinion of some investigators,
the temperature for long-term storage should not rise above −100° C
(Meryman, 1962, 1963; Moline, 1962). From this standpoint, preservation in liquid nitrogen at −190° C is both practical and effective. Freshly
isolated cells as well as permanent cell strains can be recovered efficiently after storage at this temperature (Nagington and Greaves, 1962).
Liquid nitrogen has also been successfully employed for the preservation
of cell lines maintained in a protein-free, chemically defined medium
(Evans, de Oca, Bryant, Schilling, and Shannon, 1962). Although occasional claims to the contrary have been made, there is no good evidence that temporary or prolonged storage by any of these procedures
leads to permanent alterations in cellular characteristics. Antigenic
specificity, karyotypic patterns, drug responses, and other specific properties appear to be unchanged in original and recovery cultures, respectively (Hauschka, Mitchell, and Niederpruem, 1959; Moline, 1962).

Despite the success of empirical methods for the preservation of
cells for long periods at low temperatures, the rationale for these procedures and the exact changes that cells undergo in freezing are only

imperfectly understood (see Smith, 1954; Hauschka, Mitchell, and Niederpruem, 1959; Meryman, 1960, 1962, 1963). During the past few years there has been a considerable evolution of concepts concerning the basis for cellular damage in the freezing process. Prior to the employment of glycerol and other additives, the destructive effects of freezing were attributed largely to mechanical injury by ice crystals. From this viewpoint, rapid freezing appeared to offer advantages, since if the rate of cooling is sufficiently great, water may pass into a "vitreous" or glassy state without the appearance of crystalline foci (Luyet and Gehenio, 1940). However, all efforts to achieve a generalized protection by ultra-rapid freezing have failed, and experimental proof is lacking that a state of vitrification in biological materials has ever been achieved (Smith, 1954; Meryman, 1962, 1963). In any event, the now widely confirmed benefits of slow freezing in many systems indicates that mechanical damage from ice crystals need not occur if the latter do not arise within individual cells. At moderate rates of cooling, formation of ice crystals appears to take place only in the extracellular fluid, and leads to a loss of cell water that can take place rapidly enough to maintain the cell contents below the freezing point. Eventually only "bound" water remains (Smith, 1954). Apparently, such cells may collapse passively between external ice crystals without direct mechanical injury, but there is an increasing tendency for biochemical denaturation as dehydration occurs (Meryman, 1962). Under these conditions, the lethal effects of freezing seem to be based primarily on the increasing concentration of cell solutes, a tendency that can be counterbalanced by pretreatment with glycerol or other additives. This concept offers a working explanation for the behavior of animal cells during the freezing process as ordinarily carried out. Rapid rates of freezing are therefore injurious because abundant crystallization occurs within cells as well as in the external fluid under these conditions. These explanations may be oversimplified, however, in certain respects (Mazur, 1962). Of interest, for example, is the fact that such substances as sodium nitrate and glycine confer protection during freezing of bone marrow cells, although there seems to be no obvious reason for this on a solute concentration basis. It is equally puzzling to find that polyvinylpyrrolidone can protect erythrocytes from hemolysis during freeze-thawing, for the compound in this case is a large polymer, and does not even pass through the cell membrane. Finally, there is the fact that certain microbial cells may be relatively unaffected by desiccation per se, but are still subject to destruction by freezing or freeze-drying. Thus the possibility that the basis for freezing injury may differ among cell types or that multiple mechanisms come into play requires further study.

CELLULAR ORGANIZATION IN
PRIMARY POPULATIONS

The properties of somatic cells in isolated systems are conditioned by developmental factors, particularly during the period immediately following explantation. This fact has been frequently overlooked in studies dealing only with permanent cell strains. In primary cell populations, conspicuous changes in the level of organization may occur, either directly upon isolation or in successive subcultures. The evolution of efficient methods for the disaggregation of fresh tissues has provided experimental tools for the analysis of these changes. Among the questions that relate to the developmental potential of dissociated cells are the following: First, does dissociation per se interfere with the potential for morphogenetic development? To what extent can isolated somatic units reaggregate and undergo histotypic or organotypic differentiation in characteristic fabrics? Secondly, if primary populations are maintained *in vitro* as dissociated systems, what transitions take place in the level of differentiation within individual cells? How may such changes be interpreted? Although the development of these problems is still proceeding, a number of aspects have been usefully clarified by experimental researches during the past few years.

Reconstruction of Tissues by Dissociated Cells The ability of dissociated cells to reaggregate in organized groupings was first discovered by H. V. Wilson (1907, 1911) through his classical investigations on sponges. Wilson found that these simple animals could be effectively disassembled by forcing the sponge body through silk bolting cloth of fine mesh. Surprisingly, this drastic treatment does not cause complete destruction of the organism, but allows merely a mechanical separation that yields a suspension of tissue clumps and isolated cells. If the resulting preparation is then placed in a container of fresh sea water, the individual cells settle down on the glass substrate and come together in new assemblages, from which sponges quite normal in structure finally emerge. The process of reconstitution seems to be mediated by cellular migration in its early phases, leading to a random association and progressive formation of cell aggregates. Within these aggregates, a further sorting out occurs by differential cell movements, as choanocytes, archeocytes, and other specific cell types are rearranged in characteristic groupings. The organization of new units thus appears to be based on reshuffling and regrouping rather than on a process of redifferentiation as such within individual cells.

For many years these remarkable results in sponges were looked upon as a unique example of reconstitution from the cellular level, possible only in organisms that possessed simple body patterns and a wide range of regenerative powers. That similar faculties reside within the embryonic tissues of higher organisms was first demonstrated by Holtfreter (1939) in a study on the interaction of cells and tissues from amphibian embryos *in vitro*. Using a "sandwich" technique, Holtfreter prepared explants by uniting pieces of germ layers and other primordia in varying combination. If these simple "organoids" are cultured in salt solution, the cells of given rudiment show a tendency for mutual coherence, but the fragment as a whole reacts variably to the presence of other cell types. Some combinations separate completely; as, for example, pieces of ectoderm and endoderm. Other unions, such as ectoderm and mesoderm, come together firmly to develop in composite patterns.

As a framework of explanation, Holtfreter developed the concept of selective affinities between the cells and tissues of developing organisms. He was able to test this principle experimentally by devising new techniques for the disassembly of embryonic rudiments (Holtfreter, 1944). Thus, if the amphibian pronephros is exposed to solutions of high *p*H, the individual cells lose their coherence and separate easily. When a random mass of these cells is returned to saline at a physiological *p*H level, however, the separated cells reaggregate and give rise to typical pronephric structures. Townes and Holtfreter (1955) later employed this technique to examine the affinities of embryonic cells in a systematic fashion. Suspensions of cells were prepared from amphibian ectoderm, endoderm, mesoderm, neural plate, and other embryonic rudiments, and from these were constructed composite and randomized aggregates of various different types. Such combinations resume development if returned to normal salt solution, and the fate of individual cells can be followed by utilizing differences in pigmentation and size as markers. Townes and Holtfreter showed that if uniform mixtures of different cells are prepared, a process of selective reassociation subsequently occurs, with progressive segregation and reassortment of the individual components. Ectoderm or epidermal cells, for example, migrate to a peripheral position if combined with cells from neural plate or mesoderm, which move within.

The reconstitution of tissues and organs from dissociated cell populations can also be observed with avian or mammalian embryos, and these systems have in fact provided the most incisive analysis of the events concerned. A major stimulus for work in this field was the innovation by Moscona (1952) of methods for the tryptic disaggregation of chick embryonic organs. After separation with trypsin, the cell suspensions, if incubated in a hollow glass slide, give rise to random aggregates (see Figure 3.11). These can be transferred, if desired, to plasma clots

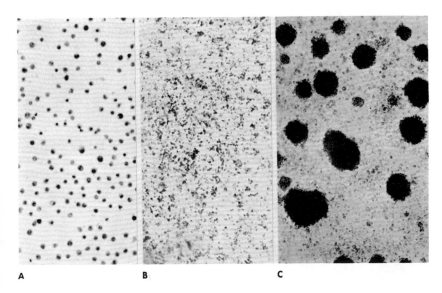

A   B   C

FIG. 3.11. Dissociation and reaggregation of embryonic cartilage cells *in vitro.* (A) Typical suspension of chondrogenic cells, obtained by digesting limb buds from 4-day chick embryos and 12-day mouse embryos. (B) Mixed suspension of chick and mouse chondrogenic cells, beginning to form nonspecific clumps after 2 hours in culture. (C) A similar culture after 36 hours of incubation. Note the appearance of large aggregates. (From Moscona, 1957.)

or to the chorioallantoic membrane of chick embryos for further development in organotypic fashion. Alternatively, the onset of primary aggregation can be mediated by swirling cell suspensions in the presence of centripetal forces of low intensity (Moscona, 1961). A restitution of tissue and organ structure occurs within these masses of recombined embryonic cells (see Figure 3.12). Dissociated populations of chick kidney, for example, form typical tubular structures, and cartilage masses appear within aggregates from limb bud mesenchyme (Moscona and Moscona, 1952). Numerous other studies have shown that suspensions of cells from such varied sources as embryonic heart, skeletal muscle, liver, lung, skin, and retina are all capable of reassociation in characteristic tissue fabrics (see Moscona, 1960, 1962a, 1962b; Trinkaus, 1961).

In composite aggregates from avian or mammalian embryos, selective reassortment follows the pattern described previously for amphibian cells. Useful information can be obtained, for example, by mixing suspensions of cells from chick mesonephros with chondrogenic elements from wing bud mesenchyme (Trinkaus and Groves, 1955; Moscona,

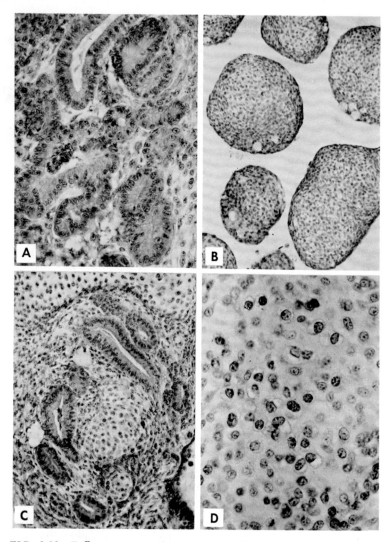

FIG. 3.12. Differentiation within aggregates formed from suspensions of embryonic cells. (A) Re-establishment of epithelial tubules within an aggregate of cells from chick kidney. (B) Masses of cartilage, reconstituted from dissociated chick chondrogenic cells. (C) Type-specific reassortment within a mixed aggregation of chick cartilage and chick kidney cells. Segregation of different cells into discrete groupings occurs; kidney cells form epithelial tubules and chondrogenic cells give rise to typical cartilage masses. (D) Chimeric cartilage mass, formed as a common tissue fabric by a mixed aggregate of mouse and chick chondrogenic cells. Nuclei of mouse origin may be recognized by their larger size and more deeply stained appearance. (From Moscona, 1956, 1959.)

1956). Cartilage and kidney tubules appear in different parts of the composite aggregate, implying that segregation of cell types occurs in accordance with their origins. The proportion of the two components, however, has a significant bearing on the results obtained. If the percentage of either mesonephric or chondrogenic cells is reduced below a certain minimum, the corresponding tissues do not develop in typical form within the composite aggregate. The same absolute number of cells when placed in culture alone regularly gives rise to normal tissue structures. Evidently the process of reassociation within mixtures does not take place effectively if there is too great a dilution by nonhomologous cells.

The actual evidence for selective reassortment within complex aggregates is not immediately obvious, since chondrogenic and nephrogenic cells from chick embryos, for example, are indistinguishable in the dissociated form. In fact, Trinkaus and Groves (1955) raised the question of exact correspondence of precursors and definitive tissue masses. Some experiments, particularly with mixtures of cell populations from embryos of differing age, gave equivocal results. However, clear proof for the selective affinity of individual cell types has been provided by the studies of Moscona (1957). His experiments were stimulated by the preceding work of Wolff (1954) on the growth of mouse and chick explants in composite culture. Wolff showed that although the cells of the two species might intermingle freely, they could be consistently distinguished by differences in nuclear size and staining properties. With the use of these markers in mind, Moscona prepared suspensions of various embryonic mouse and chick organs (for example, mouse chondrogenic cells and chick mesonephros) and combined these materials to form interspecific aggregates. After histologically recognizable tissues had been differentiated, it was clear that an actual segregation had occurred. All the nuclei in cartilage masses were of mouse origin, whereas mesonephric tubules were uniformly constructed from chick cells.

Selective segregation from mixtures is a process that takes place only in heterotypic systems; that is, composite aggregates containing cells of two or more histogenetic types. Where isotypic mixtures (of identical cell type) are prepared, no such separation of the two components occurs. The results are particularly striking when isotypic populations are constructed from cells of two different species; for example, combinations of mouse and chick chondrogenic cells (Moscona, 1957). In this case, a single tissue fabric develops in which the cells of the two species are randomly interspersed (see Figure 3.12). The resulting chimeric masses of cartilage arise by a normal process of histogenesis. They show no break in continuity of the intercellular matrix and persist for long intervals as stable structures. In the same way, mixtures of liver cells from the two species can be prepared; these give rise to unified hepatic cords in which both types of cells later form glycogen or fat. From these observations it appears that reassociation between embryonic cells *in vitro* is based on tissue-specific rather than on species-specific properties. Mutual affinity between cells of a given histotype, whatever the means of recognition, seems to depend on characteristics that transcend species boundaries.

The mechanisms that underlie this far-reaching process of reconstitution by dissociated cell populations have as yet been only partially analyzed. The initial aggregation of separated cells into larger masses appears to be a nonspecific process, mediated by random contacts and a generalized adherence, even of quite different cell types, to form larger clusters (Moscona, 1960). Such preliminary associations must be viewed as dynamic in character. Time-lapse photography reveals a constant reshuffling and shifting as cell masses arise and are re-formed over successive periods of time. Just how the selective sorting out of cell types occurs within these aggregates is far from clear. After a careful analysis of time-lapse pictures covering contacts between individual cells, Weiss (1958) concluded that selective attraction as such does not occur between two units of the same histotype. On the other hand, processes that oppose random dispersal may be important. Abercrombie and his collaborators have shown that fibroblasts and other cells *in vitro* show a cessation of movement in areas of mutual proximity, a phenomenon that they have termed contact inhibition (Abercrombie and Heaysman, 1954; Abercrombie and Ambrose, 1958; Abercrombie, 1961). Direct interactions between cells in this fashion may be reflected in a statistical limitation on locomotion and a tendency for regionalization. Contact inhibition alone, however, fails to explain the selective features of reassortment from mixtures, unless the further assumption is made that cell types differ in their individual properties of cohesion and adhesion (Steinberg, 1958, 1962a, 1962b). If this premise is adopted, the positional relationships of definitive tissue masses formed in complex aggregates may be looked upon as the end result of processes tending to maintain the surface free energy of the system at minimum levels (Steinberg, 1962c, 1963a).

An alternative basis for selective reassortment can be found by assuming that this process depends on an ordered system of cues in the microenvironment of segregating cell populations (Moscona, 1960, 1962a, 1962b). It is well known that oriented movements of cells do take place in response to physicochemical features of the immediate surroundings. A large body of information on such changes has been accumulated by

Weiss and his collaborators over a period of years, under the heading of contact guidance (see Weiss, 1945, 1958, 1961). In this context, Moscona has suggested that dissociated embryonic cells release exudates, which then function to condition the processes of reassociation. The extruded materials are thought to serve as specific ground substances, within which the assembly and histogenesis of particular cell types may occur. Evidence for such extracellular materials (ECM) is based on the detection of mucoidal residues left as trails by cells migrating on glass (Rosenberg, 1960), as well as on the abundant accumulation of similar substances in agitated suspensions of embryonic cells (Moscona, 1960, 1961). The latter materials can be shown to facilitate the processes of reconstitution in shake cultures. When populations of chick and mouse cells are intermingled, for example, both the initial aggregation and subsequent self-sorting of tissues take place more rapidly in a gently swirling suspension than in stationary cultures (Moscona, 1961). Thus the extracellular material released by dissociated embryonic cells is cast in a twofold role: (1) as a structural matrix and binding agent for the reassembly of cells in definitive patterns, and (2) as an information system providing orientation and cues for selective histogenesis.

This interpretation may need modification in the light of more recent experiments, which show that tissue reconstruction from dissociated cells does not require the presence of mucoidal exudates of gross dimensions. Auerbach and Grobstein (1958) showed that if fresh tissues are disaggregated with pancreatin instead of trypsin, the slimy materials associated with the latter procedure are removed or fail to appear. Employing pancreatin, Steinberg (1962a) found with chick cells that both reaggregation and formation of tissue structure can take place without detectable traces of overt extracellular materials. He has expressed the view that the extracellular material (ECM) of Moscona may be an experimental artifact, resulting from the breakup of cells damaged in dissociation and reaggregation processes (Steinberg, 1963). In support of this concept, studies are offered on composition of ECM as released from cells prepared by tryptic digestion. The product isolated appears to be in large measure a hydrated deoxyribonucleoprotein gel, possibly derived from the chromosomes of ruptured cells following the enzymatic removal of a part of the chromosomal protein by tryptic action. These experiments with pancreatin appear to rule out the requirement of a structured external matrix as a basis for reassembly of dissociated cells. It does not follow, however, that intercellular cementing materials in less obvious form are necessarily dispensable. Moscona (1962a) has in fact obtained evidence that soluble components released from pancreatin-treated cells are capable of promoting specific aggregation, as does the mucoidal ECM. It is apparent from these data that more than one model can be proposed for the directive interaction of embryonic cells in complex aggregates, and further study will be required to resolve the existing conflicts.

To round out the discussion of reconstitution, it should perhaps be emphasized that this phenomenon in higher animals is essentially confined to populations of embryonic cells. There is no evidence that the dissociated units of adult tissues and organs are similarly capable of processes leading to the restoration of pre-existing patterns. Even within the embryonic period, a decline in capability can be noted. Thus, Moscona (1962a) observed that the capacity of chick embryonic cells for reaggregation in shake cultures decreases progressively as a function of donor age. In preparations derived from a variety of tissue rudiments, there is a falling off in number and size of individual aggregates as test populations are obtained from embryos of advancing stages. Cells dissociated toward the end of development, or later, are unable to re-establish functional associations, even when combined in mixed aggregates with cells from younger embryos. A similar picture is evident from the studies of Ansevin and Buchsbaum (1962) on the capacity for reconstruction in populations of kidney cells obtained from newborn to 27-month-old mice. None of these suspensions proved capable of spontaneous aggregation in depression slides. The cells could, however, be brought together mechanically by centrifugation and embedded in a plasma clot for purposes of handling. Under these conditions, dissociated kidney cells from newborn mice may undergo a limited histological reorganization, if cultured further in vitro or transplanted to the chorioallantoic membrane of chick embryos. Cells from donors as old as two months can construct nephric tubules in occasional instances, but little capacity for morphogenesis is observed in cell populations from older animals. Various explanations can be offered for this decline in morphogenetic potential. Conceivably, the acquisition of specialized properties in differentiated cells may preclude the secretion of exudates essential to the restitution of tissue fabrics. It is interesting, however, that older cells do not reassociate even when mixed with embryonic populations of contrasting histotype (Moscona, 1962a). Alternatively, coherence and selective reassortment might depend on surface properties present initially but superseded by other patterns as cellular differentiation takes place. If this is the case, there is evidently little or no tendency for the reassumption of embryonic capabilities under conditions that have been imposed so far. In these experiments, modifications in the ability for reconstitution appear to proceed in one direction only.

Stability of Differentiation in Isolated Systems What factors govern the continuity of specialized features or their regression within primary cell populations? This question is a strategic one in assessing the changes in apparent level of differentiation that may occur in freshly isolated cells and their immediate derivatives. From the preceding discussion it is clear that disaggregation as such does not alter the histotypic or organotypic potential of individual cells, at least not in embryonic materials. The stability of cell markers cannot be similarly assured, however, if dissociation is coupled with an extended period of cultivation in an isolated state; for example, in the form of monolayers. The degree of continuity varies for individual characteristics. Some cell properties may persist indefinitely, even in long-term culture; others may disappear temporarily *in vitro,* but can again be expressed if the culture system is altered appropriately; still others may conceivably be lost irreversibly during serial propagation.

Stability of cellular properties in dispersed cell populations is best illustrated by the continued production of species-specific products by populations cultivated for long periods in heterologous media. Fischer (1946) reported, for example, that a strain of neoplastic mouse cells continued to produce tumors when reimplanted into the hosts of origin, even after 14 years of serial propagation in a medium consisting of chicken plasma and chick embryo extract. More precise data on this point are available from immunological studies on those antigens which provide the basis for species and strain identification. In one form, this analysis concerns the hemagglutinins that are elicited when strains of cultured cells are inoculated into laboratory animals. With suitable cross-absorptions, the reagents so obtained can be made diagnostic for the species of origin (Brand and Syverton, 1960, 1962). Under these conditions, all strains derived from a given species give essentially the same hemagglutination pattern, regardless of cell type or conversion in some cases to permanent cell lines (Brand, 1962). The antigens that confer species-specificity thus seem to be remarkably constant accompaniments of cell populations under all conditions of culture. Persistence of identification markers *in vitro* can also be demonstrated for the differential series of isoantigens that occur among inbred lines of a single species, such as the mouse (see Chapter 8). By using serological methods, Herzenberg and his collaborators have shown that cells of the mouse lymphoma *P*-388 still possess transplantation antigens identical with the inbred subline of origin (*DBA/2*), although this cell strain has been cultivated for six years in the absence of homologous products (Herzenberg, 1962; Cann and Herzenberg, 1963a, 1963b).

A number of other isolated examples can be cited where specialized characteristics appear to persist indefinitely within dispersed cell cultures (see Grobstein, 1959; Morris, 1962). Paradoxically, some of the best illustrations are to be found in neoplastic cell populations. For instance, mast cell tumors in culture may continue to synthesize 5-hydroxytryptamine and histamine as *in vivo* (Schindler, Day, and Fischer, 1959; Day and Green, 1962), whereas cells in a culture of hydatid mole have been reported to produce gonadotropin for long intervals (Waltz, Tullner, Evans, Hertz, and Earle, 1954). In general, however, tumors in culture display no greater tendency for the preservation of differentiated characteristics than do neoplasms within the intact organism. As previously noted (see Chapter 1), occasional tumors may be found, even *in vivo,* which possess specialized structural or metabolic properties despite marked anaplastic change in other respects; for example, the occurrence of high levels of alkaline phosphatase in osteogenic sarcoma.

On the opposing side, it may be useful to group together the various simplifications of structure and function that occur in culture under the general heading of dedifferentiation. The use of this term requires some definition, in view of the controversies that have occurred from time to time on the nature and reality of dedifferentiation as a biological phenomenon. Some early investigators, notably Champy (1912), suggested that cultured somatic cells may revert to a generalized embryonic state, but no evidence has ever been presented to justify this conclusion. Although isolated cells may lose certain specialized features, they do not in fact regain a broader pattern of embryonic potentialities. On the contrary, it seems likely that the regional "stamp" associated with specific tissues and organs rarely if ever completely disappears *in vitro* (see Grobstein, 1959). For these reasons, it seems simplest to use dedifferentiation in a purely descriptive sense as a means of characterizing regressive changes in cell cultures. No more should be read into this term than the simple expression of shifts to less specialized states, without specification of mechanism or connotation of retracing embryonic sequences.

Defined in this way, there can be little doubt that dedifferentiation is a prominent and widespread phenomenon in dissociated cell populations (Willmer, 1960; Levintow and Eagle, 1961; Morris, 1962). In morphological terms, this process is exemplified by the tendency for convergence in primary cultures toward three basic categories of cells, which has been mentioned previously. Obviously, morphological dedifferentiation in some cases is a necessary accommodation to conditions *in vitro.* For example, the formation of tubules, acini, and other three-dimensional units is scarcely possible in a monolayer system. But more subtle events are involved in the morphological dedifferentiation that may take place within individual cells; for example, the disappearance of a brush border from kidney epithelial cells *in vitro* (Holtzer and Holtzer, 1960).

Dedifferentiation in some cases may involve the regression or disappearance of characteristic secretion products such as hormones. An example of this process is seen in the experiments of Reusser, Smith, and Smith (1962), who explanted human anterior pituitary cells in glass substrate cultures and subsequently looked for evidence of somatotropin synthesis. Some elements in serial culture did preserve the eosinophilic or basophilic granules characteristic of pituitary epithelial cells, but when fluorescein-labeled antibody specific for human growth hormone was added, selective localization failed to occur. Thus no indication of hormone production could be obtained in the proliferating population.

Loss of responsiveness to specific hormones may also occur in dispersed cell populations. For this purpose, it is instructive to compare the reactivity of cells while growing as simple sheets with similar populations maintained in organotypic culture. Such a study is that of Franks and Barton (1960), who explanted mouse ventral prostate as an intact organ on a plasma clot. Development for the most part was restricted to processes of organized growth within the central mass, but sheets of unorganized epithelium also grew out irregularly on the plasma clot. The cells within these sheets were characterized by marked alterations in ultrastructural pattern and showed no response when testosterone propionate was added to the culture medium. The same cells, growing in organotypic fashion within the central mass, however, were markedly influenced in appearance by testosterone, and as long as hormone was provided, they showed normal ultrastructural patterns. Along the same lines, Algard (1960) reported that a hormone-dependent kidney tumor from hamsters showed contrasting patterns of behavior according to the conditions of culture. This neoplasm proliferates as a monolayer without addition of estrogen, but if maintained in the form of an organ culture, progressive growth then occurs only when the medium is supplemented with this hormone. Whether these differences in responsiveness to specific hormones in monolayers are based on cellular changes as such, or merely on the removal of stromal associations required to mediate endocrine stimulation, has not yet been determined.

The question of whether dedifferentiation obliterates regional differences is a particularly interesting one. Do cells of the same general type, but derived from different location in the body, become indistinguishable after a period of culture *in vitro*? The investigations of Parker (1933) on races of fibroblasts from chick embryos have often been quoted in this regard. In these experiments, Parker isolated a number of primary strains of fibroblasts from various tissues and organs and followed these populations serially *in vitro*. After a few passages in explant culture, the separate strains appeared to be identical in appearance and colonial growth forms. Nevertheless, certain of the cell lines could be identified individually by utilizing such criteria as rate of outgrowth, degree of proliferation in the absence of embryo extract, or ability to liquefy the plasma clot. Periosteal fibroblasts, for example, gave a different spectrum of reactions than did heart fibroblasts, and both in turn differed from the fibroblasts of skeletal muscle. Differentials between these same three cell types were also observed by Kutsky and Harris (1957), who found that primary strains from the sources mentioned give quite different responses when treated with tissue extracts from adult and juvenile organs.

Regional specificity thus appears to persist, at least in part, among chick fibroblasts, and the same seems to be true for human cells (Castor, Prince, and Dorstewitz, 1962). In the latter investigation, 13 primary strains of fibroblasts were examined, originating from such sites as synovial membrane, skin, pleura, pericardium, and peritoneum. All continued to form hyaluronic acid in serial transfer, and in none could the ability to synthesize chondroitin sulfate or collagen be demonstrated under the conditions employed for culture. However, the several morphologically indistinguishable cell strains did vary in rate of proliferation, glucose uptake, and polysaccharide formation. Such data suggest that dedifferentiation applies individually to particular cell characteristics; it is not an all-or-none process (see also Konigsberg, 1963).

Perhaps the most strategic manifestations of dedifferentiation are those that affect enzymatic patterns. A representative picture of such changes can be gained from the data reported in a study by Lieberman and Ove (1958). In this case, the relative activities of a series of enzymes were determined in four different permanent strains of cells, all of which had been propagated serially for long periods *in vitro*. The findings obtained were then arrayed against similar measurements made for freshly excised rabbit kidney and for primary kidney monolayers after varying periods of culture. Two striking facts emerge from this analysis. First, the activity levels for each of 13 different enzymes appeared to be almost identical among the four permanent strains. Such a similarity contrasts sharply with the disparity in enzyme patterns that are known to characterize individual cell types *in vivo* (see Chapter 1). The analogy to convergence of metabolic patterns in tumors (Greenstein, 1954) is an obvious one, although only one of the strains under investigation had actually been derived from malignant cells. Lieberman also found that an immediate and definite shift in enzyme pattern occurs in freshly isolated populations. After several days of culture, the specific activities of such enzymes as catalase, β-glucosidase, and alkaline phosphatase had decreased greatly in rabbit kidney cells. Other enzymes (for example, acid phosphatase or β-glucuronidase) showed little change, and the specific activity of glucose-6-phosphate dehydrogenase actually increased. The latter finding is particularly interesting, since all the permanent cell lines examined also showed relatively high levels of this enzyme. Shifts of the same kind have been reported by Burlington (1959) in enzymatic studies on primary populations of cat cells. In working with first passage cultures of cat kidney, he found that the combined activity of glucose-6-phosphate dehydrogenase and phosphogluconate dehydrogenase was 40 percent higher than in the intact organ. Burlington suggested accordingly that there may be an increased activity within the hexose monophosphate shunt, operating at a higher rate than normal in order to supply ribose units required for nucleotide synthesis. Other enzymes in primary cultures of cat kidney were found to show a pronounced decline in activity, as Lieberman and Ove had observed.

These clearly defined alterations in enzymatic pattern within primary cell populations pose a dilemma in interpretation. Do the changes noted signify a population shift, with the selection of a minority cell type, or does a repatterning of enzyme activities occur at the level of the individual cell? The selection hypothesis has been favored by Sato, Zaroff, and Mills (1960) on the basis of studies on dissociated populations of liver cells. It is well known that liver epithelial cells may survive less well than stromal elements under the usual conditions of culture. However, though selection in varying degree undoubtedly modifies the composition of primary populations, it seems at most only a partial explanation for enzymatic dedifferentiation at the population level. The findings of Ebner, Hageman, and Larson (1961) are particularly strategic in this regard. Working with primary monolayer cultures of bovine mammary cells, they observed a pattern of functional decline similar in general to the changes described above. But when the kinetics of loss were followed for individual characteristics, a series of nonparallel processes emerged. Thus the production of lactose declined at a high rate, and formation of this product could not be detected in primary cultures for more than about 24 hours. UDPGal-4-epimerase activity decreased more gradually. This enzyme appeared to disappear within the cell population between 7 and 10 days after explantation. The ability to synthesize β-lactoglobulin fell even more slowly and subsided to a plateau of residual function after about two weeks (see Figure 3.13). This discontinuity in the loss of individual functions plainly poses difficulties for the

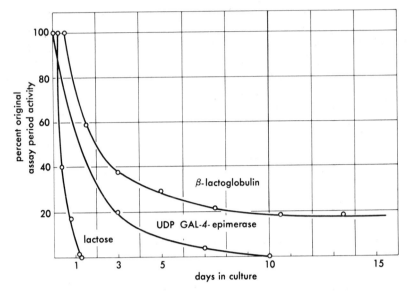

FIG. 3.13. Loss of specialized functions in first passage cultures of cells from bovine mammary gland. The three indices shown are (1) synthesis of lactose, (2) activity of uridine diphosphogalactose-4-epimerase, and (3) formation of β-lactoglobulin. Decline in each property follows a separate time course. (Redrawn from Ebner, Hageman, and Larson, 1961.)

selection hypothesis. A complex series of assumptions must be made if the results mentioned are to be looked upon as the ascendance of minority cell types with intact enzymatic patterns.

Further information on the dynamics of dedifferentiation comes from the studies of Hilfer (1962) on the properties of chick embryonic thyroid cells in monolayer culture. In a serum-saline medium, freshly isolated thyroid cells attach and spread to form continuous epithelial sheets, but no mitotic activity occurs under these conditions. The cells remain in good condition during study periods of a week or more, with a constant total count after the first day in culture. During this interval the cells retain intracellular glycoprotein and the hormone precursors moniodotyrosine and diiodotyrosine. However, the amount of thyroxine declines progressively and none can be demonstrated in cultures older than five days. Also, it is possible to detect triiodothyronine in the original cell suspensions and in the initial cultures, but the measurable levels of this substance fall to zero by about the third day. In this nonproliferating cell system, it does not seem possible to attribute the changes noted to a selective modification of the population structure. It is more reasonable to assume that functional as well as morphological dedifferentiation may occur at the cellular level, to an extent and at rates that vary for particular cell markers.

Modulation and Alternative Concepts   If the reality of dedifferentiation in a descriptive sense is granted for dispersed populations, one must still explain the significance of these events in terms of cellular information systems. The interpretation that has found most general favor is the theory of cell modulation (Weiss, 1939, 1949, 1950). This view assumes that the intrinsic specialization of cell types is not altered *in vitro*, merely the overt expression of particular characteristics. In a given environment, cells may lose morphological individuations, for example, or cease to form specific end products such as pigment, connective tissue fibers, or hormones. These shifts can be regarded as modulations, however, if one postulates that the cells in question may, under other conditions, resume output of the corresponding derivatives, or revert to pre-existing patterns of structure. From this viewpoint, the simplifications of structure and function that take place in isolated systems are in principle reversible, and the loss of specialized features is more apparent than real.

A number of investigations from the older literature on tissue culture bear in varying degree on the general concept of modulation (see Bloom, 1937; Weiss, 1949; Grobstein, 1959). Most of this earlier work was performed under insufficiently critical conditions to warrant a detailed recapitulation here. Typical of the uncertainties that exist are a number of conflicting reports on the production of cartilage or bone by morphologically dedifferentiated cells from bone-forming tissues. For example, Strangeways (1924) established a fragment of adult fowl cartilage in plasma culture and maintained the resulting population for 23 serial passages. At this stage, culture was implanted subcutaneously into an adult host and gave rise to cartilage masses, although no vestige of the original cartilage as such could be detected *in vitro*. However, Burrows (1933) found that if the central fragment of cartilage was removed during serial culture, the population that was restored from more peripheral cells did not produce cartilage on subcutaneous tests in assay hosts. Aside from the implied heterogeneity of population structure, there is an additional uncontrolled factor that prevents a clear interpretation in such experiments. This is the possibility of an induction process, which might lead to the formation of cartilage by host cells rather than those of the graft.

Other experiments have dealt with the question of whether a process of redifferentiation can give rise to cartilage and bone directly *in vitro*. For this purpose, Fischer and Parker (1929) performed experiments in which cells were isolated from the marginal growth zone of a culture established 7 to 9 months earlier from the frontal bone of a chick embryo. No extracellular matrix was demonstrable in these populations. In seeking conditions that might favor differentiation rather than growth, they omitted the embryonic extract usually present in the culture medium. Within this more restricted milieu, a new ground substance appeared, passing through a fibrous stage and later becoming more homogeneous. Although superficially the events mentioned appeared to simulate the formation of osteoid materials, the closer study of Burrows (1933) proved that this was not the case. His results showed that the staining reactions in such a system were of the collagenoid type and did not indicate the occurrence of calcification.

One of the most explicit expressions of cellular modulation is to be seen through the varying function of the pigmentation system in cultures of chick iris epithelium. Several studies show that the formation of pigment *in vitro* can be cut off or re-established by appropriate manipulation of environmental conditions. The initial experiments of Ebeling (1924) suggested that iris epithelium may grow as a colorless sheet for a year or more if maintained in a state of proliferation. In a reduced medium containing only serum and saline in the fluid phase, the cells formed pigment in conspicuous amounts. Similar observations were made by Doljanski (1930), who found pigment formation to be inversely proportional to the concentration of embryonic extract in the culture medium. However, the recent studies of Whittaker (1963) on cultures of chick retina indicate that progressive dilution or inactivation of melanogenic mechanisms by cell division is not the sole factor responsible for depigmentation *in vitro*. It would appear that the inverse correlation between mitosis and differentiation in this system has been oversimplified, a conclusion that parallels that of Hilfer (1962) in the experiments mentioned above. Aside from these considerations, it is important to note that I. Fischer (1938) long ago demonstrated that propigment granules are retained in colorless sheets of chick iris epithelium. Thus modulation in this context refers only to the disappearance or reappearance of the final storage products rather than to a loss and restoration of the entire pigment-forming system.

The induction of enzymes as a reversible process obviously falls within the general framework of cell modulations. It should be emphasized, however, that adaptive phenomena at this level in somatic cells do not have the broad significance that has frequently been the case for microbial populations (see Chapter 2). Within the intact organism, most of the enzymes that have been examined appear to be strictly constitutive. In some instances, however, the activities of individual factors can be influenced by administration of hormones or specific substates (see Knox, Auerbach, and Lin, 1956; Knox, 1961). Examples of regulation of enzyme levels can also be found *in vitro*, as Burkhalter, Jones, and Featherstone (1957) first showed with cultures of chick embryonic lung. In their experiments, cholinesterase activity was measured as a function of adding acetylcholine to the culture medium. In the presence of substrate, the specific cholinesterase activity rose to a high level over a period of several days, and was maintained at this point as long as the culture medium contained acetylcholine (see Figure 3.14). On removal of this substance, activity declined rapidly to control levels.

Increased levels of arginase in the presence of high concentrations of arginine in the culture medium have also been reported for a series of permanent cell lines by Klein (1961) and Schimke (1962). Curiously, arginase activity in this case is enhanced if yeast RNA is added to the culture medium. Whether the effect is mediated by an alteration in enzyme concentration, or merely by the incidental introduction of an activator present as an impurity in the RNA preparations, has not been determined. In freshly isolated mouse or chick cells, the initial activity of arginase declines sharply, as previously described for other enzymes.

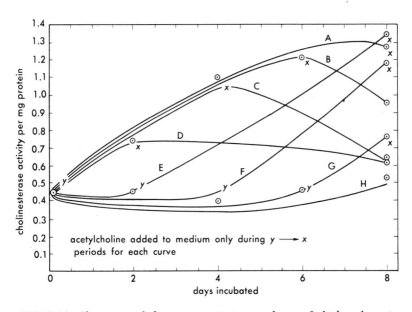

FIG. 3.14. Changes in cholinesterase activity in cultures of chick embryonic lung as a result of adding acetylcholine to the external medium. Each point shown represents the mean value of determinations made separately on four roller tubes. (From Burkhalter, Jones, and Featherstone, 1957.)

There is some evidence that, in this case, the trend may be slowed or prevented by the provision of increased arginine plus yeast RNA (Klein, 1960). Since the final arginase activities do not rise above levels observed in freshly isolated cells, however, this phenomenon seems to come under the heading of maintenance rather than induction in the usual sense.

Studies on alkaline phosphatase offer the most clear-cut system where enzyme activity in isolated cell populations can be regulated by extrinsic factors. In contrast to the general rule, the activity levels of alkaline phosphatase fluctuate greatly among different cell lines, even between clones isolated from a single population (Nitowsky and Hertz, 1961; Maio and de Carli, 1962a). In nine strains of primary fibroblasts derived from human skin, Cox and Pontecorvo (1961) were unable to demonstrate any alkaline phosphatase activity as long as the cell populations were maintained in conventional media. Increases of up to 40-fold the minimal detectable amount of alkaline phosphatase activity can be obtained, however, if organic monophosphates such as phenylphosphate or β-glycerophosphate are added to the nutrient. The effect appears to be one of substrate induction, since these activating substances are known to exist *in vivo*, where they are acted upon by both acid and alkaline phosphatase. Interestingly, the same compounds at moderate concentrations do not produce elevations of alkaline phosphatase activity in epithelial cell strains. Marked rises in the latter, however, can be obtained by treatment with the hydrocortisone analogue prednisolone (Cox and MacLeod, 1961, 1962). Prednisolone, in turn, does not induce or activate alkaline phosphatase in strains of fibroblasts. Some cell lines appear to be refractory to both treatments. The explanation for these differences in response is unknown, as is the molecular basis for altered enzyme activity with the two inductors. Particularly in the case of prednisolone it is not clear whether elevated function stems from increased enzyme synthesis, the mobilization of inactive precursors, or decreased leakage of alkaline phosphatase into the surrounding medium (Melnykovych, 1962).

Enzyme repression by external factors has also been documented for several cell systems *in vitro*. Lieberman (1957) reported that the incubation of mouse cells in culture with diphosphopyridine nucleotide (DPN) resulted in a specific disappearance of DPNase activity. The growth rate and activities of other enzymes were not lowered. In a related vein, it may be noted that although high levels of arginine can cause elevations of arginase in mammalian cell lines, the specific activities of arginosuccinate synthetase and lyase are depressed by this compound (Schimke, 1962). It may also be mentioned that cystine and cysteine serve as repressors for alkaline phosphatase in human cell cultures (Cox and MacLeod, 1963). An interesting example of reversible enzyme activation and repression has been described by DeMars (1958). The system in question is instrumental for adaptation to a medium that contains glutamic acid instead of glutamine. If the former is supplied alone, De-Mars found with a permanent strain of mouse cells that growth is minimal. Eventually, however, cell proliferation rises again to an optimal rate. This change coincides with an increase in specific activity of glutamine synthetase, which in fully adapted strains is 15 times higher than for cells grown in glutamine. If such populations are then returned to a medium containing glutamine alone, or a mixture of glutamine and glutamic acid, the activity of glutamine synthetase rapidly drops to control levels.

Summing up, there is evidence for the general concept of modulative change in the reversible changes in morphology or the accumulation of specialized products that can occasionally be observed in cell cultures. Model systems can be found in the induction or repression of certain enzymes as well as in the experimental "turning on" or "turning off" of pigment formation and other specialized syntheses. It seems fair to say, however, that this limited documentation falls far short of the broad confirmation needed to establish the validity of modulation as a general explanation for processes of dedifferentiation *in vitro*. Only with freshly dissociated embryonic tissues or rudiments are there convincing proofs that cell populations which lack overt functional and structural specializations can in fact re-establish these patterns extensively and completely. In long-term culture, this conclusion is less certain. An increasing number of observations now cast doubt on the assumption that differentiated states are necessarily propagated *in vitro* as a reversible expression of cell potential (Trinkaus, 1956; Grobstein, 1962). For at least some markers, the possibility of a *de facto* deletion during serial culture must be considered even though the genetic information covering these characteristics remains intact at the chromosomal level.

Conceivably, a disappearance of cell markers may underlie the progressive decline of histogenetic potential *in vitro*. This phenomenon can be noted when dissociated cells are propagated as monolayers for varying periods and are then subsequently reaggregated. The work of Holtzer and his colleagues on cartilage provides an illuminating model system (Holtzer, Abbott, Lash, and Holtzer, 1960; Holtzer, 1961; Stockdale, Abbott, Holtzer, and Holtzer, 1963). The vertebral rudiments from 10-day chick embryos represent particularly favorable material, since the cartilage cells within these structures are demonstrably capable *in vivo* of dividing without loss of specialization. By means of tryptic dissociation, a suspension consisting almost entirely of chondrocytes can be obtained, and these cells will grow either as a thin layer in plasma-coated flasks or as aggregates on an agar substrate. In agreement with the work of others, freshly isolated cartilage cells can be aggregated by centrifuging in this system, and the resulting pellet regularly gives rise to a typical mass of cartilage if maintained as an organ culture. However, the same cells, if propagated in monolayers, do not give rise to cartilage, although there is a logarithmic increase in cell number.

Proceeding from this background of information, Holtzer and his associates examined the histogenetic potential of cartilage cells in monolayer cultures by harvesting the populations at successive intervals with trypsin. The accumulated cells were reaggregated by centrifugation and cultured as a pellet on an agar substrate. Cells reassociated in this way after not more than three days as a thin layer in flask cultures retain the typical features of differentiated chondroblasts or chondrocytes: (1) close packing in aggregates, (2) formation of matrix with specific staining properties, and (3) synthesis of chondroitin sulfate as determined by incorporation of S^{35}. If populations are maintained for longer intervals in monolayer form, there is a progressive decline in these chondrogenic properties. After 10 days or more of proliferation in thin layers, the cells remain healthy and can be subcultured for a number of additional passages, but no longer exhibit the ability to form visible cartilage matrix or to synthesize chondroitin sulfate when reaggregated into pellets. Although the possibility of selective overgrowth by another cell type cannot be rigorously excluded in these cases, it should be emphasized that the initial populations consist almost entirely of chondrocytes. Their uninterrupted proliferation in logarithmic fashion makes it unlikely that growth in this system can be attributed to the selective activity of a minor component. A number of attempts were made by Holtzer and his colleagues to induce cartilage formation from dedifferentiated populations, but all attempts were unsuccessful. Cartilage failed to form in pellets derived from cells that had been cultivated for a period in the absence of embryo extract or in pellets grafted to the chorioallantoic membrane and coelom of chick embryos. These facts suggest that dedifferentiation of cartilage cells cannot be explained by the preferential synthesis of DNA alone, as suggested by Stockdale, Abbott, Holtzer, and Holtzer (1963), for even if the substrates and enzymes required for cartilage formation are diluted out during active cell division, there should be renewed synthesis of these factors when DNA formation is later repressed.

While the progressive loss of histogenetic potential can thus be seen particularly well with cartilage cells (see also Kuroda, 1963), the underlying events seem to be common to other differentiating cell systems. Moscona (1960) found, for example, that neuroretinal cells from 7-day chick embryos characteristically form concentric structures, or rosettes, if aggregated soon after dissociation. When cultured instead as monolayers and tested periodically by aggregation in shaker flasks, a gradual decline in ability to form rosettes can be noted. The same sequence of events is observed with dissociated skin cells from mouse embryos. Freshly dissociated preparations readily recombine in clusters and form sheets of skin with hair follicles when placed on plasma clots. If a period of monolayer culture is interposed, the cells reaggregate less readily. When reassembled by centrifugation, these populations give rise merely to unorganized outgrowths of epithelial cells and fibroblasts, without the formation of hair follicles. Along somewhat similar lines, Hilfer (1962) has noted that after a few days in monolayer culture, aggregates derived from chick thyroid cells are unable to form follicles or produce thyroxin, although these properties can be readily asserted in tissue masses reconstituted from freshly disaggregated thyroid. Even the ability for type-specific reassortment within three-dimensional groupings seems to decline when cell populations are maintained in dispersed form. Moscona (1962a) reports that monolayer-modified embryonic cells remain scattered within complex aggregates and do not segregate as usual into foci of common histotype.

It is reasonable to suggest from these findings that cellular dedifferentiation *in vitro* may be a function of irreversible loss as well as modulative changes in phenotype. A model that is consistent with this thesis can be devised by assuming that differentiation consists in the establishment by primary gene action of cytoplasmic control systems and that the actual continuity of somatic properties depends more directly on the latter. According to current information theory, these control systems might be visualized in one sense as stable forms of messenger RNA, or complexes with cytoplasmic particulates. Alternatively, they could represent steady states, in the sense of Delbrück (see Chapter 2), or even selectively modified patterns of structure within the cell. If the maintenance of differentiated states does depend on peripheral regulation, these mechanisms may be particularly subject to epigenetic change under the special conditions that obtain in monolayers or other dispersed cell systems. The replication of cytoplasmic determinants might become depressed or asynchronous, for example, as a result of unbalanced growth or even through the progressive leaching of key metabolites from monolayers (see Chapter 5). Thus the activity of control systems regulating particular cell markers could diminish to the vanishing point. If the molecular ecology within these isolated cells did not permit a reassertion of primary gene action, the characteristics in question would disappear as effectively as by direct genetic deletion.

Parallels to the foregoing concept can be cited from experiments with microorganisms (see Chapter 2). The production of vegetative petites in yeast offers a particularly useful comparison (Ephrussi, 1953). As noted earlier, this condition arises from the permanent loss of cytoplasmic factors essential for the synthesis of respiratory enzymes. Such changes take place regularly in a few cells during vegetative growth; they can be induced more uniformly by chemical agents, temperature treatments, or even by nutritional deficiencies (Sarachek and Fowler, 1961). The common end result can be explained by assuming that a number of environmental influences may depress or prevent the replication of cytoplasmic determinants for the corresponding enzyme-forming systems. Significantly, these factors cannot then be replaced, even though the necessary information would seem to be present in the nuclear genes. A second analogy arises from the studies of Sonneborn on the so-called kappa particles in *Paramecium*. By manipulating environmental conditions appropriately, the replication of kappa can be made asynchronous with that of the organism. In this case, the cell as a whole literally outstrips the plasmid in rate of multiplication and the latter is effectively eliminated (Sonneborn, 1959). It is not yet known whether there are conditions of growth in the culture of freshly isolated somatic cells that may likewise interfere with the balanced duplication of cytoplasmic control systems, and if so, whether deletion is a possible sequel. However, these and other novel mechanisms of dedifferentiation deserve more careful study. The attractiveness of the modulation concept has tended to inhibit the examination of other models of cellular change. Conceivably, some of these may be of restricted but strategic significance.

CELL POPULATIONS IN
LONG-TERM CULTURE

One of the principal objectives in the early days of tissue culture was to establish the principal cell types from chick embryos and other sources as "pure" lines, which could be propagated indefinitely as lineages comparable to stock strains of microbial cells. The concept of homogeneity was considerably oversimplified in an era that preceded the development of cloning procedures, but nevertheless a number of lines were isolated that consisted of a single histotype, such as chick iris epithelium (Fischer, 1922), chick monocytes (Carrel and Ebeling, 1922), and thyroid epithelium (Ebeling, 1925). Unfortunately, this initially promising perspective proved to be an inadequate one. With the benefit of more modern techniques for cytological analysis, it has become increasingly clear that most, if not all, of the cell lineages that multiply without limit *in vitro* are modified strains. Far from representing the persistence of an unchanged component within the precursor population, these permanent cell lines must be regarded as deviants. Ordinarily they are found to have aberrant karyotypes, novel morphological patterns, and other emergent properties not readily explicable on the basis of modulation or other processes of morphogenetic change. The evolution of primary cells into variant forms thus constitutes an additional area of interest in the dynamics of long-term cultures. In these transitions may be found models of possible significance for other types of cell alterations.

Progressive Changes in Primary Populations Carrel and other pioneer investigators believed that somatic units could proliferate indefinitely without change from the original cell types, provided the conditions of culture were made sufficiently favorable. This concept stems in the main from observations on a famous line of chick heart fibroblasts, reputed to have survived in serial transfer for 34 years before it was finally closed out (Carrel, 1912, 1914; Ebeling, 1913, 1922; Parker, 1961). The cells were carried routinely in the form of explants in plasma culture; the degree of proliferation and outgrowth were variable, but usually very vigorous; and the populations in late generations did not seem to depart significantly in appearance or colonial pattern from those of early transfers or of recently established cultures. From such experiments came the widely heralded view of Carrel that tissue cells are potentially immortal if maintained as continuously proliferating strains *in vitro* (Carrel, 1914; Ebeling, 1922).

Although these classic investigations have never been seriously challenged, it no longer seems possible to accept at face value the conclusions offered. No other investigators have reported a similar success in maintaining populations of primary cells in unmodified form for a period of years, and the question of alternative explanations needs to be examined. Techniques for karyotypic analysis had not been worked out at this earlier period; thus it is conceivable the persisting population was an aneuploid variant rather than one of the original cell types present at the outset. The possibility of sporadic contamination by fresh cells also requires consideration in view of the stringent precautions now known to be necessary to assure the purity of cell lines (see pages 178–179). In this connection, it should be noted that unfiltered chick embryonic extract was routinely added to Carrel's stock cultures, and inevitably contained a few fresh cells. These contaminants could effectively "seed" stock populations in dormant phases, giving rise to foci of active growth from which the strain might be continued effectively. There is no point in pursuing conjectures of this type in detail, but it should be emphasized that rigorous proof is lacking for the indefinite continuity of primary cells in Carrel's investigations.

The results of more recent studies with chick cells point in another direction. Typical of this newer work are the experiments of Harris (1957) on the serial cultivation of chick skeletal muscle fibroblasts as monolayers. Primary cultures can be established reproducibly with this material, and a number of individual strains were examined. All proliferated luxuriantly in logarithmic fashion for a number of successive transfers. Eventually, however, every strain passed into a static condition and was lost. In this process, the growth rate and total yield declined to zero, the cells became ragged and heterogeneous with the occurrence of bizzare forms, and large amounts of intercellular debris appeared. Such changes could not be attributed to progressive damage by the trypsin used to harvest cell populations at the end of each growth cycle, for the decline in older cultures was equally marked when strains were transferred exclusively by mechanical means. Evidently the limited viability of primary chick cells is not restricted to monolayer populations either, for Parker (1961) has observed the repeated decline of chick fibroblasts in plasma cultures after a finite number of transfer generations. A number of other investigators have obtained substantially similar results with various cell systems, and it seems clear that the limited proliferation of primary cells is a general phenomenon (see Swim and Parker 1957; Swim, 1959; Madin, 1959). In primary cultures of both human and animal cells, three phases have usually been described: (1) an interval of progressive growth, often vigorous, through a number of serial passages; (2) a dormant period, in which the majority of cell strains are lost; and (3) the emergence in occasional instances of variants as permanent cell lines. This pattern is by no means a uniform one nor is it predictable in all cases; first and third phases, for example, may merge indistinguishably (Madin and Darby, 1958; Foley, Drolet, McCarthy, Goulet, Dokos, and Filler, 1960).

The apparent inability of primary cell populations to proliferate indefinitely poses a fundamental problem. Is this restriction an artifact of method, or is it the expression of an intrinsic cellular change? The first alternative has been championed by Puck and his associates, who claimed to have developed techniques that permit the propagation of primary cells without limit in serial culture (Puck, 1958, 1959). As previously noted, these workers were the first to isolate clonal populations in routine fashion from first passage cultures of human and animal tissues. Primary strains of human fibroblasts that originate in this way are uniformly euploid (that is, with a normal diploid chromosome pattern) and have been carried by serial transfer for periods up to a year without loss of karyotypic integrity (Puck, Cieciura, and Robinson, 1958; Puck, 1958, 1959). Technical measures that preserve the normal chromosome pattern were believed the key to the indefinite continuity of such populations. Conversely, deleterious cultural conditions were thought to interfere with cell division, leading to the ultimate decline and loss of primary strains or causing modifications in karyotype that are reflected in conversion to a permanent strain of aneuploid character. With this concept in mind, Puck has recommended a number of refinements in culture techniques, including gentle trypsinization and handling of cells, precise control of pH and incubation temperatures, and the use of media pretested for toxicity. He has stressed the avoidance of mitotic inhibitors and the use of serum from embryonic or newborn animals rather than from adult sources. Selected batches of fetal calf serum have been thought especially suitable for the indefinite cultivation of primary diploid cells of human origin.

There can be little doubt that the variability and properties of isolated cells are on occasion a function of particular conditions prevailing in culture. However, it is increasingly unlikely that the finite survival of primary strains with their diploid patterns can be accounted for in this fashion. Contrary to the views of Puck (1958, 1959) and Moser (1960), the stability of karyotype in primary cells does not appear to depend on the precise control of environmental variables or on the exacting exclusion of toxic factors. The careful analysis of Hayflick and Moorhead (1961) is particularly illuminating on this point. In their experiments, fetal tissues of human origin were used to establish some 25 different strains, all of which grew ultimately with the morphology of fibroblasts. These populations exhibited flourishing growth and continued to proliferate for periods as long as those reported by Puck; that is, up to approximately a year in some instances. In every case, the diploid pattern remained intact during the interval of months in which vigorous multiplication took place. This result was achieved by routine culture methods without elaborate precautions in the handling and maintenance of cell populations. The culture media contained ordinary calf serum and were not pretested for inhibitors. None of 15 separate pools of serum employed during the investigation seemed to affect adversely the karyotypic integrity of primary cells. Ferguson and Wansbrough (1962) have likewise been able to maintain diploid strains for long intervals and without recourse to specialized procedures. In view of these newer findings, therefore, it seems logical to conclude that factors responsible for maintenance of the euploid state reside primarily within the cell rather than in the surrounding microenvironment.

The demonstrated ability of certain human cells to proliferate as primary lines for as long as a year may actually be somewhat misleading, for there are as yet no indications that these strains as such can survive indefinitely. This qualification is supported by the comprehensive data amassed by Hayflick and Moorhead (1961) in the investigation mentioned above. According to these authors, the various diploid strains of human cells, as in other systems, are characterized by a finite limit of subcultivation. The limit appears to be an individual one for particular cell lines, but does not extend beyond a maximum of about 50 serial passages (or about one year *in vitro*) under the conditions that have been imposed. The history of primary strains as described by Hayflick and Moorhead follows a familiar pattern. Thus, single populations were found to proliferate reproducibly for 2 to 10 months if maintained continuously in logarithmic growth. During this time, the cells remained comparatively uniform in appearance, and there were no signs of deterioration in the culture as a whole (see Figure 3.15). Later, mitotic

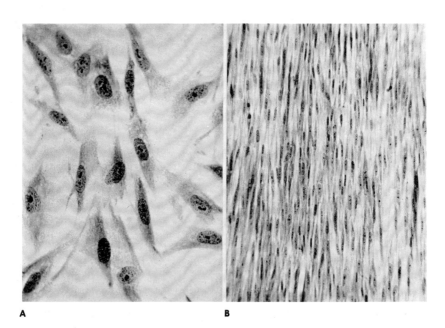

A   B

FIG. 3.15. Primary diploid strains of cells derived from human fetal lung. May-Grünwald Giemsa strain. (A) Appearance of individual cells after 35 subcultivations and 9 months *in vitro*. (B) Colonial pattern in mass population from same cell line. Note typical directional orientation of cells. (From Hayflick and Moorhead, 1961.)

activity decreased, and degenerative changes set in, with ragged cells, aberrant nuclei, and the accumulation of debris at cell surfaces (see Figure 3.16). Initially it was believed that a diploid chromosome pattern was preserved during the degenerative phase of primary human strains, but it is now clear that aneuploidy can be demonstrated during this interval (Saksela and Moorhead, 1963). Such observations bring the evolution of human cell lines into closer agreement with the transitional changes of karyotype known to occur within animal cell populations (see Chapter 4).

Hayflick and Moorhead were unable to reverse the degenerative trends in their primary cultures by changes in media, subcultivation, or the pooling of populations. They did, however, effectively rule out the direct action of toxic factors in the external medium as an explanation for decline and loss of cell strains at this stage. Young strains, for example, were able to proliferate vigorously in the same pool of medium in which older strains progressively deteriorated. More significantly, if a cell sample that had been preserved by freezing from an earlier

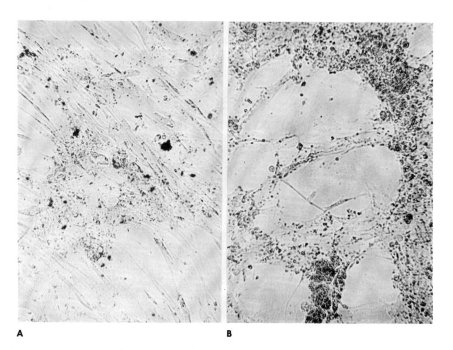

A   B

FIG. 3.16. Degenerative changes in human primary cell strains. Living unstained preparations. (A) Deteriorating line of cells derived from human fetal lung, in fiftieth serial passage. Note granular debris and heterotypic cell morphology. (B) Another area of same culture. (From Hayflick and Moorhead, 1961.)

passage of a declining strain was thawed and established in the same nutrient, growth occurred in a rapid and optimal fashion. The implication of these findings is plain: The ultimate growth failure seems to stem primarily from an intrinsic sequence of change. In cultures of freshly isolated human cells, this process may be long and drawn out as compared to that for certain other cell types, but it is no less progressive.

The finite capacity for subcultivation of primary cells is an important and as yet unexplained phenomenon. Conceivably, the limiting factors might be related to mechanisms of dedifferentiation discussed earlier, and indeed, failure of growth could represent the final phase in a sequential regression at the primary level. It has been pointed out that the decline of individual cell markers appears to proceed at different rates during the dedifferentiation that occurs following explantation, and the control systems affecting cell growth and reproduction may well be the last affected by this trend. On such an assumption, it is not unreasonable that primary cells seem to pass through a stage in which the capacity for proliferation remains intact, although mechanisms for the expression of more specialized characters may be grossly impaired. If the replication of cell patterns during this phase does not represent a steady state, the progressive deterioration of control systems may extend ultimately to those concerned with chromosome duplication, mitotic division, and homeostatic regulation of the cell as an intact unit. In this case, the onset of disorganization, dormancy, and eventual loss of the population could be expected, unless a reshuffling of genetic materials incident to these processes resulted in the emergence of variants. The latter might then selectively re-establish equilibrium conditions for growth as a permanent cell strain. A number of experimental data, to be described in the following section, are in accord with this hypothesis, although critical proofs have not yet been provided.

The limited viability of primary strains may also have implications for the behavior of organized cell systems *in vivo*. Hayflick and Moorhead have suggested that this phenomenon may be the expression of senescence at the cellular level, that is, the antithesis of Carrel's earlier views. They point out that experiments of analogous design can be carried out in transplant systems. Thus the long-term culture of primary cells may be simulated to a degree by the serial transfer of normal tissues between young animals with an appropriate common background of histocompatibility factors (see Chapter 8). This parallel has not been examined directly, but the work of Krohn (1962) has contributed a number of interesting findings. In a limited series of transplantations with mice, he was unable to obtain serial growth of ovary or thyroid for more than three transplant generations, but better success was achieved with skin. Grafts of skin from young mice survived in tandem transfer for about 1000 days, although evidently with declining ability for proliferation, since the final areas of donor tissue were minute. Transplants of older skin on young hosts were also initially healthy and normal in appearance, but remained so for shorter periods. After intervals that ranged from 100 to 250 days in some combinations or approximately 600 days in others, these grafts underwent a chronic progressive deterioration. Simultaneous transplants of old and young skin made to the same individual suggest that the factors responsible for this eventual downfall are intrinsic to the graft; that is, after a period of time, the older grafts in certain combinations passed regularly into decline while the transplants of young skin on the same host continued to survive in a healthy and vigorous condition. While transplantation studies with age-chimeras of this type are obviously quite preliminary, the results mentioned are consistent with the view that *in vivo*, as *in vitro*, the ability of normal cell lineages to proliferate may not be unlimited.

Origins of Permanent Cell Strains Although cell populations adapted to a permanent existence in culture are now commonplace, their advent is of comparatively recent date. In this development, Earle's well-known L strain of mouse cells can be regarded as a prototype. Originating as a by-product of experiments on carcinogenesis *in vitro* (see Chapter 7), strain L was initiated in 1940 from an explant of subcutaneous tissue (see Earle, 1943). In the course of serial transfer in plasma culture, the cell population was treated with methylcholanthrene, and eventually produced sarcomas when injected into the subline of origin (C_3H). In 1947, strain L was established in glass substrate cultures (Evans and Earle, 1947); later, these were used to initiate a clonal subline (Sanford, Earle, and Likely, 1948). The derivative population can be designated strain L, clone 929, or $NCTC$-929, and has been widely distributed. Clone 929 was also the first cell type adapted for indefinite cultivation in a protein-free, chemically defined medium (Evans, Bryant, McQuilkin, Fioramonti, Sanford, Westfall, and Earle, 1956). The chromosome pattern of strain L and its sublines is markedly aneuploid, and the modal karyotype varies significantly among numerous existing substrains in different laboratories (see Chapter 4). Like many other permanent lines, strain L has undergone morphological alterations in the course of serial culture. As a variant form, it does not now resemble normal fibroblasts in primary culture. For this reason, the occasional description of strain L cells as "fibroblasts" is misleading. Figure 3.17 shows the appearance of strain L, clone 929, which is subject to minor modulations in appearance and colonial pattern in accordance with the varying conditions of culture (see also Figure 5.10).

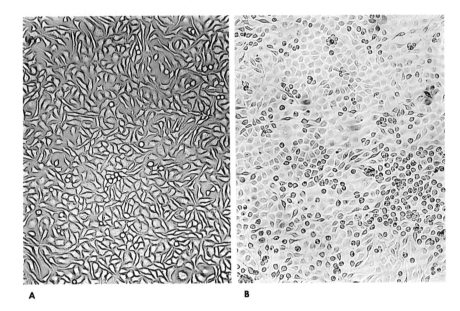

A   B

FIG. 3.17. Populations of clone 929, strain L mouse cells, illustrating modulations in morphological appearance under different cultural conditions. (Unpublished photographs, courtesy of R. C. Parker.)

Another cell line that has become equally familiar is strain HeLa, derived originally from a carcinoma of the human cervix. The early passages of this population were carried in plasma and, later, directly on a glass substrate (Gey, Coffman, and Kubicek, 1952; Gey, 1955). At about the same time, procedures for tryptic dispersion of cells were coming into use, and strain HeLa was the first to be propagated serially by this method (Scherer, Syverton, and Gey, 1953). In the expanding application of cell cultures to problems in virology, HeLa cells frequently provided a convenient experimental system (Syverton, 1956). Like strain L mouse cells, HeLa now occurs as a spectrum of sublines in many different laboratories. Two of the best known derivatives are the S_1 and S_3 substrains, obtained originally as clones by Puck, Marcus, and Cieciura (1956).

Numerous other permanent strains of cells have been obtained from tumors, although by no means all neoplastic populations will grow indefinitely from the outset *in vitro*, and some are more difficult to cultivate than are primary normal cells. Among the better known human lines that have come into general use are HEP-2, derived from a carcinoma of the larynx (Moore, Sabachewsky, and Toolan, 1955); *KB*, which originated as a carcinoma of the nasopharynx (Eagle, 1955); Detroit-6, of probable origin from a metastatic carcinoma of the lung (Berman, Stulberg, and Ruddle, 1955); and *J*-111, a line of monocytic leukemia (Osgood and Brooke, 1955). A variety of cell lines that proliferate continuously have also been isolated from animal tumors.

It should not be inferred, however, that permanent cell lines originate only from tumors or from populations that, as in the case of strain *L*, have acquired demonstrable neoplastic properties *in vitro*. Permanent strains can also arise directly from primary populations of embryonic or adult cells in which there has been no indication of neoplastic conversion. Over the past few years, many such lines have been established, both for man and various laboratory animals (see Ross and Syverton, 1957; Swim, 1959; Madin, 1959; Paul, 1960; Hayflick, 1962). The tabulation of Hayflick cites references for some 91 cell lines derived from nonneoplastic tissues, most if not all presumably capable of indefinite proliferation. Karyotypic analyses are available for a large number of these, with modal chromosome numbers that depart characteristically from the diploid value. Heteroploidy as such, however, is not completely diagnostic for permanent cell strains. A few lines are pseudodiploid (that is, with balanced gain and loss of single chromosomes within the set), and others may differ only by minor structural changes from a euploid pattern (see Chapter 4). It should be noted, too, that although the morphology of permanent cell lines arising from primary populations is characteristically variant, it may occasionally conform to the pre-existing profile (Swim and Parker, 1957).

Because contaminations between cell strains are known to have occurred in certain laboratories within recent years (see following section), some investigators have expressed the view that most, if not all, so-called alterations in long-term culture are to be regarded as artifacts. Proof that this view is too extreme can be found in experiments such as those of Rothfels and Parker (1959). Using stringent precautions to rule out any possibility of cell contaminations, they nevertheless observed repeatedly the emergence of morphological variants in serial cultures of mouse kidney cells. The variant forms grew as modified mosaics, which closely resembled *HeLa* cells in colonial pattern (see Figure 3.18). However, when karyotypic studies were performed, the chromosomes were unmistakably those of mouse cells. All these continuously propagating lines were aneuploid, and the deviations in chromosome number and structure proved to be individualized for the various different strains. These results offer an explicit demonstration

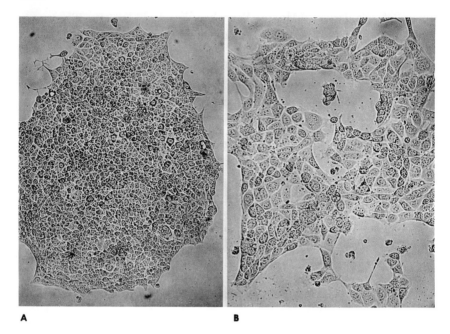

A   B

FIG. 3.18. Cell morphology and colonial pattern in a permanent strain of mouse kidney cells. (A) Clonal population arising as a colony from an isolated cell. (B) Typical mosaics formed by association of altered kidney cells in a pavement membrane. (Unpublished photographs, courtesy of R. C. Parker.)

that permanent cell lines do arise as variants from primary populations, even though the occurrence of contaminations at times in the past has tended to obscure this pattern of change.

Epithelial derivatives have been particularly useful in characterizing the transition from primary to permanent cell strains; among the first to work with these populations was Chang (1954). Using human surgical specimens, he initiated cultures from conjunctiva, liver, kidney, and appendix. Although growth during the early passages was often sparse and irregular, permanent cell lines were eventually obtained from each source. The initial monolayers contained a mixture of cell types, but after 15 to 30 transfers, only epithelial-like cells remained. These were remarkably generalized in character, grew vigorously in culture, and appeared to be essentially similar in appearance for all four established strains. In each case, the cells assumed a simple polygonal outline and grew in close apposition as an undifferentiated pavement epithelium. Subsequent studies have shown that the Chang strains are all markedly aneuploid, with variant chromosome patterns (see Chapter 4).

Chang's experimental design did not reveal whether permanent strains arise by a generalized conversion within the population as a whole or by discontinuous focal alterations followed by a selection process. However, the latter alternative can be demonstrated for some cell systems. One of the most favorable for this purpose seems to be human amnion, which can be established reproducibly in the form of primary monolayers from surgical specimens (Zitcer, Fogh, and Dunnebacke, 1955). The populations that arise are epithelial in character and can be maintained for extended periods, although with little or no proliferation in the nutrients that were initially recommended. Within such cultures, Fogh and Lund (1957) observed the appearance of a variant cell type. When isolated in subculture, these cells grew rapidly and could be propagated indefinitely as a derivative strain (*FL*). Similar lines of modified amnion cells have been described by several investigators.

The stages that intervene in the conversion of primary amnion cultures have been the subject of study by Zitcer and Dunnebacke (1957) as well as by Hayflick (1961) and Fogh (1961). In each case, the origin of rapidly proliferating strains has been traced to variant colonies that arise in small numbers within dormant primary populations. The interval required for the onset of this transition varies from 35 days to several months in culture. New colonies can be recognized when as few as 8 to 20 cells are present, owing to characteristic deviations in appearance from primary amnion (see Figure 3.19). Within these foci, the incidence of cell division is high, but no mitotic activity can be discerned in the adjacent primary population. Selection thus proceeds rapidly, and with continuing subculture, the primary cells are eliminated in favor of the altered cell types. Cells of the derivative strains exhibit a generalized epithelial morphology that is, however, clearly distinct from that of freshly isolated amnion (Fogh and Edwards, 1959). In a series of these populations, characteristic differences can be found in growth patterns, details of morphology, and reactions to heterologous sera (Zitcer and Dunnebacke, 1957; Fogh, 1961). The focal origin of variant cells and the individuality of derivative lines suggest that the establishment of permanent strains in this system is based on spontaneous random changes rather than on modulation or physiological adaptation. A rigorous analysis in terms of population dynamics, however, has yet to be made.

The interplay of mechanisms that may lead to the emergence of permanent lines can be documented in more detail by the studies of Rothfels, Kupelwieser, and Parker (1963). As mentioned previously, these workers established primary monolayers of mouse embryo cells in serial passage. At successive transfer generations, routine determina-

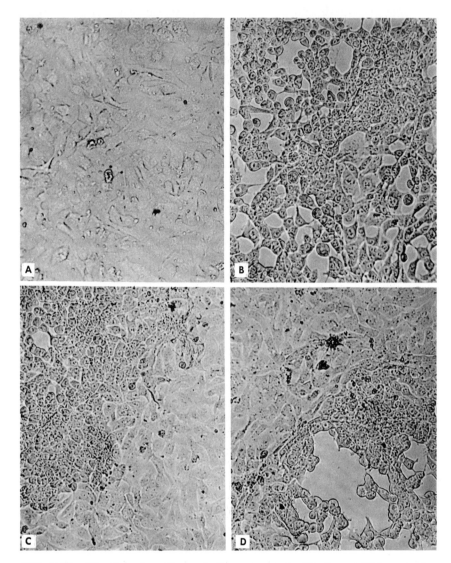

FIG. 3.19. Alterations in cell morphology associated with the establishment of a permanent strain of human amnion cells. (A) An area in a primary cell sheet. The unstained cells are very transparent and show few mitoses. (B) Central region in a colony of altered cells. There is great mitotic activity and a few multinucleated elements have formed. No primary cells can be seen. (C–D) Areas of primary cells adjacent to foci of altered cells. The latter are more granular and refractile. (From Hayflick, 1961.)

tions were made of mitotic frequency and chromosomal pattern. The findings for a representative strain can be illustrated with the data shown in Figure 3.20. The sequence of mitotic decline, chromosomal diversification, and renewed proliferation is seen here in diagrammatic fashion. An obvious question posed by these observations is whether a causal relation exists between growth failure and the later onset of aneuploidy. Such does not seem to be the case, for Rothfels and his colleagues were able to eliminate the growth stasis of primary cells through the use of feeder systems. By combining a primary population at each transfer with a nondividing aliquot of irradiated feeder cells, the strain can be propagated for long periods without decline in mitotic activity. All the populations do become aneuploid eventually, but the onset of chromosomal changes is considerably delayed. Sublines taken off feeder at an earlier stage become aneuploid more rapidly. Just how a feeder system could retard the development of aneuploidy in primary populations is far from clear. Conceivably, the progressive leaching of

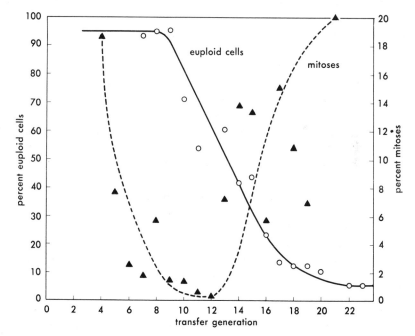

FIG. 3.20. Transitional changes between a primary and permanent cell strain. Data obtained from cultures of mouse embryonic cells, transferred at biweekly intervals. Note the sharply declining frequency of mitosis after four transfer generations, the progressive disappearance of diploid cells in the ensuing dormant phase, and the final emergence of an actively growing aneuploid population. (From Rothfels, Kupelwieser, and Parker, 1963.)

cell constituents may be sufficient to initiate mitotic irregularities even if the rate of loss is insufficient to inhibit the division process as such. In this case, the provision of similar products by feeder cells may tend to prevent or compensate for attrition in serial culture.

Some uncertainties still exist concerning the origins of particular cell lines now in general use. For example, a series of epithelial-like cells have been reported to develop from cultures of human bone marrow or even from peripheral blood (Berman and Stulberg, 1956, 1958; Berman, Stulberg, and Ruddle, 1957). The populations in question have become known as the Detroit lines, and were originated through attempts to maintain bone marrow cells in long-term culture. Freshly isolated populations from this source contain a complex array of cells. In general, most of these are short-lived, with fibroblasts as the usual persisting growth form. In some cases, however, Berman and Stulberg found isolated islands of another cell type. These grew as compact, polygonal elements in closely adherent mosaics. The derivative populations were markedly aneuploid and could be maintained indefinitely. A number of similar strains were also obtained directly from peripheral nonleukemic blood, using cultures initiated from the buffy coat (Berman and Stulberg, 1958).

The remarkable appearance of epithelial elements in cultures of bone marrow and blood has never been satisfactorily accounted for. Other investigators working with human bone marrow have been unable to confirm the original findings (Berg and Rosenthal, 1961; Ang, Jaross, and McAllister, 1962). Using rabbit bone marrow, Goldstein and Havas (1960) could isolate permanent strains of fibroblasts routinely, but although some of these were carried for as long as 4½ years, no transitions to epithelial-like cells were observed. Similarly, there have been no further reports of aneuploid, epithelial-like cells in cultures of peripheral blood. A possible explanation may stem from the fact that the first of the Detroit strains (Detroit-6) was isolated from a patient with carcinoma of the lung. The subsequent Detroit lines of epithelial character appear to differ only in minor respects from this population. The possibility that the entire group originated by inadvertent contamination of cultures with Detroit-6 cells must therefore be considered. On the other hand, epithelial transformations have again been described in cultures of human synovial connective tissue cells by Castor, Prince, and Dorstewitz (1961), and more study of this problem is evidently needed.

Taken as a group, permanent cell strains must be regarded as novel cell systems. Their aneuploid chromosome patterns, pleomorphic appearance, and other variant features depart from the characteristics of normal cell types *in vivo*. For this reason, some investigators have been inclined to homologize permanent cell lines with tumors and to equate their origins with a process of neoplastic conversion (Leighton, Kline, and Orr, 1956). This view finds support in numerous studies that show that neoplastic transformations can take place *in vitro*. Indeed, with mouse cells, it appears that most, if not all, long-term populations eventually acquire tumor-producing properties (Rothfels, Kupelwieser, and Parker, 1963). However, even in these systems it has become clear that the onset of neoplastic change cannot be directly correlated with the appearance of aneuploidy or with the alterations in growth pattern that usher in a permanent strain (see Chapter 7). Furthermore, if cell lines from other types of animals are considered, it appears that spontaneous conversions to malignancy *in vitro* are much less frequent. Permanent lines derived from non-neoplastic tissues seem to differ as a rule in transplantation behavior from those that originate from tumors. In most cases, at least, a differential distinction between the two can be made by assays performed in the cheek pouch of the hamster (Foley, Handler, Adams, and Craig, 1962). On the basis of the evidence now available, it may be reasonable to view the transition from primary to permanent lines as opening up merely a broader spectrum of cellular variation. Some, but not all, of the changes that arise may confer tumor-producing properties if the cells are returned to the original organism.

In concluding this discussion, it should be pointed out that cell lines have been characterized by more than one system of terminology in the research literature. Earlier investigators, for example, frequently referred to "established" strains. As Madin (1959) emphasizes, however, this label does not have a clear-cut connotation. In a sense, both primary and permanent cell lines are "established." Because of this ambiguity, it seems best to refer to established strains, if at all, in a purely descriptive fashion. An established strain is thus one that multiplies serially, whether for long or short intervals. Still another system of reference has been suggested by Hayflick and Moorhead (1961). These workers would make explicit the distinction between primary and permanent populations by designating the former as *strains* and the latter as *lines*. Unfortunately, the terms strain and line, from a common-sense standpoint, connote very nearly the same thing, and up to this point they have in fact been used interchangeably in the research literature. For this reason, it seems unlikely that an arbitrary redefinition of terms will gain general acceptance. The underlying distinction can be made more effectively in the concept of primary versus permanent populations, using strain and line as synonymous in meaning.

Problems of Recognition and Identification   The long-term culture of somatic cells is plainly marked by transitions and discontinuities. Primary strains may converge in properties; permanent lines, in their origin and evolution feature diversification. The clarification of these changes depends in part on the availability of means for the recognition and specific identification of cell populations. Objective criteria are necessary to establish the identity of cell lines that resemble one another and especially to assure that altered cell populations are in fact derived by modification of the original cell types. The practical importance of safeguarding the identity of stock strains requires little emphasis in microbiology, where on occasion contamination of reference materials has introduced artifacts into the research literature. That this problem is equally critical for the management of somatic cell lines, however, has only recently come to be appreciated. A number of well-documented instances of cross-contamination between strains have now been described. These were disclosed only through the development of procedures that made possible a differential diagnosis of the cells concerned.

The experience of Parker and his collaborators offers an instructive example of population changes that at first appeared to represent spontaneous variation but eventually were traced by careful analysis to the introduction of an extraneous cell type. Over a period of years, these investigators repeatedly witnessed population changes in cultures from a variety of sources. In each case, conversion was initiated by the appearance of cells that were quite different in morphology from those already present. These, by vigorous growth, soon replaced the initial population (Parker, 1955, 1958; Parker, Castor, and McCulloch, 1957). Emergence of the new cell type did not coincide with a declining phase of population growth. The phenomenon seemed rather to be equally characteristic of first passage primary cultures and permanent strains. However, the derivative lines were remarkably similar in appearance, whether obtained from freshly isolated monkey kidney cultures, chick embryo cultures, or populations of other types. All closely resembled Earle's strain L mouse cells. They could be propagated in free suspension, were resistant to polio virus, and proliferated without limit in serial culture. In view of these facts, the suspicion grew that most, if not all, of the population changes noted could be attributed to a process of recurrent contamination from L cells maintained in the same laboratory. This conclusion was ultimately borne out by karyotypic studies performed in painstaking detail (Rothfels, Axelrad, Siminovitch, McCulloch, and Parker, 1959). The chromosomal patterns of the various altered strains were found to coincide with the karyotype of clone 929 cells in all general features as well as the morphological details of several characteristic markers. Their origin from L cells was then confirmed independently by transplantation specificity tests.

Several other instances of cross-contamination between cell strains have been detected through chromosome analysis. Hsu and Klatt (1958) described a line of cells that was clearly murine in karyotype, although derived originally from a culture of cartilage from human fetal foot. In this case, it appeared also that strain L mouse cells had inadvertently been introduced at some point during serial cultivation. Similarly, Ford and Yerganian (1958) traced unexplained modifications in a Chinese hamster line to contamination with human cells, probably *HeLa*. The latter, which grows vigorously, has probably replaced a number of other cell strains. Rothfels and his collaborators, in the study mentioned above, examined three lines of cells supposedly derived by Westwood, Macpherson, and Titmuss (1957) from cultures of embryonic rabbit kidney, human liver, and monkey kidney. All these, and in addition a strain of cells originating from cultures of monkey heart (Salk and Ward, 1957), proved to be indistinguishable in appearance and karyotype from *HeLa* cells. Such reports emphasize the infective potential of *HeLa*, strain L, and other rapidly growing cell types (see also Brand and Syverton, 1962). Clearly, the management of somatic cells in serial culture requires the same rigid exclusion of cross-contamination recognized to be essential in the handling of more typical infectious agents.

Although differential diagnosis of cells by karyotype is often useful, it requires the presence of suitable markers. Where the populations in question have fairly similar chromosome patterns, other measures must be used. If species recognition is the crucial factor, several serological procedures can be employed. As previously noted, Brand and Syverton (1960, 1962) have adapted hemagglutination techniques for this purpose. For example, rabbit, human, or monkey cells may be used to immunize an appropriate host whose serum after absorption will then selectively agglutinate erythrocytes of the corresponding species. Cross-reactions do occur in some instances, but these are minimal in comparison to the broad overlap found between species in complement fixation or cytotoxicity tests. Brand and Syverton have used the hemagglutination technique to check the identity of lines that showed unexpected departures in viral susceptibility and other cellular properties from the stated species of origin. Some 17 strains in this category, derived from a number of laboratories, were found to be incorrectly labeled. Stocks ostensibly from monkey, rabbit, swine, calf, hamster, or duck tissues were either mouse or human in hemagglutination properties (Brand and Syverton, 1962).

A second immunological procedure that can be used for species identification of cells *in vitro* is the mixed agglutination reaction. This method was originally developed by Coombs, Bedford, and Rouillard (1956) for demonstrating common antigens on the surface of red blood cells and tissue cells. The reacting groups, if similar, may be linked from cell to cell by a specific antibody. A positive result is evidenced by a cluster of erythrocytes around each individual tissue cell, and this phenomenon is readily detected by phase microscopy. The mixed agglutination reaction can be applied to the diagnosis of unknown cell types on the assumption, so far apparently valid, that these surface antigens are species-specific (Coombs, Daniel, Gurner, and Kelus, 1961a, 1961b; Coombs, 1962). In practice, antisera are prepared against an array of erythrocytes from various species, and are suitably absorbed to render them selective in their action. The individual reagents are then applied in turn to aliquots of an unknown cell type. Specific binding, if it occurs, is detected by washing the treated cells and adding indicator erythrocytes corresponding to the antiserum used. Numerous tests show that mixed agglutination occurs only if erythrocytes, antiserum, and test cells correspond to the same species. By this means, Coombs and his co-workers have been able to identify selectively mouse, rat, bovine, pig, guinea pig, rabbit, Rhesus monkey, and human cells from culture.

The identification antigens for individual species can also be detected by immunofluorescence, using reagents selective for the cells in question (Stulberg, Simpson, and Berman, 1961). Other indices for group identification can be based on the varying susceptibility of cell strains to a spectrum of viruses (Hull and Tritch, 1962). A combination of criteria in most cases offers the most efficient means of validating species labels as Defendi, Billingham, Silvers, and Moorhead (1960) showed in tests with 11 different cell strains. These were compared individually with respect to morphology, sensitivity to antisera prepared against nucleoproteins, detectable transplantation antigens, susceptibility to polio virus, and chromosome patterns. Particular criteria differed in usefulness for characterizing cell strains, but the over-all profiles for each population were distinctive. Further classifications of this kind are undoubtedly valuable, but it is fair to say that the only satisfactory method in the long run for securing the identity of stock strains lies in the use of genetic markers. Where such labels are sufficiently individualized and can be employed in combination, the identity of the cell lines becomes clear and unmistakable.

Although permanent cell lines may be labeled with unique chromosomes (Chapter 4), and it is possible to incorporate such characteristics as drug resistance into these strains (Chapter 6), naturally occurring markers within cell lines are particularly useful. The presence or absence of specific enzymes, for example, may often be determined with precision in isolated populations. Some chromogenic reactions for enzymes may even be applied to the detection and isolation of variants on a clonal basis (Maio and de Carli, 1962b). In a few cases, unique materials are available directly from human patients or animals with inherited metabolic deficiencies. Thus, cells from galactosemic individuals (who are unable to utilize galactose normally) can be shown to lack the enzyme galactose-1-phosphate uridyl transferase, which is otherwise found in human tissues (Krooth and Weinberg, 1961). Similarly, skin biopsies from acatalasic patients give cultures without detectable catalase (Krooth, Howell, and Hamilton, 1962), and cells originating from individuals known to be deficient in, or heterozygous for, variant patterns of glucose-6-phosphate dehydrogenase reflect the corresponding patterns *in vitro* (Gartler, Gandini, and Ceppellini, 1962; Davidson, Nitowsky, and Childs, 1963). These markers offer a valuable series of unit characters for broader investigations of cellular change.

There is an additional practical matter that needs mention, since it may affect the properties of cell lineages in subtle fashion. This is the prevalence of pleuropneumonia-like organisms (PPLO) as infections in stock cell strains (see Parker, 1961; Coriell, 1962; Barile, Malizia, and Riggs, 1962). Such organisms are tiny, soft forms without a cell wall, like the *L* phases of certain bacteria. PPLO can accordingly pass through ordinary sterility filters. They are difficult to cultivate on ordinary test media, and may frequently pass unnoticed. Contaminations with PPLO do not necessarily cause growth disturbances, but their presence cannot be ignored. The presence of PPLO may cause confusion in the antigenic characterizations of cell lines, for example. Similarly, artifacts can arise in physiological studies that represent microbial activity rather than that of the host cell. Paradoxically, the rise of PPLO infections in cell strains can be correlated with the routine use of antibiotics in the culture medium. Contaminations are not ordinarily observed in freshly isolated cells, and they rarely appear if populations are maintained serially in the absence of antimicrobial agents. The explanation for this phenomenon may lie in a close affinity between PPLO and *L* forms, and this controversial area is still poorly defined (see Klieneberger-Nobel, 1962). However, penicillin is known to induce regularly the appearance of *L* forms in some bacteria, and although reversion to the more typical bacterial phase commonly occurs, stable *L* forms have also been produced. Experimentally, the latter are difficult to distinguish from PPLO. It has in fact been suggested that the contaminants observed in cell lines may in the main arise from bacteria, under the induction and selection pressure of penicillin or other antibiotics in the culture medium (see Barile, Malizia, and Riggs, 1962). PPLO or L forms can in some instances be eliminated from cell lines by treatment with heat, specific antiserum, or agents such as kanamycin. Preferably, these contaminants are to be avoided by the omission of antibiotics from the culture environment (Coriell, 1962).

■ References

ABERCROMBIE, M. 1961. The bases of locomotory behavior of fibroblasts. Exptl. Cell Res., Suppl., **8**: 188–198.

ABERCROMBIE, M., and AMBROSE, E. J. 1958. Interference microscope studies of cell contacts in tissue culture. Exptl. Cell Res., **15**: 332–345.

ABERCROMBIE, M., and HEAYSMAN, J. E. M. 1954. Observations on the social behavior of cells in tissue culture. II. "Monolayering" of fibroblasts. Exptl. Cell Res., **6**: 293–306.

ALGARD, F. T. 1960. Hormone-induced tumors. I. Hamster flank-organ and kidney tumors *in vitro*. J. Natl. Cancer Inst., **25**: 557–571.

ANG, B., JAROSS, L., and McALLISTER, R. M. 1962. Studies of fibroblast-like cells from the bone marrow of leukemic and nonleukemic children. Proc. Soc. Exptl. Biol. Med., **109**: 467–471.

ANSEVIN, K. D., and BUCHSBAUM, R. 1962. Capacity for histological reconstruction by mouse kidney cells in relation to age. J. Gerontol., **17**: 130–137.

AUERBACH, R., and GROBSTEIN, C. 1958. Inductive interaction of embryonic tissues after dissociation and reaggregation. Exptl. Cell Res., **15**: 384–397.

BARILE, M. F., MALIZIA, W. F., and RIGGS, D. B. 1962. Incidence and detection of pleuropneumonia-like organisms in cell cultures by fluorescent antibody and cultural procedures. J. Bact., **84**: 130–136.

BERG, R. B., and ROSENTHAL, M. S. 1961. Studies of fibroblastic cells cultivated from bone marrow of leukemic and non-leukemic patients. Proc. Soc. Exptl. Biol. Med., **106**: 614–617.

BERMAN, L., and STULBERG, C. S. 1956. Eight culture strains (Detroit) of human epithelial-like cells. Proc. Soc. Exptl. Biol. Med., **92**: 730–735.

BERMAN, L., and STULBERG, C. S. 1958. The Detroit strains of human epithelial-like cells from non-leukemic peripheral blood. Blood, **13**: 1149–1167.

BERMAN, L., STULBERG, C. S., and RUDDLE, F. H. 1955. I. Report of isolation of a strain of cells resembling epithelial cells from bone marrow of a patient with carcinoma of the lung. Blood, **10**: 896–911.

BERMAN, L., STULBERG, C. S., and RUDDLE, F. H. 1957. Human cell culture. Morphology of the Detroit strains. Cancer Res., **17**: 668–676.

BILLINGHAM, R. E., and MEDAWAR, P. B. 1952. The freezing, drying, and storage of mammalian skin. J. Exptl. Biol., **29**: 454–468.

BLOOM, W. 1937. Cellular differentiation and tissue culture. Physiol. Revs., 17: 589–617.

BORGHESE, E. 1958. Organ differentiation in culture. *In: A Symposium on the Chemical Basis of Development*, pp. 704-773. W. D. McElroy and B. Glass, eds. Baltimore: The John Hopkins Press.

BRAND, K. G. 1962. Persistence and stability of species-specific haemagglutinogens in cultivated mammalian cells. Nature, 194: 752–754.

BRAND, K. G., and SYVERTON, J. T. 1960. Immunology of cultivated mammalian cells. I. Species specificity determined by hemagglutination. J. Natl. Cancer Inst., 24: 1007–1019.

BRAND, K. G., and SYVERTON, J. T. 1962. Results of species-specific hemagglutination tests on "transformed," nontransformed, and primary cell cultures. J. Natl. Cancer Inst., 28: 147–157.

BREEDIS, C. 1942. The action of extreme cold on leukemic cells of mice. J. Exptl. Med., 76: 221–240.

BREEDIS, C., and FURTH, J. 1938. The feasibility of preserving neoplastic cells in the frozen state. Science, 88: 531–532.

BURKHALTER, A., JONES, M., and FEATHERSTONE, R. M. 1957. Acetylcholine-cholinesterase relationships in embryonic chick lung cultivated *in vitro*. Proc. Soc. Exptl. Biol. Med., 96: 747–750.

BURLINGTON, H. 1959. Enzyme patterns in cultured kidney cells. Am. J. Physiol., 197: 68–70.

BURROWS, H. J. 1933. The intercellular product of a pure culture of osteogenic cells *in vitro*. Arch. exptl. Zellforsch. Gewebezücht., 14: 202–209.

CANN, H. M., and HERZENBERG, L. A. 1963a. *In vitro* studies of mammalian somatic cell variation. I. Detection of H-2 phenotype in cultured mouse cell lines. J. Exptl. Med., 117: 259–265.

CANN, H. M., and HERZENBERG, L. A. 1963b. *In vitro* studies of mammalian somatic cell variation. II. Isoimmune cytotoxicity with a cultured mouse lymphoma and selection of resistant variants. J. Exptl. Med., 117: 267–284.

CARREL, A. 1912. On the permanent life of tissues outside of the organism. J. Exptl. Med., 15: 516–528.

CARREL, A. 1914. Present condition of a strain of connective tissue twenty-eight months old. J. Exptl. Med., 20: 1–2.

CARREL, A. 1924. Tissue culture and cell physiology. Physiol. Revs., 4: 1–20.

CARREL, A., and EBELING, A. H. 1922. Pure cultures of large mononuclear leucocytes. J. Exptl. Med., 36: 365–378.

CASTOR, C. W., PRINCE, R. K., and DORSTEWITZ, E. L. 1961. "Epithelial transformation" of human synovial connective tissue cells: Cytologic and biochemical consequences. Proc. Soc. Exptl. Biol. Med., 108: 574–578.

CASTOR, C. W., PRINCE, R. K., and DORSTEWITZ, E. L. 1962. Characteristics of human "fibroblasts" cultivated *in vitro* from different anatomical sites. Lab. Invest., 11: 703–713.

CHAMPY, C. 1912. Sur les phénomènes cytologiques qui s'observent dans les tissus cultivés en dehors de l'organisme. Compt. Rend. Soc. Biol., **72**: 987–988.

CHANG, R. S. 1954. Continuous subcultivation of epithelial-like cells from normal human tissues. Proc. Soc. Exptl. Biol. Med., **87**: 440–443.

CHEN, J. M. 1954. The cultivation in fluid medium of organized liver, pancreas and other tissues of foetal rats. Exptl. Cell Res., **7**: 518–529.

COHEN, E. P., and EAGLE, H. 1961. A simplified chemostat for the growth of mammalian cells: Characteristics of cell growth in continuous culture. J. Exptl. Med., **113**: 467–474.

COOMBS, R. R. A. 1962. Identification and characterization of cells by immunologic analysis, with special reference to mixed agglutination. Nat. Cancer Inst. Monogr., **7**: 91–103.

COOMBS, R. R. A., BEDFORD, D., and ROUILLARD, L. M. 1956. A and B blood group antigens on human epidermal cells demonstrated by mixed agglutination. Lancet, **270**: 461–463.

COOMBS, R. R. A., DANIEL, M. R., GURNER, B. W., and KELUS, A. 1961a. Recognition of the species of origin of cells in culture by mixed agglutination. I. Use of antisera to red cells. Immunology, **4**: 55–56.

COOMBS, R. R. A., DANIEL, M. R., GURNER, B. W., and KELUS, A. 1961b. Species-characterizing antigens of "L" and "ERK" cells. Nature, **189**: 503–504.

CORIELL, L. L. 1962. Detection and elimination of contaminating organisms. Natl. Cancer Inst. Monogr., **7**: 33–53.

COX, R. P., and MACLEOD, C. M. 1961. Hormonal induction of alkaline phosphatase in human cells in tissue culture. Nature, **190**: 85–87.

COX, R. P., and MACLEOD, C. M. 1962. Alkaline phosphatase content and the effects of prednisolone on mammalian cells in tissue culture. J. Gen. Physiol., **45**: 439–485.

COX, R. P., and MACLEOD, C. M. 1963. Repression of alkaline phosphatase in human cell cultures by cystine and cysteine. Proc. Natl. Acad. Sci., **49**: 504–510.

COX, R. P., and PONTECORVO, G. 1961. Induction of alkaline phosphatase by substrates in established cultures of cells from individual human donors. Proc. Natl. Acad. Sci., **47**: 839–845.

DAVIDSON, R. G., NITOWSKY, H. M., and CHILDS, B. 1963. Demonstration of two populations of cells in the human female heterozygous for glucose-6-phosphate dehydrogenase variants. Proc. Natl. Acad. Sci., **50**: 481–485.

DAY, M., and GREEN, J. P. 1962. The uptake of amino acids and the synthesis of amines by neoplastic mast cells in culture. J. Physiol., **164**: 210–226.

DEFENDI, V., BILLINGHAM, R. E., SILVERS, W. K., and MOORHEAD, P. 1960. Immunological and karyological criteria for identification of cell lines. J. Natl. Cancer Inst., **25**: 359–386.

DEMARS, R. 1958. The inhibition by glutamine of glutamyl transferase formation in cultures of human cells. Biochim. et Biophys. Acta, **27**: 435–436.

DOLJANSKI, L. 1930. Sur le rapport entre la prolifération et l'activité pigmentogène dans les cultures d'épithélium de l'iris. Compt. Rend. Soc. Biol., **105**: 343–345.

DOUGHERTY, R. M. 1962. Use of dimethyl sulphoxide for preservation of tissue culture cells by freezing. Nature, **193**: 550–552.

DULBECCO, R. 1952. Production of plaques in monolayer tissue cultures by single particles of an animal virus. Proc. Natl. Acad. Sci., **38**: 747–752.

EAGLE, H. 1955. Propagation in a fluid medium of a human epidermoid carcinoma, strain KB. Proc. Soc. Exptl. Biol. Med., **89**: 362–364.

EARLE, W. R. 1943. Changes induced in a strain of fibroblasts from a strain C₃H mouse by the action of 20-methylcholanthrene. (Preliminary report). J. Natl. Cancer Inst., **3**: 555–558.

EARLE, W. R., BRYANT, J. C., SCHILLING, E. L., and EVANS, V. J. 1956. Growth of cell suspensions in tissue culture. Ann. N. Y. Acad. Sci., **63**: 666–682.

EBELING, A. H. 1913. The permanent life of connective tissue outside of the organism. J. Exptl. Med., **17**: 237–285.

EBELING, A. H. 1922. A ten year old strain of fibroblasts. J. Exptl. Med., **35**: 755–759.

EBELING, A. H. 1924. Cultures pures d'épithélium proliférant *in vitro* depuis dix-huit mois. Compt. Rend. Soc. Biol., **90**: 562–563.

EBELING, A. H. 1925. A pure strain of thyroid cells and its characteristics. J. Exptl. Med., **41**: 337–346.

EBNER, K. E., HAGEMAN, E. C., and LARSON, B. L. 1961. Functional biochemical changes in bovine mammary cell cultures. Exptl. Cell Res., **25**: 555–570.

EPHRUSSI, B. 1953. Nucleo-cytoplasmic relations in micro-organisms. Oxford: Clarendon Press. 127 pp.

EVANS, V. J., and EARLE, W. R. 1947. The use of perforated cellophane for the growth of cells in tissue culture. J. Natl. Cancer Inst., **8**: 103–119.

EVANS, V. J., EARLE, W. R., SANFORD, K. K., SHANNON, J. E., and WALTZ, H. K. 1951. The preparation and handling of replicate tissue cultures for quantitative studies. J. Natl. Cancer Inst., **11**: 907–927.

EVANS, V. J., BRYANT, J. C., McQUILKIN, W. T., FIORAMONTI, M. C., SANFORD, K. K., WESTFALL, B. B., and EARLE, W. R. 1956. Studies of nutrient media for tissue cells *in vitro*. II. An improved protein-free chemically defined medium for long-term cultivation of Strain L-929 cells. Cancer Res., **16**: 87–94.

EVANS, V. J., deOCA, H. M., BRYANT, J. C., SCHILLING, E. L., and SHANNON, J. E. 1962. Recovery from liquid-nitrogen temperature of established cell lines frozen in chemically defined medium. J. Natl. Cancer Inst., **29**: 749–757.

FELL, H. B. 1951. Histogenesis in tissue culture. *In: Cytology and Cell Physiology*, pp. 419–443. G. H. Bourne, ed. Oxford: Clarendon Press.

FELL, H. B. 1956. Skeletal development in tissue culture. *In: The Biochemistry and Physiology of Bone*, pp. 401–441. G. H. Bourne, ed. New York: Academic Press Inc.

FELL, H. B., and ROBISON, R. 1929. The growth, development and phosphatase activity of embryonic avian femora and limb-buds cultivated *in vitro*. Biochem. J., **23**: 767–784.

FERGUSON, J., and WANSBROUGH, A. 1962. Isolation and long-term culture of diploid mammalian cell lines. Cancer Res., **22**: 556–562.

FISCHER, A. 1922. A three months old strain of epithelium. J. Exptl. Med., **35**: 367–372.

FISCHER, A. 1930. Gewebezüchtung. Munich: Müller and Steinecke. 661 pp.

FISCHER, A. 1946. Biology of tissue cells. New York: Hafner Publishing Company. 348 pp.

FISCHER, A., and PARKER, R. C. 1929. Proliferation und Differenzierung. Arch. exptl. Zellforsch. Gewebezücht., **8**: 297–324.

FISCHER, I. 1938. Die Pigmentbildung des Irisepithels *in Vitro*. Ein Beitrag zu den Beziehungen zwischen Differenzierung, Wachstum, und Funktion. Arch. exptl. Zellforsch. Gewebezücht., **21**: 92–154.

FOGH, J. 1961. Transformation of cultured human amnion cells. Path. et Biol. (Paris), **9**: 559–568.

FOGH, J., and EDWARDS, G. A. 1959. Ultrastructure of primary culture amnion cells and transformed FL cells in continuous culture. J. Natl. Cancer Inst., **23**: 893–923.

FOGH, J., and LUND, R. O. 1957. Continuous cultivation of epithelial cell strain (FL) from human amniotic membrane. Proc. Soc. Exptl. Biol. Med., **94**: 532–537.

FOLEY, G. E., DROLET, B. P., McCARTHY, R. E., GOULET, K. A., DOKOS, J. M., and FILLER, D. A. 1960. Isolation and serial propagation of malignant and normal cells in semi-defined media: Origins of CCRF cell lines. Cancer Res., **20**: 930–939.

FOLEY, G. E., HANDLER, A. H., ADAMS, R. A., and CRAIG, J. M. 1962. Assessment of potential malignancy of cultured cells: further observations on the differentiation of "normal" and "neoplastic" cells maintained *in vitro* by heterotransplantation in Syrian hamsters. Natl. Cancer Inst. Monogr., **7**: 173–204.

FORD, D. K., and YERGANIAN, G. 1958. Observations on the chromosomes of Chinese hamster cells in tissue culture. J. Natl. Cancer Inst., **21**: 393–425.

FRANKS, L. M., and BARTON, A. A. 1960. Effects of testosterone on the ultrastructure of the mouse prostate *in vivo* and in organ cultures. Exptl. Cell Res., **19**: 35–50.

GARTLER, S. M., GANDINI, E., and CEPPELLINI, R. 1962. Glucose-6-phosphate dehydrogenase deficient mutant in human cell culture. Nature, **193**: 602–603.

GEY, G. O. 1955. Some aspects of the constitution and behavior of normal and malignant cells maintained in continuous culture. Harvey Lectures, **50**: 154–229. New York: Academic Press Inc.

GEY, G. O., COFFMAN, W. D., and KUBICEK, M. T. 1952. Tissue culture studies of the proliferative capacity of cervical carcinoma and normal epithelium. Cancer Res., **12**: 264–265.

GOLDSTEIN, M. N., and HAVAS, E. 1960. Routine development of permanent strains of fibroblasts from bone marrow of adult rabbits. Proc. Soc. Exptl. Biol. Med., **104**: 75–77.

GREENSTEIN, J. P. 1954. Biochemistry of cancer. Second edition. New York: Academic Press Inc. 653 pp.

GROBSTEIN, C. 1959. Differentiation of vertebrate cells. In: The Cell. Biochemistry, Physiology, Morphology, Vol. 1, pp. 437–496. J. Brachet and A. E. Mirsky, eds. New York: Academic Press Inc.

GROBSTEIN, C. 1962. Levels and ontogeny. Am. Scientist, **50**: 46–58.

HARRIS, M. 1948. Specificity and mode of action of cytotoxins produced against alien transplants in rats. J. Exptl. Zool., **107**: 439–454.

HARRIS, M. 1957. Quantitative growth studies with chick myoblasts in glass substrate cultures. Growth, **21**: 149–166.

HARRIS, M. 1959. Growth measurements on monolayer cultures with an electronic cell counter. Cancer Res., **19**: 1020–1024.

HARRISON, R. G. 1907. Observations on the living developing nerve fiber. Proc. Soc. Exptl. Biol. Med., **4**: 140–143.

HAUSCHKA, T. S., MITCHELL, J. T., and NIEDERPRUEM, D. J. 1959. A reliable frozen tissue bank: viability and stability of 82 neoplastic and normal cell types after prolonged storage at −78°C. Cancer Res., **19**: 643–653.

HAYFLICK, L. 1961. The establishment of a line (WISH) of human amnion cells in continuous cultivation. Exptl. Cell Res., **23**: 14–20.

HAYFLICK, L. 1962. Cell lines from non-neoplastic tissue. In: Growth, including Reproduction and Morphological Development, pp. 156–160. P. L. Altman and D. S. Dittmer, eds. Washington, D.C.: Federation of American Societies for Experimental Biology.

HAYFLICK, L., and MOORHEAD, P. S. 1961. The serial cultivation of human diploid cell strains. Exptl. Cell Res., **25**: 585–621.

HERZENBERG, L. A. 1962. I. Steps toward a genetics of somatic cells in culture. II. Maternal isoimmunization as a result of breeding in the mouse. J. Cellular Comp. Physiol., **60**(Suppl. 1): 145–157.

HILFER, S. R. 1962. The stability of embryonic chick thyroid cells in vitro as judged by morphological and physiological criteria. Dev. Biol., **4**: 1–21.

HOLTFRETER, J. 1939. Gewebeaffinität, ein Mittel der embryonalen Formbildung. Arch. exptl. Zellforsch. Gewebezücht., **23**: 169–209.

HOLTFRETER, J. 1944. Experimental studies on the development of the pronephros. Rev. Can. Biol., **3**: 220–250.

HOLTZER, H. 1961. Aspects of chondrogenesis and myogenesis. In: Synthesis of Molecular and Cellular Structure, pp. 35–87. D. Rudnick, ed. New York: The Ronald Press Company.

HOLTZER, H., ABBOTT, J., LASH, J., and HOLTZER, S. 1960. The loss of phenotypic traits by differentiated cells in vitro. I. Dedifferentiation of cartilage cells. Proc. Natl. Acad. Sci., **46**: 1533–1542.

HOLTZER, H., and HOLTZER, S. 1960. The in vitro uptake of fluorescein labelled plasma proteins. I. Mature cells. Compt. Rend. Lab. Carlsberg, **31**: 373–408.

Hsu, T. C., and Klatt, O. 1958. Mammalian chromosomes *in vitro*. IX. On genetic polymorphism in cell populations. J. Natl. Cancer Inst., **21:** 437–473.

Hull, R. N., and Tritch, O. J. 1962. Characterization of cell strains by viral susceptibility. Natl. Cancer Inst. Monogr., **7:** 161–172.

Klein, E. 1960. On the substrate induced enzyme formation in animal cells cultured *in vitro*. Exptl. Cell Res., **21:** 421–429.

Klein, E. 1961. Studies on the substrate-induced arginase synthesis in animal cell strains cultured *in vitro*. Exptl. Cell Res., **22:** 226–232.

Klieneberger-Nobel, E. 1962. Pleuropneumonia-like organisms (PPLO). New York: Academic Press Inc. 157 pp.

Knox, W. E. 1961. The adaptive control of enzyme activity in animals. *In: Synthesis of Molecular and Cellular Structure*, pp. 13–33. D. Rudnick, ed. New York: The Ronald Press Company.

Knox, W. E., Auerbach, V. H., and Lin, E. C. C. 1956. Enzymatic and metabolic adaptations in animals. Physiol. Revs., **36:** 164–254.

Konigsberg, I. R. 1963. Clonal analysis of myogenesis. Science, **140:** 1273–1284.

Krohn, P. L. 1962. Review lectures on senescence. II. Heterochronic transplantation in the study of aging. Proc. Roy. Soc. (London) Ser. B., **157:** 128–147.

Krooth, R. S., Howell, R. R., and Hamilton, H. B. 1962. Properties of acatalasic cells growing *in vitro*. J. Exptl. Med., **115:** 313–327.

Krooth, R. S., and Weinberg, A. N. 1961. Studies of cell lines developed from the tissues of patients with galactosemia. J. Exptl. Med., **113:** 1155–1171.

Kuroda, Y. 1963. Changes in aggregation and differentiation of cartilage cells grown in monolayer cultures. Exptl. Cell Res., **30:** 446–448.

Kutsky, R. J. 1953. Stimulating effect of nucleoprotein fraction of chick embryo extract on homologous heart fibroblasts. Proc. Soc. Exptl. Biol. Med., **83:** 390–395.

Kutsky, R. J., and Harris, M. 1957. Effects of nucleoprotein fractions from adult and juvenile tissues on growth of chick fibroblasts in plasma cultures. Growth, **21:** 53–72.

Leighton, J., Kline, I., and Orr, H. C. 1956. Transformation of normal human fibroblasts into histologically malignant tissue *in vitro*. Science, **123:** 502–503.

Levintow, L., and Eagle, H. 1961. Biochemistry of cultured mammalian cells. Ann. Rev. Biochem., **30:** 605–640.

Lieberman, I. 1957. The mechanism of the specific depression of an enzyme activity in cells in tissue culture. J. Biol. Chem., **225:** 883–898.

Lieberman, I., and Ove, P. 1958. Enzyme activity levels in mammalian cell cultures. J. Biol. Chem., **233:** 634–636.

Likely, G. D., Sanford, K. K., and Earle, W. R. 1952. Further studies on the proliferation *in vitro* of single isolated tissue cells. J. Natl. Cancer Inst., **13:** 177–184.

LOVELOCK, J. E., 1953. The mechanism of the protective action of glycerol against hemolysis by freezing and thawing. Biochim. et Biophys. Acta, 11: 28–36.

LUYET, B. J., and GEHENIO, P. M. 1940. Life and death at low temperatures. Normandy, Missouri: Biodynamica. 341 pp.

LWOFF, A., DULBECCO, R., VOGT, M., and LWOFF, M. 1955. Kinetics of the release of poliomyelitis virus from single cells. Virology, 1: 128–139.

MADIN, S. H. 1959. Tissue culture in veterinary medical research. Adv. Vet. Sci., 5: 329–417.

MADIN, S. H., and DARBY, N. J., JR. 1958. Established kidney cell lines of normal adult bovine and ovine origin. Proc. Soc. Exptl. Biol. Med., 98: 574–576.

MAIO, J. J. and DE CARLI, L. L. 1962a. Distribution of alkaline phosphatase variants in a heteroploid strain of human cells in tissue culture. Nature, 196: 600–601.

MAIO, J. J., and DE CARLI, L. L. 1962b. The use of chromogenic reactions for the study of enzymic markers in populations of mammalian cells cultured *in vitro*. Cytogenetics, 1: 353–361.

MARCUS, P. I., CIECIURA, S. J., and PUCK, T. T. 1956. Clonal growth *in vitro* of epithelial cells from normal human tissues. J. Exptl. Med., 104: 615–628.

MAZUR, P. 1962. Mechanisms of injury at subzero temperatures. Natl. Cancer Inst. Monogr., 7: 13–15.

McLIMANS, W. F., DAVIS, E. V., GLOVER, F. L., and RAKE, G. W. 1957. The submerged culture of mammalian cells: The spinner culture. J. Immunol., 79: 428–433.

MELNYKOVYCH, G. 1962. Effect of corticosteroids on the formation of alkaline phosphatase in HeLa Cells. Biochem. et Biophys. Res. Comm., 8: 81–86.

MERCHANT, D. J., KAHN, R. H., and MURPHY, W. H., JR. 1960. Handbook of cell and organ culture. Minneapolis: Burgess Publishing Co. 188 pp.

MERCHANT, D. J., KUCHLER, R. J., and MUNYON, W. H. 1960. Population dynamics in suspension cultures of an animal cell strain. J. Bioch. Microbiol. Technol. Eng., 2: 253–265.

MERYMAN, H. T. 1960. General principles of freezing and freezing injury in cellular materials. Ann. N. Y. Acad. Sci., 85: 503–509.

MERYMAN, H. T. 1962. Freezing of living cells: biophysical considerations. Natl. Cancer Inst. Monogr., 7: 7–15.

MERYMAN, H. T. 1963. Preservation of living cells. Federation Proc., 22: 81–89.

MOEN, J. K. 1935. The development of pure cultures of fibroblasts from single, mononuclear cells. J. Exptl. Med., 61: 247–260.

MOLINE, S. W. 1962. The low-temperature preservation of tissue and cell cultures. Technical Bulletin F-1649. New York: Linde Company (Division of Union Carbide Corporation). 9 pp.

MOORE, A. E., SABACHEWSKY, L., and TOOLAN, H. W. 1955. Culture characteristics of four permanent lines of human cancer cells. Cancer Res., **15:** 598–602.

MORRIS, C. C. 1962. Maintenance and loss in tissue culture of specific cell characteristics. Adv. Appl. Microbiol., **4:** 117–212.

MOSCONA, A. 1952. Cell suspensions from organ rudiments of chick embryos. Exptl. Cell Res., **3:** 535–539.

MOSCONA, A. 1956. Development of heterotypic combinations of dissociated embryonic chick cells. Proc. Soc. Exptl. Biol. Med., **92:** 410–416.

MOSCONA, A. 1957. The development *in vitro* of chimeric aggregates of dissociated embryonic chick and mouse cells. Proc. Natl. Acad. Sci., **43:** 184–194.

MOSCONA, A. 1959. Tissues from dissociated cells. Sci. Am., **200:** 132–144.

MOSCONA, A. 1960. Patterns and mechanisms of tissue reconstruction from dissociated cells. *In: Developing Cell Systems and Their Control,* pp. 45–70. D. Rudnick, ed. New York: The Ronald Press Company.

MOSCONA, A. 1961. Rotation-mediated histogenetic aggregation of dissociated cells. A quantifiable approach to cell interactions *in vitro.* Exptl. Cell Res., **22:** 455–475.

MOSCONA, A. 1962a. Analysis of cell recombinations in experimental synthesis of tissues *in vitro.* J. Cellular Comp. Physiol., **60** (Suppl. 1): 65–80.

MOSCONA, A. 1962b. Cellular interactions in experimental histogenesis. Int. Rev. Path., **1:** 371–428.

MOSCONA, A., and MOSCONA, H. 1952. The dissociation and aggregation of cells from organ rudiments of the early chick embryo. J. Anat. **86:** 287–301.

MOSER, H. 1960. Modern approaches to the study of mammalian cells in culture. Experientia, **16:** 385–398.

MURRAY, M. R. 1959. Recent advances of tissue culture in cancer research. Experientia, **15:** 289–294.

MURRAY, M. R., and KOPECH, G. 1953. A bibliography of the research in tissue culture (1884–1950). Vol. I and Vol. II. New York: Academic Press Inc. 1741 pp.

NAGINGTON, J., and GREAVES, R. I. N. 1962. Preservation of tissue culture cells with liquid nitrogen. Nature, **194:** 993–994.

NITOWSKY, H. M., and HERTZ, F. 1961. Alkaline phosphatase activity of human cell cultures. Proc. Soc. Exptl. Biol. Med., **107:** 532–534.

OSGOOD, E. E., and BROOKE, H. J. 1955. Continuous tissue culture of leukocytes from human leukemic bloods by application of "gradient" principles. Blood, **10:** 1010–1022.

OWENS, O. VON H., GEY, M. K., and GEY, G. O. 1954. Growth of cells in agitated fluid medium. Ann. N. Y. Acad. Sci., **58:** 1039–1055.

PARKER, R. C. 1933. The races that constitute the group of common fibroblasts. III. Differences determined by origin of explant and age of donor. J. Exptl. Med., **58:** 401–414.

PARKER, R. C. 1955. Cultivation of tumor cells *in vitro.* Canad. Canc. Conf., **1:** 42–54.

PARKER, R. C. 1958. Alterations in clonal populations of monkey kidney cells.

In: *Papers and Discussions Presented at the Fourth International Poliomyelitis Conference (Geneva)*, pp. 257–267. Philadelphia: J. P. Lippincott Company.

PARKER, R. C. 1961. Methods of tissue culture. Third edition. New York: Hoeber-Harper Inc. 358 pp.

PARKER, R. C., CASTOR, L. N., and McCULLOCH, E. A. 1957. Altered cell strains in continuous culture: A general survey. Spec. Publ. N. Y. Acad Sci., **5**: 303–313.

PARKES, A. S. 1945. Preservation of human spermatozoa at low temperatures. Brit. Med. J., **2**: 212–213.

PARSHLEY, M. S. 1959. Tissue culture of adult tissue. *In: Transplantation of Tissues*, Vol. 2, pp. 593–633. L. A. Peer, ed. Baltimore: The Williams and Wilkins Company.

PAUL, J. 1960. Cell and tissue culture. Second edition. Edinburgh: E. and S. Livingstone, Ltd. 312 pp.

PENSO, G., and BALDUCCI, D. 1963. Tissue cultures in biological research. Amsterdam: Elsevier Publishing Co. 468 pp.

POLGE, C., SMITH, A. U., and PARKES, A. S. 1949. A revival of spermatozoa after vitrification and dehydration at low temperatures. Nature, **164**: 666.

PORTERFIELD, J. S., and ASHWOOD-SMITH, M. J. 1962. Preservation of cells in tissue culture by glycerol and dimethyl sulphoxide. Nature, **193**: 548–550.

PUCK, T. T. 1958. Growth and genetics of somatic mammalian cells *in vitro*. J. Cellular Comp. Physiol., **52**(Suppl. 1): 287–311.

PUCK, T. T. 1959. Quantitative studies on mammalian cells *in vitro*. Rev. Mod. Phys., **31**: 433–448.

PUCK, T. T., CIECIURA, S. J., and FISHER, H. W. 1957. Clonal growth *in vitro* of human cells with fibroblastic morphology. Comparison of growth and genetic characteristics of single epithelioid and fibroblast-like cells from a variety of human organs. J. Exptl. Med., **106**: 145–158.

PUCK, T. T., CIERCIURA, S. J., and ROBINSON, A. 1958. Genetics of somatic mammalian cells. III. Long-term cultivation of euploid cells from human and animal subjects. J. Exptl. Med., **108**: 945–956.

PUCK, T. T., and MARCUS, P. I. 1955. A rapid method for viable cell titration and clone production with HeLa cells in tissue culture: The use of X-irradiated cells to supply conditioning factors. Proc. Natl. Acad. Sci., **41**: 432–437.

PUCK, T. T., MARCUS, P. I., and CIECIURA, S. J. 1956. Clonal growth of mammalian cells *in vitro*. Growth characteristics of colonies from single HeLa cells with and without a "feeder" layer. J. Exptl. Med., **103**: 273–284.

REUSSER, F., SMITH, C. G., and SMITH, C. L. 1962. Investigations on somatotropin production of human anterior pituitary cells in tissue culture. Proc. Soc. Exptl. Biol. Med., **109**: 375–378.

RINALDINI, L. M. J. 1958. The isolation of living cells from animal tissues. Intern. Rev. Cytol., **7**: 587–647.

ROSENBERG, M. D. 1960. Microexudates from cells grown in tissue culture. Biophys. J., **1**: 137–159.

Ross, J. D., and Syverton, J. T. 1957. Use of tissue cultures in virus research. Ann. Rev. Microbiol., 11: 459–508.

Ross, J. D., Treadwell, P. E., and Syverton, J. T. 1962. Cultural characterization of animal cells. Ann. Rev. Microbiol., 16: 141–188.

Rothfels, K. H., Axelrad, A. A., Siminovitch, L., McCulloch, E. A., and Parker, R. C. 1959. The origin of altered cell lines from mouse, monkey and man, as indicated by chromosome and transplantation studies. Canad. Canc. Conf., 3: 189–214.

Rothfels, K. H., Kupelwieser, E. B., and Parker, R. C. 1963. Effects of X-irradiated feeder layers on mitotic activity and development of aneuploidy in mouse-embryo cells *in vitro*. Canad. Canc. Conf. 5: 191–223. New York: Academic Press Inc.

Rothfels, K. H., and Parker, R. C. 1959. The karyotypes of cell lines recently established from normal mouse tissues. J. Exptl. Zool., 142: 507–520.

Rous, P., and Jones, F. S. 1916. A method for obtaining suspensions of living cells from the fixed tissues, and for the plating out of individual cells. J. Exptl. Med., 23: 549–555.

Ruddle, F. H. 1962. Morphological transformation in an established line of pig kidney cells. Proc. Soc. Exptl. Biol. Med., 109: 116–118.

Saksela, E., and Moorhead, P. S. 1963. Aneuploidy in the degenerative phase of serial cultivation of human cell strains. Proc. Natl. Acad. Sci., 50: 390–395.

Salk, J. E., and Ward, E. N. 1957. Some characteristics of a continuously propagating cell derived from monkey heart tissue. Science, 126: 1338–1339.

Salzman, N. P. 1961. Animal cell cultures. Science, 133: 1559–1565.

Sanford, K. K., Covalesky, A. B., Dupree, L. T., and Earle, W. R. 1961. Cloning of mammalian cells by a simplified capillary technique. Exptl. Cell Res., 23: 361–372.

Sanford, K. K., Earle, W. R., Evans, V. J., Waltz, H. K., and Shannon, J. E. 1951. The measurement of proliferation in tissue cultures by enumeration of cell nuclei. J. Natl. Cancer Inst., 11: 773–795.

Sanford, K. K., Earle, W. R., and Likely, G. D. 1948. The growth *in vitro* of single isolated tissue cells. J. Natl. Cancer Inst., 9: 229–246.

Sarachek, A., and Fowler, G. L. 1961. Induction of heritable respiratory deficiency in *Saccharomyces* by pantothenate starvation. Nature, 190: 792–794.

Sato, G., Zaroff, L., and Mills, S. E. 1960. Tissue culture populations and their relation to the tissue of origin. Proc. Natl. Acad. Sci., 46: 963–972.

Scherer, W. F., and Hoogasian, A. C. 1954. Preservation at subzero temperatures of mouse fibroblasts (Strain L) and human epithelial cells (Strain HeLa). Proc. Soc. Exptl. Biol. Med., 87: 480–487.

Scherer, W. F., Syverton, J. T., and Gey, G. O. 1953. Studies on the propagation *in vitro* of poliomyelitis viruses. IV. Viral multiplication in a stable strain of human malignant epithelial cells (Strain HeLa) derived from an epidermoid carcinoma of the cervix. J. Exptl. Med., 97: 695–709.

SCHIMKE, R. T. 1962. Repression of enzymes of arginine biosynthesis in mammalian tissue culture. Biochim. et Biophys. Acta, **62:** 599–601.

SCHINDLER, R., DAY, M., and FISCHER, G. A. 1959. Cultures of neoplastic mast cells and their synthesis of 5-hydroxytryptamine and histamine *in vitro.* Cancer Res., **19:** 47–51.

SHAFFER, B. M. 1956. The culture of organs from the embryonic chick on cellulose-acetate fabric. Exptl. Cell Research, **11:** 244–248.

SMITH, A. U. 1954. Effects of low temperatures on living cells and tissues. *In: Biological Applications of Freezing and Drying,* pp. 1–62. R. J. C. Harris, ed. New York: Academic Press Inc.

SONNEBORN, T. M. 1959. Kappa and related particles in *Paramecium.* Advan. Virus Res., **6:** 229–356.

STEINBERG, M. S. 1958. On the chemical bonds between animal cells. A mechanism for type-specific association. Am. Naturalist, **92:** 65–81.

STEINBERG, M. S. 1962a. On the mechanism of tissue reconstruction by dissociated cells. I. Population kinetics, differential adhesiveness, and the absence of directed migration. Proc. Natl. Acad. Sci., **48:** 1577–1582.

STEINBERG, M. S. 1962b. Mechanism of tissue reconstruction by dissociated cells. II. Time course of events. Science, **137:** 762–763.

STEINBERG, M. S. 1962c. On the mechanism of tissue reconstruction by dissociated cells. III. Free energy relations and the reorganization of fused, heteronomic tissue fragments. Proc. Natl. Acad. Sci., **48:** 1769–1776.

STEINBERG, M. S. 1963a. Reconstruction of tissues by dissociated cells. Science, **141:** 401–408.

STEINBERG, M. S. 1963b. ECM: Its nature, origin, and function in cell aggregation. Exptl. Cell Res., **30:** 257–279.

STOCKDALE, F. E., ABBOTT, J., HOLTZER, S., and HOLTZER, H. 1963. The loss of phenotypic traits by differentiated cells. II. Behavior of chondrocytes and their progeny *in vitro.* Dev. Biol., **7:** 293–302.

STRANGEWAYS, T. S. P. 1924. Tissue culture in relation to growth and differentiation. Cambridge: W. Heffer & Sons, Ltd. 50 pp.

STRANGEWAYS, T. S. P., and FELL, H. B. 1926a. Experimental studies on the differentiation of embryonic tissues growing *in vivo* and *in vitro.* I. The development of the undifferentiated limb-bud (a) when subcutaneously grafted into the post-embryonic chick and (b) when cultivated *in vitro.* Proc. Roy. Soc. (London) Ser. B., **99:** 340–366.

STRANGEWAYS, T. S. P., and FELL, H. B. 1926b. Experimental studies on the differentiation of embryonic tissues growing *in vivo* and *in vitro.* II. The development of the isolated early embryonic eye of the fowl when cultivated *in vitro.* Proc. Roy. Soc. (London) Ser. B., **100:** 273–283.

STULBERG, C. S., SIMPSON, W. F., and BERMAN, L. 1961. Species-related antigens of mammalian cell strains as determined by immunofluorescence. Proc. Soc. Exptl. Biol. Med., **108:** 434–439.

STULBERG, C. S., SOULE, H. D., and BERMAN, L. 1958. Preservation of human epithelial-like and fibroblast-like cell strains at low temperatures. Proc. Soc. Exptl. Biol. Med., **98:** 428–431.

Swim, H. E. 1959. Microbiological aspects of tissue culture. Ann. Rev. Microbiol., **13:** 141–176.

Swim, H. E., Haff, R. F., and Parker, R. F. 1958. Some practical aspects of storing mammalian cells in the dry-ice chest. Cancer Res., **18:** 711–717.

Swim, H. E., and Parker, R. F. 1957. Discussion: Cells in continuous culture. Spec. Publ. N. Y. Acad. Sci., **5:** 351–355.

Syverton, J. T. 1956. Cells in continuous culture for study of viruses. Am. J. Trop. Med. Hyg., **5:** 430–439.

Townes, P. L., and Holtfreter, J. 1955. Directed movements and selective adhesion of embryonic amphibian cells. J. Exptl. Zool., **128:** 53–120.

Trinkaus, J. P. 1956. The differentiation of tissue cells. Am. Nat., **90:** 273–289.

Trinkaus, J. P. 1961. Affinity relationships in heterotypic cell aggregates. *In: La Culture Organotypique. Associations et Dissociations d'Organes en Culture in Vitro*, pp. 209–226. Paris: Colloq. Intern. Centre Natl. Recherche Sci.

Trinkaus, J. P., and Groves, P. W. 1955. Differentiation in culture of mixed aggregates of dissociated tissue cells. Proc. Natl. Acad. Sci., **41:** 787–795.

Waltz, H. K., Tullner, W. W., Evans, V. J., Hertz, R., and Earle, W. R. 1954. Gonadotrophic hormone secretion from hydatid mole grown in tissue culture. J. Natl. Cancer Inst., **14:** 1173–1185.

Weiss, P. 1939. Principles of development. New York: Holt, Rinehart and Winston, Inc. 601 pp.

Weiss, P. 1945. Experiments on cell and axon orientation *in vitro:* the role of colloidal exudates in tissue organiztion. J. Exptl. Zool., **100:** 353–386.

Weiss, P. 1949. Differential growth. *In: The Chemistry and Physiology of Growth*, pp. 135–186. A. K. Parpart, ed. Princeton, N.J.: Princeton University Press.

Weiss, P. 1950. Perspectives in the field of morphogenesis. Quart. Rev. Biol., **25:** 177–198.

Weiss, P. 1958. Cell contact. Intern. Rev. Cytol., **7:** 391–423.

Weiss, P. 1961. Guiding principles in cell locomotion and cell aggregation. Exptl. Cell Res., Suppl. **8:** 260–281.

Westwood, J. C. N., Macpherson, I. A., and Titmuss, D. H. J. 1957. Transformation of normal cells in tissue culture: its significance relative to malignancy and virus vaccine production. Brit. J. Exptl. Path., **38:** 138–154.

White, P. R. 1963. The cultivation of animal and plant cells. Second edition. New York: The Ronald Press Company. 246 pp.

Whittaker, J. R. 1963. Changes in melanogenesis during the dedifferentiation of chick retinal pigment cells in cell culture. Dev. Biol., **8:** 99–127.

Wildy, P., and Stoker, M. 1958. Multiplication of solitary HeLa cells. Nature, **181:** 1407–1408.

Willmer, E. N. 1958. Tissue culture. Third edition. London: Methuen and Co., Ltd. 191 pp.

Willmer, E. N. 1960. Cytology and evolution. New York: Academic Press Inc. 430 pp.

WILSON, H. V. 1907. On some phenomena of coalescence and regeneration in sponges. J. Exptl. Zool., **5**: 245–258.

WILSON, H. V. 1911. On the behavior of the dissociated cells in hydroids, *Alcyonaria*, and *Asterias*. J. Exptl. Zool., **11**: 281–338.

WOLFF, E. 1954. Potentialités et affinités des tissus, révélées par la culture *in vitro* d'organes en associations hétérogènes et xénoplastiques. Bull. Soc. Zool. de France, **79**: 357–468.

WOLFF, E., and HAFFEN, K. 1952. Sur une methode de culture d'organes embryonnaires *"in vitro."* Texas Repts. Biol. Med., **10**: 463–472.

ZAROFF, L., SATO, G., and MILLS, S. E. 1961. Single-cell platings from freshly isolated mammalian tissue. Exptl. Cell Res., **23**: 565–575.

ZITCER, E. M., and DUNNEBACKE, T. H. 1957. Transformation of cells from the normal human amnion into established strains. Cancer Res., **17**: 1047–1053.

ZITCER, E. M., FOGH, J., and DUNNEBACKE, T. H. 1955. Human amnion cells for large-scale production of polio virus. Science, **122**: 30.

Variation in
chromosome
patterns

chapter

4

Chromosomes offer a tangible expression of the information systems within cells, and conventional genetic studies show that karyotypic alterations may be reflected in phenotypic change. The examination of chromosomal patterns in isolated cell populations thus assumes obvious significance as a potential indicator of cytogenetic variation. Studies in this field have developed rapidly within the last few years. In the resulting flow of investigation, two quite different objectives can be recognized. One of these has been to define in precise terms the normal chromosome configurations of man and of other animals, and to identify karyotypic anomalies that may be associated with congenital abnormalities or other heritable defects. It is now well known, for example, that Mongolism is associated with the presence of an extra autosome in the human karyotype, giving a chromosome number of 47 instead of 46. Several other previously obscure conditions have similarly been linked with chromosome aberrations (see Stern, 1960; Hsu, 1963). A second focus in chromosome studies, and the principal theme in the discussion to follow, concerns the evolution of karyotype in isolated cell systems. Changes of this kind are regularly observed within tumors as well as among cell populations maintained in long-term culture. They have been the subject of detailed study and frequent comment in past years (see reviews by Levan, 1956c, 1959; Hauschka, 1957, 1958, 1961; Hsu, 1959a, 1961). Despite these efforts, the significance of karyotypic shifts within isolated cell populations is far from clear. Particularly intriguing is the parallelism between chromosomal remodeling within tumors *in vivo* and permanent cell strains *in vitro*. An analysis of these changes forms the subject matter of the succeeding sections.

196

METHODS FOR CHROMOSOME
ANALYSIS

In the definition of chromosome patterns, a series of technical advances have served to open the way effectively. With these methods, a degree of resolution can be achieved which scarcely seemed possible at an earlier period. Classical cytologists relied for the most part on cells within tissue sections for karyotypic studies. While adequate procedures for fixation and straining were available, the closely arrayed chromosome groupings proved difficult to analyze. The degree of uncertainty in these pioneer investigations is symbolized by the fact that only recently was the true diploid number for human cells settled at 46 (Tjio and Levan, 1956a; Tjio and Puck, 1958b).

Among measures that contributed to a more precise definition of karyotype, the first was perhaps the adaptation of squash techniques to animal cells. Used initially by Heitz (1936) on plant materials, this method provides for the controlled flattening of dividing cells in order to position the chromosomes in a plane more favorable for observation. Squash procedures cannot be used to advantage on tissue sections, but the large, well-isolated cells of ascites tumors proved to be quite suitable for this method (Hauschka and Levan, 1951). Ascites cells have consequently been employed as material for numerous karyologic studies (Hauschka, 1953a, 1958; Hauschka and Levan, 1953; Levan, 1956c). When methods became available for the disaggregation of fresh tissues and the dispersion of cell populations in culture, squash techniques were extended to these systems and are now used widely (see Ford, 1962; Yerganian, 1963). With suitable care, it is possible to flatten and spread the chromosome complement at metaphase without rupturing the cell membrane. The loss of individual chromosomes can be controlled by counting intact, well-isolated cells. With some materials, excellent chromosome spreads can be prepared by a simple air-drying technique without recourse to mechanical pressure for flattening (Rothfels and Siminovitch, 1958; Tjio and Puck, 1958a; Moorhead, Nowell, Mellman, Battips, and Hungerford, 1960).

The study of chromosome patterns has also been facilitated by the introduction of pretreatments for the dispersion of individual units within chromosome groupings. The introduction of hypotonic saline for this purpose was a significant breakthrough (Hughes, 1952; Hsu and Pomerat, 1953). By immersing the cells in a solution of lowered osmotic pressure prior to squashing, marked swelling can be induced. Furthermore, spindle formation is disrupted. Thus the chromosomes do not become aligned in the equatorial plate, but remain instead widely scattered in the cytoplasm. As an additional aid in chromosome study, cultures can be exposed to colchicine or related compounds, which in appropriate dilution specifically block the formation of the spindle (Levan, 1954; Ford and Hamerton, 1956; Ford, 1962). By this means, it is possible to accumulate large numbers of dividing cells for subsequent analysis. Colchicine pretreatment also causes a marked condensation of chromosomes into compact rodlike structures, further aiding in the exact determination of chromosome number.

Several conventions have been adopted for the representation of chromosomal changes. Fluctuations in chromosome number can be conveniently indicated by using frequency distributions for metaphase cells in a representative sample. The histograms prepared from such data show the modal or most frequent chromosome number, also referred to as the stem line (see page 223). The degree of departure from this central tendency within the population is thus evident, together with the character of secondary modes, if any. Chromosome variation that involves structural rather than numerical changes is more readily shown by karyotypes. These depict the metaphase chromosomes of typical cells by drawings or photomicrographs rearranged into an arbitrary sequence for purposes of illustration. Each chromosome at this stage consists of a pair of chromatids connected by a centromere, which serves as a point of attachment to the division spindle. The centromere has a characteristic position within each chromosome, and this may have diagnostic value for the classification of groups within the total chromosome complement. Chromosomes with the centromere in an apparently terminal position are said to be telocentric, although in practice, it is difficult to distinguish these from subtelocentrics in which the short arms of the chromatids are merely inconspicuous. The latter are sometimes referred to under the heading acrocentric. By contrast, chromosomes with a medial or near-medial centromere may be defined as metacentric. These designations are convenient for recognition purposes, or as a means of characterizing structural rearrangements.

A number of terms are in general use to describe the chromosome set as a whole, and it may be well to clarify their respective meanings (see also Swanson, 1957). A distinction is often made, for example, between diploid and heteroploid states. The latter covers all departures from the diploid pattern, whether mediated by changes involving individual chromosomes or the whole set (that is, polyploidy). Alternatively, the terms euploid and aneuploid may be applied to cells or cell populations. Euploidy implies a balanced chromosome complement; thus, haploids, diploids, or any exact multiples thereof come under this definition. Aneuploid combinations arise whenever there are losses or gains of individual elements. If these changes can be referred to particular chromosomes within the normal karyotype, it may be possible to characterize variant cells as monosomic or trisomic for the unit in question. Where a more extensive degree of aneuploidy exists, it is often useful to indicate by appropriate designation the nearest euploid state. Thus, such words as subdiploid, hypertriploid, and hypotetraploid are permissible as descriptive terms. On the other hand, in dealing with aneuploid states that are exact multiples of a basic stem line, it may be desirable to avoid confusion with euploid values. In this case, the nonspecific terms low-ploid and high-ploid may be invoked (Harris and Ruddle, 1960).

The effectiveness of karyotypic analysis is a function both of chromosome number and morphology. Obviously, numerical changes are most readily detected when the total chromosome number is small. Structural modifications, on the other hand, can be identified only if there is an appreciable diversification in the appearance of individual units. The chromosomal patterns of various species differ greatly in their suitability for study in this light. The normal complement in mouse cells, for example, is 40; all the chromosomes are telocentric or acrocentric, and the intergradation in size is essentially continuous (Levan, Hsu, and Stich, 1962). Under these conditions, individual chromosomes cannot in general be identified as such. Karyotype analysis is thus limited to the detection of morphological variants (for example, newly appearing dicentric or metacentric chromosomes) or to changes in size distribution among the units of the chromosome set. In other species, the chromosomes are often more heteromorphic. One of the most favorable forms in this respect is the Chinese hamster (*Cricetulus griseus*). Cells from this animal offer material of choice for cytogenetic studies (Yerganian, 1952, 1959, 1963). There are only 11 pairs of chromosomes, and 5 of these show distinctive morphological features. Size differences are useful for comparisons of the remaining autosomes, whereas the sex chromosomes are dissimilar in appearance and serve as convenient markers. Diploid or near-diploid populations have been derived from the Chinese hamster in the form of cell strains (Yerganian and Leonard, 1961). These may be particularly useful for investigating the relations between karyotype and cellular phenotype.

AN INVENTORY OF KARYOTYPIC ALTERATIONS

The chromosome configurations of normal cells and tissues *in vivo* provide a standard of reference for assessing the changes that take place within isolated cell populations. In the past, constancy in chromosome patterns within the intact organism has generally been assumed, although substantial proof for uniformity was slow in forthcoming. A few investigators did not have this view, and some in fact reported extensive aneuploidy in human tissues, with wide fluctuations of chromosome number among individual cells (Timonen and Therman, 1950). There is now ample evidence, however, that these and similar claims from the older literature are erroneous, based on artifacts in technique. In more recent investigations with improved methods of analysis, the chromosome number of mammalian cells *in vivo* shows remarkably little variation. Typically, the mode is precisely defined at the diploid level, with no departures other than a small proportion of polyploid cells. The latter are more prominent in certain tissues, such as the rodent liver, where they constitute a substantial fraction of the cell population. True aneuploidy doubtless does arise occasionally through mitotic irregularities, but in general, the consistency of chromosome number within normal tissues is striking (Beatty, 1957; Levan, 1959; Hsu, 1959a, 1961, 1963). There is likewise little or no evidence that morphological variation occurs to any extent within the karyotype of normal cells *in situ*. Where individual members of the chromosome set can be distinguished, the size and appearance of particular units are highly reproducible. These generalizations, based on the study of cells and tissues taken directly from intact organisms, have been repeatedly confirmed and extended by observations on primary cell strains *in vitro* (Tjio and Puck, 1958a; Hayflick and Moorhead, 1961).

Changes in Chromosome Numbers   The karyotypes of tumors and of permanent cell strains present a striking contrast to the stable euploid patterns of normal tissues. These variant systems are for the most part clearly aneuploid, with modal values that depart significantly from the balanced euploid series. Moreover, there is an appreciable fluctuation around the mode, even in clonal populations, so that a histogram is necessary to depict population structure in terms of chromosome number.

This picture can be illustrated more specifically by the numerous chromosome studies that have been made on ascites tumors of mice and rats. One of the earliest of these to be investigated systematically was the Yoshida sarcoma of rats (Makino, 1952; Makino and Kanô, 1953). Smears made from such neoplasms show a broad spread of chromosome numbers in the cell population, centering at 40 chromosomes instead of the value of 42 typical of normal rat cells. Large V-shaped chromosomes are observed as a unique feature, apparently arising from the fusion of smaller units. Various neoplasms among a series of related tumors were found to share these features, although individual differences were found in the detailed karyotypic patterns. A more general survey was subsequently made (Makino, 1957), and it became evident that the features of any single tumor must be fitted into a broader spectrum of variation. Neoplasms within the rat, like other animals, can be found with modal numbers that range from diploid to tetraploid levels in individual cases.

These studies proceeded simultaneously with more extensive investigations on ascites tumor populations in mice. The data of Bayreuther (1952), Hauschka and Levan (1951, 1953), and Levan and Hauschka (1952) revealed chromosome numbers for selected strains in the neighborhood of diploid or tetraploid levels but with a much broader numerical fluctuation around the modal point than can be found in normal cell populations. A number of other karyotypic analyses were performed on mouse ascites tumor populations, and the findings are usefully summarized in several reviews (Levan, 1956c, 1958, 1959). Hyperdiploid or hypotetraploid modes are observed most frequently. However, neoplasms occur with intermediate numbers as well, and the gradation in a series of tumors is essentially continuous (see Figure 4.1). In some cases, the modal value coincides nominally with the diploid or tetraploid number. It is probable, however, that none of the tumors in this category are actually euploid. Mutually compensating additions, losses, deletions, or structural changes appear to have taken place in these instances, as later discussion will make clear.

The variant chromosome patterns of ascites populations, like their growth forms, might well be regarded as examples of neoplastic progression, and heteroploidy in general is a characteristic feature among tumors, especially those that have been transplanted serially (Levan, 1956c, 1959; Hauschka, 1958, 1961; Klein and Klein, 1959; Hsu, 1959a, 1961). It was more surprising to learn, however, that aneuploidy is equally prominent in permanent cell strains derived from nonneoplastic tissues. The unique configuration of these systems was first revealed by Levan (1956a), who examined two of the Chang lines isolated from normal human liver and conjunctiva, respectively. After two years in serial culture, both strains proved to have chromosome numbers ranging from 72 to 80. Numerically, the Chang lines could be termed hypertriploid, but Levan found that the total did not correspond to any multiple of the basic chromosome set. There were proportionately more

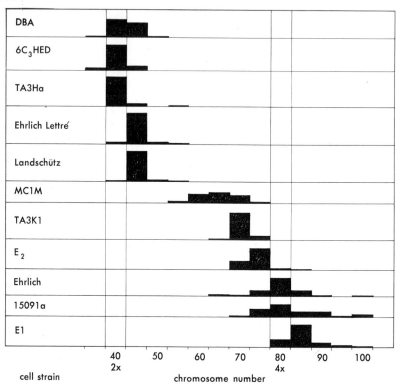

FIG. 4.1. Distribution of modal chromosome numbers in 11 mouse ascites tumors. Diploid and tetraploid levels are marked 2X and 4X, respectively. Only the stem-line region is shown for each tumor. (Redrawn from Levan, 1958.)

telocentric and subtelocentric chromosomes than in normal cells, an observation pointing to the occurrence of structural rearrangements. These observations were soon confirmed and extended by numerous other investigators. Hsu and Moorhead (1957) reported the results of chromosome analysis on eight different human cell strains, four of which had been derived from normal tissues but had plainly undergone a radical change in karyotype. Heteroploid shifts were also described for mouse cell strains (Hsu and Klatt, 1958; Rothfels and Parker, 1959) and for those of the Chinese hamster (Ford and Yerganian, 1958; Tjio and Puck, 1958a; Ford, 1959); the phenomenon has come to be recognized as a general one (see Levan, 1959; Hsu, 1961).

As the discussions of Chapter 3 have indicated, karyotypic diversification typically accompanies the emergence of permanent strains from primary populations, and cell lines that can proliferate without limit are as a rule found to be aneuploid in pattern. A few exceptions should perhaps be noted, and the experiments of Yerganian and Leonard (1961) appear to provide a case in point. In line with others, they observed that cell strains isolated from the Chinese hamster for the most part diverge after a time from the classic diploid configuration. One exceptional line, however, preserved a stable euploid karotype for long periods with no sign of deviation in stock cultures. Significantly, this strain grew with unusual rapidity, with a generation time of 14 hours or less. Yerganian has accordingly suggested that the euploid cells in question may be variants that grow more rapidly than aneuploids, whereas in most cell strains, the reverse appears to be true at the critical stage when the shift to a heteroploid state occurs. The basis for this variation in growth properties is unknown.

Some cell lines may also stabilize at or near the diploid level for serial propagation in spite of clear changes in karyotype. A good illustration is provided by the permanent strain of pig kidney cells analyzed in some detail by Ruddle (1961). Although this line had been maintained *in vitro* for more than five years, the stock population and many of its clonal derivatives showed a modal chromosome number of 38, which is the normal diploid complement for this species. When karyotypes of the long-term strains were compared with those of freshly isolated pig kidney cells, however, minor structural rearrangements could be detected within the chromosome set. More subtle deviations in karyotype were revealed only by a detailed inventory of chromosomes within the individual cells of clonal populations. A close scrutiny of these data showed that minor spread of chromosome numbers around the modal value stems primarily from the loss or gain of single chromosomes, presumably from irregularities in chromosome behavior during cell division. Frequently the absence of a chromosome of one kind can be compensated for at random by an extra chromosome of another variety; in this way, the total number may remain at a technically diploid level. Variations of the latter type were first discovered by Yerganian, who coined the term "quasidiploid" for purposes of description (Tonomura and Yerganian, 1956). Obviously, a quasidiploid (or pseudodiploid) condition can be most readily detected where the chromosomes of a set are distinctive and can be recognized individually. It seems likely, however, that this phenomenon is of very general occurrence among permanent cell strains.

The striking shifts in modal chromosome number that may take place when diploid cells from normal tissues are cultivated for extended periods have frequently been regarded as indicative of conversion to malignancy *in vitro* (see pages 240–241). It is significant, however, that equally drastic alterations in karyotypic profile may occur within cell populations explanted directly from tumors, even when the neoplasm is already demonstrably aneuploid *in vivo*. A typical illustration of these adjustments can be seen in the experiments of Hsu and Klatt (1959) on the Novikoff rat hepatoma. This neoplasm is serially transplantable in the ascites form, and during animal passage, the chromosome pattern is consistently heteroploid, with a major mode at the subdiploid level (39 chromosomes) and a minor peak at twice this value (78 chromosomes). Hsu and Klatt established three strains of cells from the Novikoff tumor and followed the resulting populations in long-term culture. In each line, the modal chromosome number shifted upward, stabilizing eventually at 67 to 68, 59 to 61, and 74 to 75 in the three series, respectively. After 8 to 10 months of continuous cultivation, each strain exhibited a rather narrow range of chromosome numbers, and none of the low-ploid cells characteristic of the tumor *in vivo* could be found. Similar shifts in modal chromosome number have been described by Okumura, Takaoka, and Katsuta (1958), in cultures isolated from another rat ascites tumor, and by Ely and Gray (1961), and DiPaolo (1962) for strains explanted from mouse ascites tumors. In the majority of these instances, the cell lines in culture retained the ability to produce tumors on reinoculation, despite drastic reorganization of chromosome patterns. These observations emphasize that karyotypic remodeling can be expected within explanted tumors as well as in populations derived originally from normal tissues. The common basis for numerical shifts or other changes may be one of adaptive adjustment by variation and selection to conditions in culture, irrespective of the presence or absence of neoplastic properties in the cells concerned.

In earlier studies of heteroploidy, there was some question whether aneuploid strains arise from changes after explantation or merely by the progressive growth of aneuploids present as rare variants in the original cell population. The first alternative can be affirmed, for variation in chromosome number is a continuing process within permanent lines and has been found to occur even among clonal populations derived from single cells. A good illustration of this tendency is provided by the analysis of sublines derived over a period of years from NCTC-929 (strain L) and maintained separately in various laboratories under somewhat different conditions. A number of these subclones have been gathered together and examined with respect to chromosome pattern (Hsu and Klatt, 1958; Hsu, 1959b). None of 12 different substrains were found to have an identical chromosome configuration, despite their common derivation from the same cell. The modal chromosome number varied from 65 to 72 in particular lines, and each substrain showed a characteristic incidence of structural rearrangements. Such findings can be confirmed with other cell lineages and are typical of the relative instability of chromosome patterns within permanent cell strains. The onset of aneuploidy is thus but the first step in an unfolding sequence of chromosomal alterations. In this respect, the lack of chromosomal variation within primary strains that remain at the euploid level offers a clear contrast.

Structural and Morphological Shifts   In the analysis of karyotypic changes, emphasis has often been placed on numerical aberrations because these are the most readily determined departures from normal chromosome patterns. Structural alterations in individual chromosomes also occur, however, and the differences may be striking. Characteristically, these changes accompany fluctuations in chromosome number; over a period of time, the accumulated differences may represent a conspicuous remodeling of the normal karyotype. In permanent strains of mouse cells, for example, the commonest morphological change lies in the formation of metacentric chromosomes. These contrast sharply with the uniform profile of telocentrics that is observed for mouse cells *in vivo* or in primary culture. The incidence of metacentric chromosomes varies between permanent cell lines. Surveying a series that had been recently established from mouse kidney, Rothfels and Parker (1959) found numbers ranging from none to three. However, populations that have been cultivated for long periods typically show more biarmed chromosomes. In five such strains examined by Hsu and Klatt (1958), the characteristic number of metacentrics and subtelocentrics lay between 10 to 20 per cell. A number of mechanisms have been suggested for the appearance of these metacentric units, such as the terminal union of two acrocentric chromosomes. Such a possibility can be visualized particularly well in pig kidney cells, where large metacentric chromosomes may appear *de novo* with an attenuated centromeric region (Ruddle, 1961). In this case, interaction of the short arms of the two acrocentric chromosomes may bring the two centromeres into close functional association. However, Hsu, Billen, and Levan (1961) consider that the majority of metacentrics in mouse cells arise by centromeric breakage, followed by sister chromatid fusion; still other mechanisms remain to be evaluated.

In human cells, where all the chromosomes show two arms, telocentric units may arise as morphological variants. Chromosomes with this configuration have been described in cultures of *HeLa* cells by Chu and Giles (1958) and in other human cell strains by Norryd (1959). In populations of Chinese hamster cells, Ford and Yerganian (1958) frequently observed telocentric chromosomes, which do not occur normally in the karyotype for this species. It seemed possible that such variants might arise from metacentric chromosomes by centrometric fracture, with the persistence of two halves as functional units. This explanation was reinforced in some instances by coincidental disappearance of a large metacentric chromosome in the hamster cells.

Other types of morphological variation have also been detected in the chromosome patterns of tumors and established cell strains. Minute and nearly telocentric chromosomes were found to occur regularly as markers in two sarcoma-producing lines of mouse cells examined by Chu, Sanford, and Earle (1958), and minutes of a similar character are reported to occur in varying number within different sublines of NCTC-929 cells (Hsu, 1959b). Dicentrics are observed less often. These can occasionally be found as variants within single cells of tumors or permanent strains, but the stable perpetuation of a dicentric condition is not ordinarily to be expected, owing to bridge formation and chromosome breakage at anaphase. At least one line of mouse cells (L–P55) seemed originally to offer an exception, but the apparent dicentric condition was eventually explained as the consequence of a deep secondary construction on a subtelocentric chromosome (Hsu and Klatt, 1958; Hsu, 1959b).

Less obvious types of chromosomal rearrangements clearly do take place in tumors and in isolated cell populations, but it is difficult in most cases to document their occurrence. Small deletions or inversions within individual chromosomes, as well as reciprocal exchanges between two chromosomes of similar morphology, are ordinarily impractical to detect by present methods. Deletions have been demonstrated cytologically in cells of the Chinese hamster (Ford, Wakonig, and Yerganian, 1958). However, for a precise estimate of the extent and kind of chromosomal rearrangements within isolated cell populations, new refinements in technique will be required. The methods presently available for karyotype analysis in mitotic cells do not begin to approach the resolving power than can be attained routinely in salivary gland preparations of *Drosophila*.

As Levan first demonstrated, structural rearrangements in tumors or permanent cell strains seem to take place more freely in polyploids than at a low-ploid level, possibly because the increased gene dosage buffers against imbalance or specific deficiency incident to any single loss. His painstaking studies on mouse ascites tumors bring out this relationship clearly (Levan, 1956b, 1956c). The data consist of detailed comparisons between karyotypes made from normal mouse spermatogonia and from three mammary adenocarcinomas that had been converted to the ascites form. One of the tumors had a modal frequency near the normal diploid value; the others were hypotetraploid. All three tumor populations exhibited a consistent telocentric pattern throughout the whole chromosome complement. By measuring the relative lengths of individual chromosomes, Levan was able to prepare comparable size distributions for the several different karyotypes (see Figure 4.2). Interestingly, the distributions for spermatogonial cells and the near-diploid tumor line practically coincided, but both hypotetraploid tumors showed a variant pattern. The chromosomes of the latter displayed an accentuated size gradient, with more extreme differences at either end of the spectrum. Such alterations could be produced only by many interchanges between individual chromosomes, and at least some must have involved unequal translocations to give chromosomes longer or shorter than those of the normal karyotype. Since rearrangements of this type are likely to pass unnoticed in a casual inspection of karyotypes, Levan referred to them as cryptostructural changes. The fact that these alterations accumulate more readily in cells of higher ploidy correlates significantly with the selective advantage that these populations may show in the evolution of tumors or long-term cultures.

The induction of chromosome aberrations by X irradiation or other agents has occupied the attention of numerous workers in cell culture,

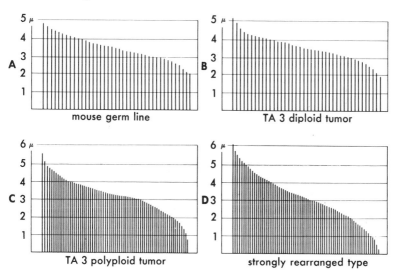

FIG. 4.2. Cryptostructural variation in the chromosome patterns of mouse cells. (A) Average idiogram taken from spermatogonial metaphases. (B–C) Increased variation in chromosome length due to the occurrence of structural rearrangements between chromosomes. The divergence is more marked in the polyploid tumor. (D) A hypothetical idiogram representing the end result of random structural interchange between mouse germ-line chromosomes of average size. (After Levan, 1956b.)

as well as in more conventional systems (see Muller, 1954; Lea, 1955; Swanson, 1957; Puck, 1959; Evans, 1962). The complexities of this topic lie beyond the confines of the present discussion, but it can be pointed out that experimental modification of the chromosomal complement does not necessarily lead to a decline in growth vigor. The loss of viability after X irradiation is a graded process within mass populations, and a surviving fraction can be isolated with undiminished powers of

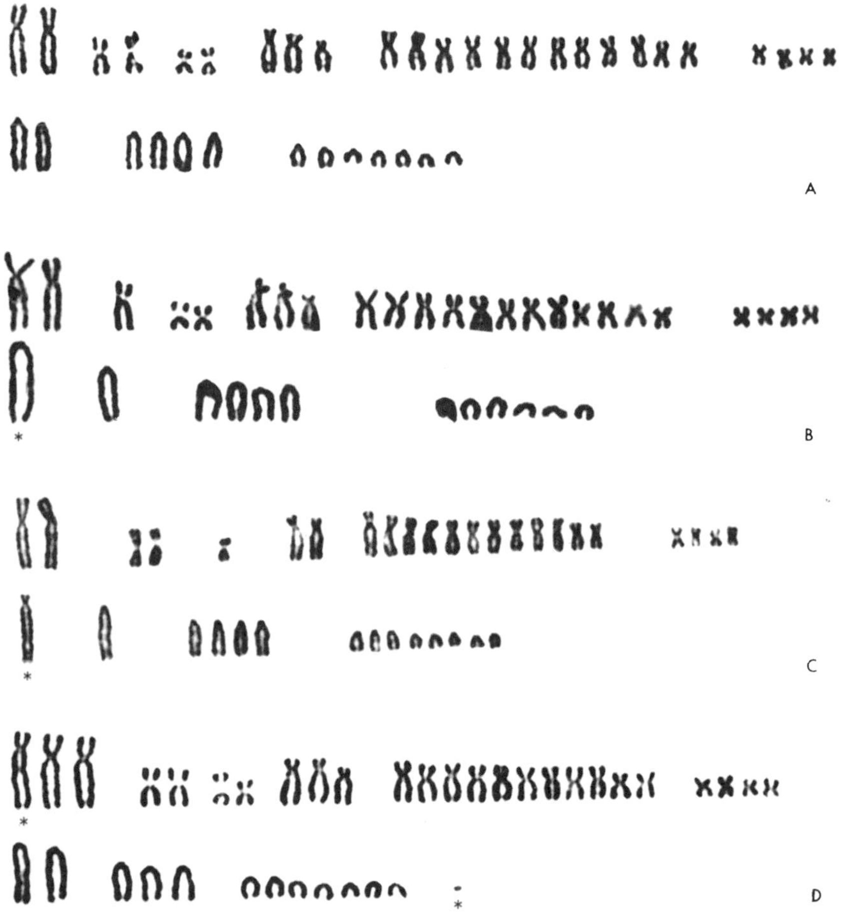

FIG. 4.3. Photo-karyotypes of a permanent strain and clonal sublines of pig kidney cells, showing marker chromosomes induced by X irradiation. (A) Representative chromosomal pattern from cell of parental line. (B–D) Clonal derivatives from survivors of an irradiated population. Marker chromosomes, present in 100 percent of cells in each of the respective sublines, are indicated by asterisks. (After Ruddle, 1961. Copyright, University of Chicago Press.)

proliferation even after comparatively large doses (for example, 500 r). This fact makes it possible to derive lines with specific cytological markers, since translocations and other chromosomal aberrations may be expected frequently at these high levels of radiation exposure. Morphological variations were in fact reported even after doses of 50 to 150 r in cultures of primary human cells (Puck, 1958). Ring chromosomes, dicentrics, and other structural novelties were observed in this study, although the isolation of clonal lines bearing these markers was not accomplished. Similarly, Wakonig and Ford (1960) observed minute chromosomes, ring forms, and chromatid interchanges in populations of Chinese hamster cells exposed to low doses of X irradiation.

The only systematic effort to produce marker strains by X irradiation, however, is that of Ruddle (1961), who used a permanent line of pig kidney cells for the purpose. Starting with a recently cloned population, cultures were exposed to X irradiation at dose levels of 300 to 800 r. From the survivors, a number of new clones were isolated, and these were screened for gross chromosomal changes. Fourteen of the recovery lines showed well-defined marker chromosomes. All were similar in growth pattern to unirradiated populations in serial culture over a period of 12 to 16 months. The most readily detected aberrations were those involving differences in position of the centromere or in size of individual chromosomes (see Figure 4.3). Large telocentric or subtelocentric markers appeared in some lines. These seemed to originate through the fusion of two smaller chromosomes, followed by the elimination of one centromere. Other clones among the recovery cultures showed large metacentrics, and in at least one strain, a minute chromosome emerged that is not found ordinarily in the pig complement. The various marker chromosomes proved to be surprisingly stable, occurring consistently in all cells of the corresponding populations for periods of more than a year. Moreover, drug resistant variants were isolated from certain of the marker strains (see Chapter 6). In each case, the identifying chromosomes persisted unchanged in the derivative strains (see Figure 4.4). This remarkable continuity is correlated with the origin of markers in most cases by fusion between two nonhomologous chromosomes. The consistent retention of the fusion product may reflect a strong selection against the loss of such extensive complements of genes (Ruddle, 1961).

The effective application of these markers for the analysis of cellular variation can be seen in further experiments, which involve morphological conversions in clones of pig kidney cells (Ruddle, 1962a). The populations in question are typically epithelial in appearance, with individual cells arranged in the form of a contiguous mosaic. In one clone

FIG. 4.4. Marker chromosomes in two cells from a clonal subline of pig kidney cells resistant to 2,6-diaminopurine. Asterisks in the photo-karyotypes show (1) a minute chromosome at extreme right, lower row, and (2) a large acrocentric chromosome with constriction, left side, upper row. Both chromosome markers were present in cells of the sensitive precursor population and have persisted without change in the drug-resistant subline. (From Harris and Ruddle, 1961.)

that had grown for 11 months according to this pattern, round cell variants appeared and eventually increased to become the dominant cell type (see Figure 4.5). Both epithelioid and round cells could be isolated in pure form from the mixed population, and these perpetuated their respective growth forms in serial culture. Although cellular contamination seems an obvious explanation, this possibility was rigorously excluded by the presence of a very long telocentric chromosome peculiar to cells of the parent strain. When various subclones of epithelioid and round cells were examined, all showed this characteristic marker. Interestingly, the presence of this chromosome seems to be indicated even in nondividing cells (Ruddle, 1962b). In the parental clone as well as its variants, about 50 to 80 percent of the interphase nuclei show a conspicuous nipplelike projection (see Figure 4.6). This curious structure arises as a bleblike protrusion of the nucleus, evidently as a reaction to the abnormally long marker chromosome. In telophase preparations, the association of the two can be seen directly.

Experimental modifications in karyotype thus offer a means for individualizing the sublines of permanent cell strains. The creation of visible differences by X irradiation or other means has an obvious utility in monitoring cytogenetic variation as well as in securing the identity of stock strains. However, it is frequently desirable to utilize intrinsic

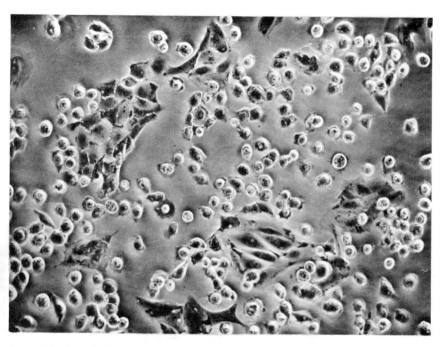

FIG. 4.5. Morphological transformation within a clone of pig kidney cells. The original line grew uniformly in an epithelioid pattern. Rounded elements later appeared and increased in subculture, to become dominant. Both cell types are shown in this photograph. Living culture, phase contrast. (From Ruddle, 1962a.)

hereditary markers, particularly within primary diploid populations in which the induction of aberrations would disrupt the euploid configuration. For some organisms, the X or Y chromosomes may be sufficiently distinctive in appearance to serve as marker elements. This is true, for example, with cells of the Chinese hamster (Yerganian, 1959), chicken (Pontén, 1962), or even the mouse (Stich and Hsu, 1960). Alternatively, sexual dimorphism among interphase nuclei can be used as an identifying tag. The feature in question is the so-called sex chromatin mass, found characteristically in the female cells of certain mammals. Barr and Bertram (1949) first discovered this structure in neurons of the cat, and subsequent studies have revealed the existence of sex chromocenters in varying frequency within female interphase nuclei of a variety of species, including man (see Barr 1960; Hamerton, 1961). Like other chromatin masses, the sex chromatin stains with basophilic dyes and is Feulgen-positive. It is larger, however, than other particles of chromatin, and is situated typically as a compact body on the inner surface of the nuclear

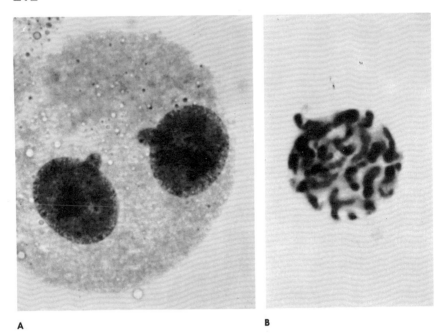

A   B

FIG. 4.6. Nuclear bleb as an interphase marker in pig kidney cells. (*A*) Binucleate cell at interphase, with symmetrical orientation of blebs. (*B*) Appearance of bleb as nuclear membrane re-forms at telophase. Note protrusion of chromosome in bleb region. (From Ruddle, 1962b.)

membrane. Various explanations can be advanced for the appearance of sex chromatin in female cells, but it seems likely that this structure derives from heterochromatic regions of the X chromosomes, perhaps one only (Hamerton, 1961; Melander, 1962).

Sex chromatin may persist as a marker *in vitro*, as *in vivo*, but significant differences are to be noted in this respect between primary and permanent cell strains. Euploid cells of female origin exhibit characteristic chromocenters even after numerous serial passages, although the proportion of positive cells varies (Burlington, 1959; Fraccaro and Lindsten, 1959; Hayflick and Moorhead, 1961). In the experiments of Fraccaro, the percentage of female interphase nuclei with sex chromatin ranged from 34 percent for human adrenal cells to 88 per cent for human liver. Some of this variability can be explained by the observation of Therkelsen and Petersen (1962) that the frequency of Barr-positive cells fluctuates in accordance with the population growth cycle. In primary cultures of human embryonic fibroblasts, for example, the proportion of nuclei with sex chromatin rose from 60 percent in log phase to nearly

100 per cent in the postlogarithmic period. The consistent occurrence of sex chromatin in primary diploid cells thus matches the stability of karyotype known to exist within these populations. By contrast, the presence of sex chromatin in tumors and in permanent cell lines is more variable. Sex chromocenters were found by Orsi and Ritter (1958) in a cultured line recently established from a human mammary tumor, but no Barr-positive cells could be observed in HeLa populations or in a long-term line of female cells derived from rabbit kidney. Miles (1959) surveyed a more extensive spectrum of cultures derived from primary human neoplasms. A substantial proportion of cells freshly isolated from these tumors contained sex chromatin, but only in those where the neoplasms had originated from females. However, Miles found that two neoplasms of female origin that had been serially transferred for many generations were Barr-negative. Sex chromatin may in general be difficult to demonstrate among cell lines maintained in long-term culture. For example, the incidence of chromocenters resembling sex chromatin was determined for 12 permanent strains of human cells by DeWitt, Rabson, Legallais, Del Vecchio, and Malmgren (1959). The various populations on this list, including such well-known lines as HeLa, J-111, Chang liver and conjunctiva, Detroit 6, and KB, all showed low counts of chromatin bodies. The frequency with which these structures occurred could not be correlated with the sex of the original donor. It thus seems reasonable to regard the decreased expression of sex chromatin as an example of progression within established tumors and other heteroploid systems, regardless of whether the cells in question are maintained in vivo or in vitro. Conceivably, such changes may be mediated directly by loss or modification of X chromosomes during serial passage, but cytological proof for this view is not yet available.

POPULATION DYNAMICS IN KARYOTYPIC CHANGE

Polymorphism in chromosome patterns is clearly a fundamental property of the aneuploid groupings that characterize most tumors and permanent cell strains. In these karyotypic mosaics, the exact configuration may depend on random drift as well as a shifting balance between emergent cell types (Levan, 1956c; Hauschka, 1957, 1961; Hsu, 1961). From this standpoint, heteroploidy and the diversification of chromosome patterns represent problems in population dynamics. The interplay of events appears to dictate an indefinite process of evolution within the cell systems concerned.

Transitions to Heteroploid States   In the remodeling of karyotypes, a useful distinction may be drawn between mechanisms that lead to population shifts (for example, changes in ploidy) and those that are expressed more simply by aneuploid fluctuation around a modal balance point (Hsu and Moorhead, 1956). The latter arise from mitotic irregularities, which distribute the chromosomes to daughter cells in an unsymmetrical fashion. Multipolar spindles, for example, are especially frequent in *HeLa* cells and in certain other stock strains. Hsu (1954) estimated that up to 35 percent of the division spindles of *HeLa* cells were multipolar during the early phases of proliferation after subculture, decreasing to a maximum of 10 percent at one week under the conditions of study. Most of the abnormalities appeared to originate in multinucleated cells as a result of partial fusion between two or more spindles. But motion pictures make clear that tripolar spindles can arise even from cells with a single nucleus (Hsu and Moorhead, 1956). The pronounced instability of mitotic processes in *HeLa* cells is not necessarily representative, and multipolar spindles are comparatively rare in many cell strains. However, unequal distribution of chromosomes in this fashion does give rise to a broad spectrum of numerical variants, some at least of which are viable. A second, and perhaps most common, mechanism of numerical fluctuation within the chromosome complement is the process of nondisjunction. This phenomenon occurs when the two chromatids that are united initially by a common centromere do not separate at anaphase and pass to opposite poles of the division spindle but remain together instead. In this case, one of the daughter cells becomes trisomic when the other is left monosomic for the chromosome in question. Less often, monosomy may arise through lagging or simple loss of one chromatid during the division process. The frequency of these events is difficult to document by direct observation (Hsu and Moorhead, 1956), but the existence of quasidiploid cells as a class leaves no doubt as to their reality.

With respect to the mechanisms that account for modal shifts in chromosome patterns, polyploidy appears to be a frequent although not invariable intermediate in many systems. There are several ways in which the doubling of chromosome complements may occur. One of these is the process of endomitosis, a term coined originally by Geitler (1937) to describe changes noted in cells of the water strider, *Gerris lateralis*. Typically, the chromosomes here appear within the nucleus and undergo a doubling in number, but without the disappearance of the nuclear membrane, formation of a spindle, or division of the cytoplasm. A variation of endomitosis can sometimes be seen when the chromosome number doubles during interphase. In this event, groupings of four chromatids are seen at metaphase for the next cell division, instead of the usual two. Such a phenomenon has been termed endoreduplication by Levan and Hauschka (1953).

Other mitotic abnormalities may also contribute to a multiplication in chromosome numbers. For example, doubling may occur if the spindle mechanism fails to form normally during division, with the reconstitution of the duplicated chromosome group within a single nucleus. Such effects are often termed "C-mitotic," in recognition of the fact that changes of the same type can be induced by colchicine. Alternatively, an increase in ploidy may follow the appearance of binucleate cells. The latter can arise from the failure of cytoplasmic division to occur at telophase, or by a refusion of the two daughter cells, a process described as teloreduplication (Moorhead and Hsu, 1956). Mitotic changes tend to be synchronized within binucleate cells, and if the two groups of chromosomes are aligned on a common spindle, polyploid derivatives can be formed. A sequence of this type is believed to account for the frequent occurrence of polyploidy in mammalian liver (Wilson and Leduc, 1948).

The relative importance of individual mechanisms for polyploidization differs for particular cell types. Levan and Hauschka (1953) found that endoreduplication is a prominent feature in some mouse ascites tumors, but not in others; the incidence ranged from zero to 20 percent of all metaphase figures. Other forms of endomitosis also fluctuated. An equally variable picture has been observed for cell strains *in vitro*. Endoreduplication takes place frequently in various lines of mouse sarcoma-producing cells (Chu, Sanford, and Earle, 1958). In cultures of *HeLa* cells, however, endoreduplication can be only rarely observed (Chu and Giles, 1958), and endomitosis is not particularly common (Hsu, 1954). In these populations, polyploidy for the most part can be attributed to other types of mitotic abnormalities, including C-mitosis (Hsu and Moorhead, 1956). Cell division occurs in more regular fashion in permanent lines of pig kidney cells, and Ruddle (1960) found no instances of C-mitosis in stock cultures. Endomitosis also appears to be lacking, and the incidence of endoreduplication seems much too low to account for the polyploidy observed. Binucleate cells occur frequently (0.1 to 1.0 percent), and in this material it is likely that the majority of polyploids arise via nuclear fusion.

Although polyploidy is found to some degree in most, if not all, cell populations, the mere occurrence of this phenomenon does not imply a population shift. The more significant requirement is an altered balance between the low-ploid and high-ploid components that proliferate together in a common environment. That an equilibrium does exist even within aneuploid strains is indicated by the studies of Hsu and Kellogg (1960) on strain *L–P*59, a subline of *NCTC*-929 cells. In this line, the incidence of high-ploid cells remains constant at 1 to 2 percent, although if clones are isolated, the high-ploid derivatives produce only half as many cells as the low-ploid sublines at the plateau growth phase. This selective disadvantage must be offset in mixed populations by the continuous production of new polyploids, in order to account for the constant proportion of the two types of cells.

The equilibrium between high-ploid and low-ploid components can also be seen when attempts are made to shift their relative proportions experimentally. For example, doubling of chromosome number can be induced within ascites tumors by colchicine treatment (Hauschka, 1953b; Levan, 1954), but the alteration of mass populations is not an enduring one. Despite the advent of numerous polyploid elements, the incidence of high-ploid cells declines to the former level soon after the administration of colchicine is discontinued. Yet polyploids as such are not inherently unstable in these populations and do not revert to a low-ploid state. If ascites tumors in mice are established from single high-ploid cells, the elevated chromosome number is regularly retained in serial passage (Révész and Norman, 1960).

Perhaps the most striking example of dynamic balance is seen in the fact that primary cell strains may retain a diploid pattern in stable fashion for long periods, despite the fact that from the outset these populations contain a low but regularly occurring proportion of polyploid cells (Tjio and Puck, 1958a; Hayflick and Moorhead, 1961). Ultimately, however, these primary cells are replaced by heteroploid derivatives if the population transforms to become a permanent cell line. What, then, shifts the stable equilibrium that existed earlier so that it favors cell types with a higher chromosome number? The appearance of aneuploids as dominant components can be explained by assuming that these variants possess favorable growth characteristics, but it is more difficult to see why this change should be more probable in high-ploid than in low-ploid cells. An explanation may lie in the fact that, as previously mentioned, karyotypic remodeling appears to take place more freely in polyploids. In primary cell lines, the competitive differential between diploid and polyploid cells may lead to a rapid turnover of the latter, so that chromosomal variants derived from polyploids do not accumulate to any degree in serial passage.

It may be significant that karyotypic shifts commonly seem to coincide with progressive slowing of population growth and decline in cell numbers to a low level (Hsu and Moorhead, 1956; Rothfels and Parker, 1959). As indicated in Chapter 3, this critical stage might be reached by a slow but progressive functional decline during serial culture; for example, by leakage of enzyme proteins, information-type RNA, or other key cellular components not replaced at a rate commensurate with cell multiplication. Since cell volume is a function of ploidy (Fankhauser, 1945; Hauschka, Grinnell, Révész, and Klein, 1957), the larger polyploid cells with a more favorable surface-volume relationship could be expected to show a selective advantage at this stage. Increased persistence of polyploids might thus allow opportunity for the accumulation of variations at the high-ploid level. By the loss of nonessential chromosomes, structural rearrangements and other alterations in karyotype, variant cell lineages may arise. Although aneuploid, these may have more favorable genomes for growth and proliferation under the conditions existing in culture.

These concepts of heteroploid shifts can be illustrated more specifically with the Novikoff hepatoma as a model system (Hsu and Klatt, 1959). This tumor is particularly convenient for the analysis of numerical changes because of several unique chromosomes that serve as identifying markers. These were used by Hsu and Klatt to rule out cell contaminations as a possible artifact in population changes. As noted previously, the Novikoff hepatoma shows two principal peaks of chromosome distribution *in vivo*, which are near to, but not identical with, diploid and tetraploid reference points. The modification of this pattern differs in detail for individual strains of cells established *in vitro*, but a common sequence consists in a preliminary emphasis of cells at the high-ploid level, followed by a broad diversification of cell types containing somewhat lower chromosome numbers. Eventually, cells corresponding to the original low-ploid and high-ploid modes disappear completely, with the population stabilizing at some intermediate value (see Figure 4.7).

Sequential diversification of karyotype may also take place through polyploidization in other cell strains. This process is exemplified in the evolutionary patterns described by Ruddle (1960, 1961) in experiments with pig kidney cells (see Figure 4.8). Starting with an uncloned parental population, it proved possible to isolate heteroploid and near-diploid clones readily (for example, clones *PK*–13, *PK*–14). Within sample populations of the latter, only a small proportion of high-ploid cells can be found initially. These are near tetraploids, with double the basic chromosome complement. Few, if any, cells depart toward more aneuploid patterns. However, in later transfers, a new mode builds up, usually at a hypotetraploid or hypertriploid level, as in the parental strain. Cells can be isolated from this component, and give rise to subclones with the corresponding chromosome number. The cycle of change ac-

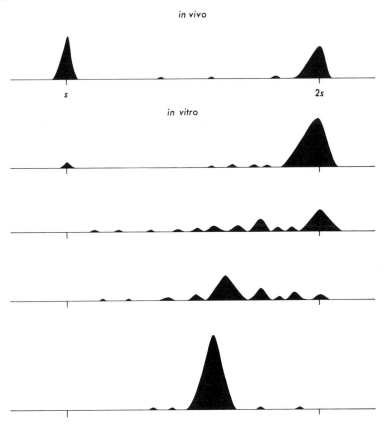

FIG. 4.7. Schematic representation of chromosomal changes in populations of Novikoff rat hepatoma cells grown in culture. Ascites populations *in vivo* (top figure) show near-diploid (s) and near-tetraploid ($2s$) components. Sublines established in culture show a predominance at first of the $2s$ component, followed by a marked heteroploid shift, with the eventual establishment of a new modal equilibrium. (Redrawn from Hsu and Klatt, 1959.)

cordingly begins again. Polyploids of a new order appear by chromosome doubling within the heteroploid stem cells, and diversification can be observed once more at the higher level. Differences in the tendency for diversification can be observed among a series of clones, even where these represent subclones derived from the same cell. Some clonal populations persist for long periods in a predominantly low-ploid state. Others convert completely to a new heteroploid mode, and still other sublines contain variable proportions of low- and high-ploid components after a series of consecutive transfers. These observations illustrate the

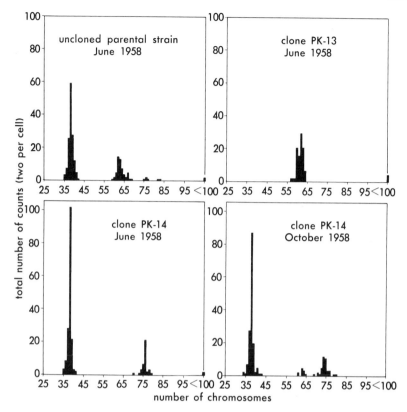

FIG. 4.8. Distributions of chromosome number in a permanent strain of pig kidney cells and its clonal derivatives. (After Ruddle, 1961. Copyright, University of Chicago Press.)

futility of using clonal origin as a measure of uniformity or purity of cell lines. The fact is that diversification begins early in clones derived from these and other permanent cell strains, and may even be accentuated by the cloning process as such (Ruddle, 1961). Thus the term clone is meaningful only in an operational sense, that is, to connote the origin of a given population from a single cell. It is misleading when used as a criterion of homogeneity.

Although polyploidization may represent a common stepping stone in the transition to aneuploidy, or to new heteroploid balance points, it is by no means essential for the occurrence of these shifts. The existence of hyperdiploid and subdiploid states within the spectrum of tumors and permanent cell strains indicates that comparatively stable cell lineages can arise by direct loss or gain of varying numbers of chromosomes within a low-ploid complement. Even if individual alterations are minor, a succession of changes can account for marked shifts in modal distribution. Furthermore, deletion of one or more chromosomes can be coupled, in some cases at least, with a secondary polyploid doubling, to yield populations with elevated chromosome numbers. In this case, the sequence diploidy → subdiploidy → hypotetraploidy replaces the more common diploid → tetraploid → hypotetraploid pattern (Hsu, Billen, and Levan, 1961). A plurality of mechanisms must thus be envisioned as a basis for heteroploid shifts within isolated cell populations, including the possibility that some aneuploid lines may arise from random cell fusions (see pages 228–233).

The factors that initiate karyotypic transformation of diploid systems have remained surprisingly obscure. As yet, no definite explanation can be offered for the decline in homeostatic mechanisms that seems to usher in the occurrence of chromosomal changes on a continuing basis. It is clear that chromosome aberrations may be created by such means as X irradiation, but the degree to which experimental treatments may induce karyotypic instability as such requires further study. In this area, the effects of viral agents may provide useful model systems. Evidence now at hand indicates that chromosome irregularities can be demonstrated in cells harboring viruses of several different kinds. Hampar and Ellison (1961, 1963), for example, inoculated herpes simplex virus into cultures of Chinese hamster cells and noted subsequently the appearance of chromatid and chromosome breaks, translocations, and constrictions or elongations in centromeric regions. These effects proved to be temporary. No changes in chromosome number were observed, perhaps owing to the fact that herpes virus does not multiply in Chinese hamster cells and persists for a short time only in a carrier state. Chromosomal breakage has also been reported in cultures of cells taken from the blood of human patients suffering from measles (Nichols, Levan, Hall, and Östergren, 1962).

More striking modifications in karyotype can be noted in primary cell populations exposed to simian vacuolating virus (SV_{40}). This agent first appeared in cultures established from rhesus and cynomolgus monkeys, and it grows in a variety of mammalian cells, including primary isolates from human tissues. SV_{40} attracted considerable interest because when it is inoculated into newborn Syrian or golden hamsters (*Mesocricetus aureus*), tumors are produced in high frequency (Eddy, Borman, Berkeley, and Young, 1961). Carcinogenicity of SV_{40} for man has not yet been shown, but pronounced effects of the virus can be demonstrated on human cells *in vitro*. When primary cultures of human skin or human kidney are treated with this agent, foci of morphologically altered cells appear (Shein and Enders, 1962; Koprowski, Pontén, Jensen, Ravdin, Moorhead, and Saksela, 1962). A general discussion of these transformations is deferred to Chapter 7, but in the present context it can be pointed out that morphological alterations are accompanied or soon followed by the occurrence of marked abnormalities in chromosome pattern (see Moorhead and Saksela, 1963). A large proportion of cells are aneuploid or quasidiploid, and trisomy or monosomy occurs often. Structural changes are equally prominent. Koprowski and his collaborators found dicentrics or other evidence of chromosome rearrangements in more than half of the cells of a quasidiploid population. Abnormally long chromosomes, acentric fragments, and minutes can also be seen. These phenomena are not peculiar to cultures of human cells, for Black and Rowe (1963) have reported analogous changes in populations of primary kidney cells from the golden hamster. Cultures of this type when treated with SV_{40} show clear-cut transformations in morphology, and the derivative lines are markedly heteroploid.

The transformations induced with SV_{40} bear a striking similarity to the focal changes that can be induced in hamster cell cultures by treatment with polyoma virus (Vogt and Dulbecco, 1960). Here, also, karyotypic changes coincide with alterations in morphology and growth behavior or follow as a sequel (Vogt and Dulbecco, 1963). The most conspicuous event in polyoma-treated cells is the occurrence of chromatid breaks. These can be demonstrated in high incidence soon after the isolation of focal variants, and continue to appear, although with decreasing frequency, for a number of serial passages. Vogt and Dulbecco observed the occurrence of chromatid bridges in over 50 percent of the focal cells during early transfers. This fact seemed to account for an unusually large number of dead cells in these populations, as well as the onset of aneuploidy in variant strains. Since trypsinization has also been reported to cause chromatid breaks (Levan and Biesele, 1958), some focal lines were transferred serially without trypsin treatment. The incidence of chromosome changes was not lessened by this procedure, thus reinforcing the view that the viral agent serves here as the primary cause.

Polyoma virus disappears as such in transformed hamster cultures, but Vogt and Dulbecco (1963) have suggested that the prolonged instability of karyotype in these cells, as in populations treated with SV_{40}, may reflect the persistence of a specific agent, perhaps viral DNA. This contingency has not been entirely ruled out (see Chapter 7), but the common occurrence of karyotypic instability in cell populations having no known contact with viruses argues for a more general explanation. One speculation to be considered is the possibility that karyotypic integrity may depend on a balanced feedback from cytoplasmic systems. Distortion of this information transfer might initiate instability and irreversible changes in chromosome pattern. The eventual decline of primary cells in long-term culture provides one setting in which the deterioration of nucleocytoplasmic correlations could be expected; alternatively, more abrupt modification might be induced by the intervention of viruses or chemical agents.

Several models from nuclear transplantation in amphibian embryos (see Chapter 1) support the concept that cytoplasmic modification can be reflected in karyotypic changes. It will be recalled, for example, that even a brief sojourn of nuclei in foreign cytoplasm of another species can result in lasting alterations. Thus, if nuclei of R. pipiens are allowed to divide a few times in eggs of R. sylvatica and are then transferred back into native cytoplasm, the capacity for proliferation as such is unimpaired. However, a persisting instability in chromosome behavior is induced by this treatment. The resulting cell populations are characteristically aneuploid, and may contain chromosome types not found in the usual complement of R. pipiens, as well as clearly abnormal ring forms, minutes, and acentric fragments (Briggs, 1962; Hennen, 1963).

A comparable syndrome can be produced without recourse to interspecific transfers by treating the eggs and embryos of R. pipiens with nitrogen mustard (Grant and Stott, 1962). Not surprisingly, when intact cells are exposed to this agent, the nuclei show chromosome abnormalities, but the same result can apparently be achieved by cytoplasmic treatment alone. For such a test, unfertilized eggs are treated with nitrogen mustard, enucleated, and then provided with a normal sperm nucleus or a nucleus transferred from a control blastula. Under these conditions, cleavage proceeds as usual, mitotic activity is normal, and a high proportion of embryos give rise to blastulae. Further development, however, is severely inhibited. Cytological studies reveal a pattern of karyotypic instability similar to that described above (that is, aneuploidy, fragmentation, ring chromosomes, and anaphase bridges). The parallel with interspecific transfers can be made a close one by returning nuclei from these experimental blastulae to untreated eggs. With rare exceptions the second generation embryos are again blocked at gastrulation, or soon thereafter, and chromosome abnormalities continue to arise within these nuclei, now replicating in normal cytoplasm.

Finally, it can be pointed out that the developmental potential of R. pipiens nuclei may even be restricted by injecting zygotes with homologous proteins from adult liver (Markert and Ursprung, 1963). Here again, development proceeds to the blastula stage, but is consistently blocked at this point, as well as in serial transfer embryos resulting from transplantation of the corresponding nuclei. Chromosomal aberrations regularly occur, but at least some nuclei within transfer embryos exhibit a normal chromosome complement. The inference seems clear, therefore, that karyotypic anomalies are not merely perpetuated by mitosis from the original egg that received an inoculation of liver proteins.

The origins of karyotypic diversity must accordingly be construed to include the possible influence of cytoplasmic changes as well as factors that impinge directly on the chromosome complement as such. In detail, these processes are obscure, and whether the chromosomal changes that take place in untreated primary cells can in fact be arrayed with those induced by viral and chemical agents remains to be seen. It is encouraging to note, however, that several systems are now available in which transitions to aneuploidy can be brought under experimental scrutiny.

Clonal Analysis and Stem-Line Concepts The mosaicism of karyotype in established tumors and permanent cell strains has stimulated numerous discussions in an adaptive vein. In order to account for the balance and predominance of cell types, the concept of stem lines has frequently been invoked. Development of this idea is often attributed to Makino (1952, 1956, 1957), but similar views are expressed or implicit in papers by Hauschka and Levan (1953), Hauschka (1953a, 1957), Levan (1956c, 1958), and numerous other investigators. The stem-line theory was formulated originally as an explanation for the chromosome patterns of ascites tumors. According to this view, each tumor is characterized by one or more stem cells of specific karyotype, which serve as the principal progenitors of the neoplastic population. The stem line corresponds to the modal cell karyotype in frequency distributions. Continuity of chromosome patterns as well as the heritable characteristics of a given neoplasm are attributed to the persistence of stem cells in tumor lineages. In the simplest case, each tumor can be represented by s, the stem-line number of chromosomes, and the usual small polyploid component in such populations by $2s$.

The stem-line concept has undergone a number of modifications within the past few years. The original views of Makino (1952) and Makino and Kanô (1953) implied that stem cells are the chief, if not the sole, component of tumor populations in which continuing cell division takes places. They noted the frequent occurrence of mitotic abnormalities within the Yoshida sarcoma and other rat ascites tumors. To account for the spread of chromosome numbers around the stem-line value, Makino suggested that mitotic aberrations within stem cells give rise continually to variant karyotypes, these being incapable in most cases of continued proliferation. However, for some tumors at least, this view proved to be an oversimplification. When means were developed for the transfer of certain neoplasms by single cells (Furth and Kahn, 1937; Ishibashi, 1950), it became possible to sample population structure more directly. Clones of ascites cells obtained in this way did not necessarily show in each case the same modal chromosome number as that of the parental population (Hauschka, 1953a; Makino and Kanô, 1955).

The plasticity of ascites tumors has been demonstrated convincingly through the extensive clonal studies of Hauschka and Levan (1958). Using the Krebs-2 and Ehrlich ascites tumors, they isolated 19 clones by single-cell inoculations. These were maintained in Swiss mice as separate strains for a period of years. The individual tumors of this group showed well-defined and fairly constant chromosome numbers, with modes that varied but ranged between 72 and 85. The parental populations were less constant, and showed a downward drift from tetraploid to hypotetraploid levels during the same period. Structurally, the chromosome patterns of a number of clones proved to be individualized. Metacentrics and minutes, as well as extra long chromosomes were observed as unique features. The differences in karyotype among this spectrum of clones were accompanied by equally clear-cut differentials in other characters, including relative virulence for the mouse host, nature of the ascitic exudate, and compatibility with a resistant strain of mice (129/Rr Jax). These findings make clear that ascites tumors are frequently, if not usually, a complex of cell types, more than one of which may be capable of serial proliferation on clonal isolation.

The actual complexity of stem lines within tumors, however, can be made evident only through recourse to an additional technique for the analysis of populations, namely, microspectrophotometry. By this means, DNA measurements may be obtained on individual cells within complex groupings, and the values obtained can then be arrayed in frequency distributions. The time scale for measurement is unrestricted. Whereas the study of chromosome patterns is of necessity confined to metaphase cells, observations on DNA content can be performed at any point within the cell cycle. If the cell types under study differ sufficiently in characteristic DNA values, it is possible to recognize one or more stem lines and to compare their contributions during proliferation of the population as a whole. The observations of Stich and Steele (1962) illustrate these broadened horizons. In their survey, DNA measurements were performed on eight different human tumors. The results for each neoplasm were then classified and arranged according to the various phases of cell division. The patterns that appeared are shown in Figure 4.9. Distinctive differences can be observed for particular tumors. In the simplest case (A), the DNA values of all cells in metaphase are

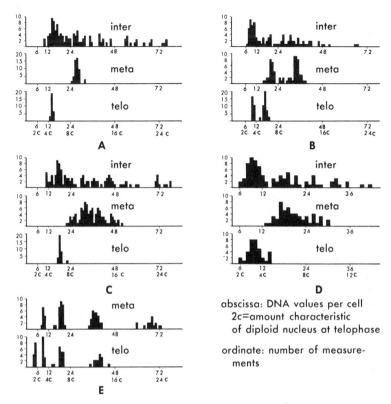

abscissa: DNA values per cell
2c=amount characteristic
of diploid nucleus at telophase

ordinate: number of measurements

FIG. 4.9. Stem-line patterns of several human tumors, as reconstructed from DNA measurements during successive phases of the mitotic cycle. (A) An adenocarcinoma of the stomach. DNA values of interphase nuclei are widely scattered, indicating the presence of many cells containing different chromosome numbers. Only cells of a particular DNA content enter metaphase and complete mitosis; the dividing cell population is characterized by a single hypertetraploid cell type. (B) Leiomyosarcoma of the colon. The nondividing cell population has a mosaic composition, from which two components carry through cell division. These are not multiples in terms of DNA values; thus proliferation of this tumor is characterized by two stem lines. (C) Adenocarcinoma of the breast. A mixture of cell types characterizes the nondividing population. A number of these are capable of entering metaphase, but only one component, sharply defined, completes the division cycle. (D) Carcinoma of the breast. Many cell types are present, and most of these appear able to complete mitosis. No dominant stem line can be found. (E) Bronchiogenic carcinoma. The histogram of DNA values at metaphase and telophase shows definite modes at exact multiples of the lowest amount of DNA. The numerous dividing cell types seem to represent polyploids of the subdiploid cell line. (Redrawn from Stich and Steele, 1962.)

sharply defined at approximately the same point; at telophase, one-half of this amount remains. By contrast, the DNA measurements for cells in interphase are widely scattered, much more than can be accounted for by postulating time differences in doubling of DNA within individual cells. The nondividing population seems, therefore, to be a mosaic of cell types, of which only one functions as a stem line to perpetuate the tumor. In another neoplasm (C) there is evidence that more than one cell type proceeds to metaphase, but only a single component carries through the division cycle. Still other tumors appear to have multiple stem lines. These can be independent components, lacking in any simple ratio of DNA values (B); or a harmonic polyploid series may exist as exact multiples of a basic cell type (E). Finally, at least some tumors seem to lack a dominant stem line and exhibit a variety of cell types that appear to continue through mitosis (D). These data illustrate the individuality that may obtain within aneuploid systems, and show the need to avoid oversimplification in the analysis of population structure.

The extent to which a given stem-line complex may persist, regardless of its exact configuration, has occasioned much discussion. Earlier, Makino (1956, 1957) expressed the view that stem lines represent lineages of intrinsic stability within tumors and are maintained when the population is exposed to a variety of altered environmental conditions. However, even within the Yoshida sarcoma, much used for these studies, many deviations from the normal karyotype can be found among the stem cells (Tjio and Levan, 1956b). The stem-line elements in this and other aneuploid systems are accordingly the product of remodeling at some stage, and typically these changes continue. In more recent discussions it has become recognized that tumors and permanent cell strains are in a state of karyotypic flux and that the constancy of stem lines is not absolute (Makino and Sasaki, 1958; Hauschka and Levan, 1958; Hsu and Klatt, 1958).

The interpretation most frequently offered for the modification of stem lines during serial propagation is that of variation and selection (Hsu, 1961; Hauschka, 1961). On this view, karyotypic diversification corresponds to a spectrum of cells with markers of differential selective value. Aneuploid systems are thought to be buffered in this way against a changing microenvironment through the availability of genomes differing in physiological optima or other features of adaptive significance. The stem line thus would refer merely to the cell type or types proliferating most vigorously under conditions that prevail at a particular time, without implication of an intrinsic continuity.

Several lines of evidence have been put forward to support the concept of adaptive shifts in stem line within tumors and permanent cell strains. For example, although the modal chromosome number for ascites tumors tends to remain constant during serial transfer, both spontaneous and induced changes may occasionally take place. Thus, Hauschka and Levan (1958) observed a progressive decline in chromosome number within the near tetraploid Krebs-2 and Ehrlich tumors when those neoplasms were propagated by serial transfer in Swiss mice instead of the hosts with more variable genotype, which had been used previously. During this period, other lines of the tumors that were maintained in the original host animals showed no alteration in modal chromosome number. Hauschka and Levan interpreted these shifts as adaptive adjustments to the histocompatibility differential imposed by the change in hosts (see Chapter 8). This explanation has been supported in more direct fashion by the experiments of Ising (1955, 1958), who maintained Ehrlich tumor lines for long periods in a heterologous environment. When these cells were carried serially in hamsters instead of in mice, the modal chromosome number dropped progressively from 79 to 72. A more far-reaching effect was revealed when detailed measurements were made of individual chromosomes. These showed as much as 20 percent reduction in aggregate length. The loss of chromosomal material is mediated by cryptostructural changes, and seems clearly related to the genetic incompatibility of graft and host, for if the hamster hosts were treated with cortisone to minimize immunological responses, there was little if any elimination of chromosomes from the Ehrlich cells. The basis for this quantitative and qualitative decline is unknown, although it has been suggested that the deletion of specific chromosomes or their appropriate parts may confer a selective advantage through reduced expression of identification antigens (Levan, 1959). This possibility will be considered in more detail in Chapter 8.

The concept of genetic polymorphism within aneuploid systems implies the possibility of manipulating the structure of populations by experimental means. If the patterns of environmental selection can be suitably altered, it should be possible to favor cell types that under ordinary circumstances are subsidiary to the modal elements. An example of this approach can be seen in the experiments of Hsu and Kellogg (1960) on L–P59 cells. Colchicine was introduced as a modifying factor into sample populations on the premise that the actively dividing stem cells in a mosaic grouping would be inhibited to a greater extent than more slowly growing components. The effect of this procedure was in part to emphasize the proportion of high polyploid cells, which ranged in frequency from 13 to 100 percent among various treated strains. Among the low-ploid component, there was a replacement of the usual modal cells by variants that could be recognized by the presence of unique marker chromosomes. Evidently this new modal type was selected for (rather than induced by) colchicine treatment, since cells with the same markers could be found in low frequency within control populations. The changes in population structure induced by colchicine proved to be reversible within certain limits. If exposure to this agent was not prolonged, the original stem cells selectively multiplied in recovery cultures and regained in a few days their former position of dominance.

In a subsequent study, Hsu (1960) has described cyclic fluctuations in the structure of untreated $L-P59$ cells during the normal growth cycle. A long subtelocentric chromosome with a prominent secondary constriction was utilized as a marker in these experiments. This element, termed the D chromosome, varies in occurrence within the $L-P59$ populations. Cells may be found with none, one, two, or three D chromosomes. Immediately after a routine transfer, cells with none or one D chromosome are the predominant type. At late stages in the growth cycle, with the population essentially stationary in numbers, the most frequent karyotypes are those with two or three D chromosomes. Hsu found that frequent subculturing causes population shifts in the direction of cell types with a low number of D chromosomes. Conversely, if young populations are treated with used medium from older cultures, the frequency of cells with a large number of D chromosomes rises.

These observations are obviously in line with the view that aneuploid populations are adaptively determined complexes, in which the balance of competing genotypes shifts in response to environmental conditions or changes in growth potential of the various individual components. It does not seem desirable, however, to push the selection model too far as an explanation for karyotypic changes (see page 233). The relatively high rate of chromosome aberrations in tumors and in permanent cell strains suggests that many, or most of, these shifts may have little adaptive significance for population growth or cell proliferation. The chance accumulation of different chromosome changes within separated populations can thus account for the individuation of sublines by a process of genetic drift, quite apart from any selective pressures. In this sense, the microevolution of clones resembles that of organisms isolated in small groups, where speciation can be accomplished by random diversification as well as by selection as such.

Hybridization of Cell Strains Karyological analysis has also provided the entering wedge for a new study, which may become one of the most significant aspects of population dynamics. This is the question of genetic interchange between individual somatic units. Until recently, such processes have been known only for gametes and in microbial systems (see Chapter 2). There is still no indication that recombination takes place freely at any time among somatic cell populations, but the possibility of genetic transfer under special conditions can no longer be excluded. Several reports now demonstrate that fusion or interaction may occur in mixtures of certain permanent strains, with the production of composite cell types. These variants can be extracted by clonal isolation to yield hybrid cell strains. Hybridization in this fashion offers a tool of obvious significance for genetic analysis, particularly if complementary processes of reduction or segregation can be found to occur. So far, there are no signs of the latter in the cell systems that have been examined, but a comprehensive investigation may be more fruitful.

The hybridization phenomenon in somatic populations was first discovered by Barski and his collaborators in experiments with sarcoma-producing lines of mouse cells (Barski, Sorieul, and Cornefert, 1960, 1961). The strains in question had been derived earlier in another laboratory (Sanford, Likely, and Earle, 1954) as part of a program in experimental carcinogenesis, which will be detailed in Chapter 7. At the present juncture it need be indicated only that these lines originated in common from a single cell, isolated from a culture of normal subcutaneous tissue of a C_3H mouse. Two sublines of the clonal population were maintained for an extended interval in serial culture and diverged progressively in a number of properties. One of these was a differential ability to produce tumors on reinjection into C_3H mice. The cell lineages have accordingly been referred to as "high-tumor" and "low-tumor" strains, respectively. Numerous other contrasting characters were found, including disparity in cell morphology, tumor growth forms, and chromosome patterns (Chu, Sanford, and Earle, 1958).

These distinctions in marker properties have been effectively used by Barski and his co-workers to demonstrate that cell fusions occur when populations of the two types are cultivated together. The evidence for hybridization rests primarily on chromosome patterns, and thus the karyotypic features of each strain are significant. The specific sublines employed, termed $N1$ and $N2$ for simplicity, were derived from the high-tumor strain $NCTC$-2472 and the low-tumor $NCTC$-2555, respectively. $N1$ populations show a modal chromosome number of 55, and with rare exceptions the individual elements are all telocentric. One very long telocentric chromosome serves as a marker. By contrast, the number of chromosomes within the $N2$ strain shows a mode at 62. In this strain, there are regularly 9 to 19 metacentrics present.

In actual experiments, mass cultures were established by mixing 1×10^6 cells from each of the two marker lines. The composite populations were then maintained by serial transfer over a period of several months. During the early phases, both $N1$ and $N2$ cells could be recognized by their characteristic differences in morphology, but a selective advantage led to predominance of the $N2$ component. During the third or fourth month of culture, a new type appeared. These elements, designated M cells, progressively increased in relative number. The chromosome pattern of the M cells proved to be distinctive. These units were high polyploids, with a modal number at 115 to 116, a value that is close to the expected sum of the chromosomal complements from $N1$ and $N2$ cells. More significantly, markers from both $N1$ and $N2$ lines occurred regularly within the same cell. Variants of the M type consistently showed 9 to 15 metacentric units, and 45 of 48 cells examined contained the extra long telocentric chromosome. Subsequent studies have shown that M cells can be isolated as clones from mixed populations and that the karyotypic pattern described persists within these derivative strains (Barski, 1961; Barski and Cornefert, 1962).

An obvious interpretation which might be placed on mixture experiments is that the variants that appear are merely double stem-line elements, derived by polyploidy and structural remodeling within one or another of the original strains. This possibility seems to be ruled out within the system in question. Barski and his co-workers found that double stem-line cells are indeed present in the separate strains as well as in composite populations. They do not, however, show markers appropriate to both cell lines, and are readily recognized as multiples of a basic chromosome complement. Cells of truly intermediate karyotype, on the other hand, appear only in mixed cultures and cannot be detected within the individual stock lines. The conclusion that hybrid elements are formed by fusion or cellular interaction thus seems to be the only explanation consistent with the facts. This view has also been expressed by Sorieul and Ephrussi (1961), who repeated the mixture experiments with $NCTC$-2472 and $NCTC$-2555 in a separate investigation.

If hybridization can actually take place between somatic cells, the generality of this phenomenon becomes an important question. Evidently the production of hybrid variants is not restricted to a unique pair of strains, although derivation from the same single cell of the two that have been described might suggest such a possibility. The recent observations of Ephrussi and Sorieul (1962a, 1962b) are particularly pertinent in this regard. In order to determine the specificity of hybridization, they combined aliquots of $NCTC$-2555 with cells of other types. Clear evidence for the appearance of hybrids was obtained in at least one instance with an unrelated partner strain. The latter, clone Py 198-1, had been derived earlier from a culture of cells from Swiss mice rendered neoplastic *in vitro* by treatment with polyoma virus (Vogt and Dulbecco,

1960). The *Py* 198-1 strain characteristically exhibits a modal chromosome number of 74, a uniform telocentric configuration, and two chromosomes with heterochromatic gaps in staining, which serve as good markers. When cultures were established by mixing *Py* 198-1 and *NCTC*-2555, variants ultimately appeared, which showed 144 chromosomes, 15 to 16 metacentrics, and the expected markers with heterochromatic specializations. These cells seem clearly to be composites on the basis of chromosome pattern. Analogous findings have been reported by Gershon and Sachs (1963), who likewise obtained karyological evidence of fusion between mouse tumor cells from two inbred strains. In this case, the fusion products were found to possess isoantigens corresponding to both original parental types. Thus the formation of hybrids can be observed in more than one combination, and is not confined to paired strains of closely similar genotype.

The specific mechanisms of hybridization, where it does occur, are little known. In an effort to secure information on this point, Barski and Belehradek (1963) prepared composite explants that consisted of mouse normal embryonic tissue plus aggregates of the *N*1 cells mentioned earlier. The areas of contact between the two cell populations were then examined with lapsed-time cinemicrography. Two examples of apparent transfer of nuclei between cells were detected. In both cases, this seemed to proceed by penetration of one nucleus into a second cell to form a binucleate structure, the cytoplasm of the donor cell remaining outside. These fragmentary observations suggest the interesting possibility that hybridization may be mediated by nuclear contribution only. However, a broad series of studies is obviously needed to determine whether hybrids in general arise by the fusion of intact cells, transfer of nuclei, or a combination of mechanisms.

Aside from chromosomal patterns, the expression of markers within hybrid cells has been examined only for recombinants between the *N*1 and *N*2 strains (Barski and Cornefert, 1962). Morphologically, the various clones of *M* cells that have been isolated are similar and intermediate between the two precursors. In common with *N*2 rather than *N*1 cells, the hybrid variants give rise to well-developed nodules on the chick chorioallantoic membrane, and are not destroyed completely by the addition of polyoma virus. But in terms of capacity to produce sarcomas on injection into C_3H mice, clonal populations of *M* cells closely resemble the *N*1 strain. Nearly 100 percent of mice receiving 1×10^6 or more *M* cells develop tumors, and the growth curves for these neoplasms coincide with the *N*1 pattern. Histologically, however, the *M* cell tumors are made up of rounded or polygonal elements in irregular growth forms, quite unlike the spindle-cell sarcomas typical of the *N*1 line or the more anaplastic round-cell tumors produced by the *N*2 strain. These observations are limited in scope, but it is evident that the expression of markers within hybrid cells does not follow a simple pattern. Yet the composite series of characteristics appears to be relatively stable. Barski and Cornefert found, during observation periods that ranged up to approximately one year, that the specific features of hybrid populations persist unchanged in serial passage.

A broader exploration of hybridization between isolated cell strains is clearly indicated by these findings. The experimental conditions requisite to hybrid formation are in need of definition; it may be that this phenomenon can be selectively induced. As yet untouched are the questions of whether hybridization can occur within diploid, as well as aneuploid populations, and in nonneoplastic strains as opposed to those with tumor-producing properties. Conceivably, hybridization may prove to be a specialized event in somatic systems. However, this does not necessarily lessen the potential usefulness of hybrid cells for genetic analysis. It is well to recall that the discovery of strain *K*-12 of *E. coli* (Chapter 2), with its high frequency of recombination, opened the way to the study of gene transfer in bacteria. The exploitation of favorable materials that permit genetic interchange may be similarly fruitful at the somatic level.

In a continuing search for appropriate models, the processes associated with formation of syncytia and giant cells *in vivo* or *in vitro* may bear a closer examination. Within the intact organism, polynuclear states occur, for example, in osteoclasts and fetal trophoblast; and the fact that skeletal muscle fibers arise by the fusion of myoblasts has been demonstrated experimentally (Stockdale and Holtzer, 1961). Giant cells are also a familiar feature of foreign-body reactions and certain other types of pathological processes. Those formed from macrophages or monocytes in culture have offered a convenient material for experimental study (Lewis, 1927; Goldstein, 1954; Franklin, 1958). In this system, it is clear that direct fusion of mononucleate cells occurs; that single cells can be added to an existing syncytium; and that both cytoplasm and nuclei merge indistinguishably with the common mass.

Within recent years it has also become clear that polynuclear giant cells may arise *in vivo* or in cell cultures following infection with certain viruses such as measles, herpes, and varicella (see Roizman, 1962; Okada and Tadokoro, 1962; Thomison, 1962). There is evidence that these polykaryocytes arise by aggregation and fusion of cells that differ phenotypically as a result of viral infection in a limited fraction of the population (Roizman, 1962). At first the union seems to be a partial one, and the merging components can be dissociated with trypsin; later, this treatment is ineffective. Aside from these observations, little direct analysis has been made of extrinsic factors affecting giant cell formation. However, low pH (Franklin, 1958), reduced concentrations of magnesium ions (Owens, Gey, and Gey, 1958), and certain types of sera (Kawana, 1960) are reported to promote the appearance of multinucleate elements in particular cell systems. These scattered observations raise the possibility that the fusion of cells may be regulated experimentally in order to produce binucleate products rather than random polynuclear aggregates. It remains to be seen whether the controlled hybridization of cell strains can be achieved on a broader basis by this procedure.

KARYOTYPES AND CELLULAR PHENOTYPES

Much of the work on karyotypic variation within tumors or isolated cell strains has been predicated on the assumption that alterations in chromosome pattern are expressed by changes in the phenotypic properties of these materials. This is not an unreasonable starting point in view of the many demonstrations that spontaneous or induced chromosome aberrations can lead to detectable variation in developing organisms. Cytogenetic studies in *Drosophila* and other conventional systems show that deletions within individual chromosomes, the development of monosomic conditions by nondisjunction, or various types of somatic segregation may permit the expression of recessive alleles previously masked in a heterozygous state. Similarly, trisomic conditions and the differential loss of chromosomes in heteroploids may introduce changes in dosage and in genic balance, and the occurrence of structural rearrangements can provide a basis for position effects.

All of these chromosome aberrations can be found within neoplastic populations and permanent cell lines. However, it has been remarkably difficult to demonstrate that specific variation in cellular properties occurs as a result of chromosomal changes in isolated systems, although there has been no lack of effort to do so (see Hauschka, 1958, 1961; Vogt, 1959; Harris and Ruddle, 1960; Hsu, 1961). For example, the chromosome patterns of aneuploid populations may vary widely and evolve progressively with time, but the nutritional requirements in all these cell lines are essentially identical and remain unchanged in serial passage (see Chapter 5). Conversely, variant cells arise within tumors or permanent cell strains with selective resistance to particular drugs; yet no consistent karyotypic shift can be associated with this transition (see Chapter 6). The correlation of cell properties with karyotypic fluctuation has occasionally been reported (Vogt, 1959; Konigsberg and Nitowsky, 1962), but no real evidence exists to rule out a fortuitous rather than causal association in these cases.

Obviously, karyotypic aberrations are only one of a series of mechanisms that may operate to produce heritable alterations in cellular phenotype. Variants arising by point mutation or extrachromosomal changes, for example, may be expected to show an intact karyotypic pattern. Yet the low apparent correlation between chromosomal modifications that do occur and any obvious phenotypic changes requires further comment. It may be that few of the alterations in chromosome pattern are actually of selective significance in these aneuploid populations. There is good reason to assume that somatic cells, unlike microorganisms, require only a small fraction of the total genome to direct processes of unorganized growth. Genetic information concerned with the events of differentiation, the specialized functioning of tissues and organs, and the mediation of organismal correlations is presumably dispensable under these conditions. Chromosomal changes affecting the majority of loci within isolated somatic cells may therefore fail to find any overt phenotypic expression. Consistent with this view are the experiments of Ragni and Szybalski (1962), which show that in comparison to bacteria, permanent lines of human cells are highly resistant to inactivation by radioactive decay of DNA-incorporated radiophosphorus. The haploid state of the bacterial genome accounts only in part for this differential. On balance, it thus seems reasonable to expect occasional instances of correlation between karyotypic and phenotypic variation in isolated cell systems, although no general association can be established (Hsu, 1961).

The clearest indications of alteration in cellular properties as a direct expression of disparity in chromosome pattern are to be found among populations that differ only in level of ploidy. However, it should be emphasized that chromosome number alone is an inadequate parameter for such studies. This is illustrated graphically by the investigations of Kit and his collaborators on biochemical processes in Chinese and Syrian hamsters (Kit, Fiscus, Ragland, Graham, and Gross, 1959). These two animals show 22 and 44 chromosomes per cell, respectively, and have been regarded as a possible example of speciation by polyploidy in mammals. But despite this difference in chromosome number, the cellular content of DNA is found to be the same in both animals. Thus it is not clear whether a mere rearrangement of the genetic apparatus has occurred or whether gene dosage has been altered as well. Both are suggested by biochemical data obtained with the two types of cells. Kit and his associates observed, for example, that transaminase activity per gamma DNA is about the same in Chinese and Syrian hamster tissues; yet succinoxidase activity and cytochrome oxidase activity per gamma DNA are twice as high in the Chinese hamster. On the other hand, differences in free amino acid patterns are less between the two species than among the various tissues of either one taken separately.

It follows that a close examination of ploidy effects in isolated cell populations can be made only if the DNA charge as well as the number of chromosomes is controlled. These conditions are fulfilled in studies that Hauschka has reported on hyperdiploid and hypertetraploid lines of Ehrlich ascites tumors (Hauschka, Grinnell, Révész, and Klein, 1957). The high-ploid lines (*ELT*) were derivatives of the hyperdiploid parent stock (*ELD*), with an exact doubling in chromosome number in the stem cells as the only difference in karyotype. Measurements of cell volume and DNA content per cell indicate a 2:1 ratio between these strains. The high-ploid and low-ploid cells do not differ in relative virulence for mouse hosts, but exhibit a different pattern of growth. During the early phases of a growth cycle, *ELD* and *ELT* cells multiply rapidly, with a mean doubling time that is approximately the same. At later stages, the division rate of *ELT* cells declines, so that the growth curves diverge progressively. The maximum counts with ELT cells are approximately twice those of *ELD* populations, indicating that total mass rather than cell number is the limiting factor. This spectrum of characteristics for cell strains differing in ploidy can be extended by the functional studies of Kit and Gross (1959). With histologically similar mouse tumors near diploid and tetraploid levels, the ratio of DNA to respiration, anaerobic glycolysis, dry weight, and the activities of certain enzymes remained constant. These observations indicate that elevation of chromosome number by polyploid shifts tends to be expressed by a corresponding expansion of cellular size and activity. However, this increase inevitably alters surface-volume relationships and introduces other problems of scale, so that a simple doubling of cellular parameters cannot be expected in all cases.

The complexities of relating cellular phenotype to chromosome number can be illustrated more adequately by considering as a model system the radiosensitivity of isolated cell populations. Since the lethal effects of ionizing radiation on cells are commonly attributed to chromosome damage (Puck, 1959), it is reasonable to look for a numerical association between the two phenomena. A clear dependence of radiosensitivity on ploidy level has in fact been demonstrated for yeast cells by the experiments of Mortimer (1958). In these investigations, survival curves with increasing doses of X irradiation were determined for populations that ranged from haploid to hexaploid, respectively, in terms of chromosome sets. Mortimer found that haploid yeast cells are markedly more sensitive than are diploids. However, when higher levels of ploidy are examined, the trend is in the opposite direction (see Figure 4.10, part *A*). In this case, susceptibility to X irradiation increases as a function of chromosome number. According to Mortimer, these data may reflect the production of both dominant and recessive lethals. It is the latter that represent the major cause of mortality within haploid cells, whereas in an ascending polyploid series, the rising probability of dominant lethals becomes limiting.

More typically, the intrinsic resistance of cells and organisms to ionizing radiation rises continuously as the number of chromosome sets is increased (see Révész and Norman, 1960). Among plants, where the data are most extensive, radiosensitivity declines regularly among higher polyploids, regardless of whether the parameter in question is mitotic inhibition, germination of seeds, growth of young plants, or survival in the field. Such findings are consistent with the view that mortality stems from the inactivation of critical genetic sites, more of which must be altered in polyploid cells. Among animals, it has been more difficult to find materials appropriate for a test of ploidy effects on radiosensitivity. The related *ELD-ELT* pair of Ehrlich ascites tumors are useful for this purpose, since they differ only in chromosome number. Révész and Norman (1960) irradiated samples of both populations and assayed the test cells by placing them within porous Millipore filter chambers,

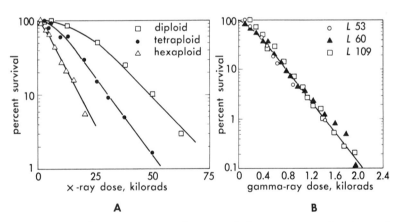

FIG. 4.10. Radiosensitivity as a function of chromosome number in yeast and strain *L* mouse cells. (*A*) Progressive increase in sensitivity to X irradiation in strains of yeast with rising ploidy levels. (After Mortimer, 1958.) (*B*) Mortality curves in sublines of *L* cells with modal chromosome numbers of 53, 60, and 109, respectively. The radiosensitivity of these populations appears to be identical. (After Till, 1961.)

KARYOTYPES AND CELLULAR PHENOTYPES

which were then inserted into the peritoneal cavity of mice. For a given dose of X irradiation, the hypertetraploid *ELT* cells started to grow earlier and/or reached a larger population than did the hyperdiploid *ELD* cells. This is essentially the same result that Berry (1963) obtained with two mouse lymphocytic leukemias, where a tetraploid population was found to be relatively more radioresistant than the accompanying diploid neoplasm.

Certain data on animal cells in tissue culture have been difficult to fit into this picture of radiosensitivity as a function of chromosome pattern. For example, Till (1961) compared the responses of three sub-lines of strain *L* mouse cells chosen for study because the stem-line values ranged from 53 for one strain to 109 for another. Survival patterns after graded exposure to γ irradiation were determined for each of the substrains within this group (see Figure 4.10, part *B*). Contrary to the cases outlined above, Till's data do not reveal any significant difference in mortality that might be correlated with chromosomal variation. All three survival patterns are clearly covered by a single dose-response curve. In the same way, Lockart, Elkind, and Moses (1961) compared the radiosensitivity of three lines of *HeLa* cells, which varied in modal chromosome number from 65 to 103. Some differences in response to X irradiation were noted among the group, but it did not prove possible to correlate either the minimum lethal dose or extrapolation number with the chromosomal complements of individual strains.

These varying results can be harmonized in part by recent discoveries, which show that the effect of chromosome number on radiosensitivity can be masked by the presence of oxygen during the irradiation procedure (Silini and Hornsey, 1962; Glas and Révész, 1962; Révész, Glas, and Hilding, 1963). With Ehrlich ascites tumors of near diploid and tetraploid constitution, the differential in sensitivity that has been described is consistently observed when the cells are irradiated in nitrogen. However, if exposure is carried in an atmosphere of oxygen instead, the dose-response curves for cells of the two types become identical. Thus the failure of Till (1961) and Lockart, Elkind, and Moses (1961) to observe differences in radiosensitivity between populations with a large disparity in chromosome number may be a consequence of the aerobic conditions, which doubtless existed in these cultures during irradiation.

Smaller numerical variations in the chromosome complement appear in practice to be of little or no significance as an index of radiosensitivity. This point is illustrated by the experimental data of Révész, Glas, and Hilding (1963). On testing several clones isolated from X-irradiated populations of *ELD* cells, they found that some of the sublines were identical in radiosensitivity under anoxic conditions, despite the fact that they varied in stem-line number. On the other hand, other clones were discovered that varied materially in sensitivity to irradiation and yet displayed a karyotype identical with the modal cells of the parental population. Révész and his co-workers have concluded accordingly that the relation between chromosome number and radiosensitivity may be wholly fortuitous unless the chromosome sets compared are exact multiples of each other.

Considering the difficulty in attempting to correlate chromosome pattern with well-defined changes in somatic cells, it is understandable that the role of chromosome anomalies in the much more complex problem of carcinogenesis is a controversial topic. This question, however, has been of continuous interest for many years. Since the time of Boveri (1912), there have been many suggestions that chromosome changes represent an etiological factor in the origin of tumors or are part of a broader spectrum of mutational changes in carcinogenesis. The enormous number of descriptive studies that bear on this problem include many of the investigations mentioned in this chapter. It is not possible without extensive discussion to sift these details further, but summaries and critical evaluation can be found in the comprehensive reviews of Levan (1956c, 1958, 1959), Hauschka (1957, 1961), Koller (1960), Hsu (1961), and Stich (1963).

If chromosomal changes are directly implicated in neoplastic transformations, it might be reasonable to expect in some cases a consistent pattern of karyotypic lesions with the onset of malignancy. This prediction seems to be verified for at least one tumor type. In 1960, Nowell and Hungerford detected an atypical chromosome in otherwise diploid cells from the peripheral blood of human patients with chronic granulocytic leukemia. The minute element in question has subsequently been observed with considerable regularity in other tumors of the same kind (Nowell and Hungerford, 1961; Tough, Court Brown, Baikie, Buckton, Harnden, Jacobs, King, and McBride, 1961). This marker can be referred to as the Philadelphia, or Ph[1], chromosome; it appears to be derived from chromosome 21 within the human karyotype. Conceivably, a causal relation may exist in this case between the loss or translocation of genetic loci and the onset of neoplastic change. However, the Ph[1] chromosome does not occur in acute granulocytic leukemia or in other types of myeloproliferative disorders (Hungerford and Nowell, 1962; Nowell and Hungerford, 1962), and there are no indications that individualized chromosome lesions can be found for tumors in general.

The frequency with which deviations of any kind can be detected in the chromosome patterns of developing neoplasms has been difficult to ascertain until recently, owing to the problem of obtaining good preparations from solid tumors in early stages. Even though this technical hurdle has now been surmounted, the resulting data have not been easy to interpret. Among the various shades of opinion, Bayreuther (1960) has taken the position that many or most primary neoplasms retain an intact diploid pattern, with chromosomal changes intervening only as a secondary progression within established tumors. His conclusions are based on the preliminary survey of a series that included both spontaneous and induced tumors within a variety of laboratory animals. In these materials, normal chromosome complements were reported to predominate, with abnormal karyotypes appearing ordinarily only in tumors of large size or after transplantation.

It is difficult to reconcile the views of Bayreuther with a number of other studies that document the occurrence of karyotypic abnormalities in an appreciable proportion of primary tumors. For example, Ford, Hamerton, and Mole (1958) detected increased numerical variation in most of a series of primary reticular tumors of the mouse. Usually there was a small shift in modal chromosome number as well, and in some cases, the appearance of marker chromosomes. Only a relatively small percentage of these tumors showed normal karyotypes. Similarly, Hellström (1959) observed considerable variability in chromosome numbers within all of 14 primary fibrosarcomas induced in mice by methylcholanthrene. The cytogenetic patterns noted ranged widely. Ten of the tumors were aneuploid, with predominant chromosome numbers at hyperdiploid, triploid, or even hypotetraploid levels. In other neoplasms, the chromosome number fluctuated broadly without any well-defined mode. But even the tumors with nominal diploid patterns showed an increased frequency of cells in the hyperdiploid region, suggesting a tendency for karyotypic variation in all the tumors, although progressing at different rates within any given neoplasm.

In more recent investigations dealing with this problem, it has become clear that chromosomal deviations must be regarded as a frequent, although not invariable, feature of primary tumor populations. For example, Hauschka (1961) found that 76 percent out of a sample of 104 untreated human neoplasms were aneuploid, and at least some of the remainder were pseudodiploid. Wide differences are to be expected between cell types, however, and among mouse leukemias the predominant picture at early stages is an intact diploid karyotype (see Miller, 1961). Some of the disparity encountered may stem from technical problems of assessing the true chromosomal picture of developing neoplasms *in vivo*. For example, short-term cultures from the blood or marrow of leukemia patients often present a normal karyotype; yet when aliquots of bone marrow are examined directly, a considerable incidence of aneuploidy can be found. In these cases, the normal diploid cells apparently possess a considerable growth advantage over the leukemic variants in culture, although not within the intact organism (Sandberg, Ishihara, Miwa, and Hauschka, 1961; Sandberg, Ishihara, Crosswhite, and Hauschka, 1962).

Although chromosomal instability thus seems to be a characteristic feature of neoplasms in early stages, there is also general agreement now that at least some frankly malignant tumors show no immediate shift in chromosome pattern (Koller, 1960; Hsu, 1961; Hauschka, 1961; Miller, 1961). This consideration appears to rule out gross karyotypic changes as a necessary feature in the initial transition from normal to neoplastic states. It does not, however, preclude the possibility that chromosomal aberrations may be one of a number of events that serve to trigger neoplastic transformations, or that chromosomal changes may reinforce this process by providing genetic implementation for variability initiated by another cause (see Hauschka, 1963).

Obviously, the role of chromosome changes in carcinogenesis cannot be resolved by descriptive studies alone. In principle, the correlation of neoplastic with karyotypic transformations can be carried on more profitably *in vitro*, where the selective manipulation of factors affecting both processes can be explored. As indicated previously, heteroploidy in isolated populations is not in itself indicative of neoplastic conversion. For example, Hsu (1961) has described experiments in which the repeated injection of aneuploid lines from C_3H mouse cells into the corresponding hosts failed to elicit tumors, and similar experiments have been reported by others (Wallace, Orsi, Ritter, and Moyer, 1961; de Bruyn and Hansen-Melander, 1962).

More illuminating are the experiments of Levan and Biesele (1958), in which the acquisition of aneuploidy and ability to produce tumors were followed simultaneously. In this work, particular attention has been devoted to a strain established from mouse embryonic skin, and which was monitored at regular intervals during serial transfer (see Figure 4.11). These cultures proliferated vigorously for two or three passages and then exhibited the usual decline into a sluggish state. Ultimately, a vigorously growing derivative appeared by focal variation after the tenth subculture. Cytologically, polyploid cells were numerous even in early stages. However, diploids predominated until passage 12, when the karyotypic profile shifted over to a broad grouping in the hypotetraploid region. Neither this gross karyotypic alteration nor the earlier change in cultural characteristics seemed to be directly associated with a malignant transformation, for cell reimplantation that was begun at passage 16 at first gave negative results. Not until passage 22 was a spindle-cell sarcoma finally obtained in the hosts of origin. To account for this timing, Levan (1958) has speculated that extensive structural remodeling in the hypotetraploid cells may have occurred over several passages, finally giving rise to a variant with properties for progressive growth *in vivo*. This concept offers an attractive explanation, but it is possible that the staggered time sequence may signify merely that chromosomal alteration and neoplastic conversion here are independent events. The clonal analysis of populations in transition may perhaps provide a more explicit picture.

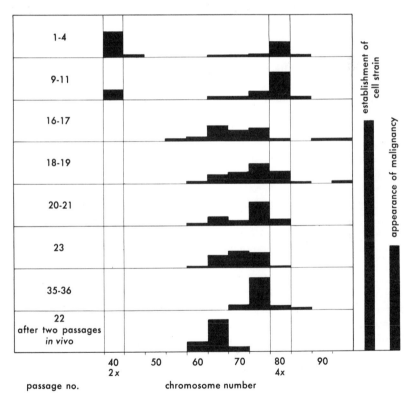

FIG. 4.11. Chromosome number distributions during the serial cultivation of a population of normal embryonic mouse skin cells, which eventually underwent malignant conversion. A prominent heteroploid shift can be observed, which coincides with the period of transition from a primary to a permanent cell strain rather than with the onset of tumor-producing properties. (Redrawn from Levan, 1958.)

■ References

BARR, M. L. 1960. Sexual dimorphism in interphase nuclei. Am. J. Human Genet., **12**: 118–127.

BARR, M. L., and BERTRAM, E. G. 1949. A morphological distinction between neurones of the male and female, and the behavior of the nucleolar satellite during accelerated nucleoprotein synthesis. Nature, **163**: 676–677.

BARSKI, G. 1961. Clones cellulaires "hybrides," isolés à partir de cultures mixtes. Compt. Rend. Acad. Sci., **253**: 1186–1188.

BARSKI, G., and BELEHRADEK, J., JR. 1963. Transfert nucleaire intercellulaire en cultures mixtes in vitro. Exptl. Cell Res., **29**: 102–111.

BARSKI, G., and CORNEFERT, F. 1962. Characteristics of "hybrid"-type clonal cell lines obtained from mixed cultures in vitro. J. Natl. Cancer Inst., **28**: 801–821.

BARSKI, G., SORIEUL, S., and CORNEFERT, F. 1960. Production dans des cultures in vitro de deux souches cellulaires en association, de cellules de caratère "hybride." Compt. Rend. Acad. Sci., **251**: 1825–1827.

BARSKI, G., SORIEUL, S., and CORNEFERT, F. 1961. "Hybrid" type cells in combined cultures of two different mamalian cell strains. J. Natl. Cancer Inst., **26**: 1269–1291.

BAYREUTHER, K. 1952. Der Chromosomenbestand des Ehrlich-Ascites-Tumors der Maus. Z. Naturforsch., Teil B, **7**: 554–557.

BAYREUTHER, K. 1960. Chromosomes in primary neoplastic growth. Nature, **186**: 6–9.

BEATTY, R. A. 1957. Chromosome constancy in the corneal epithelium of the mouse. Chromosoma, **8**: 585–596.

BERRY, R. J. 1963. Quantitative studies of relationships between tumor cell ploidy and dose response to ionizing radiation in vivo. Modification of radiation response in a previously irradiated tumor. Radiation Res., **18**: 236–245.

BLACK, P. H., and ROWE, W. P. 1963. Transformation in hamster kidney monolayers by vacuolating virus, SV–40. Virology, **19**: 107–108.

BOVERI, T. 1912. Zur Frage der Entwicklung maligner Tumoren. Jena. English translation, The Origin of Malignant Tumors, by M. Boveri, 1929. Baltimore: The Williams and Wilkins Company, 119 pp.

BRIGGS, R. 1962. Comments on paper by J. A. Moore. J. Cellular Comp. Physiol., **60**(Suppl. 1): 32–33.

BURLINGTON, H. 1959. Sex chromatin in cultured cells. Exptl. Cell Res., **16**: 218–219.

CHU, E.H.Y., and GILES, N. H. 1958. Comparative chromosomal studies on mammalian cells in culture. I. The HeLa strain and its mutant clonal derivatives. J. Natl. Cancer Inst., **20**: 383–401.

CHU, E.H.Y., SANFORD, K. K., and EARLE, W. R. 1958. Comparative chromosomal studies on mammalian cells in culture. II. Mouse sarcoma-producing cell strains and their derivatives. J. Natl. Cancer Inst., **21**: 729–752.

DE BRUYN, W. M., and HANSEN-MELANDER, E. 1962. Chromosome studies on the MB mouse lymphosarcoma. J. Natl. Cancer Inst., **28**: 1333–1354.

DEWITT, S. H., RABSON, A. S., LEGALLAIS, F. Y., DEL VECCHIO, P. R., and MALMGREN, R. A. 1959. Chromocenters resembling sex chromatin in human tissue culture cell lines. J. Natl. Cancer Inst., **23**: 1089–1095.

DIPAOLO, J. A. 1962. Establishment of long-term cultures of Ehrlich ascites tumor cells. Proc. Soc. Exptl. Biol. Med., **109**: 616–618.

EDDY, B. E., BORMAN, G. S., BERKELEY, W. H., and YOUNG, R. D. 1961. Tumors induced in hamsters by injection of rhesus monkey kidney cell extracts. Proc. Soc. Exptl. Biol. Med., **107**: 191–197.

ELY, J. O., and GRAY, J. H. 1961. Chromosome number of *in vivo* and *in vitro* cultured Krebs-2 carcinoma of mice: the selective property of the *in vitro* culture medium. Cancer Res., **21**: 1002–1023.

EPHRUSSI, B., and SORIEUL, S. 1962a. Nouvelles observations sur l'hybridation *in vitro* de cellules de souris. Compt. Rend. Acad. Sci., **254**: 181–182.

EPHRUSSI, B., and SORIEUL, S. 1962b. Mating of somatic cells *in vitro*. *In: Approaches to the Genetic Analysis of Mammalian Cells*, pp. 81–97. D. J. Merchant and J. V. Neel, eds. Ann Arbor: University of Michigan Press.

EVANS, H. J. 1962. Chromosome aberrations induced by ionizing radiations. Intern. Rev. Cytol., **13**: 221–321.

FANKHAUSER, G. 1945. The effects of changes in chromosome number on amphibian development. Quart. Rev. Biol., **20**: 20–78.

FORD, C. E. 1962. Methods in human cytogenetics. *In: Methodology in Human Genetics*, pp. 227–259. W. J. Burdette, ed. San Francisco: Holden-Day, Inc.

FORD, C. E., and HAMERTON, J. L. 1956. A colchicine, hypotonic citrate, squash sequence for mammalian chromosomes. Stain Technol., **31**: 247–251.

FORD, C. E., HAMERTON, J. L., and MOLE, R. H. 1958. Chromosomal changes in primary and transplanted reticular neoplasms of the mouse. J. Cellular Comp. Physiol., **52**(Suppl. 1): 235–269.

FORD, D. K. 1959. Chromosomal changes occurring in Chinese hamster cells during prolonged culture *in vitro*. Can. Cancer Conf., **3**: 171–188.

FORD, D. K., WAKONIG, R., and YERGANIAN, G. 1958. Further observations on the chromosomes of Chinese hamster cells in tissue culture. J. Natl. Cancer Inst., **22**: 765–800.

FORD, D. K., and YERGANIAN, G. 1958. Observations on the chromosomes of Chinese hamster cells in tissue culture. J. Natl. Cancer Inst., **21**: 393–425.

FRACCARO, M., and LINDSTEN, J. 1959. Observations on the so-called "sex chromatin" in human somatic cells cultivated *in vitro*. Exptl. Cell Res., **17**: 536–539.

FRANKLIN, R. M. 1958. Some observations on the formation of giant cells in tissue cultures of chicken macrophages. Z. Naturforsch. Part B, **13**: 213–214.

FURTH, J., and KAHN, M. C. 1937. The transmission of leukemia of mice with a single cell. Am. J. Cancer, **31**: 276–282.

GEITLER, L. 1937. Die Analyse des Kernbaus und der Kernteilung der Wasser-läufer *Gerris lateralis* und *Gerris lacustris (Hemiptera heteroptera)* und die Somadifferenzierung. Z. Zellforsch. mikroscop. Anat., **26:** 641–672.

GERSHON, D., and SACHS, L. 1963. Properties of a somatic hybrid between mouse cells with different genotypes. Nature, **198:** 912–913.

GLAS, U., and RÉVÉSZ, L. 1962. Radiosensitivity of selected sub-lines of a tumour-cell population tested in the presence or absence of oxygen. Intern. J. Radiation Biol., **6:** 69–80.

GOLDSTEIN, M. N. 1954. Formation of giant cells from monocytes cultivated on cellophane. Anat. Record, **118:** 577–591.

GRANT, P., and STOTT, P. M. 1962. Effect of nitrogen mustard on nucleocyto-plasmic interactions. *In: Biological Interactions in Normal and Neoplastic Growth,* pp. 47–73. M. J. Brennan and W. L. Simpson, eds. Boston: Little, Brown & Co.

HAMERTON, J. L. 1961. Sex chromatin and human chromosomes. Intern. Rev. Cytol., **12:** 1–68.

HAMPAR, B., and ELLISON, S. A. 1961. Chromosomal aberrations induced by an animal virus. Nature, **192:** 145–147.

HAMPAR, B., and ELLISON, S. A. 1963. Cellular alterations in the MCH line of Chinese hamster cells following infection with herpes simplex virus. Proc. Natl. Acad. Sci., **49:** 474–480.

HARRIS, M., and RUDDLE, F. H. 1960. Growth and chromosome studies on drug resistant lines of cells in tissue culture. *In: Cell Physiology of Neoplasia,* pp. 524–546. Austin: University of Texas Press.

HARRIS, M., and RUDDLE, F. H. 1961. Clone strains of pig kidney cells with drug resistance and chromosomal markers. J. Natl. Cancer Inst., **26:** 1405–1411.

HAUSCHKA, T. S. 1953a. Cell population studies on mouse ascites tumors. Trans. N. Y. Acad. Sci., Ser. II, **16:** 64–73.

HAUSCHKA, T. S. 1953b. Methods of conditioning the graft in tumor trans-plantation. J. Natl. Cancer Inst., **14:** 723–740.

HAUSCHKA, T. S. 1957. Tissue genetics of neoplastic cell populations. Can. Cancer Conf., **2:** 305–345.

HAUSCHKA, T. S. 1958. Correlation of chromosomal and physiologic changes in tumors. J. Cellular Comp. Physiol., **52**(Suppl. 1): 197–233.

HAUSCHKA, T. S. 1961. The chromosomes in ontogeny and oncogeny. Cancer Res., **21:** 957–974.

HAUSCHKA, T. S. 1963. Chromosome patterns in primary neoplasia. Exptl. Cell Res., Suppl. **9:** 86–98.

HAUSCHKA, T. S., GRINNELL, S. T., RÉVÉSZ, L., and KLEIN, G. 1957. Quantita-tive studies on the multiplication of neoplastic cells *in vivo.* IV. Influence of doubled chromosome number on growth rate and final population size. J. Natl. Cancer Inst., **19:** 13–31.

HAUSCHKA, T. S., and LEVAN, A. 1951. Characterization of five ascites tumors with respect to chromosome ploidy. Anat. Record, **111:** 467.

HAUSCHKA, T. S., and LEVAN, A. 1953. Inverse relationship between chromosome ploidy and host-specificity of sixteen transplantable tumors. Exptl. Cell Res., **4**: 457–467.

HAUSCHKA, T. S., and LEVAN, A. 1958. Cytologic and functional characterization of single cell clones isolated from the Krebs-2 and Ehrlich ascites tumors. J. Natl. Cancer Inst., **21**: 77–135.

HAYFLICK, L., and MOORHEAD, P. S. 1961. The serial cultivation of human diploid cell strains. Exptl. Cell Res., **25**: 585–621.

HEITZ, E. 1936. Die Nukleal-Quetschmethode. Deut. Botan. Ges., **53**: 870–878.

HELLSTRÖM, K. E. 1959. Chromosomal studies on primary methylcholanthrene-induced sarcomas in the mouse. J. Natl. Cancer Inst., **23**: 1019–1033.

HENNEN, S. 1963. Chromosomal and embryological analyses of nuclear changes occurring in embryos derived from transfers of nuclei between *Rana pipiens* and *Rana sylvatica*. Develop. Biol., **6**: 133–183.

HSU, T. C. 1954. Cytological studies on HeLa, a strain of human cervical carcinoma. I. Observations on mitosis and chromosomes. Texas Rept. Biol. Med., **12**: 833–846.

HSU, T. C. 1959a. Numerical variation in chromosomes in higher animals. *In: Developmental Cytology*, pp. 47–62. D. Rudnick, ed. New York: The Ronald Press Company.

HSU, T. C. 1959b. Mammalian chromosomes *in vitro*. XI. Variability among progenies of a single cell. Biological contributions, Pub. No. 5914, U. Texas, pp. 129–134. Austin: University of Texas Press.

HSU, T. C. 1960. Mammalian chromosomes *in vitro*. XIII. Cyclic and directional changes of population structure. J. Natl. Cancer Inst., **25**: 1339–1354.

HSU, T. C. 1961. Chromosomal evolution in cell populations. Intern. Rev. Cytol., **12**: 69–161.

HSU, T. C. 1964. Genetic cytology. *In: The Biology of Cells and Tissues in Culture*. E. N. Willmer, ed. New York: Academic Press, Inc. In press.

HSU, T. C., BILLEN, D., and LEVAN, A. 1961. Mammalian chromosomes *in vitro*. XV. Patterns of transformation. J. Natl. Cancer Inst., **27**: 515–541.

HSU, T. C., and KELLOGG, D. S. 1960. Mammalian chromosomes *in vitro*. XII. Experimental evolution of cell populations. J. Natl. Cancer Inst., **24**: 1067–1093.

HSU, T. C., and KLATT, O. 1958. Mammalian chromosomes *in vitro*. IX. On genetic polymorphism in cell populations. J. Natl. Cancer Inst., **21**: 437–473.

HSU, T. C., and KLATT, O. 1959. Mammalian chromosomes *in vitro*. X. Heteroploid transformation in neoplastic cells. J. Natl. Cancer Inst., **22**: 313–339.

HSU, T. C., and MOORHEAD, P. S. 1956. Chromosome anomalies in human neoplasms with special reference to the mechanisms of polyploidization and aneuploidization in the HeLa strain. Ann. N. Y. Acad. Sci., **63**: 1083–1094.

HSU, T. C., and MOORHEAD, P. S. 1957. Mammalian chromosomes *in vitro*. VII. Heteroploidy in human cell strains. J. Natl. Cancer Inst., **18**: 463–471.

HSU, T. C., and POMERAT, C. M. 1953. Mammalian chromosomes *in vitro*.

II. A method for spreading the chromosomes of cells in tissue culture. J. Heredity, **44**: 23–29.

HUGHES, A. 1952. Some effects of abnormal tonicity on dividing cells in chick tissue cultures. Quart. J. Microscop. Sci., **93**: 207–219.

HUNGERFORD, D. A., and NOWELL, P. C. 1962. Chromosome studies in human leukemia. III. Acute granulocytic leukemia. J. Natl. Cancer Inst., **29**: 545–565.

ISHIBASHI, K. 1950. Studies on the number of cells necessary for the transplantation of the Yoshida sarcoma. Gann, **41**: 1–14.

ISING, U. 1955. Chromosome studies in Ehrlich mouse ascites cancer after heterologous transplantation through hamsters. Brit. J. Cancer, **9**: 592–599.

ISING, U. 1958. Effect of heterologous transplantation on chromosomes of ascites tumors. A contribution to our knowledge of environmental influence on tumour cells. Acta Pathol. et Microbiol. Scand., Suppl. **127**: 1–102.

KAWANA, M. 1960. Effects of sera on the appearance of multinucleated cells in tissue culture of Strain L cells (mouse fibroblasts). Japan. J. Exptl. Med., **30**: 307–318.

KIT, S., FISCUS, J., RAGLAND, R. S., GRAHAM, O. L., and GROSS, A. L. 1959. Biochemical studies on the Chinese hamster (22 chromosomes) and the Syrian hamster (44 chromosomes). Exptl. Cell Res., **16**: 411–417.

KIT, S., and GROSS, A. L. 1959. Quantitative relationships between DNA content and glycolysis or histones of diploid and tetraploid cells. Biochim. et Biophys. Acta, **36**: 185–191.

KLEIN, G., and KLEIN, E. 1959. Nuclear and cytoplasmic changes in tumors. *In: Developmental Cytology*, pp. 63–82. D. Rudnick, ed. New York: The Ronald Press Company.

KOLLER, P. C. 1960. Chromosome behavior in tumors: readjustments to Boveri's theory. *In: Cell Physiology of Neoplasia*, pp. 9–48. Austin: University of Texas Press.

KONIGSBERG, U. R., and NITOWSKY, H. M. 1962. Studies of the karyotype of clonal strains of Chang liver differing in alkaline phosphatase activity. J. Natl. Cancer Inst., **29**: 699–710.

KOPROWSKI, H., PONTÉN, J. A., JENSEN, F., RAVDIN, R. G., MOORHEAD, P., and SAKSELA, E. 1962. Transformation of cultures of human tissue infected with simian virus SV40. J. Cellular Comp. Physiol., **59**: 281–286.

LEA, D. E. 1955. Actions of radiations on living cells. Second edition. Cambridge: The University Press. 416 pp.

LEVAN, A. 1954. Colchicine-induced C-mitosis in two mouse ascites tumors. Hereditas, **40**: 1–64.

LEVAN, A. 1956a. Chromosome studies on some human tumors and tissues of normal origin, grown *in vivo* and *in vitro* at the Sloan-Kettering Institute. Cancer, **9**: 648–663.

LEVAN, A. 1956b. The significance of polyploidy for the evolution of mouse tumors. Strains of the TA3 mammary adenocarcinoma with different ploidy. Exptl. Cell Res., **11**: 613–629.

LEVAN, A. 1956c. Chromosomes in cancer tissue. Ann. N. Y. Acad. Sci., **63:** 774–792.

LEVAN, A. 1958. Cancerogenesis. A genetic adaptation on the cellular level. *In: Achste Jaarboek van Kankeronderzoek en Kankerbestrijding in Nederland,* pp. 110–126. Lund: Carl Bloms Boktryckeri.

LEVAN, A. 1959. Relation of chromosome status to the origin and progression of tumors: the evidence of chromosome numbers. *In: Genetics and Cancer,* pp. 151–182. Austin: University of Texas Press.

LEVAN, A., and BIESELE, J. J. 1958. Role of chromosomes in cancerogenesis, as studied in serial tissue culture of mammalian cells. Ann. N. Y. Acad. Sci., **71:** 1022–1053.

LEVAN, A., and HAUSCHKA, T. S. 1952. Chromosome numbers of three mouse ascites tumors. Hereditas, **38:** 251–255.

LEVAN, A., and HAUSCHKA, T. S. 1953. Endomitotic reduplication mechanisms in ascites tumors of the mouse. J. Natl. Cancer Inst., **14:** 1–43.

LEVAN, A., HSU, T. C., and STICH, H. F. 1962. The idiogram of the mouse. Hereditas, **48:** 677–687.

LEWIS, W. H. 1927. The formation of giant cells in tissue cultures and their similarity to those in tuberculous lesions. Am. Rev. Tuberc., **27:** 616–628.

LOCKART, R. Z., JR., ELKIND, M. M., and MOSES, W. B. 1961. Radiation responses of mammalian cells grown in culture. II. Survival and recovery characteristics of several subcultures of HeLa S3 cells after X-irradiation. J. Natl. Cancer Inst., **27:** 1393–1404.

MAKINO, S. 1952. A cytological study of the Yoshida sarcoma, an ascites tumor of white rats. Chromosoma, **4:** 649–674.

MAKINO, S. 1956. Further evidence favoring the concept of the stem cell in ascites tumors of rats. Ann. N. Y. Acad. Sci., **63:** 818–830.

MAKINO, S. 1957. The chromosome cytology of the ascites tumors of rats, with special reference to the concept of the stemline cell. Intern. Rev. Cytol., **6:** 25–84.

MAKINO, S., and KANÔ, K. 1953. Cytological studies of tumors. IX. Characteristic chromosome individuality in tumor-strain cells in ascites tumors of rats. J. Natl. Cancer Inst., **13:** 1213–1235.

MAKINO, S., and KANÔ, K. 1955. Cytological studies of tumors. XIV. Isolation of single-cell clones from a mixed-cell tumor of the rat. J. Natl. Cancer Inst., **15:** 1165–1182.

MAKINO, S., and SASAKI, M. 1958. Cytological studies of tumors. XXI. A comparative ideogram study of the Yoshida sarcoma and its subline derivatives. J. Natl. Cancer Inst., **20:** 465–488.

MARKERT, C. L., and URSPRUNG, H. 1963. Production of replicable persistent changes in zygote chromosomes of *Rana pipiens* by injected proteins from adult liver nuclei. Develop. Biol., **7:** 560–577.

MELANDER, Y. 1962. Chromosome behavior during the origin of sex chromatin in the rabbit. Hereditas, **48:** 645–661.

MILES, C. P. 1959. Sex chromatin in cultured normal and cancerous human tissues. Cancer, **12:** 299–305.

MILLER, J.F.A.P. 1961. Etiology and pathogenesis of mouse leukemia. Advan. Cancer Res., 6: 291–368.

MOORHEAD, P. S., and HSU, T. C. 1956. Cytologic studies of HeLa, a strain of human cervical carcinoma. III. Durations and characteristics of the mitotic phases. J. Natl. Cancer Inst., 16: 1047–1066.

MOORHEAD, P. S., NOWELL, P. C., MELLMAN, W. J., BATTIPS, D. M., and HUNGERFORD, D. A. 1960. Chromosome preparations of leukocytes cultured from human peripheral blood. Exptl. Cell Res., 20: 613–616.

MOORHEAD, P. S., and SAKSELA, E. 1963. Non-random chromosomal aberrations in SV$_{40}$-transformed human cells. J. Cellular Comp. Physiol., 62: 57–83.

MORTIMER, R. K. 1958. Radiobiological and genetic studies on a polyploid series (haploid to hexaploid) of Saccharomyces cerevisiae. Radiation Res., 9: 312–326.

MULLER, H. J. 1954. The nature of the genetic effects produced by radiation. In: Radiation Biology, Vol. 1, Part 1, pp. 351–374. A. Hollaender, ed. New York: McGraw-Hill Book Co., Inc.

NICHOLS, W. W., LEVAN, A., HALL, H., and ÖSTERGREN, G. 1962. Measles-associated chromosome breakage. Hereditas, 48: 367–370.

NORRYD, C. 1959. The chromosomes of three human cell strains. Hereditas, 45: 449–460.

NOWELL, P. C., and HUNGERFORD, D. A. 1960. Chromosome studies on normal and leukemic human leukocytes. J. Natl. Cancer Inst., 25: 85–110.

NOWELL, P. C., and HUNGERFORD, D. A. 1961. Chromosome studies in human leukemia. II. Chronic granulocytic leukemia. J. Natl. Cancer Inst., 27: 1013–1035.

NOWELL, P. C., and HUNGERFORD, D. A. 1962. Chromosome studies in human leukemia. IV. Myeloproliferative syndrome and other atypical myeloid disorders. J. Natl. Cancer Inst., 29: 911–931.

OKADA, Y., and TADOKORO, J. 1962. Analysis of giant polynuclear cell formation caused by HVJ virus from Ehrlich's ascites tumor cells. II. Quantitative analysis of giant polynuclear cell formation. Exptl. Cell Res., 26: 108–118.

OKUMURA, H., TAKAOKA, T., and KATSUTA, H. 1958. Comparative studies on chromosomes among rat ascites hepatoma cells before and after the establishment of cell strains in tissue culture. Japan. J. Exptl. Med., 28: 419–432.

ORSI, E. V., and RITTER, H. B. 1958. A report of sex chromatin in human tumor tissue culture. Exptl. Cell Res., 15: 244–246.

OWENS, O. VON H., GEY, M. K., and GEY, G. O. 1958. The effect of calcium and magnesium on the growth and morphology of mouse lymphoblasts (MB III, de Bruyn) in tissue culture. Cancer Res., 18: 968–973.

PONTÉN, J. 1962. Sex chromosomes as markers in transplanted chicken leukaemic cells. Nature, 194: 97.

PUCK, T. T. 1958. Action of radiation on mammalian cells. III. Relationship between reproductive death and induction of chromosome anomalies by X-irradiation of euploid human cells in vitro. Proc. Natl. Acad. Sci., 44: 772–780.

Puck, T. T. 1959. Quantitative studies on mammalian cells *in vitro*. Rev. Mod. Phys., **31**: 433–448.

Ragni, G., and Szybalski, W. 1962. Molecular radiobiology of human cell lines. II. Effects of thymidine replacement by halogenated analogues on cell inactivation by decay of incorporated radiophosphorus. J. Mol. Biol., **4**: 338–346.

Révész, L., Glas, U., and Hilding, G. 1963. Relation between chromosome number and radiosensitivity of tumour cells. Nature, **198**: 260–261.

Révész, L., and Norman, U. 1960. Relationship between chromosome ploidy and radiosensitivity in selected tumor sublines of common origin. J. Natl. Cancer Inst., **25**: 1041–1064.

Roizman, B. 1962. Polykaryocytosis induced by viruses. Proc. Natl. Acad. Sci., **48**: 228–234.

Rothfels, K. H., and Parker, R. C. 1959. The karyotypes of cell lines recently established from normal mouse tissues. J. Exptl. Zool., **142**: 507–520.

Rothfels, K. H., and Siminovitch, L. 1958. An air-drying technique for flattening chromosomes in mammalian cells grown *in vitro*. Stain Technol., **33**: 73–77.

Ruddle, F. H. 1960. Chromosome variation in cell populations. Ph.D. Thesis, University of California, Berkeley. 88 pp.

Ruddle, F. H. 1961. Chromosome variation in cell populations derived from pig kidney. Cancer Res., **21**: 885–894.

Ruddle, F. H. 1962a. Morphological transformation in an established line of pig kidney cells. Proc. Soc. Exptl. Biol. Med., **109**: 116–118.

Ruddle, F. H. 1962b. Nuclear bleb: a stable interphase marker in established line of cells *in vitro*. J. Natl. Cancer Inst., **28**: 1247–1251.

Sandberg, A. A., Ishihara, T., Crosswhite, L. H., and Hauschka, T. S. 1962. Chromosomal dichotomy in blood and marrow of acute leukemia. Cancer Res., **22**: 748–756.

Sandberg, A. A., Ishihara, T., Miwa, T., and Hauschka, T. S. 1961. The *in vivo* chromosome constitution of marrow from 34 human leukemias and 60 nonleukemic controls. Cancer Res., **21**: 678–689.

Sanford, K. K., Likely, G. D., and Earle, W. R. 1954. The development of variations in transplantability and morphology within a clone of mouse fibroblasts transformed to sarcoma-producing cells *in vitro*. J. Natl. Cancer Inst., **15**: 215–237.

Shein, H. M., and Enders, J. F. 1962. Transformation induced by simian virus 40 in human renal cell cultures. I. Morphology and growth characteristics. Proc. Natl. Acad. Sci., **48**: 1164–1172.

Silini, G., and Hornsey, S. 1962. Studies on cell survival of irradiated Ehrlich ascites tumor. III. A comparison of the X-ray survival curves obtained with a diploid and a tetraploid strain. Intern. J. Radiation Biol., **5**: 147–153.

Sorieul, S., and Ephrussi, B. 1961. Karyological demonstration of hybridization of mammalian cells *in vitro*. Nature, **190**: 653–654.

Stern, C. 1960. Principles of human genetics. Second edition. San Francisco: W. H. Freeman and Company. 753 pp.

STICH, H. F. 1963. Chromosomes and carcinogenesis. Canad. Canc. Conf., **5:** 99–115.

STICH, H. F., and HSU, T. C. 1960. Cytological identification of male and female somatic cells in the mouse. Exptl. Cell Res., **20:** 248–249.

STICH, H. F., and STEELE, H. D. 1962. DNA content of tumor cells. III. Mosaic composition of sarcomas and carcinomas in man. J. Natl. Cancer Inst., **28:** 1207–1218.

STOCKDALE, F. E., and HOLTZER, H. 1961. DNA synthesis and myogenesis. Exptl. Cell Res., **24:** 508–520.

SWANSON, C. P. 1957. Cytology and cytogenetics. Englewood Cliffs, N.J.: Prentice-Hall, Inc., 596 pp.

THERKELSEN, A. J., and PETERSEN, G. B. 1962. Frequency of sex-chromatin-positive cells in the logarithmic and postlogarithmic growth phases of human cells in tissue culture. Exptl. Cell Res., **28:** 588–623.

THOMISON, J. B. 1962. Evolution of measles giant cells in tissue culture. Analysis by time lapse microcinematography. Lab. Invest., **11:** 211–219.

TILL, J. E. 1961. Radiosensitivity and chromosome numbers in Strain L mouse cells in tissue culture. Radiation Res., **15:** 400–409.

TIMONEN, S., and THERMAN, E. 1950. Variation of the somatic chromosome number in man. Nature, **166:** 995–996.

TJIO, J. H., and LEVAN, A. 1956a. The chromosome number of man. Hereditas, **42:** 1–6.

TJIO, J. H., and LEVAN, A. 1956b. Comparative idiogram analysis of the rat and the Yoshida rat sarcoma. Hereditas, **42:** 218–234.

TJIO, J. H., and PUCK, T. T. 1958a. Genetics of somatic mammalian cells. II. Chromosomal constitution of cells in tissue culture. J. Exptl. Med., **108:** 259–268.

TJIO, J. H., and PUCK, T. T., 1958b. The somatic chromosomes of man. Proc. Natl. Acad. Sci., **44:** 1229–1237.

TONOMURA, A., and YERGANIAN, G. 1956. Aneuploidy in the regenerating liver of the Chinese hamster. Genetics, **41:** 664–665.

TOUGH, I. M., COURT BROWN, W. M., BAIKIE, A. G., BUCKTON, K. E., HARNDEN, D. G., JACOBS, P. A., KING, M. J., and McBRIDE, J. A. 1961. Cytogenetic studies in chronic myeloid leukaemia and acute leukaemia associated with mongolism. Lancet, **1:** 411–417.

VOGT, M. 1959. A study of the relationship between karyotype and phenotype in cloned lines of strain HeLa. Genetics, **44:** 1257–1270.

VOGT, M., and DULBECCO, R. 1960. Virus-cell interaction with a tumor-producing virus. Proc. Natl. Acad. Sci., **46:** 365–370.

VOGT, M., and DULBECCO, R. 1963. Steps in the neoplastic transformation of hamster embryo cells by polyoma virus. Proc. Natl. Acad. Sci., **49:** 171–179.

WALLACE, R. E., ORSI, E. V., RITTER, H. B., and MOYER, A. W. 1961. Observations during *in vitro* growth of cells derived from rabbit kidney. Exptl. Cell Res., **25:** 671–686.

WAKONIG, R., and FORD, D. K. 1960. Chromosome aberrations in irradiated cells of Chinese hamster grown in tissue culture. Can. J. Zool., **38**: 203–207.

WILSON, J. W., and LEDUC, E. H. 1948. The occurrence and formation of binucleate and multinucleate cells and polyploid nuclei in the mouse liver. Am. J. Anat., **82**: 353–385.

YERGANIAN, G. 1952. Cytogenetic possibilities with the Chinese hamster, *Cricetulus barabensis griseus.* Genetics, **37**: 638–639.

YERGANIAN, G. 1959. Chromosomes of the Chinese hamster, *Cricetulus griseus.* I. The normal complement and identification of sex chromosomes. Cytologia (Tokyo), **24**: 66–75.

YERGANIAN, G. 1963. Cytogenetic analysis. *In: Methodology in Mammalian Genetics*, pp. 469–510. W. J. Burdette, ed. San Francisco: Holden-Day, Inc.

YERGANIAN, G., and LEONARD, M. J. 1961. Maintenance of normal *in situ* chromosomal features in long-term tissue cultures. Science, **133**: 1600–1601.

Nutrition and progression in cell cultures

chapter

5

Nutritional studies on isolated cell populations pose a number of different problems. One practical goal has been the definition of requirements for growth and maintenance of cell strains *in vitro* and the formulation of appropriate nutrients in known chemical terms. Although the long-term cultivation of cell populations in plasma, serum, and tissue extracts was achieved many years ago, it has been more difficult to eliminate completely these complex natural ingredients. Some cell strains, however, can now be propagated in nutrients of precisely known composition, the advantages of which are obvious for chemical and metabolic studies. The determination of nutritional essentials for isolated cells as contrasted to those of the intact organism offers another area of interest, as does the comparison of cultural requirements for different cell types *in vitro,* including neoplastic cell populations. So far, at least, the minimum array of factors required for growth has been surprisingly similar among cultured cells of all kinds, although some compounds in this list are not dietary requirements for the animals of origin. Primary cell strains, however, may be more exacting in cultural properties than are permanent cell strains. This has led to a search for differences that might correlate with transitions between the two that have already been described in Chapters 3 and 4.

Still another topic for study concerns the possibility of nutritional variation in the form of spontaneous or induced changes within isolated somatic populations. Among microorganisms, markers involving the loss or gain of specific requirements for growth are a familiar index of genetic change. But nutritional variants do not seem to arise spontaneously with a similar frequency within somatic cell strains, nor have they been produced by any reliable procedure so far (Eagle, 1960a).

However, studies on drug resistance, to be described in Chapter 6, show clearly that somatic cells can in fact undergo a variety of heritable changes in biosynthetic patterns. There is no reason to assume that cellular adjustments that may lead to the loss or gain of specific nutritional requirements are different in principle from those that confer adaptive responses to particular drugs. Thus the difficulty in obtaining nutritional variants from somatic cell populations may in part be a matter of designing more efficient selection mechanisms (DeMars and Hooper, 1960).

DEFINITION OF REQUIREMENTS FOR
THE GROWTH OF CELL STRAINS

A broad array of studies, performed by different methods, have sought to determine the individual role of micro- and macromolecular constituents in nutrient media for cell growth. These developments are outlined briefly as a background for further discussion. More comprehensive treatments are to be found in a number of recent reviews (Biggers, Rinaldini, and Webb, 1957; Morgan, 1958; Swim, 1959; Paul, 1960; Levintow and Eagle, 1961).

Approaches and Experimental Systems Early investigators in the field of cell nutrition were hampered by the necessity of using explant techniques as well as a culture medium containing complex and unknown additives. In retrospect, progress was also hindered by the belief of Carrel and others that embryo juice and tissue extracts contained unique substrates that were essential for cell growth in general. This conclusion stemmed largely from experiments on chick fibroblasts growing as explants in a plasma coagulum. In such cultures, growth is conspicuously increased by the addition of embryonic extract, and activity can be found in both protein and nonprotein fractions (Baker and Carrel, 1926a, 1926b). Consequently, many efforts were made to isolate essential growth factors from tissue extracts over a period of years (see summaries in Stewart and Kirk, 1954; Waymouth, 1954). The characterization of nutritional components for cell growth, however, made very little headway by these analytical methods. It did not prove possible to isolate and identify the specific amino acids, vitamins, and other constituents presumed to be essential for proliferation and maintenance of isolated cell strains.

In view of these failures, later studies of nutrition in isolated cells and tissues shifted to a purely synthetic approach. Natural media were discarded completely, and efforts were made to replace them with empirical mixtures of chemically defined compounds, free from proteins or other additives of unknown composition. Investigations of this type were initiated by White (1946, 1949), who sought to obtain a synthetic medium for the growth and maintenance of chick embryonic cells. Basing his formulations on data from nutritional studies at the organismal level, White included the amino acids known to maintain nitrogen equilibrium in the rat, various vitamins, and a balanced array of salts, together with glucose as an energy source. Fragments of chick embryonic tissues survived for considerable periods in this medium, without supplementation with serum or macromolecular constituents of any kind, but growth as such failed to occur. These results were confirmed by Morgan, Morton, and Parker (1950), who devised an improved nutrient termed Medium 199 for surviving chick cells. The composition of this mixture was generally similar to those of White, but contained a broader array of cofactors and intermediary metabolites of possible nutritional significance. Like other synthetic nutrients to be described, Medium 199 can be used in combination with serum to cultivate a variety of permanent cell strains derived from mammalian sources. Despite this practical usefulness, neither the original formula nor minor modifications thereof (Pasieka, Morton, and Morgan, 1956) proved capable of supporting progressive growth of freshly isolated cells in the absence of supplementation with protein. It was not possible to demonstrate a net increase in mass in primary chick explants cultivated in Medium 199, nor even to prolong survival of these cells for more than a few weeks or months.

Depletion techniques, however, were eventually devised to reveal the limiting character of specific components in Medium 199 for cell survival (Morton, Pasieka, and Morgan, 1956). If, for example, embryonic chick tissues are incubated in saline alone for 3 to 4 days before adding synthetic nutrients, it is possible to demonstrate significant decreases in survival time when specific amino acids are omitted (Morgan and Morton, 1957). With some exceptions, the results of such depletion studies are in reasonable agreement with the data on cell nutrition as derived from other sources (Morgan, 1958). It seems questionable, however, that the factors which limit progressive attrition and cell death in a surviving system can be equated, except on an empirical basis, with those that determine synthesis in an actively growing population. Significant contributions to the study of nutrition in synthetic media are for the most part possible only under conditions that permit a continuing propagation. As subsequent discussions will make clear, this problem has been solved for some, and perhaps most, permanent cell strains with more recently derived nutrients. To date, however, adaptation and selection have been complicating factors. The additional innovations that may be necessary to promote the growth of primary cells as unmodified stocks in chemically defined media are still unknown.

From a practical standpoint, the most productive approach in cell nutrition up to the present time has been a combination of analytic and synthetic methods. This point of departure stems from the early experiments of Fischer (1941, 1946) with dialyzed media. Recognizing the difficulties inherent in devising a completely synthetic nutrient for chick fibroblasts, Fischer retained the classic plasma-embryonic extract-serum medium, but simplified each of the components by dialysis against saline prior to use. Outgrowth of cells from explanted fragments failed to take place in cultures containing the dialyzed macromolecular constituents alone, but could be restored by adding back the micromolecular components; for example, the dialysate from chick embryo extract. Owing in part to technical complexities (Harris, 1952), Fischer did not succeed in defining completely the active compounds within these dialysates, but his work laid the basis for simpler and more incisive investigations in cell nutrition with dialyzed media.

Essential Factors for Mass Cultures   To Eagle and his collaborators must be given the principal credit for the rapid development of studies on cell nutrition within recent years. In an outstanding series of papers, these workers identified a series of amino acids, vitamins, and other specific micromolecular factors that are required for the growth of freshly isolated populations, as well as for cell strains *in vitro* (see summaries in Eagle, 1960a; Levintow and Eagle, 1961). The experiments of Eagle began with the basic observation that cell types such as *HeLa* or strain *L* will grow readily in a synthetic nutrient if the medium is fortified with a small amount of dialyzed serum protein. As little as 1 to 5 percent serum may suffice, provided the accompanying synthetic nutrient contains an adequate complement of amino acids, vitamins, glucose, and salts. Omission of a single essential constituent will block proliferation and growth in this system; thus it becomes possible to demonstrate the effects of specific nutritional deficiencies at the cellular level in clear-cut fashion.

In his initial studies with this technique, Eagle (1955a) demonstrated that 13 amino acids are essential for the growth of strain *L* mouse cells: arginine, cystine, histidine, leucine, isoleucine, lysine, methionine, phenylalanine, threonine, tryptophan, tyrosine, valine, and glutamine. The deletion of any one of these compounds from the culture medium leads rapidly to a complete arrest of both growth and cell division. A characteristic syndrome of cytopathologic changes is also seen when the cultures are examined microscopically. Up to a point, such deficiency states are reversible, and if the missing amino acid is restored, the test populations resume a normal appearance and proliferate at a rate similar to that of control cultures. Effects of this type are not produced by the addition or subtraction of other amino acids, and those that are nonessential include glycine, alanine, serine, aspartic acid, glutamic acid, proline, and hydroxyproline. Compounds of this group can be synthesized from simpler precursors and are not required by mass populations of *L* cells. For those amino acids that are essential, dose-response curves show individual and often sharply defined optimum concentrations for promoting maximal cell growth (Figure 5.1). Only the L-configurations are biologically active; D-isomers are inert, although not growth-inhibiting in moderate concentrations.

The pattern of amino acid requirements determined for *L* cells has proved to be remarkably similar to that of other cell types when grown as mass cultures in the presence of dialyzed serum. *HeLa* cells show some differences in quantitative responses, but the same 13 amino acids must be provided if proliferation is to occur (Eagle, 1955b). This finding is applicable to a number of other mammalian cell strains as well (Eagle,

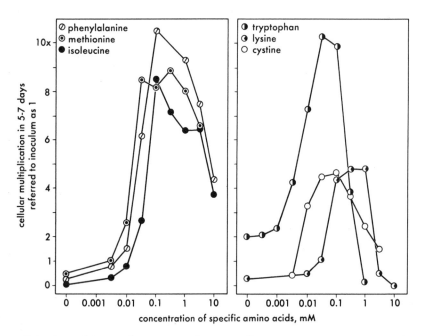

FIG. 5.1. The growth response of *HeLa* cells to varying concentrations of essential amino acids. Inhibition, as shown here, is frequently observed at concentrations in excess of an optimal level. (Redrawn from Eagle, 1955b.)

1955c, 1959; Swim and Parker, 1958a). There seem to be no basic differences in the amino acids required for the growth of freshly isolated cells as compared to established lines. Primary populations of chick embryonic lung cells, for example, will grow progressively in dialyzed media supplemented with synthetic nutrients, but only if all 13 essential amino acids are made available (Neuman and Tytell, 1960a). Similarly, freshly isolated monkey kidney cells can be propagated successfully with the amino acids required by established lines (Eagle, Freeman, and Levy, 1958). In this case, however, the addition of glycine greatly increases the growth that takes place, and is essential for successful subculture of these populations.

Several other minor variations in the pattern of amino acid requirements have been described. Thus cells of the Walker rat carcinoma and mouse leukemia L-5178Y are reported to grow only if provided with asparagine in culture (McCoy, Maxwell, and Neuman, 1956; Haley, Fischer, and Welch, 1961). Serine has likewise been asserted to be necessary for proliferation in one strain of rabbit fibroblasts (Haff and Swim, 1957a). The investigations of Eagle and Piez (1962), which will be detailed in the following section, now show that serine and asparagine are examples of nutritional requirements which are dependent on population density. The need for such metabolites disappears in closely arrayed cell groupings. When this factor is taken into account, there is little if any significant evidence for variation in amino acid requirements between the cell types that have been examined.

Among those amino acids required generally for growth in cell culture, several are noteworthy because they do not represent dietary essentials at the organismal level. Cystine, tyrosine, and glutamine are not included in the list of ten amino acids needed to support the growth of rats (Rose, Oesterling, and Womack, 1948), and even arginine and histidine can be omitted from the human diet if mere maintenance of nitrogen equilibrium rather than growth is used as a criterion (Rose, Haines, and Warner, 1954). None of these five amino acids is dispensable in culture, however, regardless of whether the cells used for assay are derived from human or animal sources. Particular attention has been given to the utilization *in vitro* of glutamine, since it is well known that this compound can be synthesized *in vivo* from other precursors. Although glutamic acid at high levels can substitute for glutamine in the nutrition of *HeLa* cells (Eagle, Oyama, Levy, Horton, and Fleischman, 1956), a similar response does not occur directly with *L* cells. For the latter, a preliminary adaptation is necessary, which as previously described (Chapter 3) appears to involve an induced increase in glutamine synthetase activity. Levintow, Eagle, and Piez (1957) have studied the metabolic fate of labeled glutamine in *HeLa* cells. In this system, glutamine appears to function as an essential building block for cell proteins. Both glutamic acid and glutamine residues occur within newly synthesized protein, but each originates independently by direct incorporation of the corresponding precursors from the nutrient medium. Glutamine can also be transformed in *HeLa* cells to aspartic acid and proline, but the amide nitrogen does not appear to contribute to α-amino groups. Other experiments with *HeLa* cells show that glutamine participates actively in pyrimidine biosynthesis and also, to a lesser extent, in the formation of purines (Salzman, Eagle, and Sebring, 1958).

That glutamine is essential for freshly isolated cells, however, has been questioned recently by Morgan and his associates (Pasieka and Morgan, 1959; Pasieka, Morton, and Morgan, 1960). They observed that glutamine does not extend the survival of chick tissues in protein-free synthetic nutrients and actually accumulates in the external medium. In the same environment, or in synthetic nutrients supplemented with serum, several permanent cell strains were found to utilize glutamine in significant amounts. The significance of this difference is doubtful, however, since the freshly isolated cells were not studied under conditions that would permit growth rather than mere temporary survival. In other experimental systems where chick cells can grow, glutamine does seem to be essential. Where dialyzed media are used for assay, freshly isolated chick cells exhibit a definite growth requirement for glutamine (Neuman and Tytell, 1960a), as indeed Fischer and his colleagues had demonstrated some years ago (Fischer, Astrup, Ehrensvärd, and Oehlenschläger, 1948).

A number of general interpretations have been suggested for the anomalous finding that cell populations *in vitro* appear to have basic amino acid requirements that are additional to those of the whole organism (Eagle, 1959, 1960a). It is conceivable, for example, that modulation or dedifferentiation might lead to a systematic reduction in potential for amino acid biosynthesis within cell strains that have been cultivated in isolation for extended periods. As an over-all explanation, this line of argument seems effectively countered by the fact that even in freshly isolated cells, the same amino acid requirements are to be found. A more convincing concept is the possibility of occasional biosynthetic specialization among cell types *in vivo*, leading to an expanded array of nutritional requirements for single components in culture. At least one pertinent example of this process can be cited. Isolated cell strains are in general unable to hydroxylate phenylalanine to tyrosine (Eagle, Piez, and Fleischman, 1957); and the basis for this deficiency lies in the restriction of phenylalanine hydroxylase, even *in vivo*, to cells of the liver. Since both tyrosine and phenylalanine are required for protein synthesis, a deficiency of either *in vitro* effectively produces a metabolic block. Alternatively, the inability to synthesize particular amino acids *in vitro* could result from the fact that certain essential precursors or cofactors are lacking in this artificial milieu. Eagle (1960a) has in fact shown that monkey kidney cells in primary culture have a reduced ability to convert folic acid to folinic acid, which in turn is reflected in a suboptimal production of glycine from serine, for which folinic acid is a requisite cofactor. The glycine requirement for active growth of these cells, mentioned previously, can be eliminated by providing folinic acid directly in the culture medium. The principal explanation for disparities that exist between amino acid requirements *in vivo* and *in vitro*, however, lies in another direction. This is the assumption that while biosynthesis of certain amino acids (for example, cystine) may proceed at rates sufficient for the needs of tissue cells within the closely arrayed populations of the intact organism, the same yields are inadequate for the requirements of cell strains in monolayers and other isolated systems, particularly during active growth. Considerable experimental support can be marshaled for this concept, which will be considered in more detail in the following section.

The essential role of specific vitamins for cell growth *in vitro* has also been documented by the researches of recent years. As another facet of his initial studies, Eagle (1955d) examined the effects of omitting single vitamins from the synthetic nutrient used in conjunction with dialyzed serum for the cultivation of strain *L* and *HeLa* cells. Seven vitamins were identified as nutritionally essential in this first group of experiments: choline, folic acid, nicotinamide, pantothenate, pyridoxal, riboflavin, and thiamine. The omission of any of these factors ultimately leads to cell death, but deficiency states do not develop immediately. A preliminary period of cultivation in media lacking the vitamin is required to deplete cell reserves. This interval extends for 5 to 15 days with particular vitamins of the foregoing group. Eventually, growth ceases and the cell populations degenerate with characteristic cytopathologic changes. Administration of the missing vitamin, if not delayed too long, can promptly reverse the deficiency syndrome. Some inconsistent results obtained initially were later cleared up by the finding that inositol must be provided for the growth of human cell strains and, with the exception of strain *L*, for animal cell lines as well (Eagle, Oyama, Levy, and Freeman, 1956, 1957). It appears that cell strains in general are able to form inositol to some extent, but only in occasional lines (for example, strain *L*) does biosynthesis reach levels sufficient for sustained growth *in vitro* (Eagle, Agranoff, and Snell, 1960).

These investigations of Eagle, as well as those of Swim and Parker (1958b), indicate that for most cell types at least eight known vitamins must be added to insure growth in a dialyzed medium. Additional needs may eventually be demonstrated, but up to the present time, none of the fat-soluble vitamins (for example, A, D, K, tocopherol) have been found essential for growth within this system, nor has it been possible to show a requirement for biotin or lipoic acid. Whether certain of these are in fact present as trace contaminants of chemical reagents, are included in bound form with serum protein, or are merely nonessential under particular conditions of growth *in vitro* remains to be determined. For those vitamins that are demonstrably essential, a variable level of activity can be found in substitution experiments with precursors and congeners (Eagle, 1956a). In populations of L cells, for example, pyridoxine and pyridoxal have an identical effect on growth, and there is no significant difference in the activity of thiamine as compared to that of cocarboxylase. Some vitamin conjugates, however, are actually less active in this system than are the parent vitamins. Thus pyridoxal phosphate is less efficient on a molar basis than is pyridoxal, and coenzyme A has a lower activity than does pantothenic acid. These differences appear to reside in differential permeability of cells to the compounds concerned, but definite evidence on this point has not yet been obtained. One instance can be cited in which the metabolic conversion product is more effective than the vitamin precursor. As previously noted, folinic acid or citrovorum factor is more active than folic acid in promoting cell growth and biosynthesis of glycine in monkey kidney cells. There are also indications that provision of nonessential amino acids in the culture medium may, at least for some cells, eliminate the requirement for pyridoxal (Swim and Parker, 1958b).

The assessment of mineral requirements for cell growth, as for vitamins, has merely established a minimum group of essentials for proliferation in the assay system used. Eagle (1956b) showed that six ionic species must be included in balanced array for the propagation of *HeLa* or strain L cells in monolayers: Na^+, K^+, Ca^{2+}, Mg^{2+}, Cl^-, and $H_2PO_4^-$. Bicarbonate or carbon dioxide are not required as exogenous supplements, but the physiological production of CO_2 tends to mask the essentiality of this system (Figure 5.2). If suitable provision is made in culture flasks for the absorption of metabolic CO_2 as it is produced, deficiency states and an arrest of cell growth can be observed (Harris, 1954; Geyer and Chang, 1958; Swim and Parker, 1958c; McCoy, Maxwell, and Kruse, 1961). It is probable from studies on the whole organism that additional mineral requirements for cell growth remain to be substantiated *in vitro*. The apparent dispensability of these in the assay

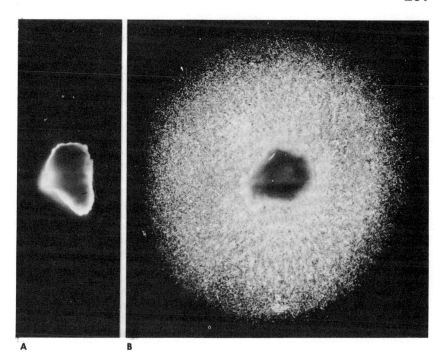

A   B

FIG 5.2. Essential role of bicarbonate for outgrowth of chick heart fibroblasts in plasma culture. (A) Explant from chick heart, cultivated 6 days in bicarbonate-free medium at pH 7.4. No growth occurs if the CO_2 produced during this period is removed continuously by NaOH in an absorption well. (B) Prominent outgrowth zone arising from a heart fragment maintained for 6 days in the same medium, but supplemented with 0.2 percent $NaHCO_3$. (From Harris, 1954. Copyright, Wistar Institute Press.)

systems used may reflect merely their inclusion in small amounts as impurities within individual reagents. From the standpoint of experimental design, the demonstration of requirements for specific inorganic compounds, and especially trace elements, thus presents a difficult problem.

An appropriate carbohydrate source is also essential for the proliferation and growth of isolated cell strains. Several types of assay systems have contributed useful information. These include primary strains of chick fibroblasts in a dialyzed plasma medium (Harris and Kutsky, 1953), monolayer cultures of permanent cell strains growing in the presence of dialyzed serum (Chang and Geyer, 1957; Eagle, Barban, Levy, and Schulze, 1958), and surviving explants of chick embryonic heart in a protein-free medium (Morgan and Morton, 1960).

The pattern of specificity that emerges from these studies is fairly well defined (Figure 5.3). In each case it has been possible to replace glucose with mannose or fructose, although the latter is less efficient on a molar basis in supporting cell growth. Conflicting results have been obtained with galactose, but in most instances this compound can substitute partially or wholly for glucose as a carbohydrate source.

Other hexose sugars appear to be relatively inert. This finding applies to pentose sugars as well, with the exception of ribose. The latter is utilized in lieu of glucose by a variety of human cell strains, and the growth response is greatly increased by the provision of pyruvate (Eagle, Barban, Levy, and Schulze, 1958). Among the disaccharides, only maltose serves as an effective substrate for cell growth, apparently by virtue of maltases that occur both within cells and in dialyzed serum (Harris and Kutsky, 1953; Morgan and Morton, 1960). Turanose shows moderate activity, but there is little evidence that sucrose or lactose are significantly metabolized by isolated cell populations. In contrast to microorganisms, somatic cells *in vitro* are not in general capable of adaptation to new carbohydrate substrates by the induced biosynthesis of appropriate

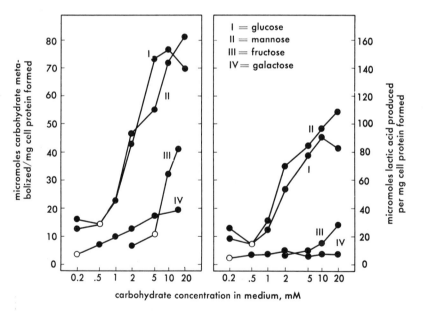

FIG. 5.3. Sugar metabolism in cultures of Chang liver cells. The amounts of carbohydrate utilized and of lactic acid produced are shown as a function of protein formed during cell growth. (Redrawn from Eagle, Barban, Levy, and Schulze, 1958.)

enzymes. There is some evidence, however, for heritable variations that may confer greater efficiency for growth at low levels of carbohydrate or for increased utilization of new carbohydrate sources, or for both. These experiments will be considered in more detail in a later section.

While the requirement for amino acids, vitamins, salts, and carbohydrate has been clearly established, certain other classes of compounds either are dispensable for the propagation of cell strains in the presence of serum protein or are active only under special circumstances. An essential role for unsaturated fatty acids, or for lipids in general, has not been demonstrated for mass populations in dialyzed media. However, cultures of Walker carcinosarcoma 256 cells in serumless media may be stimulated by the provision of methyl oleate (Neuman and Tytell, 1960c), and it has been reported that an apparent requirement of albumin in the clonal growth of Chinese hamster cells can be eliminated by the substitution of linoleic acid within a narrow concentration range (Ham, 1963). Whether or not lipids in some form are essential, it is clear that certain cells can utilize triglycerides or serum lipids extensively if these are present in the culture medium (Bailey, Gey, and Gey, 1959; Geyer and Neimark, 1959). Nucleic acid derivatives, whether in conjugated form or as free bases, need not be provided for cell growth *in vitro*, a fact that reflects active *de novo* synthesis of the necessary precursors (Salzman, Eagle, and Sebring, 1958). Both purines and pyrimidines can, however, be incorporated directly if furnished as preformed substrates in the culture medium (Salzman and Sebring, 1959).

By appropriate manipulation of media the utilization of exogenous purines can even be made obligate. This possibility arises from the fact that *de novo* synthesis of purines can be blocked by administering folic acid antagonists; for example, amethopterin. Growth ceases under these conditions, but can continue if the medium is enriched by three additives to supply the products of blocked reactions (Hakala, 1957). Thymidine and glycine are necessary, as is a preformed purine such as hypoxanthine, which can be transformed into adenine and guanine in nucleic acids and the purine components of nucleotide cofactors. In further experiments along the same lines, Hakala and Taylor (1959) found that adenine alone (Figure 5.4), or its nucleoside and nucleotide derivatives, can serve as an efficient purine source for the growth of amethopterin-blocked cells. Guanine nucleosides and nucleotides sufficed for limited growth of mouse Sarcoma 180 cells, but not for *HeLa* cells. Essentially similar results have been reported by Szybalski, Szybalska, and Ragni (1962) in a study of purine utilization in populations of Detroit *D*98 human cells derived from bone marrow.

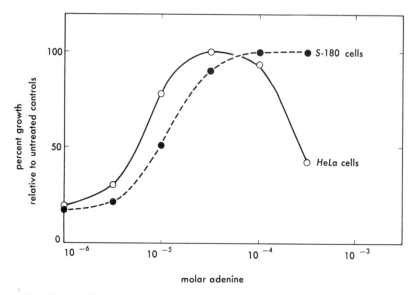

FIG. 5.4. Utilization of adenine as a purine source by *HeLa* and mouse Sarcoma 180 cells in which *de novo* synthesis of purines is blocked by amethopterin. (Redrawn from Hakala and Taylor, 1959.)

Population Density and Nutritional Requirements   Studies in cell nutrition have for the most part been designed on the view that nutritional essentials as defined for mass populations are also appropriate for the growth of single cells. While this assumption may have some validity in a culture of bacteria or protozoa, it is only partially true even within microorganisms. Sparse growth of bacteria in low population densities has frequently been observed. It would appear that somatic cells in culture have even less efficient homeostatic mechanisms. A number of metabolites that can be synthesized by these cells may become limiting for growth or survival under conditions that permit excessive losses to the surrounding medium. The tendency for such depletion passes unnoticed in mass cultures because of a mutual buffering effect between cells in close proximity. But in sparse populations, the loss of one or more metabolites imperfectly retained may increase to the point where replacement through biosynthesis is exceeded. Under these conditions, growth will fail to occur unless a compensating exogenous source is provided. Thus somatic cells in culture can simulate "leaky" mutants in microorganisms, which show clear-cut modifications in nutritional requirements according to population density.

The first indications that excessive losses of metabolites may occur in dispersed populations emerged from efforts to establish defined media suitable for the growth of clones from single cells. With this objective in mind, Sato, Fisher, and Puck (1957) established dilute populations of *HeLa* cells in dialyzed human serum, supplemented with the synthetic nutrient designed by Eagle (1955c) for the propagation of mass cultures. Clonal growth failed to occur under these conditions. The capacity for clonal proliferation could be restored, however, by adding 10 to 20 percent whole human serum to Eagle's synthetic nutrient, or alternatively, by supplementing dialyzed serum plus Eagle's nutrient with an additive containing cholesterol, ascorbic acid, coenzyme A, cocarboxylase, DNA, flavine-adenine dinucleotide, glutathione, and cysteine. Although this mixture was empirically effective under the conditions employed by Sato, other investigators have been unable to verify any general need for cholesterol or for other compounds on the prescribed list. This discrepancy probably means that with certain pretreatments, cells to be cultured can suffer unusual losses of metabolites and cofactors (Levintow and Eagle, 1961).

A more detailed study of clonal proliferation in defined media was subsequently undertaken by Lockart and Eagle (1959). In order to obviate the possibility of traumatic injury during dissociation procedures, stock populations of *HeLa, KB,* and Chang conjunctival cells were maintained continuously as suspension cultures, and were simply diluted out in nutrient medium prior to plating, without exposure to the action of enzymes or chelating agents. But even with these precautions, growth failed to occur when the inocula were small, despite presence of the 13 amino acids, 7 vitamins, and other nutritional factors demonstrably adequate for the proliferation of stock lines in mass culture. By adding also seven nonessential amino acids to the basal nutrient, however, the plating efficiency for single cells rose from zero to levels ranging from 50 to 100 percent. Of the individual amino acids studied in this context, serine showed the highest activity. In some experiments, serine was as effective in increasing the capacity for clonal growth as the entire group of seven accessory amino acids (Figure 5.5). To explain these clear-cut effects, Lockart and Eagle suggested that nonessential amino acids, and serine in particular, are readily lost from the intracellular pool to the surrounding medium, a phenomenon that can be growth-limiting if equilibrium is not restored.

Other experiments have shown that even with mass populations, growth in some instances may fail to occur unless the external medium is supplemented with one or more metabolites known to be synthesized by the cells in question. One such example has been reported by Herzenberg and Roosa (1960), who found that pyruvate is a requirement for the proliferation of *P-388* mouse lymphoma cells *in vitro.* Tracer experi-

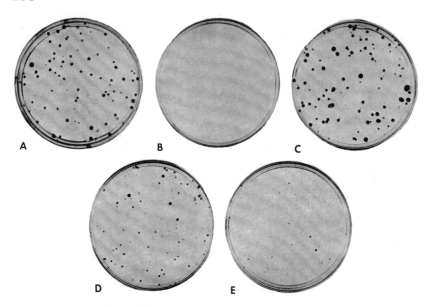

FIG. 5.5. The effect of "nonessential" amino acids on the plating efficiency of HeLa S_3 cells in dialyzed serum. The seven factors studied included alanine, asparagine, aspartic acid, glutamic acid, glycine, proline, and serine, each at 0.1 to 0.2 mM. (A) Growth of colonies from isolated cells in 10 percent whole human serum supplemented with Eagle's basal medium. (B) Same, but with dialyzed serum substituted for whole serum. (C) Growth in 10 percent dialyzed serum, Eagle's nutrient, and seven nonessential amino acids. (D) Similar to (C), but with serine alone added to dialyzed serum and Eagle's medium. (E) Glycine alone, in combination with dialyzed serum and Eagle's nutrient. (From Lockart and Eagle, 1959, with the permission of *Science*.)

ments showed that pyruvate forms as usual from glucose in cells of this strain. A high concentration of exogenous pyruvate must nevertheless be provided, far in excess of the amount actually metabolized. These facts suggest that pyruvate is lost readily from *P*-388 cells, but re-enters only with difficulty. Herzenberg and Roosa found that the pyruvate requirement of mass populations can be replaced with serine or glycine, but for purposes of cloning, both pyruvate and serine (or glycine) must be present. These observations are consistent with the findings of Neuman and Tytell (1960b), who reported that the growth of a wide variety of primary and permanent cell lines as mass cultures is stimulated significantly by the inclusion of glycine or serine in the nutrient medium.

The requirement for cystine in isolated populations is equally a function of the cultural conditions that are imposed in a given cell system (Eagle, Piez, and Oyama, 1961). Using labeled compounds, these investigators showed that each of several cell lines tested was capable of synthesizing cystine from glucose and methionine, although the cells concerned died if placed in a cystine-free medium. When traces of L-cystine (0.002 to 0.005 mM) are added, however, sustained growth takes place. Under these conditions, 16 to 80 percent of the cystine residues in newly synthesized protein derive from methionine sulfur and glucose carbon. It thus appears that externally supplied cystine prevents excessive depletion of cystine formed *de novo* within the cell, although direct incorporation of the preformed amino acid also occurs. At sufficiently high population densities, it becomes unnecessary to supplement the nutrient with cystine, presumably because the effective loss from individual cells is minimized by the increased ratio of cells to medium.

A general statement of population density as a modifying factor in cell nutrition has been formulated by Eagle and Piez (1962) on the basis of continuing studies dealing with the loss of specific constituents from somatic cells in culture. At least seven compounds (cystine, homocystine, serine, inositol, pyruvate, glutamine, tyrosine) can be implicated inferentially from the fact that each, under certain conditions, is an essential nutrient in spite of the fact that synthesis occurs at levels adequate for at least limited cell growth. From the facts that have been ascertained for serine and the other compounds listed, it is increasingly clear that the function of this group of nutritional factors is to condition the microenvironment so that suitable equilibria can be established between intra- and extracellular pools of the metabolites in question. Thus a hard and fast distinction cannot be drawn between essential and nonessential factors in cell nutrition. The definition is clearly an operational one, dependent on the conditions of culture and the characteristics of any given cell type. For those substrates that can be synthesized, the need for exogenous supplementation is a function of variable balances between production, utilization, and external loss.

These important studies suggest that increased attention should be given to changes in permeability, which may occur in isolated cell populations either as a result of disaggregation and other technical procedures, or as a consequence of transitions in physiologic state. This is a field of study that in the past has been all but ignored. A number of investigators have attempted to measure viability in dissociated populations by changes in dye-binding capacity (Phillips and Terryberry, 1957; Hanks and Wallace, 1958; Kaltenbach, Kaltenbach, and Lyons, 1958), but there has been no analysis of membrane alterations or other cellular shifts on which these diagnostic criteria have been presumably based.

It has been generally recognized that trypsin treatment may result in cell injury, for example, but actual experimental data about this phenomenon are few. Weiss (1958) noted, however, that significant losses in dry mass occurred in mouse Sarcoma 37 cells that had been exposed to trypsin, although the mean cell diameter and viability appeared to be unchanged. Danes, Broadfoot, and Paul (1963) similarly observed a fall in respiration of strain *L* cells following trypsinization, owing to the loss of Krebs cycle intermediates to the surrounding medium. Several other permanent lines reacted similarly, but some were unaffected by enzyme treatment.

Tracer methods involving the incorporation of P^{32} have been used by Levine (1960) to assess the effect of manipulative procedures on *HeLa* cells. Trypsinization causes a significant loss of label, as do repeated rinsings in saline, which appear to alter the permeability of the cell membrane. More drastic methods of tissue disaggregation may result in marked functional losses in the resulting cell suspensions, even when morphological integrity is preserved. This is demonstrated particularly well in the experiments of Zimmerman, Devlin, and Pruss (1960), in which single cell preparations were obtained from rat kidney and liver by homogenizing in calcium-free solution. After isolation, the cells appeared to be morphologically intact, but an extensive leakage of enzymes had occurred, and the final suspensions were incapable of carrying on anaerobic glycolysis. Artifacts may thus arise as a result of damage incurred during the dissociation and handling of cells, particularly in the establishment of primary cultures. There is an obvious need for quantitative information about the factors that may be limiting for the maintenance of membrane integrity during isolation procedures.

GROWTH EFFECTS ASSOCIATED WITH PROTEINS

Cell populations within the animal body are constantly immersed in protein-containing fluids. The complexity of this macromolecular environment is well known, although the precise functions of individual proteins remain for the most part to be specified. Speculation has been active concerning the possible role of these large molecules in cell growth. It has been asserted frequently that proteins as such are indispensable in nutrition at the cellular level. Carrel, Fischer, and others looked upon the action of embryonic extracts as dependent on the selective utilization of protein substrates. But despite the considerable attention that has been given to this problem, no universal role for proteins in cell nutrition has been established. Even where proteins are requisite for cell growth *in vitro*, their functions appear to be accessory and diverse in nature. Rather than serving as direct substrates, proteins have been implicated in numerous growth-promoting processes; for example, as passive carriers of essential micronutrients, participants in cell-substrate binding mechanisms, or possible regulators of permeability. This does not mean that proteins are necessarily dispensable for cell growth in general, although a number of isolated cell strains can now be propagated in protein-free media. The multiplicity of mechanisms by which macromolecules can influence maintenance and proliferation, however, does not seem to have been previously appreciated.

Uptake of Exogenous Proteins Since the simple utilization of media proteins as a nitrogen source was the original explanation offered for the growth-promoting action of these large molecules, it may be useful at the outset to examine the evidence that bears on this possibility. The question of penetration by macromolecules, for example, has received considerable study. Contrary to the usual belief, there are a number of circumstances in which proteins can enter or leave tissue cells. Thus the discharge of digestive enzymes and the release of serum proteins from the liver are well known. Likewise, the release of trophic hormones from the pituitary and the probable entry of these proteins into target organs can be cited as other examples of macromolecular transfers.

There is a variety of experimental evidence summarized in recent reviews (Schechtman, 1956; Harris, 1958), which demonstrates the experimental uptake of proteins by particular cell types. Knight and Schechtman (1954), for example, injected bovine serum albumin into chickens and examined the protein content of eggs laid subsequently. Large amounts of bovine protein with electrophoretic properties unaltered accumulated in these eggs and could be identified by serologic methods. Other investigators have used fluorescent antibody techniques to demonstrate the passage of external proteins into tissue cells. Coons (1956) injected laboratory animals with a variety of heterologous proteins (crystalline egg albumin, human gamma globulin, crystalline bovine albumin), and found that antigen could be demonstrated within parenchymal cells of the liver, in lymphocytes, in fibroblasts, in renal epithelial cells, and in the connective tissue and reticulo-endothelial system generally.

In cell cultures, there is some evidence for the selective depletion of media proteins, although whether an uptake of macromolecules as such takes place is not clear. Kent and Gey (1957, 1960), for example, grew two permanent strains of rat tumor cells in a medium containing equal parts of human adult or placental cord serum and a balanced saline. Electrophoretic patterns of the serum proteins were obtained for media after varying periods of cell growth, as well as for incubated blanks. No changes were observed in the characteristic albumin or γ-globulin components, but a marked drop took place in the α-2 globulin fraction of used media from both cell strains (Figure 5.6). This decline after 29 days amounted to 35 to 40 percent of the levels found initially in incubated blanks. The β-globulin fraction was also depleted in used media, but characteristically to a different degree by the two cell lines concerned.

Most of these examples are of a specialized character, but they serve to suggest that the movement of macromolecules between cells and the external medium is a more frequent occurrence than has been generally realized. Where uptake does occur, the mechanisms of transfer are still not clearly understood. A number of models have been sug-

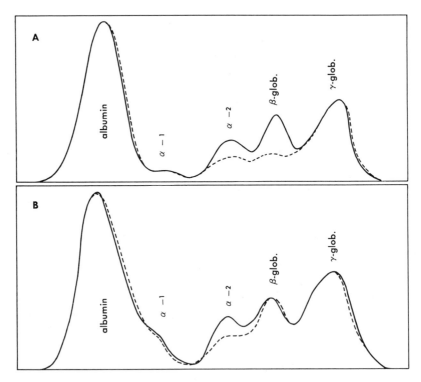

FIG. 5.6. Paper electrophoresis recordings of serum proteins in nutrients used for cultivation of rat tumor cells. *Solid lines*: incubated fluid controls. *Broken lines*: used culture media. (A) *TSAT-72* rat sarcoma. (B) *WRC-256* rat carcinoma. (After Kent and Gey, 1960. Reproduced with permission from *Science*.)

gested for the entry of proteins into cells, including such processes as facilitated diffusion and active transport (Danielli, 1954). For the most part, however, interest has focused on pinocytosis, a phenomenon that can be demonstrated commonly in amoebae as well as in cells in tissue culture (Holter, 1959, 1961). The word pinocytosis means "drinking by cells," and was coined by Lewis (1931) to describe the formation at the cell surface of fluid-filled globules that then pass into the interior. Such pinocytotic vesicles may contain dissolved substances as well as proteins bound to the original cell membrane (Nachmias and Marshall, 1961). In amoebae, the vesicles arise by invaginations that form vesicles and are pinched off from the surface. Cells in tissue culture, however, exhibit membranous ruffle pseudopodia; these, by infoldings, enwrap small quantities of fluid (Gey, 1956). In either case, the pinocytotic vesicles after their formation may coalesce as larger vacuoles or shrink to form granular masses. There is no apparent lower limit in the size of globules taken in by pinocytosis, and this has given rise to speculations that pinocytotic vesicles have a functional relationship with the endoplasmic reticulum or other cytoplasmic organelles (Holter, 1961).

Pinocytosis thus suggests the existence of a dynamic transport mechanism for the permeation of macromolecules into living cells, and it has been tempting to assume that extracellular protein may gain ingress in this way and thereby be utilized in significant amounts for cell growth. An accumulating array of facts, however, militates against this concept. Chief among the evidence are the observations of Holter and his collaborators on the relative potential for pinocytosis in tissue cells (Holter and Holtzer, 1959; Holtzer and Holtzer, 1960). These investigators have used tissue slices and cell cultures to survey a wide variety of cell types for their ability to pinocytose heterologous proteins *in vitro*. For this purpose various plasma proteins (normal rabbit globulin, rabbit antichickmyosin, bovine plasma albumin) were labeled with fluorescein according to the methods of Coons (1956). When these preparations are incubated with cell cultures or tissue slices, pinocytosis can be detected by the appearance of fluorescent substance as discrete droplets in the cytoplasm. Extensive uptake of fluorescein-conjugated proteins were observed in cells of the reticulo-endothelial series, such as macrophages, leukocytes, and Kupffer cells of the liver. Pinocytotic vesicles were also prominent in epithelial cells from tissue slices of the kidney or ileum of newborn mice and in cultures of several tumors (*HeLa*, Ehrlich, and *DBA* ascites cells). On the other hand, strain *L* mouse cells failed to show pinocytosis, indicating that the presence of this phenomenon is not a diagnostic feature of cells with neoplastic properties. Negative results were obtained with cartilage, muscle, and fibroblasts in tissue slices, as well as with parenchymal cells from such organs as stomach, bladder, adrenal, or pancreas. Likewise, normal fibroblasts, kidney, and human amnion in cell culture failed to show uptake. Considered as a whole, these results have led Holtzer and his collaborators to suggest that pinocytosis may be characteristic only of a rather restricted group of cell types, which can be considered specialized for this purpose (for example, cells of the reticulo-endothelial system).

Even if pinocytosis could be correlated more closely with cell growth, there is a formal difficulty in assuming that protein taken up in this way may be directly metabolized. In all instances studied so far, pinocytotic vesicles are bounded by a membrane. This structure is persistent and does not disappear at any stage to leave the inner contents free to mingle with the surrounding cytoplasm (Holter, 1961). A graphic illustration can be provided by experiments with ferritin, a protein that, because of its high iron content, is capable of high electron scatter and consequently can be visualized with the electron microscope. Easton, Goldberg, and Green (1962) conjugated ferritin with normal gamma globulin as well as with immune antibodies directed against ascites tumor cells, and studied the interaction process *in vitro*. Electron micrographs show that ferritin conjugates do not in either case appear able to pass through the cell membrane. Where ferritin can be visualized in the cell interior, it is always contained within membrane-bounded profiles (Figure 5.7). Similar observations using ferritin alone have been reported by Ryser, Caulfield, and Aub (1962). These results emphasize that the physical uptake of macromolecules does not necessarily connote functional entry into the cytoplasmic matrix. Participation in metabolic sequences of protein taken up by pinocytosis is corresponding unlikely.

A clear-cut answer to the question of whether extracellular protein serves as a nitrogen source in cell growth, however, can be obtained only by chemical methods. The careful studies of Eagle and Piez (1960) now appear to have provided decisive information of this kind. For the work in question, *HeLa* cells were cultivated in media containing labeled proteins plus an adequate complement of known crystalloidal nutrients. In some series the macromolecular supplement consisted of C^{14}-labeled rabbit serum protein or rabbit serum specifically marked with C^{14}-L-lysine. Eagle and Piez also considered the possibility that homologous protein may be incorporated according to a pattern differing from that of heterologous proteins. Accordingly, they prepared a nondialyzable extract, derived directly from stock populations of *HeLa* cells propagated in the presence of C^{14}-phenylalanine. This labeled fraction was added

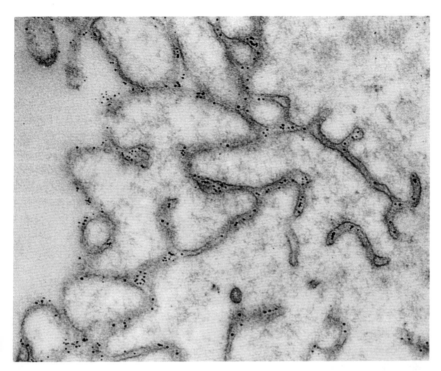

FIG. 5.7. Electron micrograph showing zone of surface folding in Krebs ascites tumor cell incubated with immune ferroglobulin. Ferritin molecules provide an "electron stain," showing the localization of ferroglobulin along surface membranes. No ferritin is visible within the cytoplasmic matrix. (From Easton, Goldberg, and Green, 1962.)

to assay cultures in combination with, or as a substitute for, serum protein. In each of these experiments, newly synthesized proteins were isolated after a standard growth interval, and specific activities were determined as a measure for the incorporation of labeled precursors. The incorporation of label was remarkably small. In none of the combinations specified did the proportion of cell protein derived from the protein of the medium exceed 3 to 6 percent. Because there are several ways in which labeling can occur without actual utilization (for example, adsorption of media proteins to the cell layers), even these estimates probably represent maximal values.

These results of Eagle and Piez thus suggest that, at least for permanent cell strains growing in synthetic nutrients, the contribution of dialyzed protein as an added nitrogen source is very minor, if it is to be considered at all. The possibility that proteins may be utilized to a greater extent by cells growing under more specialized conditions is, of course, not precluded. There is evidence, for example, that in certain tumors (Henderson and LePage, 1959), or perhaps for some embryonic systems (Francis and Winnick, 1953), such may be the case. But it is increasingly clear that the ability of extracellular proteins to promote the growth of isolated cell populations depends in general on mechanisms other than the mass provision of amino acid substrates for protein biosynthesis.

Cell Attachment Mechanisms   Physical as well as chemical concepts have been invoked to explain the apparent need for extracellular protein by cell populations propagated *in vitro*. Since the majority of strains are maintained as monolayers on a glass substrate, and often will multiply only in this fashion, some investigators have suggested that proteins act by conditioning surfaces not otherwise suitable for cell growth. According to this idea, thin films formed on glass by proteins or other surface-active agents may permit cells to adhere and proliferate in a more favored location. Several investigations in recent years have been directed toward the isolation of proteins thought to function as specific cell-attachment factors. Lieberman and Ove (1957, 1958a) fractionated bovine serum by precipitation and column extractions with diethylaminoethyl (DEAE) cellulose. The preparations obtained were assayed for ability to promote growth of Chang human appendix and other cell lines in monolayer culture. No growth occurred in the absence of serum proteins or active subfractions, which were assumed to be required for adherence and spreading of the cells concerned. By means of purification a product was obtained that showed increases of 40-fold or more in specific activity as compared to bovine serum. Lieberman and Ove did not attempt to characterize these fractions in detail, but the active factors appeared to be glycoproteins, included within the α-globulin fraction.

Proceeding independently, Fisher, Puck, and Sato (1958, 1959) likewise fractionated bovine serum and obtained subfractions that served to replace whole serum for the macromolecular requirements of *HeLa* cells. These investigators suggested that two protein components of serum are essential for cell growth, whether in mass populations or in clonal culture (1) serum albumin, thought to function at least in part as a carrier of essential small molecules, and (2) an α-globulin, believed necessary for the attachment and spreading of cells on a glass surface. In searching for an improved source of the spreading factor, Fisher noted that the active α-globulin from adult bovine serum had properties resembling those of fetuin, a mucoprotein known to be abundant in embryonic calf serum (Pedersen, 1947; Deutsch, 1954). Approximately

45 percent of the protein within fetal calf serum consists of this single component. Fetuin preparations, when assayed in culture, proved to be highly active in promoting the attachment and spreading of *HeLa* cells. Whether fetuin as such is responsible for the effects obtained, however, has been questioned by Lieberman, Lamy, and Ove (1959). By using DEAE columns for more precise chromatographic separations, an active spreading factor in bovine serum could be separated from an apparently inactive but highly purified fetuin. Actually, it appears that protein fractions with varying potential for modifying cell attachment are widespread in distribution, since practically all sera are active and the effect in culture is not species-specific. Fisher, Puck, and Sato (1958) suggested originally that the activity of cell attachment factors is based on ability to inhibit tryptic digestion, and additional support for this view can be cited from the experiments of Hebb and Chu (1960). These investigators found that strain *L* mouse cells, which had been trypsinized, remained rounded if transferred in large inocula and were unable to attach in an ordinary medium containing 2 percent calf serum. They could be made to do so even after a delay of as much as 24 hours by adding crystalline soybean trypsin inhibitor or by increasing the serum concentration to 10 percent. These effects were attributed to traces of trypsin that remained in association with the cells and continued to act unless neutralized in culture.

Proteins, however, are only one of a number of factors that may affect the association of cells with physical substrates. Later work indicates that the picture of cell adhesions has been considerably over-simplified by the assumption that cells in general will not adhere and spread on glass surfaces in the absence of extracellular protein. The work of Easty, Easty, and Ambrose (1960), and especially the detailed studies of Taylor (1961), now show that this premise is invalid. In the latter experiments, a variety of cell types were examined, including freshly trypsinized cells from chick liver, kidney, retina, mouse skin, and a permanent strain of Chang human conjunctival cells. In all these systems, cell attachment and spreading occurred rapidly and completely when preparations were incubated on a clean glass substrate in Eagle's medium containing no added protein. Approximately 80 percent of the cells adhered to the glass surface within 2 minutes; after 10 minutes, attachment was practically complete (Figure 5.8). This process does not appear to represent a physiological reaction, since the rate and extent of attachment were almost identical when formalin-fixed cells were substituted for living populations. In either case, the addition of serum to the culture medium, or precoating the glass substrate with proteins, not only served to reduce greatly the percentage of cells that

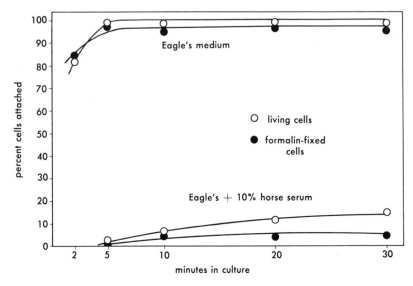

FIG. 5.8. Comparison of the rates of attachment to glass of living or formalin-killed Chang conjunctival cells, in Eagle's medium, with and without serum. (Redrawn from Taylor, 1961.)

became attached within a similar interval, but also retarded markedly the spreading process when adherence did occur. The extensive data reported from Taylor's investigations leave little doubt that extracellular protein is dispensable for primary attachment and spreading, in contrast to views held previously. This does not mean, however, that these substrate associations in protein-free media are necessarily stable or conducive to progressive growth. Taylor found that detachment and cytolysis occurred secondarily in many cases, particularly with freshly isolated cells. This fact probably explains the inability of Lieberman and Ove, as well as Fisher and his colleagues, to detect significant cell adherence and spreading in protein-free media, since observations were for the most part made at 24 hours. Thus the processes of attachment and spreading per se seem to be essentially independent from those that affect growth and survival.

A number of additional observations from Taylor's investigation are of interest in comparing the process of cell adhesion to glass substrates in the presence and absence of protein, respectively. Calcium ions, for example, have frequently been regarded as essential for cell binding and are necessary for the stability of monolayers in the presence of serum (Weiss, 1960). Nevertheless, Taylor found that omission of calcium from Eagle's medium caused no delay in attachment or decrease in the extent of spreading, if serum was also lacking. If, however, serum was added to the test media, adhesion and spreading were strongly inhibited by a calcium deficiency and could be restored to normal by the replacement of calcium ions. Similarly, although proteolytic enzymes and chelating agents are effective in removing cell populations from glass surfaces in serum-containing medium, neither trypsin treatment nor the addition of versene at 0.05 percent served to disrupt attachment and spreading in protein-free nutrients. Taylor therefore suggests that two types of bonding occur in substrate adhesions: (1) attachment mediated by an intermediate protein film, susceptible to enzymatic breakage and probably involving calcium linkages, and (2) a direct attachment of cells to clean glass surfaces. The mechanism of association in the latter case is still conjectural, since both cells and substrate appear to bear a like electrostatic charge. Counteracting London-van der Waals forces have been invoked by Curtis (1962) as an explanation, but as yet no supporting experimental evidence has been provided.

In contrast to these studies on factors that regulate primary attachment and spreading in protein-free media, very little attention has been given to the stabilization of initial cell-substrate association as a prerequisite for progressive growth of the populations concerned. Under some conditions, it appears that the specific properties of different glass substrates may be decisive in determining whether continuing adhesion and cell growth are to occur. Information on this point has been offered by Rappaport, Poole, and Rappaport (1960). These investigators have attempted to correlate the characteristics of glass surfaces with their ability to support the proliferation of monolayers in chemically defined media. As others had previously found, Rappaport and her colleagues noted that stock populations of *HeLa* or primary monkey kidney cells detach from the surfaces of Pyrex culture flasks and degenerate after 24 hours or more of incubation in protein-free media (earlier phases of attachment were not investigated). Surprisingly different results were obtained, however, when culture vessels made from certain types of soft glass with a high alkali content were used. In these, monkey kidney cells proliferated logarithmically as stable monolayers, although the same cell suspensions degenerated promptly on Pyrex surfaces. By autoclaving in sodium carbonate, even Pyrex flasks can be modified to permit the growth of *HeLa*, strain *L*, and primary monkey kidney cells in synthetic media (Rappaport and Bishop, 1960).

No attempt was made to determine whether serial subculture under these conditions could be achieved, but the differences between substrates are noteworthy. Rappaport and her collaborators have advocated an explanation based on comparative surface properties of the glasses studied. Pyrex is characterized by a much lower total negative surface charge, and because of its lesser sodium content and denser structure, has a lower proton exchange capacity than do soft glasses. The assumption is made that bonding of cells to glass surfaces may occur via cation bridges and that this process is limited on Pyrex by an inadequate number of attachment sites. Such a concept may justify more extensive tests, but it is perhaps simpler to view the stabilization of primary attachments into a monolayer growth phase as due to progressive secretion or release of protein between the cells and associated glass substrate. Experiments by Alfred and Pumper (1960), and especially those of Rosenberg (1960), show clearly that the formation of microexudates by cells attached to glass substrates does indeed occur. Further, Rappaport and her associates find that a high calcium concentration is required for the continuing stable proliferation of monolayers on appropriate substrates, and that cells can be released from this attachment during growth by chelating agents. Both properties, as mentioned previously, are characteristic of the attachment of cells to glass in the presence of protein rather than in its absence (Taylor, 1961). Considering these facts, the probable explanation for disparities in growth on Pyrex and soft glass would seem to lie in the differential ability of these substrates to elicit or retain a localized protein exudate by the cells concerned.

Liberation of Nutrients from Serum Extracellular protein may serve to modulate or stabilize cell substrate associations in monolayer cultures, but there are other functions in cell growth for which these macromolecules are even more important. The fact that serum has been required for the propagation of cell strains in free suspension as well as on glass substrates indicates that a selective contribution of nutritional factors may occur. Eagle (1955c), as well as Fisher, Puck, and Sato (1958), has accordingly suggested that the need for serum protein can be attributed to the provision of accessory small molecules found within, or bound initially to, proteins and gradually released into the nutrient medium. Precedents for this concept can be cited from microbial systems. The Reiter treponeme, for example, shows an apparent growth requirement for serum albumin (Oyama, Steinman, and Eagle, 1953). On investigation, however, the sole function of the required protein proved to be the release of an essential lipid. This factor is directly needed for growth, but has toxic effects if made available in appreciable quantities in the free form.

There are now a number of investigations that show clearly that serum protein can indeed provide specific substrates or cofactors in limited quantities for the growth of isolated somatic cells. The case that has been analyzed in greatest detail concerns the cystine requirement of mammalian cells in culture (Eagle, Oyama, and Piez, 1960). As noted previously, cystine must in general be included in the nutrients employed, but occasionally some background growth occurs in cystine-free media. This suggests that accessory mechanisms may operate to supply the exogenous cystine required by all but high-density cell populations. From further study, Eagle and his collaborators found that in the presence of dialyzed serum, a number of inorganic sulfur-containing compounds could replace free cystine as a basis for cell growth. The most obvious explanation for these results seemed to be the assumption that, as in certain microorganisms, cystine can be synthesized from inorganic precursors. When this hypothesis was tested by using S^{35}-labeled compounds, however, the cystine in newly formed cell proteins remained completely free of label. The action of compounds such as dithionite, sulfite, or thioglycollate was eventually demonstrated to be the release of free cystine, which had been initially bound as half-residues by disulfide linkages with protein-SH groups. After appropriate treatment of dialyzed protein with dithionite, for example, a cystine deficiency state can be readily demonstrated in culture unless free cystine as such is provided.

The potential availability of nutritional factors contained within, or in conjunction with, proteins in the culture medium has been further emphasized by the finding that dialyzed serum contains the complete complement of enzymes required for the degradation of protein to free amino acids (Piez, Oyama, Levintow, and Eagle, 1960). Thus, if serum is dialyzed and stored at $-20°$ C, no significant accumulation of free amino acids can be found on later thawing. But when similar preparations are left in the refrigerator at $2°$ to $5°$ C, the levels of free amino acids rise progressively and approach in as little as 11 days the concentrations typical of fresh whole serum. Proteolysis is even more rapid in culture media incubated at $37°$ C, with or without cells. From a practical standpoint, the spontaneous release of free amino acids can be somewhat reduced if serum is filtered through a Sephadex gel as a means of eliminating small molecules initially present. For example, Eagle and his collaborators found that gel-filtered serum after 5 days of incubation contained only one fifth the amount of free amino acids released in dialyzed serum during the same period. The explanation of this differential doubtless lies in a more efficient removal of proteolytic cofactors by the gel treatment.

It is unlikely that the spontaneous release of amino acids from dialyzed serum is quantitatively significant in most of the nutritional studies that have been made, since routine experiments consistently show that no cell growth occurs if even a single essential amino acid is omitted from a medium containing dialyzed serum protein. Eagle and his collaborators point out, however, that proteolysis in stored serum or on incubation can introduce an appreciable error into experiments designed to follow the utilization of amino acids at low concentrations. In one such experiment, valine labeled with C^{14} was added at 0.002 mM to a valine-free medium that contained 5 percent dialyzed serum. When the cellular proteins synthesized in this nutrient were later analyzed, the specific activity of the valine residues was only 23 percent of the precursor amino acid. Under these conditions, most of the incorporated valine had apparently originated from the valine of serum protein. Although the experimental variables were chosen to maximize this contribution, the need for effective controls in other investigations with dialyzed serum is emphasized. Clearly, nutrients based on serum protein cannot be regarded as chemically defined until the essential functions of the latter can be identified with, and restricted to, known pure compounds.

The demonstration that free amino acids are formed by proteolysis in dialyzed serum makes it probable that other types of products (for example, peptides) also can arise by degradation of extracellular proteins. Some of these may account directly for the essential role of serum protein in the nutrition of permanent cell strains. This conclusion is supported by recent studies in which protein digests have been placed in equilibrium with chemically defined media as a "feeder system" (Eagle, 1960b). Such an experimental design necessitates a specially designed dual culture vessel in which twin chambers for suspension cultures are separated by a cellophane dialyzing membrane. Dialyzed serum protein can be placed in one compartment, while the cells to be tested (*HeLa, KB*, or strain *L*) are inoculated into the opposite chamber in Eagle's synthetic nutrient containing no serum supplement. Under these conditions, the test cells fail to receive any benefit from serum protein across the dialysis membrane, and promptly die. But if a dialyzed pancreatic extract is added to the compartment containing serum, the resulting degradation products are capable of diffusion across the cellophane membrane, creating a continuing feeder action. In such cultures, the cells survive and undergo active proliferation, with mean generation times of approximately 1 to 2 days. All three strains tested could be propagated serially in this fashion without limit as long as the specified feeder system continued to act across the cellophane membrane. The vigorous growth of cell populations in this protein-free system does not appear to be the result of selective proliferation by variants especially adapted for growth. If cell populations that have been maintained in conjunction with a feeder unit for one month are subsequently returned to a standard suspension culture vessel which lacks a feeder, death ensues promptly unless serum protein is provided in the same concentration required originally by the parental stock cultures.

These findings are probably indicative of a generalized ability of permanent cell strains to proliferate in the absence of exogenous protein, if provided with dialyzable degradation products from serum (Gwatkin, 1960; Metzgar and Moskowitz, 1960; Levintow and Eagle, 1961). The exact nature of the active factors and their mechanism of liberation have not yet been ascertained. Eagle found a number of serum protein fractions to be as active as whole serum. A variety of crystalline proteolytic enzymes can also substitute for the pancreatic extract employed initially. Even without these additives, however, the enzymes present within intact serum can bring about a release of active compounds under appropriate conditions. In the experiments of Metzgar and Moskowitz (1960), horse serum was incubated at 37° C for one week, and the heat-stable dialysate was collected. When combined with an appropriate synthetic medium, this nonprotein fraction served to support the growth of several permanent cell strains as effectively as did whole serum. The active compounds released in this way from serum are apparently not to be identified among the complement of known amino acids, vitamins, and other commonly recognized cofactors, since synthetic media containing these constituents alone do not in general suffice for the growth of cell strains. A detailed investigation of peptides as growth factors seems indicated, especially since the older literature contains frequent references to growth stimulation by protein digests and degradation products (Waymouth, 1954; Stewart and Kirk, 1954). Other possibilities, however, cannot yet be ruled out.

Responses of Primary Cell Populations   The failure of primary cell lines to proliferate indefinitely, even though a stabilized period of initial growth may in some cases extend for many months, now seems to be generally established (Chapter 3). It is logical to infer that primary cells differ in one or more respects from permanently propagating cell lines, and a distinction may be found in responses to extracellular protein or associated growth factors. Thus, while permanent cell strains in general appear capable of multiplication in a protein-free synthetic medium supplemented only by dialyzable factors from serum digests, no primary cells have yet been observed to do so (Levintow and Eagle, 1961). Some of these grow very poorly in synthetic media supplemented by serum protein alone, and are markedly stimulated by extracts prepared from embryonic or adult tissues. A typical illustration can be provided by the studies of Takata and Harris (1962) on the growth of pig kidney cells in monolayer culture. If cell populations of this type are isolated directly from fetal kidney and placed in dilute serum plus Medium 199, growth in serial subculture is slow and sporadic. These primary strains respond with rapid logarithmic proliferation, however, if the basal nutrient is supplemented with a dialyzed protein extract from pig spleen, along with serum protein. No effect is obtained by increasing the total protein content of the medium to a similar degree by serum alone. This differential response to tissue proteins is not found with all primary cell lines. A number of observations have been made, however, on cell strains that in early passages were dependent upon, or were stimulated by, tissue extracts, although ultimately these additives became dispensable (Haff and Swim, 1957b).

With this background it is not difficult to appreciate the sustained interest in extracts from embryonic and adult tissues that is documented in the early literature, since the experiments in question were performed with fresh explants or primary cell strains. Numerous investigators, for example, have sought to isolate growth principles from the macromolecular fraction of chick embryonic extract, using homologous cultures of primary fibroblasts as an assay system. It is no longer necessary to view these factors as obligate components in a nutritional spectrum, since logarithmic growth may be achieved under appropriate conditions with chick cells growing in sera supplemented only with a synthetic nutrient (Harris, 1959). Nevertheless, the multiplication and growth of primary chick cells can be characteristically enhanced by protein fractions. An association of this activity with nucleoprotein components was proposed by Baker and Carrel (1926b), and later workers proceeded on a similar concept (Fischer and Astrup, 1943; Davidson and Waymouth, 1945; Fischer, 1946). Little if any success, however, was experienced in attempts to secure fractions of high specific activity.

These older investigations contain interesting data, but are difficult to evaluate because both isolation procedures and assay systems were poorly defined. In recent years the innovation of new techniques has permitted a further study of this problem. Searching for a more specific separation of nucleoproteins from embryonic extracts, Kutsky (1953) introduced the use of streptomycin as a selective precipitation agent, and isolated an active ribonucleoprotein fraction from saline extracts of chick embryos. By modifying the extraction procedures slightly, similar preparations can be obtained from adult chicken organs (Kutsky and Harris, 1957). These protein fractions have conspicuous effects on the growth of primary chick fibroblasts, especially in monolayer cultures with a basal nutrient containing serum and Medium 199 (Harris and Kutsky, 1954, 1958). Addition of nucleoprotein fractions from adult chicken spleen, for example, increases the logarithmic growth rate, and the assay populations show greater uniformity and stability of cell morphology in serial subculture (Figure 5.9). No indications of organ specificity can be seen when cultures of chick fibroblasts prepared from several organs are combined with nucleoprotein fractions similarly diverse.

The growth-stimulating action of these fractions on primary chick cells appears to be associated with the protein rather than with the nucleic acid component. By using phosphate in high ionic strength, Kutsky (1959) succeeded in removing the nucleic acid of streptomycin precipitates from embryonic extract. The residual subfraction is electrophoretically more homogeneous than is the parent nucleoprotein, with a single major peak. All growth-promoting activity can be accounted for in the protein subfraction, whereas the dissociated RNA appears to be inert. A small amount of lipid remains in association with the protein derivative, but is probably inactive, since 90 percent can be removed with lipid solvents without affecting the specific activity. This result

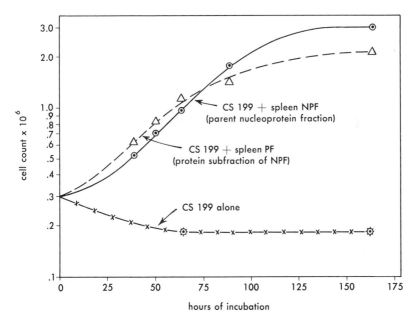

FIG. 5.9. Stimulation of the growth of chick skeletal muscle fibroblasts by a nucleoprotein fraction obtained from adult chicken spleen. The protein subfraction, derived by removing the nucleic acid, is nearly equivalent in activity to the parent material. (Redrawn from Harris and Kutsky, 1958. Copyright, University of Chicago Press.)

is not peculiar to embryonic extracts. A similar pattern of differential activity emerges when adult chicken spleen ribonucleoprotein is fractionated into protein and nucleic acid moieties (Harris and Kutsky, 1958).

Chick cells and perhaps other primary strains thus respond distinctively to protein fractions, which for permanent cell lines are clearly dispensable. The mechanism through which this activity becomes apparent has never been clarified. Several possible explanations may be considered. It can be assumed, for example, that primary populations of chick fibroblasts tend to become deficient in one or more limiting cofactors, as Eagle (1960a) has shown to be the case for folinic acid in freshly isolated monkey kidney cells. Tissue proteins might thus bind the missing cofactors or reaction products, or release active subunits, by degradation in the culture medium. Alternatively, the question of direct utilization can be re-examined. The results of Eagle and Piez (1960) show clearly that permanent cell lines do not derive any significant quantity of cellular protein from protein precursors in the external medium. Comparable experiments on primary strains have not yet been made, however, especially with protein-rich media. That further investigation on this point may be desirable is suggested by the experiments of Francis and Winnick (1953). These workers cultivated explants of chick embryo heart in media containing embryo extract labeled with C^{14}-amino acids in protein-bound form. Extensive incorporation of the labeled amino acids was reported to occur in cell proteins newly synthesized, particularly in the later stages of the growth period. The experimental design did not disclose whether this process was mediated by a preliminary breakdown of extract proteins in the culture medium. But from the results of adding relatively large concentrations of nonradioactive free amino acids as metabolic traps, Francis and Winnick concluded that most of the C^{14}-labeled amino acids were transferred from embryonic extract to cellular protein without coming into equilibrium with the extracellular free amino acid pool. The technical difficulties in labeling experiments permit alternative explanations, however, and this problem needs further study.

A more promising interpretation for the effects of tissue proteins on primary cells can be built on the concept that these factors stimulate growth by promoting the retention of specific metabolites. Since depletion is known to occur in low population densities among permanently established strains, it is not unreasonable to expect an even more extensive loss with primary cells that may be less well adapted. Supporting this view is the common observation that freshly isolated cells are usually difficult to clone, and under conditions that permit efficient multiplication of single cells from permanent lines. The data of Todaro and Green (1962, 1963) illustrate the differential more explicitly. These investigators observed that primary strains of mouse embryo and hamster cells grew readily as mass populations, but if the inoculum size was reduced, the capacity for serial proliferation was rapidly lost. With still smaller inocula, growth failed to occur even in the first passage. In the same medium, however, strain L mouse cells proliferated vigorously and indefinitely from all levels of inoculation. Since strain L has neoplastic properties that might account for this difference, Todaro and Green extended their comparisons to two tumor-producing populations. One of these had been elicited by polyoma virus in vitro (Chapter 7) and had become established as a permanently proliferating strain. The second tumor line was induced by polyoma virus in vivo and had been maintained exclusively by transplantation. Interestingly, when the latter was placed in culture, it exhibited a marked growth inhibition at low population densities, similar to that described for primary lines of normal cells. By contrast, the line of tumor cells already established in vitro was like strain L, more nearly independent of a "feeder" effect. Thus the acquisition of neoplastic properties does not necessarily confer an improved homeostasis for cells in primary culture.

That protein fractions may affect the cloning efficiency of primary populations is evident from the observations of Takata and Harris (1962). In line with the foregoing experiments, no multiplication took place when primary pig kidney cells were introduced as small inocula into dilute serum plus Medium 199, although mass cultures can be propagated slowly in the same nutrient. If adult spleen protein is added, however, clonal growth can be observed even from sparse populations. The basis for this effect may involve provision of specific micromolecular factors associated with tissue proteins to the cells concerned. But it is conceivable that the limiting loss in these dilute populations of primary cells is cellular protein as such. In this case, the provision of protein fractions externally might counter directly or indirectly the effects of cytoplasmic leaching (Harris and Kutsky, 1958). A possible model may be seen in the observation that liver extracts or catalase are protective for several types of cells when maintained in dilute populations (Lieberman and Ove, 1958b). This finding may perhaps be explained by the toxicity of certain media containing unusually high levels of cysteine, for which catalase is a specific counteracting factor (Higuchi, 1963). However, the important point in the present context is that Lieberman and Ove observed inhibition primarily in sparse populations with well-isolated cells. As these workers suggested, such a syndrome may be attributed to the leakage of catalase from the cells in question, since the effect can be reversed or prevented by adding catalase to the culture medium. On the whole, therefore, the most plausible interpretation of growth stimulation by tissue proteins appears to be an inhibition of, or compensation for, metabolite loss in primary cell cultures, although the exact mechanism remains to be determined.

MODIFICATION OF NUTRITIONAL REQUIREMENTS

No real evidence has been found to justify the view that the nutritional requirements of permanent cell strains as a group differ materially from those of primary cells. As previous discussions have made clear, there may be occasional qualitative or quantitative differences in the spectrum of factors required for the growth of specific cell types, but the over-all identity is striking. Permanent cell lines do appear to have acquired adaptive properties that permit biosynthetic patterns associated with growth to take place in an indefinitely continuing equilibrium. Whether this is mediated at least in part by dedifferentiation or modulation, or more likely by permanent heritable changes has not yet been conclusively determined. But in any event, cell strains that may converge by these processes tend to be stabilized phenotypically by common selective elements in the culture environment. This does not rule out the possibility that nutritional mechanisms may undergo additional changes within established lines if the experimental conditions adopted favor such transitions. Indeed, observations on clonal diversification of chromosomal patterns (Chapter 4), and the phenomena of drug resistance (Chapter 6) suggest that such may be the case. In practice, however, it is necessary to find suitable experimental systems, which by population shifts or selective isolation will permit an exploration for variants with novel nutritional patterns.

Growth in Chemically Defined Media   If permanent cell lines do in fact originate as variants capable of increased production or decreased loss of specific metabolities, a continuing progression might be expected where such changes conferred additional selective advantages of the same type. This seems to be the case for populations of strain L and certain other cell lines that have been adapted to grow in media containing only known crystalloidal factors. The design of nutrients for this purpose has proceeded along empirical lines. Seeking an appropriate mixture, Healy, Fisher, and Parker (1954, 1955) developed a series of elaborations on Medium 199, which had originally been designed for experiments with freshly isolated chick tissues. Significantly greater success was not achieved with chick cells, but when strain L mouse cells in monolayer culture were substituted as an assay system, much longer survival occurred. Coenzymes, nucleosides, and other supplements were added to the basic 199 formula, and in such nutrients the strain *L* cells were observed to grow for increasingly long periods without serum protein or other unknown growth factors. Eventually, media were obtained that permitted indefinite proliferation, of which the best known has been termed *CMRL* 1066 (Parker, Castor, and McCulloch, 1957). This formulation does, however, contain a concentrate of porcine coenzymes, and to this extent is not completely defined chemically.

A parallel development of synthetic media was carried on by Evans and her colleagues, resulting ultimately in chemically defined nutrients that contain only known pure constituents. These mixtures support permanent propagation of sublines from clone 929, strain *L* (Figure 5.10), as well as some other cell types (Evans, Bryant, Fioramonti,

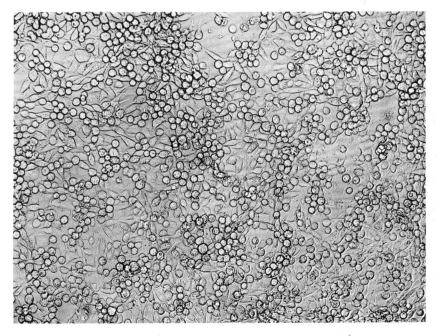

FIG. 5.10. Growth of clone 929, strain *L* mouse cells in a chemically defined medium. The nutrient employed for this experiment (*NCTC* 107) contains no serum or other unknown factors, and differs only in minor respects from the *NCTC* 109 nutrient described in the text. Photograph shows the appearance of a population maintained for 201 days, with 9 subcultures, in the nutrient specified. (From Evans, Bryant, McQuilkin, Fioramonti, Sanford, Westfall, and Earle, 1956. Copyright, University of Chicago Press.)

McQuilkin, Sanford, and Earle, 1956; Evans, Bryant, McQuilkin, Fiora-monti, Sanford, Westfall, and Earle, 1956). Of a series prepared, the formula designated *NCTC* 109 has received most intensive study (Mc-Quilkin, Evans, and Earle, 1957). This nutrient contains 69 crystalloidal compounds and has been employed for several years to maintain specific sublines of *L* cells (for example, *NCTC* strain 2071) in serial subculture. Growth proceeds more slowly than in serum-supplemented nutrients, and maximal cell populations are less, but serial transfers and replicate cultures of mass populations are achieved readily. Medium *NCTC* 109 has also been used with success to propagate a long-term strain of monkey kidney cells (Evans, Kerr, McQuilkin, Earle, and Hull, 1959) as well as a clonal population of human skin cells (Bakken, Evans, Earle, and Stevenson, 1961).

Some difficulty has been experienced in attempting to grow strain *L* or other cell types as shake cultures in chemically defined nutrients. This does not reflect any inability of the cells studied to proliferate in free suspension. Merchant and Kahn (1958), for example, were able to obtain logarithmic growth of *L* cells in shake cultures by using a nutrient based on Medium 199 plus supplements of methylcellulose and an undefined preparation of peptones. The peptone supplement for *NCTC* strain 2071 was later shown by Bryant, Evans, Schilling, and Earle (1961) to be unnecessary. These workers found that strain 2071 cells will multiply progressively in suspension with Medium *NCTC* 109 plus methylcellulose, provided the culture flasks are treated with silicone to prevent adherence and degeneration of cells in marginal areas. An alternative procedure, which may eliminate the addition of methylcellu-lose as well as siliconing, consists in adding traces of crystalline trypsin to the external medium (Sinclair, Reid, and Mitchell, 1963). Strain *L* cells are reported to multiply rapidly and without clumping in a chem-ically defined nutrient containing trypsin, apparently as the result of the digestion of an extracellular exudate by which the cells adhere to each other or to foreign surfaces. Even with these refinements, however, the proliferation of strain *L* in chemically defined media is still limited by population density. It has not been possible either in suspension or monolayer cultures to establish clones directly from single cells.

Like other synthetic media, *NCTC* 109 was formulated initially by assembling a wide array of pure compounds known or suspected to be important for the growth of cell populations *in vitro*. Certain of the original constituents are clearly dispensable in the assay systems that have been used. Thus, preformed coenzymes, including diphos-phopyridine nucleotide, coenzyme A, cocarboxylase, flavine-adenine dinucleotide, and uridine phosphate can all be omitted without affecting the growth of *NCTC* strain 2071 cells, as long as the corresponding vitamins or other precursors are provided (Evans, Fioramonti, and Earle, 1959). Similarly, thymidine and deoxycytidine are reported to stimulate this strain, but other nucleic acid derivatives may be deleted, including deoxyadenine, deoxyguanosine, and 5-methylcytosine (Evans, Fioramonti, Randolph, and Earle, 1960). Of the vitamins originally specified for *NCTC* 109, A, D, E, K, ascorbic acid, *p*-aminobenzoic acid all have been shown to be without effect on the growth of strain 2071 cells, while vitamin B_{12} stimulates some sublines but not others (Sanford, Dupree, and Covalesky, 1963). On the other hand, evidence for a biotin requirement can be found in strain 2071 cells, if these are cultivated for long periods in a variant of *NCTC* 109 deficient in nucleic acid derivatives. It is interesting also that strain 2071 cells can apparently multiply indefinitely in protein-free media without folic acid or pyridoxal (or pyridoxine), although both of these vitamins were determined by Eagle to be essential for the growth of strain *L* cells in dialyzed media. Whether this discrepancy depends on the presence or absence of macromolecules, a differing balance of accessory nutritional factors, or a variation in strain 2071 cells incident to establishment in *NCTC* 109, remains to be seen. The latter alternative seems favored by the observation that addition of dialyzed serum protein decreases, if anything, the vitamin requirements of strain 2071 (Dupree, Sanford, Westfall, and Covalesky, 1962).

A systematic analysis of various nitrogen sources within *NCTC* 109, however, shows that the spectrum of 13 amino acids required for growth in the presence of dialyzed serum protein is equally necessary for the proliferation of strain 2071 cells in chemically defined nutrients (Sanford, McQuilkin, Fioramonti, Evans, and Earle, 1958). There is no change in the requirement for glutamine under these conditions, and its omission from *NCTC* 109 leads to a sharp drop in cell number within assay populations (Peppers, Fioramonti, Westfall, Evans, and Earle, 1958). Sanford and her co-workers did find that the inclusion of a group of nonessential amino acids significantly enhances the growth of strain *L* cells in chemically defined media. They have suggested that the lack of a similar effect in the experiments of Eagle (1956a) can be attributed to provision of the accessory amino acids by serum protein. This explanation does not seem probable, since essential amino acids were not released in significant amounts under the same conditions. It is more likely that nonessential amino acids are synthesized at a lower rate in *NCTC* 109 or are lost more readily from cells in a protein-free nutrient. In either case, the resulting deficiency could be corrected by supplementing the external medium appropriately.

For strain L cells, at least, the ability to grow progressively in NCTC 109 did not appear to pre-exist in stock populations maintained previously in serum-supplemented media. In their original experiments with this nutrient, Evans and her co-workers found that clone 929 cells proliferated sporadically for six months or more before a stable growth pattern finally emerged. The subsequent investigations of McQuilkin, Evans, and Earle (1957) gave strong evidence that this process had been mediated by variation and selection. As in the preceding experiments, a series of clone 929 populations were transferred from serum-supplemented to chemically defined media. Of 56 separate attempts, 10 sublines of L cells were thus successfully adapted for progressive growth in NCTC 109. In practically all cases, a period of adjustment preceded the establishment of stable populations, during which the cultures underwent gradual or abrupt changes in cellular morphology, growth rate, and population density. Some of these sublines were returned to serum-containing media for varying intervals and could then be transferred directly to NCTC 109 without any preliminary adaptation, indicating that variations that had facilitated growth in the chemically defined medium were relatively permanent in character. Such adaptive changes are not peculiar to strain L cells. A pattern of preliminary instability and eventual cellular alteration seemed also to characterize the adaptation of human skin cells to growth in NCTC 109 (Bakken, Evans, Earle, and Stevenson, 1961). Similar changes were noted by Holmes (1959) during the cultivation of Chang liver cells in a chemically defined medium, and by Higuchi (1963) in the establishment of derivatives from primary chick embryo, dog kidney, and kitten lung cells in a serumless nutrient.

Not all cell types, however, appear to require a preliminary process of variation and selection in order to grow progressively in chemically defined media. Some are capable of progressive growth from the outset, even in nutrients such as NCTC 109, which is clearly not optimal for the immediate propagation of most permanent strains. For example, Evans, Kerr, McQuilkin, Earle, and Hull (1959) were able to cultivate monkey kidney cells directly in the NCTC 109 medium. Unlike strain L, these populations proliferated vigorously in the first passage and did not exhibit the conspicuous adaptive changes that have been described for L cells under the same conditions.

Where population shifts do take place, they are apparently not restricted to the initial establishment of cell strains in chemically defined media. It is likely that further alterations can occur if new patterns of selection are imposed. A possible example of the latter process may be seen in the experiments of Fioramonti, Evans, Mantel, and Earle

(1960) with *NCTC* strain 2071. These cells are ordinarily stimulated by a mixture of acetate, sodium glucuronate, and glucuronolactone, which are accordingly represented in the *NCTC* 109 stock formula. But when sublines of strain 2071 cells were maintained for three months without the glucuronic acid mixture, a growth response to the corresponding compounds could no longer be detected. The simplest interpretation of this result lies in assuming that nutritional simplification occurs, mediated by the accumulation of variants under selection pressure.

A somewhat similar explanation may be invoked for the observation of Merchant and Hellman (1962) that one subline of *L* cells (strain *L-M*) can be propagated serially in Eagle's medium alone. As previously noted, stock populations of strain *L* cells do not proliferate continuously under these conditions. The *L-M* subline, however, was adapted over a period of time to growth in Medium 199 with a peptone supplement, and this process appears to have selected variants capable of improved growth in the absence of protein. When the 199-peptone mixture was replaced by Eagle's synthetic nutrient, no further transitions took place. But a 2X concentration of Eagle's mixture was required for progressive growth, indicating a tendency for appreciable loss of metabolites even in these adapted cells. In addition, the lag phase seems to be accentuated with Eagle's mixture as compared to the 199-peptone medium (Figure 5.11), perhaps owing to the increased loss of nonessential amino acids

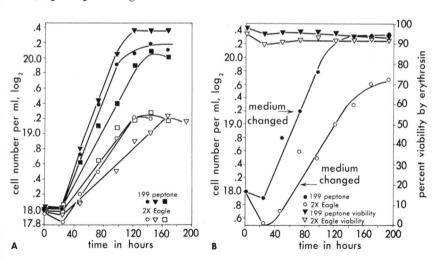

FIG. 5.11. Population changes with strain *L-M* cells cultivated in protein-free media. (A) Representative growth curves for suspension cultures maintained in Medium 199 plus peptone, as compared with cells in 2X Eagle's medium. (B) Parallel experiments with same cells and media in static monolayer cultures. (Redrawn from Merchant and Hellman, 1962.)

or other factors lacking in the simpler nutrient. These facts suggest that adaptation of the *L-M* subline to Eagle's medium as reported is incomplete, and further changes might occur on serial cultivation. In general, then, the possible evolution of nutritional patterns by adaptation to suboptimal conditions in the culture medium is therefore a factor that cannot be ignored in the long-term maintenance of cell strains.

The tendency for adaptive changes to occur in chemically defined media might be reduced if synthetic nutrients were appropriately modified to minimize or prevent losses of metabolites by the cells concerned. The experiments of Waymouth (1959) may perhaps illustrate this concept. By successive improvements, a medium termed *MB* 752/1 was developed, in which only 40 components are to be found, including glucose, salts, vitamins, glutathione, and the purine base hypoxanthine. Waymouth has found that strain *L* can be grown logarithmically from the first passage in *MB* 752/1, even when taken from stock cultures maintained previously only in serum and embryonic extract. The cells grow rather slowly, but no preliminary lag occurs on transfer to the chemically defined nutrient, and there are no detectable alterations in other cellular properties, aside from poor adherence to the glass substrate in early passages. These observations are in marked contrast to the transitional adaptations that occur when strain *L* cells are introduced into a medium such as *NCTC* 109. A possible explanation may be found in the disparity in composition of *NCTC* 109 and *MB* 752/1, respectively. The latter has fewer constituents, but has much higher concentrations of amino acids, especially arginine, histidine, lysine, and glutamine. There are also marked increases in choline, thiamine, and several other vitamins to levels far above the physiological range. These increases do not signify a corresponding rise in the incorporation of substrates into structural components, for Mohberg and Johnson (1963) showed that most amino acids in *MB* 752/1 were actually used in 1.5 to 2.5 times the quantities needed for protein synthesis. Much more glutamine, methionine, and valine in particular were metabolized than could be accounted for increases in protein, while relatively less glycine and aspartic acid disappeared than could be explained on this basis. By adjusting the relative proportion of amino acids in a modification of *MB* 752/1 to give twice the amounts actually consumed by the cells, a doubling of the cell yield was achieved.

The beneficial effects of increasing the levels of amino acids and other cofactors above the levels needed for biosynthesis have been demonstrated in this system, but the implications of these findings are uncertain. It is possible that there may be a greater tendency for loss of certain metabolites in chemically defined media as compared with those containing serum protein; this differential might be counterbalanced by increasing the external supply of the factors in question. In addition, there is the possibility of unbalanced transport for some intermediates, analogous to the requirement of mouse lymphoma P-388 cells for pyruvate. As previously noted, pyruvate seems to pass rapidly from these cells, but re-enters only with difficulty (Herzenberg and Roosa, 1960).

Further support for these concepts can be found in the successes achieved by Nagle and his collaborators in devising simplified but chemically defined media appropriate for suspension culture of several permanent cell strains (Nagle, Tribble, Anderson, and Gary, 1963). Basing their formulations on a semisynthetic nutrient containing lactalbumin hydrolysate (Higuchi, 1963; Tribble and Higuchi, 1963), these investigators assembled an array of 33 components that permitted the continuous cultivation of L, HeLa, monkey kidney, rat spleen, guinea pig kidney, and cat kidney lines. The concentrations of most amino acids were 3 to 15 times those found in NCTC 109, with the exception of cysteine, reduced from 259.9 mg/l to 75 mg/l. Previous studies had indicated that little or no growth of most cell lines occurs at concentrations of 150 mg or more per liter, although this toxicity can be neutralized if the high levels of cysteine are counteracted by adding pyruvate or catalase to the synthetic nutrient (Higuchi, 1963).

Other factors contributing to optimal results with the medium employed by Nagle include the use of glass beads, rather than trypsin, in starting the original suspensions from monolayers (Nagle, 1960), the incorporation of methylcellulose in the basic formula, and particularly the addition of insulin to the list of essential ingredients. Although it is true that insulin has an equivocal growth-promoting effect in serum-containing media (see Paul, 1960), a more clear-cut pattern seems to obtain in the absence of serum. A potentiating action by insulin on the growth of HeLa and human appendix cells in synthetic media was reported by Lieberman and Ove (1959); furthermore, most of a series of permanent strains examined by Higuchi (1963) and Tribble and Higuchi (1963) showed marked stimulation by insulin as well as by the associated protamine. Strain L cells and certain other types, however, will grow satisfactorily in monolayers with synthetic media that lack insulin. In suspension cultures with a chemically defined nutrient, Nagle and his collaborators observed a complete failure of growth by cat kidney cells unless insulin was made available. Steady progress in the design of synthetic nutrients is evident from these findings. So far, however, there are no indications that suspension cultures of primary cells can be grown with any of the chemically defined media at hand. The nature of the missing factors is an important problem.

Specific Nutritional Variations A few variants have been isolated from stock strains with altered requirements for specific micromolecular factors. Eagle, Piez, and Fleischman (1957) noted the appearance of *HeLa* cells that, unlike the parental line, could convert phenylalanine to tyrosine. The variant subline appeared spontaneously and showed limited growth in tyrosine-deficient medium, but could not be maintained indefinitely. Nutritional variants have also been obtained from cultures of the Jensen rat sarcoma by McCoy, Maxwell, Irvine, and Sartorelli (1959). Cells explanted from freshly excised neoplasms do not in this case grow unless asparagine is added to the nutrient medium. Lacking this factor, the Jensen cells degenerate in a few days. In at least two instances, however, asparagine-independent variants appeared by focal proliferation and were isolated as stable sublines (Figure 5.12). These substrains continued to grow vigorously in the absence of exogenous asparagine and even retained this characteristic through passage as transplantable tumors in the rat host.

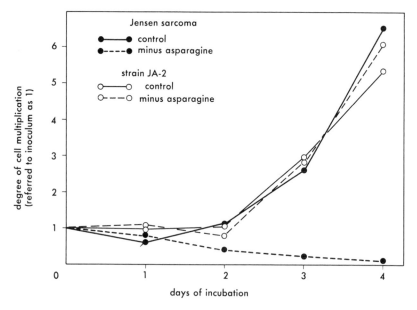

FIG. 5.12. Growth responses of Jensen rat sarcoma cells to asparagine. Stock tumor cells fail to proliferate in culture unless this factor is added, but a variant subline (strain JA-2) grows equally well in the presence or absence of exogenous asparagine. (After McCoy, Maxwell, Irvine, and Sartorelli, 1959.)

There are no indications that isolated cell strains can acquire the ability to synthesize vitamins not ordinarily produced, but at least in the case of inositol, variants independent of the usual requirement occur. Chang (1958) compared a series of *HeLa* lines obtained from different laboratories and found one strain able to proliferate without added inositol in the culture medium. According to the brief comments of Swim (1959) inositol-independent variants occur regularly in a strain (*U*12) of human uterine fibroblasts, with a frequency of 10^{-6}. The evidence available in these cases does not indicate whether nutritional independence stems from alterations in biosynthetic pattern or merely from a more efficient retention of inositol within the cultured cells. Eagle, Agranoff, and Snell (1960) have shown, however, that strains of cells that are naturally inositol-independent do release significant amounts of inositol into the culture medium. This process is sufficient to maintain the growth of dependent cells, where strains of the two types are maintained in "parabiosis" across a dialysis membrane.

The well-known faculty of microorganisms for attacking carbohydrates not ordinarily utilized raises the question of whether somatic cells are also capable of shifting to novel carbohydrate sources. In bacteria this process may be mediated by genetic change, phenotypic adaptation, or both. The findings are less clear-cut for somatic cell populations. Chang (1957, 1960) reported that *HeLa* and human conjunctival cell strains did not grow serially in media containing xylose, ribose, or lactate, respectively, as the only added carbohydrate source. Numerous variants, however, could be isolated with an increased ability for proliferation in these nutrients. During the initial transition, most of the parental population degenerates, but a few isolated foci remain, and these multiply selectively. Similar variants can be obtained from strain *L* mouse cells by the use of selective media containing galactose or xylose (Hsu and Kellogg, 1959). In this case, new properties must have originated at some stage by changes within a uniform population, since the subline employed (*L-P*55) derives ultimately from clone 929, strain *L*. Subpopulations obtained in this manner appear to be relatively stable. Hsu and Kellogg found that the ability of *L* cells to grow progressively in media containing galactose is not lost in the absence of substrate and is retained even after return for two weeks to a glucose medium. The variant characteristics thus appear to be based on heritable changes rather than on mere phenotypic adaptation. Galactose variants have also been reported in a line of human esophageal cells that does not metabolize this substrate (Bradley and Syverton, 1960, 1962). This finding must be regarded as atypical, however, since direct utilization of galactose occurs to some degree in most human cell strains (Eagle, Barban, Levy, and Schulze, 1958).

These several investigations show clearly that heritable differences in growth properties can be demonstrated by selection with alternative carbohydrate sources. There is little or no evidence, however, that any of the variant strains have actually acquired the ability to utilize normally inert substrates as an alternative to glucose. Those isolated with xylose, for example, produce little if any lactic acid in the presence of this compound. In the case of galactose, Bradley and Syverton (1962) were unable to demonstrate any significant direct utilization by sublines of human esophageal cells adapted for growth with this substrate. Chang (1960) did find that incorporation of C^{14}-labeled sugars into several cell fractions takes place to a greater degree in ribose or xylose variants than in the parental strain. But even glucose appeared to be incorporated more extensively by the variants, and these continued to show sensitivity to the analogue 2-deoxyglucose. It must be borne in mind that glucose is a demonstrable impurity in commercial preparations of other monosaccharides, and while treatment with glucose oxidase (Chang, 1960) or by yeast (Bradley and Syverton, 1962) may reduce this contamination, it is difficult to exclude residual traces. Thus the metabolic adjustments that occur in cell strains selected with various sugars may in fact be directed toward a more efficient utilization of glucose, present at threshold concentrations that are limiting for growth. Increased utilization of inert substrates such as xylose, if it occurs at all, seems to be nominal.

■ References

ALFRED, L. J., and PUMPER, R. W. 1960. Biological synthesis of a growth factor for mammalian cells in tissue culture. Proc. Soc. Exptl. Biol. Med., **103:** 688–691.

BAILEY, J. M., GEY, G. O., and GEY, M. K. 1959. Utilization of serum lipids by cultured mammalian cells. Proc. Soc. Exptl. Biol. Med., **100:** 686–692.

BAKER, L. E., and CARREL, A. 1926a. Effect of the amino acids and dialyzable constituents of embryonic tissue juice on the growth of fibroblasts. J. Exptl. Med., **44:** 397–407.

BAKER, L. E., and CARREL, A. 1926b. Action on fibroblasts of the protein fraction of embryonic tissue extract. J. Exptl. Med., **44:** 387–395.

BAKKEN, P. C., EVANS, V. J., EARLE, W. R., and STEVENSON, R. E. 1961. Establishment of a strain of human skin cells on chemically defined medium NCTC 109. Am. J. Hyg., **73:** 96–104.

BIGGERS, J. D., RINALDINI, L. M., and WEBB, M. 1957. The study of growth factors in tissue culture. Symp. Soc. Exptl. Biol., 11: 264–297.

BRADLEY, S. G., and SYVERTON, J. T. 1960. Inheritance of capability of human esophageal epithelial cells to grow with diverse carbohydrates. Proc. Soc. Exptl. Biol. Med., 103: 215–221.

BRADLEY, S. G., and SYVERTON, J. T. 1962. Characterization of a nutritional variant of human esophageal epithelial cells. Exptl. Cell Res., 27: 25–30.

BRYANT, J. C., EVANS, V. J., SCHILLING, E. L., and EARLE, W. R. 1961. Effect of chemically defined medium NCTC 109 supplemented with methocel and silicone coating the flasks on strain 2071 cells in suspension cultures. J. Natl. Cancer Inst., 26: 239–252.

CHANG, R. S. 1957. Isolation of nutritional variants from conjunctival and HeLa cells. Proc. Soc. Exptl. Biol. Med., 96: 818–820.

CHANG, R. S. 1958. Differences in inositol requirements of several strains of HeLa, conjunctival, and amnion cells. Proc. Soc. Exptl. Biol. Med., 99: 99–102.

CHANG, R. S. 1960. Genetic study of human cells in vitro. Carbohydrate variants from cultures of HeLa and conjunctival cells. J. Exptl. Med., 111: 235–254.

CHANG, R. S., and GEYER, R. P. 1957. Propagation of conjunctival and HeLa cells in various carbohydrate media. Proc. Soc. Exptl. Biol. Med., 96: 336–340.

COONS, A. H. 1956. Histochemistry with labeled antibody. Intern. Rev. Cytol., 5: 1–23.

CURTIS, A. S. G. 1962. Cell contact and adhesion. Biol. Revs., 37: 82–129.

DANES, B. S., BROADFOOT, M. M., and PAUL, J. 1963. A comparative study of respiratory metabolism in cultured mammalian cell strains. Exptl. Cell Res., 30: 369–378.

DANIELLI, J. F. 1954. Morphological and molecular aspects of active transport. Symp. Soc. Exptl. Biol., 8: 502–516.

DAVIDSON, J. N., and WAYMOUTH, C. 1945. The nucleoprotein content of fibroblasts growing in vitro. 2. The effect of tissue extracts. Biochem. J., 39: 188–199.

DEMARS, R., and HOOPER, J. L. 1960. A method of selecting for auxotrophic mutants of HeLa cells. J. Exptl. Med., 111: 559–572.

DEUTSCH, H. F. 1954. Fetuin: the mucoprotein of fetal calf serum. J. Biol. Chem., 208: 669–678.

DUPREE, L. T., SANFORD, K. K., WESTFALL, B. B., and COVALESKY, A. B. 1962. Influence of serum protein on determination of nutritional requirements of cells in culture. Exptl. Cell Res., 28: 381–405.

EAGLE, H. 1955a. The specific amino acid requirements of a mammalian cell (Strain L) in tissue culture. J. Biol. Chem., 214: 839–852.

EAGLE, H. 1955b. The specific amino acid requirements of a human carcinoma cell (Strain HeLa) in tissue culture. J. Exptl. Med., 102: 37–48.

EAGLE, H. 1955c. Nutrition needs of mammalian cells in tissue culture. Science, 122: 501–504.

EAGLE, H. 1955d. The minimum vitamin requirements of the L and HeLa cells in tissue culture, the production of specific vitamin deficiencies and their cure. J. Exptl. Med., **102:** 595–600.

EAGLE, H. 1956a. Relative growth-promoting activity in tissue culture of cofactors and the parent vitamins. Proc. Soc. Exptl. Biol. Med., **91:** 358–361.

EAGLE, H. 1956b. The salt requirements of mammalian cells in tissue culture. Arch. Biochem. Biophys., **61:** 356–366.

EAGLE, H. 1959. Amino acid metabolism in mammalian cell cultures. Science, **130:** 432–437.

EAGLE, H. 1960a. Metabolic studies with normal and malignant human cells in culture. Harvey Lectures, **54:** 156–175. New York: Academic Press, Inc.

EAGLE, H. 1960b. The sustained growth of human and animal cells in a protein-free environment. Proc. Natl. Acad. Sci., **46:** 427–432.

EAGLE, H., AGRANOFF, B. W., and SNELL, E. E. 1960. The biosynthesis of meso-inositol by cultured mammalian cells, and the parabiotic growth of inositol-dependent and inositol-independent strains. J. Biol. Chem., **235:** 1891–1893.

EAGLE, H., BARBAN, S., LEVY, M., and SCHULZE, H. O. 1958. The utilization of carbohydrates by human cell cultures. J. Biol. Chem., **233:** 551–558.

EAGLE, H., FREEMAN, A. E., and LEVY, M. 1958. The amino acid requirements of monkey kidney cells in first culture passage. J. Exptl. Med., **107:** 643–652.

EAGLE, H., OYAMA, V. I., LEVY, M., and FREEMAN, A. E. 1956. Myo-inositol as an essential growth factor for normal and malignant human cells in tissue culture. Science, **123:** 845–847.

EAGLE, H., OYAMA, V. I., LEVY, M., and FREEMAN, A. E. 1957. Myo-inositol as an essential growth factor for normal and malignant human cells in tissue culture. J. Biol. Chem., **226:** 191–206.

EAGLE, H., OYAMA, V. I., LEVY, M., HORTON, C. L., and FLEISCHMAN, R. 1956. The growth response of mammalian cells in tissue culture to L-glutamine and L-glutamic acid. J. Biol. Chem., **218:** 607–616.

EAGLE, H., OYAMA, V. I., and PIEZ, K. A. 1960. The reversible binding of half-cystine residues to serum protein and its bearing on the cystine requirement of cultured mammalian cells. J. Biol. Chem., **235:** 1719–1726.

EAGLE, H., and PIEZ, K. A. 1960. The utilization of proteins by cultured human cells. J. Biol. Chem., **235:** 1095–1097.

EAGLE, H., and PIEZ, K. 1962. The population-dependent requirement by cultured mammalian cells for metabolites which they can synthesize. J. Exptl. Med., **116:** 29–43.

EAGLE, H., PIEZ, K. A., and FLEISCHMAN, R. 1957. The utilization of phenylalanine and tyrosine for protein synthesis by human cells in tissue culture. J. Biol. Chem., **228:** 847–861.

EAGLE, H., PIEZ, K. A., and OYAMA, V. I. 1961. The biosynthesis of cystine in human cell cultures. J. Biol. Chem., **236:** 1425–1428.

EASTON, J. M., GOLDBERG, B., and GREEN, H. 1962. Demonstration of surface antigens and pinocytosis in mammalian cells with ferritin-antibody conjugates. J. Cell Biol., **12**: 437–443.

EASTY, G. C., EASTY, D. M., and AMBROSE, E. J. 1960. Studies on cellular adhesiveness. Exptl. Cell Res., **19**: 539–548.

EVANS, V. J., BRYANT, J. C., FIORAMONTI, M. C., McQUILKIN, W. T., SANFORD, K. K., and EARLE, W. R. 1956. Studies of nutrient media for tissue cells *in vitro*. I. A protein-free chemically defined medium for cultivation of Strain L cells. Cancer Res., **16**: 77–86.

EVANS, V. J., BRYANT, J. C., McQUILKIN, W. T., FIORAMONTI, M. C., SANFORD, K. K., WESTFALL, B. B., and EARLE, W. R. 1956. Studies of nutrient media for tissue cells *in vitro*. II. An improved protein-free chemically defined medium for long-term cultivation of Strain L-929 cells. Cancer Res. **16**: 87–94.

EVANS, V. J., FIORAMONTI, M. C., and EARLE, W. R. 1959. Studies of nutrient media for tissue cells *in vitro*. V. The effect of the coenzymes of medium NCTC 109 on the proliferation of NCTC Strain 2071 and NCTC Strain 2937. Am. J. Hyg., **70**: 28–33.

EVANS, V. J., FIORAMONTI, M. C., RANDOLPH, L. K., and EARLE, W. R. 1960. Studies of nutrient media for tissue cells *in vitro*. VI. The effect of the nucleic acid derivatives mixture of medium NCTC 109 on NCTC Strain 2071 and NCTC Strain 2981. Am. J. Hyg., **71**: 168–175.

EVANS, V. J., KERR, H. A., McQUILKIN, W. T., EARLE, W. R., and HULL, R. N. 1959. Growth *in vitro* of a long-term strain of monkey kidney cells in medium NCTC 109 free of any added protein. Am. J. Hyg., **70**: 275–279.

FIORAMONTI, M. C., EVANS, V. J., MANTEL, N., and EARLE, W. R. 1960. Studies of nutrient media for tissue cells *in vitro*. VII. The effect of the glucuronic acid mixture of NCTC 109 on the proliferation of NCTC Strain 2071 and NCTC Strain 3145. Am. J. Hyg., **72**: 204–210.

FISCHER, A. 1941. Die Bedeutung der Aminosaüren für die Gewebezellen *in vitro*. Acta Physiol. Scand., **2**: 143–188.

FISCHER, A. 1946. Biology of tissue cells. Cambridge: The University Press. 348 pp.

FISCHER, A., and ASTRUP, T. 1943. Untersuchungen über die chemischen Eigenschaften des tierischen Wuchstoffes aus Embryonen. Pflüg. Arch. ges. Physiol., **247**: 34–52.

FISCHER, A., ASTRUP, T., EHRENSVÄRD, G., and OEHLENSCHLÄGER, V. 1948. Growth of animal tissue cells in artificial media. Proc. Soc. Exptl. Biol. Med., **67**: 40–46.

FISHER, H. W., PUCK, T. T., and SATO, G. 1958. Molecular growth requirements of single mammalian cells: The action of fetuin in promoting cell attachment to glass. Proc. Natl. Acad. Sci., **44**: 4–10.

FISHER, H. W., PUCK, T. T., and SATO, G. 1959. Molecular growth requirements of single mammalian cells. III. Quantitative colonial growth of single S3 cells in a medium containing synthetic small molecular constituents and two purified protein fractions. J. Exptl. Med., **109**: 649–660.

FRANCIS, M. D., and WINNICK, T. 1953. Studies on the pathway of protein synthesis in tissue culture. J. Biol. Chem., 202: 273–289.

GEY, G. O. 1956. Some aspects of the constitution and behavior of normal and malignant cells maintained in continuous culture. Harvey Lectures, 50: 154–229. New York: Academic Press Inc.

GEYER, R. P., and CHANG, R. S. 1958. Bicarbonate as an essential for human cells in vitro. Arch. Bioch. Biophys., 73: 500–506.

GEYER, R. P., and NEIMARK, J. M. 1959. Triglyceride utilization by human HeLa and conjunctiva cells in tissue culture. Am. J. Clin. Nutr., 7: 86–90.

GWATKIN, R. B. 1960. Are macromolecules required for growth of single isolated mammalian cells? Nature, 186: 984–985.

HAFF, R. F., and SWIM, H. E. 1957a. The amino acid requirements of rabbit fibroblasts, strain RM 3–56. J. Gen. Physiol., 41: 91–100.

HAFF, R. F., and SWIM, H. E. 1957b. Isolation of a nutritional variant from a culture of rabbit fibroblasts. Science, 125: 1294.

HAKALA, M. T. 1957. Prevention of toxicity of amethopterin for Sarcoma-180 cells in tissue culture. Science, 126: 255.

HAKALA, M. T., and TAYLOR, E. 1959. The ability of purine and thymine derivatives and of glycine to support the growth of mammalian cells in culture. J. Biol. Chem., 234: 126–133.

HALEY, E. E., FISCHER, G. A., and WELCH, A. D. 1961. The requirement for L-asparagine of mouse leukemic cells L-5178Y in culture. Cancer Res., 21: 532–536.

HAM, R. G. 1963. Albumin replacement by fatty acids in clonal growth of mammalian cells. Science, 140: 802–803.

HANKS, J. H., and WALLACE, J. H. 1958. Determination of cell viability. Proc. Soc. Exptl. Biol. Med., 98: 188–192.

HARRIS, M. 1952. The use of dialyzed media for studies in cell nutrition. J. Cellular Comp. Physiol., 40: 279–302.

HARRIS, M. 1954 The role of bicarbonate for outgrowth of chick heart fibroblasts in vitro. J. Exptl. Zool., 125: 85–98.

HARRIS, M. 1958. Selective uptake and release of substances by cells. In: A Symposium on the Chemical Basis of Development, pp. 596–626. W. D. McElroy and B. Glass, eds. Baltimore: Johns Hopkins Press.

HARRIS, M. 1959. Essential growth factor in serum dialysate for chick skeletal muscle fibroblasts. Proc. Soc. Exptl. Biol. Med., 102: 468–471.

HARRIS, M., and KUTSKY, P. B. 1953. Utilization of added sugars by chick heart fibroblasts in dialyzed media. J. Cellular Comp. Physiol., 42: 449–470.

HARRIS, M., and KUTSKY, R. J. 1954. Synergism of nucleoprotein and dialysate growth factors in chick embryo extract. Exptl. Cell Res., 6: 327–336.

HARRIS, M., and KUTSKY, R. J. 1958. Growth rates of fibroblasts from chick skeletal muscle in cultures supplemented with homologous nucleoproteins. Cancer Res., 18: 585–591.

HEALY, G. M., FISHER, D. C., and PARKER, R. C. 1954. Nutrition of animal cells in tissue culture. IX. Synthetic medium No. 703. Can. J. Bioch. Physiol., **32**: 327–337.

HEALY, G. M., FISHER, D. C., and PARKER, R. C. 1955. Nutrition of animal cells in tissue culture. X. Synthetic medium No. 858. Proc. Soc. Exptl. Biol. Med., **89**: 71–77.

HEBB, C. R., and CHU, M. W. 1960. Reversible injury of L-strain mouse cells by trypsin. Exptl. Cell Res., **20**: 453–457.

HENDERSON, J. F., and LePAGE, G. A. 1959. Utilization of host protein by 6C3HED ascites lymphosarcoma in C_3H and Swiss mice. Cancer Res., **19**: 749–756.

HERZENBERG, L. A., and ROOSA, R. A. 1960. Nutritional requirements for growth of a mouse lymphoma in cell culture. Exptl. Cell Res., **21**: 430–438.

HIGUCHI, K. 1963. Studies on the nutrition and metabolism of animal cells in serum-free media. I. Serum-free monolayer cultures. J. Infect. Diseases, **112**: 213–220.

HOLMES, R. 1959. Long term cultivation of human cells (Chang) in chemically defined medium and effect of added peptone fraction. J. Biophys. Bioch. Cytol., **6**: 535–536.

HOLTER, H. 1959. Problems of pinocytosis, with special regard to amoebae. Ann. N. Y. Acad. Sci., **78**: 524–537.

HOLTER, H. 1961. Pinocytosis. *In: Biological Structure and Function*, Vol. 1, pp. 157–168. T. W. Goodwin and O. Lindberg, eds. New York: Academic Press, Inc.

HOLTER, H., and HOLTZER, H. 1959. Pinocytotic uptake of fluorescein-labelled proteins by various tissue cells. Exptl. Cell Res., **18**: 421–423.

HOLTZER, H., and HOLTZER, S. 1960. The *in vitro* uptake of fluorescein labelled plasma proteins. I. Mature cells. Compt. Rend. Trav. Lab. Carlsberg, **31**: 373–408.

HSU, T. C., and KELLOGG, D. S., JR. 1959. Genetics of *in vitro* cells. *In: Genetics and Cancer*, pp. 183–204. Austin: University of Texas Press.

KALTENBACH, J. P., KALTENBACH, M. H., and LYONS, W. B. 1958. Nigrosin as a dye for differentiating live and dead ascites cells. Exptl. Cell Res., **15**: 112–117.

KENT, H. N., and GEY, G. O. 1957. Changes in serum proteins during growth of malignant cells *in vitro*. Proc. Soc. Exptl. Biol. Med., **94**: 205–208.

KENT, H. N., and GEY, G. O. 1960. Selective uptake of serum globulins and glycoproteins by cells growing *in vitro*. Science, **131**: 666–668.

KNIGHT, P. F., and SCHECHTMAN, A. M. 1954. The passage of heterologous serum proteins from the circulation into the ovum of the fowl. J. Exptl. Zool., **127**: 271–304.

KUTSKY, R. J. 1953. Stimulating effect of nucleoprotein fraction of chick embryo extract on homologous heart fibroblasts. Proc. Soc. Exptl. Biol. Med., **83**: 390–395.

KUTSKY, R. J. 1959. Nucleoprotein constituents stimulating growth in tissue culture: active protein fraction. Science, **129**: 1486–1487.

KUTSKY, R. J., and HARRIS, M. 1957. Effects of nucleoprotein fractions from adult and juvenile tissues on growth of chick fibroblasts in plasma cultures. Growth, 21: 53–72.

LEVINE, S. 1960. Effect of manipulation on ^{32}P loss from tissue culture cells. Exptl. Cell Res., 19: 220–227.

LEVINTOW, L., and EAGLE, H. 1961. Biochemistry of cultured mammalian cells. Ann. Rev. Bioch., 30: 605–640.

LEVINTOW, L., EAGLE, H., and PIEZ, K. A. 1957. The role of glutamine in protein biosynthesis in tissue culture. J. Biol. Chem., 227: 929–941.

LEWIS, W. H. 1931. Pinocytosis. Bull. Johns Hopkins Hosp., 49: 17–27.

LIEBERMAN, I., LAMY, F., and OVE, P. 1959. Nonidentity of fetuin and protein growth (flattening) factor. Science, 129: 43–44.

LIEBERMAN, I., and OVE, P. 1957. Purification of a serum protein required by a mammalian cell in tissue culture. Biochim. et Biophys. Acta, 25: 449–450.

LIEBERMAN, I., and OVE, P. 1958a. A protein growth factor for mammalian cells in culture. J. Biol. Chem., 233: 637–642.

LIEBERMAN, I., and OVE, P. 1958b. Catalase requirement for mammalian cells in culture. J. Exptl. Med., 108: 631–637.

LIEBERMAN, I., and OVE, P. 1959. Growth factors for mammalian cells in culture. J. Biol. Chem., 234: 2754–2768.

LOCKART, R. Z., JR., and EAGLE, H. 1959. Requirements for growth of single human cells. Science, 129: 252–254.

McCOY, T. A., MAXWELL, M., IRVINE, E., and SARTORELLI, A. C. 1959. Two nutritional variants of cultured Jensen sarcoma cells. Proc. Soc. Exptl. Biol. Med., 100: 862–865.

McCOY, T. A., MAXWELL, M. D., and KRUSE, P. F., JR. 1961. Carbon dioxide metabolism in the Jensen and JA sarcomas in vitro. Cancer Res., 21: 997–1000.

McCOY, T. A., MAXWELL, M., and NEUMAN, R. E. 1956. The amino acid requirements of the Walker carcinosarcoma 256 in vitro. Cancer Res., 16: 979–984.

McQUILKIN, W. T., EVANS, V. J., and EARLE, W. R. 1957. The adaptation of additional lines of NCTC Clone 929 (Strain L) cells to chemically defined protein-free medium NCTC 109. J. Natl. Cancer Inst., 19: 885–907.

MERCHANT, D. J., and HELLMAN, K. B. 1962. Growth of L-M strain mouse cells in a chemically defined medium. Proc. Soc. Exptl. Biol. Med., 110: 194–198.

MERCHANT, D. J., and KAHN, R. H. 1958. Fiber formation in suspension cultures of L strain fibroblasts. Proc. Soc. Exptl. Biol. Med., 97: 359–362.

METZGAR, D. P., JR., and MOSKOWITZ, M. 1960. Separation of growth promoting activity from horse serum by dialysis. Proc. Soc. Exptl. Biol. Med., 104: 363–365.

MOHBERG, J., and JOHNSON, M. J. 1963. Amino acid utilization by 929-L fibroblasts in chemically defined media. J. Natl. Cancer Inst., 31: 611–625.

MORGAN, J. F. 1958. Tissue culture nutrition. Bact. Revs., 22: 20–45.

MORGAN, J. F., and MORTON, H. J. 1957. The nutrition of animal tissues cultivated *in vitro*. IV. Amino acid requirements of chick embryonic heart fibroblasts. J. Biophys. Biochem. Cytol., 3: 141–150.

MORGAN, J. F., and MORTON, H. J. 1960. Carbohydrate utilization by chick embryonic heart cultures. Can. J. Bioch. Physiol., 38: 69–78.

MORGAN, J. F., MORTON, H. J., and PARKER, R. C. 1950. Nutrition of animal cells in tissue culture. I. Initial studies on a synthetic medium. Proc. Soc. Exptl. Biol. Med., 73: 1–8.

MORTON, H. J., PASIEKA, A. E., and MORGAN, J. F. 1956. The nutrition of animal tissues cultivated *in vitro*. III. Use of a depletion technique for determining specific nutritional requirements. J. Biophys. Biochem. Cytol., 2: 589–596.

NACHMIAS, V. T., and MARSHALL, J. M., JR. 1961. Protein uptake by pinocytosis in amoebae: studies on ferritin and methylated ferritin. In: *Biological Structure and Function*, pp. 605–619. T. W. Goodwin and O. Lindberg, eds. New York: Academic Press, Inc.

NAGLE, S. C., JR. 1960. The suspension of mammalian tissue cell monolayers without the use of enzymes. Bact. Proc., 1960: 192.

NAGLE, S. C., JR., TRIBBLE, H. R., JR., ANDERSON, R. E., and GARY, N. D. 1963. A chemically defined medium for growth of animal cells in suspension. Proc. Soc. Exptl. Biol. Med., 112: 340–346.

NEUMAN, R. E., and TYTELL, A. A. 1960a. Amino acid requirements for growth of avian lung cultures. Proc. Soc. Exptl. Biol. Med., 103: 71–74.

NEUMAN, R. E., and TYTELL, A. A. 1960b. Stimulatory effects of glycine, L-serine, folic acid and related compounds on growth of cell cultures. Proc. Soc. Exptl. Biol. Med., 103: 763–767.

NEUMAN, R. E., and TYTELL, A. A. 1960c. Serumless medium for cultivation of cells of normal and malignant origin. Proc. Soc. Exptl. Biol. Med., 104: 252–256.

OYAMA, V. I., STEINMAN, H. G., and EAGLE, H. 1953. The nutritional requirements of treponemata. V. A detoxified lipide as the essential growth factor supplied by crystallized serum albumin. J. Bact., 65: 609–616.

PARKER, R. C., CASTOR, L. N., and McCULLOCH, E. A. 1957. Altered cell strains in continuous culture: A general survey. Spec. Pub., N. Y. Acad. Sci., 5: 303–313.

PASIEKA, A. E., and MORGAN, J. F. 1959. Glutamine metabolism of normal and malignant cells cultivated in synthetic media. Nature, 183: 1201–1202.

PASIEKA, A. E., MORTON, H. J., and MORGAN, J. F. 1956. The metabolism of animal tissues cultivated *in vitro*. I. Amino acid metabolism of chick embryonic-heart fibroblasts cultivated in synthetic medium M 150. J. Natl. Cancer Inst., 16: 995–1009.

PASIEKA, A. E., MORTON, H. J., and MORGAN, J. F. 1960. The metabolism of animal tissues cultivated *in vitro*. IV. Comparative studies on human malignant cells. Cancer Res., 20: 362–367.

PAUL, J., 1960. Cell and tissue culture. Edinburgh: E. and S. Livingstone, Ltd. Second edition. 312 pp.

PEDERSEN, K. O. 1947. Ultracentrifugal and electrophoretic studies on fetuin. J. Phys. Colloid Chem., 51: 164–171.

PEPPERS, E. V., FIORAMONTI, M. C., WESTFALL, B. B., EVANS, V. J., and EARLE, W. R. 1958. Effect of lack of glutamine on subline 2071 mouse cells. J. Natl. Cancer Inst., 21: 611–620.

PHILLIPS, H. J., and TERRYBERRY, J. E. 1957. Counting actively metabolizing tissue cultured cells. Exptl. Cell Res., 13: 341–347.

PIEZ, K. A., OYAMA, V. I., LEVINTOW, L., and EAGLE, H. 1960. Proteolysis in stored serum and its possible significance in cell culture. Nature, 188: 59–60.

RAPPAPORT, C., and BISHOP, C. B. 1960. Improved method for treating glass to produce surfaces suitable for the growth of certain mammalian cells in synthetic medium. Exptl. Cell Res., 20: 580–584.

RAPPAPORT, C., POOLE, J. P., and RAPPAPORT, H. P. 1960. Studies on properties of surfaces required for growth of mammalian cells in synthetic medium. I. The HeLa cell. II. The monkey kidney cell. III. The L cell, Strain 929. Exptl. Cell Res., 20: 465–510.

ROSE, W. C., HAINES, W. J., and WARNER, D. T. 1954. The amino acid requirements of man. V. The role of lysine, arginine, and tryptophan. J. Biol. Chem., 206: 421–430.

ROSE, W. C., OESTERLING, M. J., and WOMACK, M. 1948. Comparative growth on diets containing ten and nineteen amino acids, with further observations upon the role of glutamic and aspartic acids. J. Biol. Chem., 176: 753–762.

ROSENBERG, M. D. 1960. Microexudates from cells grown in tissue culture. Biophys. J., 1: 137–159.

RYSER, H., CAULFIELD, J. B., and AUB, J. C. 1962. Studies on protein uptake by isolated tumor cells. I. Electron microscopic evidence of ferritin uptake by Ehrlich ascites tumor cells. J. Cell Biol., 14: 255–268.

SALZMAN, N. P., and SEBRING, E. D. 1959. Utilization of precursors for nucleic acid synthesis by human cell cultures. Arch. Biochem. Biophys., 84: 143–150.

SALZMAN, N. P., EAGLE, H., and SEBRING, E. D. 1958. The utilization of glutamine, glutamic acid, and ammonia for the biosynthesis of nucleic acid bases in mammalian cell cultures. J. Biol. Chem., 230: 1001–1012.

SANFORD, K. K., DUPREE, L. T., and COVALESKY, A. B. 1963. Biotin, B_{12}, and other vitamin requirements of a strain of mammalian cells grown in chemically defined medium. Exptl. Cell Res., 31: 345–375.

SANFORD, K. K., McQUILKIN, W. T., FIORAMONTI, M. C., EVANS, V. J., and EARLE, W. R. 1958. Study of amino acid requirements for increase in cell population of NCTC Clone 929 (Strain L.) J. Natl. Cancer Inst., 20: 775–785.

SATO, G., FISHER, H. W., and PUCK, T. T. 1957. Molecular growth requirements of single mammalian cells. Science, 126: 961–964.

SCHECHTMAN, A. M. 1956. Uptake and transfer of macromolecules by cells with special reference to growth and development. Intern. Rev. Cytol., 5: 303–322.

SINCLAIR, R., REID, R. A., and MITCHELL, P. 1963. Culture of Strain L cells in suspension: replacement of polymer by traces of trypsin in a defined medium. Nature, 197: 982–984.

STEWART, D. C., and KIRK, P. L. 1954. The liquid medium in tissue culture. Biol. Revs., 29: 119–153.

SWIM, H. E. 1959. Microbiological aspects of tissue culture. Ann. Rev. Microbiol., 13: 141–176.

SWIM, H. E., and PARKER, R. F. 1958a. The amino acid requirements of a permanent strain of altered uterine fibroblasts (U12–705). Can. J. Bioch. Physiol., 36: 861–868.

SWIM, H. E., and PARKER, R. F. 1958b. Vitamin requirements of uterine fibroblasts, Strain U12–79; their replacement by related compounds. Arch. Biochem. Biophys., 78: 46–53.

SWIM, H. E., and PARKER, R. F. 1958c. The role of carbon dioxide as an essential nutrient for six permanent strains of fibroblasts. J. Biophys. Bioch. Cytol., 4: 525–528.

SZYBALSKI, W., SZYBALSKA, E. H., and RAGNI, G. 1962. Genetic studies with human cell lines. Natl. Cancer Inst. Monogr., 7: 75–89.

TAKATA, K., and HARRIS, M. 1962. Unpublished experiments.

TAYLOR, A. C. 1961. Attachment and spreading of cells in culture. Exptl. Cell Res., Suppl. 8: 154–173.

TODARO, G. J., and GREEN, H. 1962. Role of inoculum size on the growth rate of fibroblastic cells. Federation Proc., 21: 157.

TODARO, G. J., and GREEN, H. 1963. Quantitative studies of the growth of mouse embryo cells in culture and their development into established lines. J. Cell Biol., 17: 299–313.

TRIBBLE, H. R., JR., and HIGUCHI, K. 1963. Studies on the nutrition and metabolism of animal cells in serum-free media. II. Cultivation of cells in suspension. J. Infect. Diseases, 112: 221–225.

WAYMOUTH, C. 1954. The nutrition of animal cells. Intern. Rev. Cytol., 3: 1–68.

WAYMOUTH, C. 1959. Rapid proliferation of sublines of NCTC Clone 929 (Strain L) mouse cells in a simple chemically defined medium (MB 752/1). J. Natl. Cancer Inst., 22: 1003–1017.

WEISS, L. 1958. The effects of trypsin on size, viability and dry mass of sarcoma 37 cells. Exptl. Cell Res., 14: 80–83.

WEISS, L. 1960. Studies on cellular adhesion in tissue culture. III. Some effects of calcium. Exptl. Cell Res., 21: 71–77.

WHITE, P. R. 1946. Cultivation of animal tissues *in vitro* in nutrients of precisely known constitution. Growth, 10: 231–289.

WHITE, P. R. 1949. Prolonged survival of excised animal tissues *in vitro* in nutrients of known constitution. J. Comp. Cell. Physiol., 34: 221–241.

ZIMMERMAN, M., DEVLIN, T. M., and PRUSS, M. P. 1960. Anaerobic glycolysis of dispersed cell suspensions from normal and malignant tissues. Nature, 185: 315–316.

Resistance to extrinsic agents

chapter 6 Cell populations often display a remarkable ability for adaptation to inhibitory factors in their immediate surroundings. Although this phenomenon is particularly prominent at the microbial level, it is by no means confined to microorganisms. Isolated systems of somatic cells may be similarly capable of adaptive evolution. Tumors *in vivo* as well as permanent cell strains in culture undergo manifold adjustments to drugs, irradiation, and other extrinsic agents. These processes lead to progressive remodeling of population structure, and in at least some instances are clearly based on heritable changes. Such plasticity is in marked contrast to the continuity of response levels within tissues of the intact organism.

Yet neoplastic change as such does not seem to be a necessary prerequisite for the adaptive evolution of cell populations. Drug resistance, for example, can be elicited in cultures of cell strains that have no overt malignant properties, as well as in those which are frankly tumor-producing in appropriate hosts (Chapter 7). It may be that the significant element is a functional dissociation of cell groupings, which tends to occur both in tumors and in isolated cell strains. In any event, the development of resistance to environmental factors provides a focal point for examining the progressions that take place in cell populations. Adaptive responses to drugs are particularly useful for exploring unit changes in cellular phenotype. Variation in this case can frequently be expressed by the emergence of new biosynthetic patterns. The contribution of genetic and epigenetic factors to these changes can in principle be examined by appropriate experimental designs. Coupled with a variety of insights available from microbial systems, the analysis of drug resistance constitutes perhaps the most explicit approach yet made to variation within differentiated somatic cells.

RESPONSES TO DRUGS IN MICROORGANISMS

Historically, the study of drug resistance developed as an adjunct to the field of experimental chemotherapy. As early as 1907 Ehrlich began to examine arsenicals as a means for controlling trypanosome infections in mice. Among the compounds found effective was the drug parafuchsin, but eventually the protozoan parasites became refractory and were not inhibited by further treatment with this agent. The clinical importance of drug resistance, thus clearly indicated, provided a theme that has expanded with many variations. An enormous and diversified literature developed within the area of microbiology alone (see Schnitzer and Grunberg, 1957; Schnitzer, 1963). With the eventual emergence of bacterial genetics, however, drug resistance has also become an analytical tool—a means for analyzing the mechanisms of heredity at the cellular level. This new focus introduced interpretations that on occasion have led to lively disagreements in the research literature. Nevertheless, genetic approaches to the phenomenon of resistance have been increasingly fruitful (see Bryson and Szybalski, 1955; Wolstenholme and O'Connor, 1957; Bryson, 1962).

Origins of Resistance in Bacteria   The examination of drug resistance in microorganisms has extended over various groups of Protozoa (Bishop, 1959), fungi (Schnitzer and Grunberg, 1957) and many kinds of bacteria (Szybalski and Bryson, 1955), but it is the latter that have provided the principal basis for analytical studies. Here, a clear transition in concepts has taken place. Early investigators of drug resistance in bacteria emphasized the notion of "training," and attributed refractory states to the acquisition of new metabolic patterns through exposure of sensitive cells to specific compounds. The validity of this view was generally discounted when replica plating and other techniques for indirect selection demonstrated that resistant variants can arise in the absence of contact with the corresponding drug (Lederberg and Lederberg, 1952; Sneath, 1955; Cavalli-Sforza and Lederberg, 1956). The impact of such experiments was to shift the discussion of drug resistance for the most part to genetic levels. Nevertheless, certain investigators—for example, Sevag (1955) and especially Hinshelwood and his collaborators—continued to support the hypothesis of phenotypic adaptation. While agreeing that resistant variants in bacteria can originate through mutation, they have asserted that in at least some instances, resistance is conferred by shifts in cellular reaction systems against a homogeneous genetic background (Dean and Hinshelwood, 1953, 1957). The details of this controversy need not be debated here, but it is fair to say that

Hinshelwood's original views have not been accepted by most other workers (Lederberg, 1957). On the other hand, physiological adaptation in drug resistance need not be completely excluded. In some instances the presence of drugs could be instrumental in bringing about the phenotypic expression of resistance, even though the capacity for this response is conferred by genetic change. Such a mechanism might be postulated, for example, when mutations occur that merely make possible the induction of enzymes to implement refractory states (Szybalski and Bryson, 1955). In this case, subsequent exposure to the corresponding drug or other inductor would be necessary to potentiate resistance within the phenotypically sensitive variants. Lam and Sevag (1955) have reported that a composite sequence of this type occurs during the development of resistance to streptomycin in micrococci (see also Drabble and Hinshelwood, 1961).

Although some exceptions may exist, it is clear that drug resistance in bacteria does in general arise through direct genetic change. The kinetics of this process were examined by early workers by means of fluctuation tests (Demerec, 1945; Oakberg and Luria, 1947; Newcombe and Hawirko, 1949). The data indicated mutation rates from sensitivity to resistance, which were of the order of 1×10^{-9} to 1×10^{-10} for the systems studied [that is, comparable to those observed for other genetic markers (Demerec, 1957)]. Later, a number of direct proofs showed that drug resistance in bacteria is associated with altered genetic information. These include the transfer of resistance between cells by transforming DNA (Hotchkiss, 1951; Ravin, 1961), transduction with phage (Zinder and Lederberg, 1952: Hartman, 1957), and conjugation (Lederberg, 1950; Jacob and Wollman, 1961). By examining heterozygous strains of E. coli, which arise occasionally following gene transfer, Lederberg (1951) found that streptomycin resistance behaves as a recessive marker. Other experiments have shown that resistance to chloramphenicol in E. coli is dependent on multiple loci (Cavalli and Maccacaro, 1952), and similar controls may exist for the majority of drugs (Bryson, 1962).

The genetic concept of drug resistance implies the emergence of variants in a discontinuous or stepwise sequence from sensitive populations. This prediction has been amply confirmed in studies with antibiotics and other growth inhibitors in bacterial systems. Two principal types of population change may be distinguished (Demerec, 1948). The first of these can be termed a one-step pattern, in which fully resistant variants appear at the first selective isolation with the inhibitor in question. Characteristically the survivors proliferate over a wide range of concentrations that are lethal to the sensitive precursor population and tend to be similar to one another in degree of resistance. Although streptomycin resistance was used initially to illustrate the one-step pattern, this phenomenon is seen in its simplest form in such systems as azide resistance in *E. coli* (Lederberg, 1950), or sodium *p*-amino-salicylate and isoniazid resistance in *B. megaterium* (Szybalski and Bryson, 1953). In these instances, clonal isolates from primary cultures are usually fully resistant, whereas with streptomycin, a spectrum of variants ranging from partial to complete resistance is obtained (Demerec, 1948). Azide resistance thus represents an obligatory, and streptomycin resistance a facultative, one-step pattern (Bryson and Szybalski, 1955). The latter serves as a bridge to multistep patterns of drug resistance, which Demerec first described for populations acquiring a refractory response to penicillin (Figure 6.1). In this case, only partially resistant cells are obtained during the initial isolations in the presence of the drug. But if the survivors are exposed sequentially to increasing levels of antibiotic, highly resistant forms finally emerge. Multistep patterns of this sort are consistent with a polygenic mechanism, and are typical of resistance by bacteria to most antibiotics (Bryson and Szybalski, 1955; Bryson, 1962).

Whether resistance arises from a single genetic event in the bacterial cell or from mutations in tandem, the refractory state is ordinarily

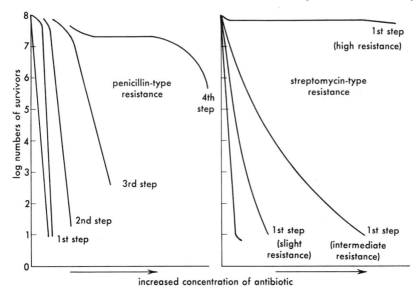

FIG. 6.1. Comparison of survival curves for bacterial populations exposed to drugs, showing penicillin and streptomycin types of resistance. (Redrawn from Bryson and Demerec, 1950.)

confined to a single drug or group of related substances, and sensitivity as a rule persists toward unrelated compounds. Thus the appearance of variants with simultaneous resistance to two different drugs would be expected only rarely, since the probability of this event as a first approximation should be the product of the separate mutation rates. This prediction is in reasonable agreement with the data actually obtained by Szybalski and Bryson (1953) for mutants in B. *megaterium* doubly resistant to sodium p-aminosalicylate and to isoniazid. For sodium p-aminosalicylate, the mutation rate is 1×10^{-6}; for isoniazid alone, the comparable frequency is 6×10^{-5}. Mutants with both markers, however, arise at a rate of only 8×10^{-10} per cell per generation. The problem of whether drugs may significantly enhance the spontaneous mutation rate has never been completely clarified. It is well known that numerous chemical agents can serve as mutagens, and this possibility is therefore not an unreasonable one (Bryson and Szybalski, 1955). Streptomycin has in fact been reported to increase the frequency of mutations to resistance in E. *coli* at concentrations that are not growth-inhibiting (Newcombe, 1955). Unrelated mutations, however, also appeared in greater numbers within the streptomycin-treated populations. So far, at least, there is no evidence in bacteria that streptomycin or any other drug can induce gene mutations specifically directed toward resistance per se.

Still another facet in the variation-selection pattern of drug responses deserves special mention. This is the paradoxical observation that in some cases, the very agent that initially inhibits sensitive cells can later become an obligatory requirement for growth and survival. Drug dependence in this sense is a rather specialized phenomenon, although scattered observations are available in microbial systems (Schnitzer and Grunberg, 1957; Schnitzer, 1963). One case has received considerable study, namely, the contrasting responses of bacteria to streptomycin. That streptomycin-dependent as well as resistant variants occur in E. *coli* was first demonstrated by Demerec (1951). Examining the survivors of sensitive populations that had been treated with streptomycin, he found that a large fraction of the survivors grew only in the presence of this drug. The mutant character was comparatively stable, although reversions to streptomycin independence did take place frequently. Subsequent studies showed that the loss of dependence is mediated by genetic change and can be accelerated by any of several agents known to induce gene mutation (Demerec, 1957). The possibility that these observations suggested originally was that sensitivity, resistance, and dependence on streptomycin are controlled by multiple alleles at a single genetic locus. This hypothesis received preliminary confirmation through recombination experiments (Newcombe and Nyholm, 1950). A more precise picture has been drawn by Hashimoto (1960), who found that streptomycin resistance and independence are actually nonidentical alleles in *E. coli*, occupying very closely linked sites within the same locus or cistron. Hashimoto also found that most, if not all, of the "reversions" from dependence to independence are in fact mediated by changes in a separate suppressor gene rather than by back mutation at the streptomycin locus.

These conclusions in general were confirmed and extended by Goldschmidt, Matney, and Bausum (1962) who showed that in *Salmonella typhimurium*, streptomycin dependence typically involves the appearance of a nutritional requirement for methionine, as well as a need for streptomycin per se. Modifier mutations at another genetic locus can abolish the requirement for methionine and reduce the dependence on streptomycin; alternatively, suppressor mutations can eliminate the need for both factors. No verified reversions to true wild type were found among any stable dependent strains, and neither modifier nor suppressor mutations were closely linked to the streptomycin dependence locus.

Extrachromosomal Systems   The documentation of drug resistance in terms of gene mutation is indeed impressive. This conclusion should not be taken to exclude alternative mechanisms, however, particularly in cell systems other than bacteria. Even in bacteria there are indications that refractory states may occasionally arise by transfer of an extrachromosomal agent. The occurrence of multiply resistant strains within the enteric group offers a case in point (Watanabe and Fukasawa, 1961a, 1961b, 1961c; see also Watanabe, 1963). Such variants were first noted clinically through the isolation from human patients of dysentery bacilli with a broad spectrum of resistance. These strains may be unresponsive, for example, to streptomycin and chloramphenicol as well as to tetracycline and sulfonamide drugs. Laboratory experiments show that multiple drug resistance can be transferred as a unit to numerous other bacteria within the *Enterobacteriaceae*, merely by introducing resistant cells into cultures of a sensitive strain (Harada, Suzuki, Kameda, and Mitsuhashi, 1960). Cell-to-cell contact is ordinarily required, but under certain conditions, transduction may succeed as well (Watanabe and Fukasawa, 1961c). Significantly, the introduction of resistance factors can occur under conditions that preclude the transfer of chromosomes between cells (Watanabe and Fukasawa, 1961a). This infective transfer of genetic characteristics is reminiscent of the behavior of the colicinogenic and *F*-factors (Chapter 2). Accordingly, Watanabe and Fukasawa have proposed that the multiple resistance factor is in fact an episome. Like other episomic agents, this unit is assumed to exist in alternative states, either replicating autonomously in the cytoplasm or in direct association with the bacterial chromosome.

Among other microorganisms the most convincing demonstration that drug resistance can be mediated by extrachromosomal patterns lies in the work of Sager (1954, 1960) on the green alga, *Chlamydomonas reinhardi*. This unicellular form is easily maintained in liquid or in solid media, and has a simple life cycle that is particularly favorable for genetic analysis (Figure 6.2). Ordinarily, *Chlamydomonas* populations consist of haploid cells that multiply by mitosis. The cells are identical in appearance, but consist of two different mating types, which are designated *plus* and *minus*, respectively. If populations of opposite mating properties are mixed, fusion ensues between complementary units, and zygotes are formed. Each zygote then undergoes meiosis, with the production of four haploid cells. The latter can be isolated individually by appropriate dissection, and can then be used to establish separate strains.

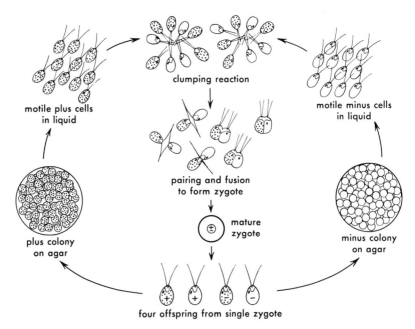

FIG. 6.2. Life cycle of the green alga, *Chlamydomonas reinhardi*. Segregation and recombination of two markers are shown: (1) mating type, denoted by plus and minus signs, and (2) ability to synthesize chlorophyll in the absence of light (*dotted*) or lack of ability (*undotted*). Only one of four possible combinations of plus and minus colonies is indicated. (Redrawn from Sager, 1960, with the permission of *Science*.)

By comparing the characteristics of these progeny populations, a simple Mendelian analysis becomes possible. A number of genetic markers have been followed in this system, and these segregate in patterns expected for chromosomal determinants (Sager, 1955).

Viewed against this background, the analysis of streptomycin resistance in *Chlamydomonas* is particularly interesting (Sager, 1954, 1955, 1960, 1961; Sager and Tsubo, 1961). Heritable variants that are refractory to growth inhibition can be obtained readily by inoculating sensitive populations on a drug agar substrate. The vast majority of these can be attributed to gene mutation. Fluctuation tests indicate that the change is a spontaneous one, occurring with a frequency of about 10^{-6} within both *plus* and *minus* strains. Characteristically, the variants that arise in this fashion are resistant to streptomycin at 100 μg/ml, but not at higher concentrations; for this reason, the mutant gene is designated *sr*-100. The inheritance of resistance in such strains follows a typical Mendelian pattern. If an *sr*-100 strain is crossed with a streptomycin sensitive (*ss*) line, segregation occurs consistently within the zygote, with a 2:2 ratio of resistant and sensitive derivatives. A chromosomal location for the *sr*-100 gene can accordingly be inferred, and mapping experiments indicate that the locus is situated approximately 15 units from the centromere in linkage group IX (Sager and Tsubo, 1961).

Among a broader spectrum of mutants isolated with streptomycin, however, a few show distinctly different properties. Physiologically, these can be recognized because of the ability to grow unhindered by drug at 500 μg/ml. Such *sr*-500 variants are very stable and do not revert to the sensitive state when maintained as haploid clones in vegetative propagation. Their genetic behavior is quite unique. Transmission of the *sr*-500 marker in crosses takes place ordinarily only where the resistant state occurs in the *plus* parent (Figure 6.3). If this condition is met, the progeny remain uniformly refractory to streptomycin through a series of backcrosses with a sensitive strain. By contrast, if resistant *minus* cells are crossed with a sensitive line, the progeny with rare exceptions are all sensitive. Other researches have shown that this uniparental mode of transmission also applies to the inheritance of streptomycin dependence (*sd*) in a single case that has been studied (Sager and Tsubo, 1961). Such a change is evidently rare in *Chlamydomonas*, since only one dependent variant has been observed among some 10,000 streptomycin-resistant colonies subjected to screening. In crosses between streptomycin-resistant and dependent strains, transmission occurs only for the marker present in the *plus* parent. Thus progeny from the cross *sd mt+* × *sr*-500 *mt−* all show dependence.

The unexpected asymmetry in patterns of inheritance for *sd* and

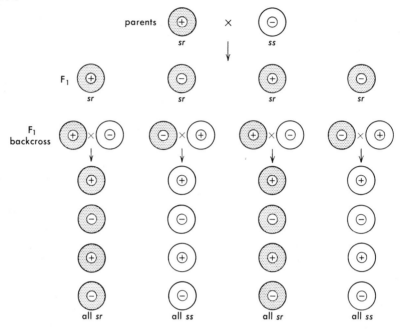

FIG. 6.3. Non-Mendelian inheritance of streptomycin resistance in *Chlamydomonas*. When resistant (*sr*-500) and sensitive (*ss*) strains are crossed, resistance is transmitted to the progeny only if present in the *plus* parent. (Redrawn from Sager, 1954.)

sr-500 determinants clearly suggests an extrachromosomal mode of transmission. There is also evidence that these factors may have a unique origin. Sager and others have been unable by means of fluctuation tests to demonstrate that the *sr*-500 variants arise spontaneously, although under similar conditions the *sr*-100 marker does appear with the expected high variance among separate sublines (Sager, 1961, 1962; Gillham and Levine, 1962). Taken together, these observations suggest that the *sr*-500 and *sd* factors have mutant properties that may derive from direct induction with streptomycin (Sager, 1960, 1962). That this drug may function in general as a mutagen for nonchromosomal determinants has been suggested by Sager and Tsubo (1962), who have shown that a specific class of chloroplast mutants in *Chlamydomonas* arises with high frequency after streptomycin treatment. The information here again favors a process of direct induction rather than a selection of pre-existing variants.

The picture of nonchromosomal determinants in *Chlamydomonas* has unfolded further through the analysis of exceptional zygotes, in which transmission of these factors occurs via a parental cell of *minus* mating type (Gillham, 1963a, 1963b; Sager and Ramanis, 1963). It appears that although extrachromosomal determinants ordinarily are somehow eliminated or inhibited in *minus* cells during mating, this process may occasionally break down. In that case, nonchromosomal factors from both parents are transmitted to haploid progeny, and during postmeiotic stages within clonal populations, segregation occurs. The extent and timing of this event are variable for different markers among the extrachromosomal group, but in no instance can segregation of known chromosomal determinants be observed during the same period (Sager and Ramanis, 1963). Somewhat similar observations are reported by Gillham (1963b), who obtained diploid populations of *Chlamydomonas* by a special selection technique during mating, and found segregation of *ss* and *sr*-500 markers to occur subsequently. These properties are consistent with the behavior of genetic particulates, and Sager and Ramanis (1963) have accordingly proposed the term nonchromosomal (NC) genes for the factors in question. Their chemical nature and location in the cell are still unknown, but the reported presence of a special type of DNA in isolated chloroplasts of *Chlamydomonas* may be suggestive (Sager and Ishida, 1963).

Acquired resistance to streptomycin in *Amoeba* has also been the subject of recent investigation (Cole and Danielli, 1963). Certain strains, at least, of *A. proteus* can be conditioned to grow at elevated concentrations if exposed sequentially to increasing concentrations of this drug. With mass populations it is not clear whether variation-selection, or a process of phenotypic adaptation takes place, but the consistent failure of Cole and Danielli to secure resistant lines by indirect means points to the latter. If an induced adaptation is responsible, the locus of change is probably nuclear rather than cytoplasmic. Nuclear transfers made between resistant and sensitive cells show that acquired resistance is conferred on hybrids by the nucleus only. However, the refractory state is transitory in the absence of streptomycin. Resistance declines progressively, reaching a normal level after a number of weeks.

Among other animal cells, suggestive evidence for the participation of extrachromosomal mechanisms in drug resistance can be found in the old experiments of Jollos (1921). These deal with the acquisition of tolerance to environmental factors by populations of *Paramecium caudatum* and *P. aurelia*. In this work, organisms were exposed to increasing concentrations of arsenious oxide or calcium, or to elevated temperatures. Eventually sublines emerged with specific resistance, and this was retained for long periods in the absence of the selecting agents. Jollos referred to these variations as "Dauermodifications," and they were characterized by distinctive properties different from those that might be expected for characteristics based on gene mutations. One of these differences was a marked effect of environmental factors on the stability of variant characters. Tolerance to arsenious oxide, for example, could be greatly decreased by subjecting resistant populations to temperature shocks or other abrupt environmental changes. If the same organisms were maintained under standard conditions of culture, the level of resistance only gradually declined over periods of 8 to 9 months. Even more interesting, however, was the observation that tolerance was retained only in populations multiplying by means of fission. Resistance disappeared abruptly in a single step whenever conjugation between individuals took place.

Beale (1954) points out that while the facts reported by Jollos appear to be substantially accurate, their significance has never been accounted for in modern genetic theory. From one viewpoint, the lability of resistance to arsenious oxide in animals subjected to environmental shocks suggests a parallel to the antigenic changes that can be induced in paramecia by similar treatments (Chapter 2). For the latter, a cytoplasmic control system must be visualized, operating with limits set by the genotype. Conceivably, the acquisition of resistance to such drugs as arsenious oxide could be accounted for by a somewhat similar explanation. Alternatively, Beale suggests that the "Dauermodifications" of Jollos may depend on a process of macronuclear differentiation. This view is consistent with the continuity of the macronucleus during vegetative multiplication as well as the disintegration and replacement of macronuclei at the time of conjugation. These uncertainties have yet to be resolved by experimental analysis, but the processes here are of considerable interest as possible genetic or developmental models.

DRUG RESISTANCE IN TUMORS

Cancer chemotherapy with its allied fields of study has become of late a major area of experimental biology and medicine. This effort stems from the successful innovation or discovery of antibiotics for the control of microbial infections. In principle, the exploitation of metabolic differences between normal and neoplastic cells could be similarly fruitful. Consistent differentials that distinguish the neoplastic state have not yet been found, however, and the use of drugs to inhibit tumors has therefore been based on multiple rationales; for example, the greater susceptibility of rapidly dividing cells to antimitotic agents, inactivation by irreversible binding of key enzymes in biosynthesis, or competitive inhibition by means of substrate analogues. The number of compounds that have been tested for these or for purely empirical reasons is legion, and varying degrees of tumor inhibition have often been reported, both clinically and in laboratory animals. It is common knowledge, however, that although temporary remissions may sometimes be achieved, all drugs that have been used so far fail eventually to halt the progress of tumor growth. These terminal refractory states may be influenced by an array of complex factors (Welch, 1961), but one element is clearly the tendency for drug resistance to develop within tumor populations. The analysis of drug resistance within neoplasms is thus a pressing practical problem as well as a tool and model system for the study of somatic cell variation.

Anticancer Drugs and Refractory States   Before taking up drug resistance within tumors as such, it may be useful to enumerate a few of the principal compounds that have received extensive study as antineoplastic agents. Most of these are antimetabolites, that is, structural analogues of vitamins, purines, pyrimidines, and other substances of physiological significance. Among the best known of these are the various antipurines (Figure 6.4). The first to be used in cancer chemotherapy was 2,6-diaminopurine (Burchenal, Bendich, Brown, Elion, Hitchings, Rhoads, and Stock, 1949), a compound that acts as an apparent antagonist of adenine. Subsequently, 8-azaguanine (Kidder, Dewey, Parks, and Woodside, 1949; Mandel, 1955), 6-mercaptopurine (Clarke, Philips, Sternberg, Stock, Elion, and Hitchings, 1953; Miner,

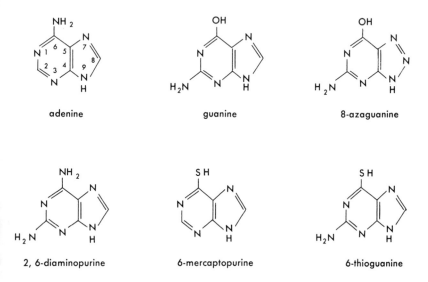

adenine   guanine   8-azaguanine

2, 6-diaminopurine   6-mercaptopurine   6-thioguanine

FIG. 6.4. Purines and purine analogues.

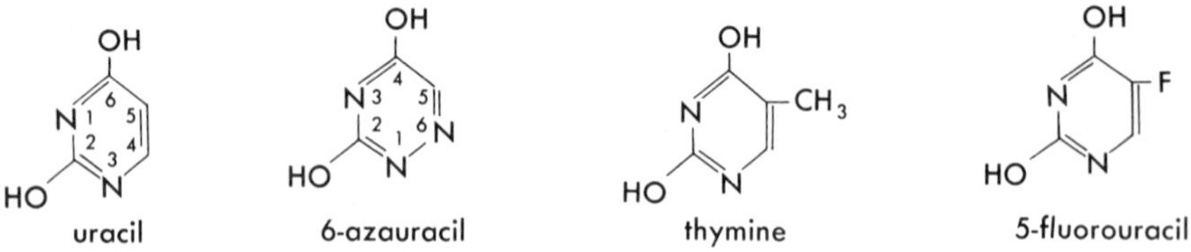

FIG. 6.5. Pyrimidines and pyrimidine analogues.

1954), 6-thioguanine (Clarke, Philips, Sternberg, and Stock, 1954), and many other substituted purines have been introduced as anticancer drugs (Timmis, 1961; Parks, 1963). Antipyrimidines also merit study as potential blocking agents in neoplastic cells (Figure 6.5). A number of tumors are inhibited by 6-azauracil (Hakala, Law, and Welch, 1956; Welch, 1961) as well as by 5-fluorouracil and related compounds (Duschinsky, Pleven, and Heidelberger, 1957; Heidelberger, 1961).

Structural analogues of vitamins have been prepared in many forms, mainly for use in nutritional and metabolic studies. At least one group of such compounds, however, the folic acid antagonists, has found extensive use in tumor chemotherapy (Figure 6.6). Starting with the observation that leukemic cells display a high requirement for folic acid, Farber and his colleagues in 1948 reported that temporary remissions of leukemia in children could be obtained with aminopterin, the 4-amino derivative of this vitamin (Farber, Diamond, Mercer, Sylvester, and Wolff, 1948). Subsequently, amethopterin (4-amino-N^{10}-methyl pteroylglutamic acid) was introduced as a slightly less toxic compound, and numerous other folic acid analogues were examined for antitumor activity (Petering, 1952; Burchenal, 1955a).

Another group of antimetabolites include the glutamine antagonists azaserine (O-diazoacetyl-L-serine) and DON (6-diazo-L-norleucine) (Figure 6.7). These compounds were isolated from cultures of *Streptomyces* in the course of screening operations directed toward the discovery of new antibiotic or antitumor agents. Both azaserine and DON inhibit reactions that require glutamine, such as the conversion of formylglycinamide to formylglycinamidine (Levenberg, Melnick, and Buchanan, 1957). It is likely, however, that these agents have multiple effects extending to several sites within the cell (Handschumacher and Welch, 1960). Animal tumors in a broad spectrum are inhibited by these glutamine antagonists (Suguira and Stock, 1955), but clinical trials in human cancer proved to be disappointing (Magill, Myers, Reilly, Putnam, Magill, Sykes, Escher, Karnofsky, and Burchenal, 1957).

A quite different category of anticancer drugs is represented by the alkylating agents, such as the nitrogen mustards and ethyleneimines

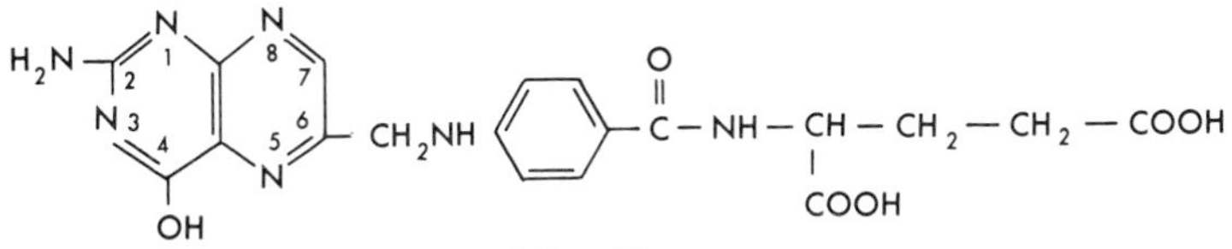

folic acid

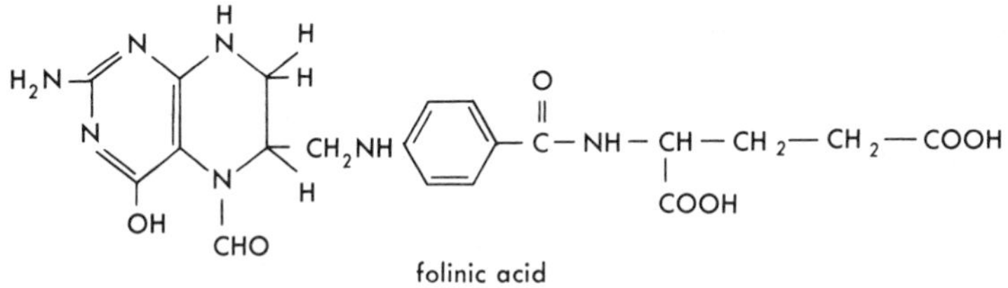

folinic acid

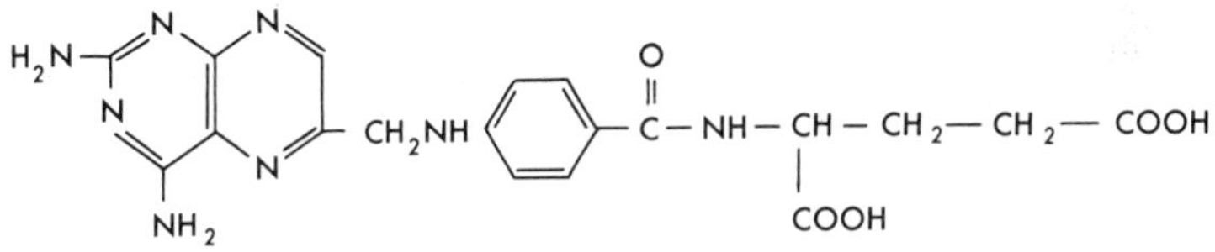

aminopterin

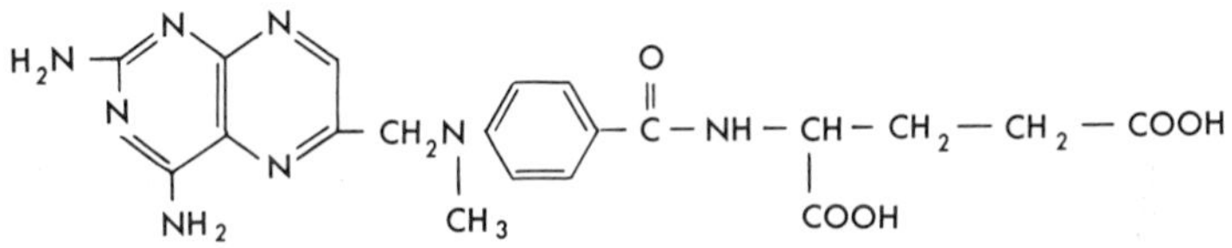

amethopterin

FIG. 6.6. Folic and folinic acids, and folic acid antagonists.

(Figure 6.8). These compounds react extensively with proteins, nucleic acids, and other components of cells. They are particularly toxic in rapidly proliferating tissues. The cytotoxic effects of agents in this group were discovered as a result of wartime researches in mustard gas and various related compounds. Subsequently the therapeutic potential of nitrogen mustards for tumor growth was pointed out (Gilman and Philips, 1946), and extensive clinical studies were made (Karnofsky, 1958). Most of this work has dealt with the compound HN_2 [that is, methyl-di-(β-chloroethyl)amine], although a variety of related mustards have been examined as well. Among other types of alkylating agents are the substance TEM (triethylene melamine) and Myleran (1,4-dimethanesulfonoxybutane), both of which have been employed extensively

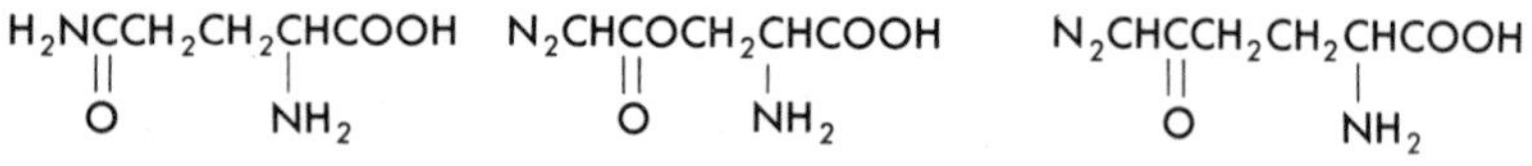

$$H_2NCCH_2CH_2CHCOOH \qquad N_2CHCOCH_2CHCOOH \qquad N_2CHCCH_2CH_2CHCOOH$$

glutamine	azaserine	DON

FIG. 6.7. Glutamine and glutamine analogues.

as anticancer drugs. The fact that alkylating agents show a broad spectrum of reaction with cellular systems has so far precluded any direct analysis of mechanisms (Mandel, 1959), although the radiomimetic effects of the nitrogen mustards have frequently been pointed out (Alexander and Stacey, 1958; Auerbach, 1958).

Many other types of compounds with antitumor activity, besides the limited number mentioned above, have received extensive study. At the present time, thousands of substances are being screened for carcinostatic action in large-scale empirical programs. The details of these complex studies belong elsewhere, but for descriptions in depth on the development and properties of antineoplastic agents, reference can be made to a number of recent comprehensive reviews (Raven, 1959; Mandel, 1959; Handschumacher and Welch, 1960; Karnofsky and Clarkson, 1963).

The development of new drugs with promise for the control of tumors has been followed regularly by descriptions of neoplasms that have become refractory to the compounds in question. This now familiar pattern was first observed by Burchenal, Robinson, Johnston, and Kushida (1950) with folic acid antagonists. For these experiments, Burchenal and his collaborators used a transplantable acute lymphocytic neoplasm of mice. The tumor was regularly sensitive to amethopterin in the first passage, with prolongation of survival time in drug-treated hosts. If, however, serial transfers of leukemic cells were made in mice to which amethopterin had been administered regularly, tumor sublines were eventually obtained in which the host survival was no longer

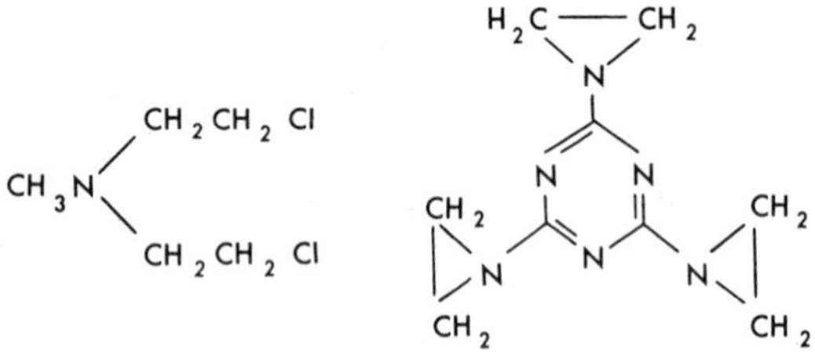

FIG. 6.8. Alkylating agents.

nitrogen mustard
(HN₂)

triethylene melamine
(TEM)

affected by the maximum tolerated dose of the drug. Law and Boyle (1950) similarly noted the development of resistance to folic acid antagonists in mice bearing a transplantable lymphoid leukemia, and showed that resistance could be documented directly by the localized growth of subcutaneous tumor implants.

Other examples of drug resistance in tumors were soon forthcoming. Using the same experimental system, Law (1951c) showed that variant populations resistant to 8-azaguanine can also be obtained by serial treatment of tumor-bearing animals. Sublines refractory to other purine analogues, such as 6-mercaptopurine (Law, 1953; Law, Taormina, and Boyle, 1954) or 6-thioguanine (Sartorelli, LePage, and Moore, 1958), may arise in the same way. Within the group of alkylating agents, it may be noted that Jackson (1954) has described the development of resistance in the Walker rat carcinosarcoma to triethylene melamine (TEM). Similarly, variants of the Yoshida rat sarcoma refractory to nitrogen mustard (HN_2) have been reported by Hirono (1955). Gluta-mine antagonists can also serve as a focal point for resistance. In a plasma-cell neoplasm of the mouse, Potter and Law (1957) observed the rapid emergence of sublines refractory to azaserine and DON, and resistance to these compounds within a mouse ascites carcinoma has also been described by Sartorelli and LePage (1958). More recently, interest has been directed toward the fluorinated pyrimidines. Sublines of mouse ascites tumors refractory to 5-fluorouracil have been reported by Heidelberger, Griesbach, Cruz, Schnitzer, and Grunberg (1958), Reichard, Sköld, and Klein (1959), and Heidelberger (1961).

These comments on the incidence of drug resistance in tumors are intended to be representative rather than inclusive, but serve to empha-size that the phenomenon is a broadly based one in neoplastic cell systems. It should be emphasized, however, that studies on drug re-sistance have for the most part been carried out with transplantable tumors. These can be subjected to a high degree of experimental selec-tion by serial passage in the presence of a given drug. The development of resistance within primary tumors or within a single host is a cor-respondingly less probable event. Many other factors besides drug re-sistance also enter into the secondary failure of cancer chemotherapy (Welch, 1959, 1961). Slow background growth of neoplastic cells may occur during treatment, for example, owing to inadequate differentials between the concentrations of drugs that are toxic to the host and those that result in complete tumor inhibition. Multiplication of tumor ele-ments may also continue disproportionately in isolated locations (for example, brain), which are difficult to reach with drugs administered systemically, and despite a reduction of neoplastic growth elsewhere.

A general discussion of these complexities lies beyond the limits of the present volume, but it is worth noting that the secondary failure of anticancer drugs to control the growth of tumors *in vivo* does not necessarily signify an altered response by the neoplastic cell population to the compound concerned.

One further variable in this system, aside from the development of resistance, is the individuality exhibited by tumors in their intrinsic responses to particular drugs. Wide differences in the degree of natural resistance are observed even among neoplasms of closely similar origins, presumably based on random progressions in metabolic pattern (Law, 1958; Klein, 1961). Pre-existing refractory states that may characterize a tumor as a whole must thus be distinguished from the secondary acquisition of similar properties by means of population change in the presence of a drug. It is the latter sequence of events that underlies the development of drug resistance in the usual sense of this term.

Transitions from Sensitivity to Resistance   The general features of drug resistance in neoplasms have been the subject of repeated discussion in recent years, and a number of comprehensive reviews are available (Law, 1956, 1958; Nichol, 1957; Welch, 1959, 1961; Handschumacher and Welch, 1960; Klein, 1961, 1963). Of the questions to be considered, perhaps the most important is whether resistance in tumors arises through inductive effects of drugs or by means of spontaneous variation and selection. The investigations of Law (1952a) have commonly been cited as definitive evidence in favor of a genetic interpretation, and are therefore worth mentioning in some detail. The experimental design for this work was the familiar fluctuation test from microbiology, adapted to examine the origin of amethopterin resistance in leukemic cells. Law used a lymphocytic neoplasm originating from *DBA* mice, designated *L*-1210, and which has provided an experimental system for numerous studies on drug resistance. The experiment was initiated with the inoculation of a small number (150) of drug-sensitive *L*-1210 cells into mice of this strain. From the resulting large subcutaneous tumor, 15 separate sublines of leukemic cells were established by parallel transplantation in untreated *DBA* hosts. At the seventh serial transfer, leukemic cells from each of these substrains were inoculated subcutaneously into groups of 10 mice, which were then injected with amethopterin. The localized mass of tumor tissue that appeared after a standard interval was used as a criterion of resistance. For control purposes, 10 replicate groups of 10 mice each were injected with leukemic cells from a single substrain. The variance in weight of lymphoma tissue among the 100 mice in the latter series was only 196, whereas a figure of 4145 was obtained for the pooled variance of tumors derived from the 15 separate sublines. These results clearly suggest that resistance to amethopterin arises at random within untreated populations of leukemic cells. A spontaneous change, rather than variations arising by induction or exposure to the drug, may thus be inferred.

This strategic experiment by Law has been widely quoted to imply that drug resistance among tumors, as in microbial cells, has a direct variation-selection basis. Very little additional evidence on this point has been provided by actual experimental studies, however. The data reported by Klein and Klein (1957) and Klein (1959) suggest that the initial picture may have been somewhat oversimplified. In these investigations the development of amethopterin resistance was again examined within populations of L-1210 cells in DBA mice, but the Kleins adopted a different experimental approach. Inocula of 10^6 sensitive cells from the stock L-1210 leukemic strain were introduced into two groups of mice, one of which received injections of amethopterin from the outset while the other was untreated. The survival times for both groups were recorded, and at the median interval the two series were continued separately by transferring 10^5 cells to each mouse within a fresh group of treated or untreated animals, respectively. A rapid and uniform loss of sensitivity occurred during serial passage of L-1210 cells in the presence of amethopterin, as shown by the convergence of survival times toward those of the untreated control series.

Reasoning that the prompt acquisition of resistance was indicative of pre-existing variants in significant numbers within sensitive populations, Klein (1959) performed a similar experiment, using a tumor grown directly from only three L-1210 cells. Resistance developed as rapidly as before, however, and the fluctuations observed among replicate series were no greater than when the initial inocula had been taken in the usual way from mass L-1210 stock populations. Klein also considered the possibility that a more sensitive assay might be needed to detect variants in low frequency. To test this hypothesis, he prepared synthetic mixtures between sensitive L-1210 populations and an established subline known to be resistant to amethopterin. When such mixtures were inoculated into DBA mice, the presence of resistant cells was evident by a lowering of survival time of drug-treated animals, even in the first passage. Differences could be detected even when the proportion of resistant cells in the initial inoculum was as low as 10^{-6}. These results suggest that variants comparable to the established resistant cells do not pre-exist within sensitive populations with a frequency of more than 10^{-6}, and the actual incidence is probably lower.

The rapid and uniform shifts toward resistance which Klein observed are difficult to reconcile with the low apparent incidence of pre-existing variants within stock populations. Several explanations for this paradox may be considered (Klein, 1959). Variation might take place at a high rate, but if the newly emerging resistant cells were at a marked selective disadvantage, their incidence would remain low. A similar result would be expected if the production of resistant variants were offset by frequent reversions to sensitivity. Klein found no evidence for a high reversion rate, however, and in model experiments with synthetic populations, resistant cells persisted along with sensitive elements in untreated mice for at least 14 serial transfers. Other possibilities include the suggestion that several intermediate changes are needed to yield fully resistant cells (Herzenberg, 1962), or that the refractory responses of cell populations under continuous drug treatment are mediated in part by epigenetic mechanisms. Decisive tests of these various explanations will necessitate the isolation of resistant sublines by indirect methods that do not require contact with the corresponding drugs. Although efforts toward this end have been reported (Klein, 1959), success has not yet been achieved.

Whatever the initial transitions may be, drug resistance, once established, is a heritable and relatively stable cell marker in tumor populations. Numerous observations have shown that refractory states tend to be maintained for long periods in the absence of selecting agents (Law, 1958; Welch, 1959; Klein, 1961). In fact, resistance to drugs in early studies of tumors was often assumed to represent an irreversible change (Law, 1954a). It is now apparent, however, that reversions to sensitivity may occasionally occur. One such instance was detailed by Potter and Law (1957), who noted the progressive loss of resistance to azaserine in a plasma cell tumor. The change took place within a variant subline over five successive transplant generations. Similarly, Heidelberger, Ghobar, Baker, and Mukherjee (1960) reported that a line of Ehrlich ascites cells with a defined resistance to 5-fluorouracil at one stage eventually regained normal sensitivity to this drug. Such observations are particularly interesting, for in combination with clonal studies to be mentioned later, they suggest that a simple deletion hypothesis may be inadequate to account for the genesis of resistant cells.

Progressions in the degree of resistance to a given agent can frequently be observed within tumor populations. With a number of drugs the level of resistance may undergo an irregular sequential modification, rising in a staircase pattern. The effect is thus analogous to the multistep acquisition of resistance to penicillin in bacteria. Multiple sequences of this type are seen, for example, in populations of L-1210 mouse leukemic cells exposed repeatedly to amethopterin (Figure 6.9), as well as in other lines within animals given 6-mercaptopurine, 6-thioguanine,

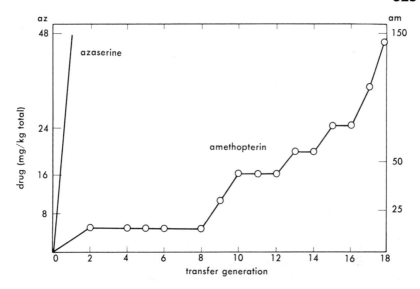

FIG. 6.9. Patterns of resistance developed in two neoplasms of mice following continuous selection with antileukemic agents. The rapid acquisition of resistance to azaserine in plasma cell neoplasm 70429 contrasts with the "stair case" phenomenon observed with lymphocytic leukemia *L*-1210 in the presence of amethopterin. (After Law, 1958.)

and 6-azauracil (Law, 1958). One-step patterns resembling the streptomycin model are also seen. Potter and Law (1957) described a plasma-cell neoplasm of the mouse, which had acquired a high level of resistance to azaserine in the course of a single transplant generation, and a similar phenomenon with DON was noted by Potter (1958) in a mast cell tumor.

As in microorganisms, tumors resistant to specific drugs commonly show cross reactions to structurally related compounds. Thus mouse leukemia cells refractory to amethopterin are also resistant to other analogues of pteroylglutamic acid, but retain sensitivity to such agents as triethylene melamine, antipurines, and azaserine (Law, 1956). Similarly, variants from the *L*-1210 line resistant to 8-azaguanine or 6-mercaptopurine are in general unaffected by antipurines, although still responsive to other types of antimetabolites. Cross resistance between unrelated compounds might also be predicted if two agents were to converge on a single metabolic target or if a common functional process were affected (for example, permeability). Linked resistance in such patterns has not yet been demonstrated for tumors, but an inverse interaction, known as collateral sensitivity (Law, 1956; Nichol, 1957), may be mentioned. This term derives from studies with bacteria in which resistance to one antibiotic is occasionally associated with increased susceptibility to another (Szybalski and Bryson, 1952). Among tumors, an apparent parallel can be found in the fact that resistance to antipurines in *L*-1210 leukemic cells potentiates the effect of folic acid antagonists on the same populations (Law, Taormina, and Boyle, 1954; Law, 1956). The interactions noted may arise from a decreased utilization of preformed purine derivatives in the resistant cells; in this case, the consequent shift toward *de novo* synthesis would imply increased sensitivity toward folic acid analogues (Law, 1956; Handschumacher and Welch, 1960).

The question of whether drug dependence as well as drug resistance can be demonstrated within neoplastic populations is a controversial one at the present time. In the course of a long series of papers, Law and his collaborators have repeatedly described the isolation of sublines from *L*-1210 mouse leukemic cells that require the continued administration of specific antimetabolites for optimal growth in *DBA* hosts. Variants dependent in this sense were observed during the earliest studies on resistance to amethopterin (Law and Boyle, 1950; Law, 1951a, 1951b), and in a few instances have been isolated from leukemias other than the *L*-1210 strain (Law, 1954a). The phenomenon, moreover, is not peculiar to the group of folic acid analogues. Sublines of *L*-1210 cells dependent on 8-azaguanine were similarly isolated from tumor-bearing mice treated with this drug (Law, 1951c). In experiments with both agents, the growth patterns of dependent variants proved to be striking (Law, 1952b, 1954b). When such neoplasms were inoculated into drug-treated hosts, the weight of tumor tissue after a standard interval frequency exceeded that of implants in untreated mice by 3- to 4-fold, and the survival time of the animals given drugs was significantly less. Skipper, Bennett, and Law (1952) extended these studies to the metabolic level and reported that amethopterin increases the incorporation of formate into nucleic acids of dependent cells while simultaneously inhibiting the same process within sensitive tissues of the host. With either amethopterin or azaguanine, a spectrum of cross dependence could be demonstrated within variant lines. Structurally related compounds were identical in effect; others had no facilitating effect on the growth of dependent tumors (Law, 1954b).

This array of careful studies leaves little doubt that drug dependence is a reproducible phenomenon in the cell systems investigated by Law and his collaborators. Whether these findings have a more general significance, however, is a moot point. If in fact drug dependence in tumors is initiated through genetic change, as in microorganisms, it is reasonable to look for additional examples of the transition to dependence in other neoplastic populations. So far, such reports have not been forthcoming, nor are there indications that drug-dependent variants emerge at the clinical level during therapy of human leukemia with anticancer drugs (Burchenal, 1955b).

At least one alternative explanation for drug dependence in the L-1210 system has been suggested, namely, that the particular strains of leukemic cells chosen for study may have harbored an infectious agent subject to inhibition by specific antimetabolites (see Handschumacher and Welch, 1960). This line of reasoning stems from a sequence of several separate studies. In 1951, Law and Dunn reported the isolation of an infectious agent from cells of the L-1210 strain; in the light of present information, this might have been the lymphocytic choriomeningitis virus. Haas and Stewart (1956) showed that this virus is specifically sensitive to amethopterin and 8-azaguanine. If either analogue is administered to mice infected with lymphocytic choriomeningitis virus, the animals exhibit a prolonged survival time, or do not succumb at all. A final link in this chain of circumstantial evidence was offered by the studies of Humphreys, Venditti, Mantel, and Goldin (1956). These investigators reported the presence of an infectious factor in a line of L-1210 cells that required amethopterin for optimal growth. The same cells, if freed of this agent experimentally, no longer showed any evidence of dependence, although they were highly resistant to amethopterin. But when the infectious agent that had been isolated in cell-free form was added back to these derivative populations, the phenomenon of drug dependence reappeared. As Handschumacher and Welch (1960) point out in their thoughtful critique, the relevance of these experiments to Law's earlier work is uncertain. No infections with lymphocytic choriomeningitis virus are definitely known to have existed within the sublines studied by Law. But in view of the demonstration that drug dependence can be mimicked by the presence of a viral passenger agent, new proofs will be required before a genetic interpretation of this phenomenon in tumors can be regarded as substantiated.

Patterns of Variation in Resistant Cells   The mechanisms that implement drug resistance must be ultimately expressed at the cellular level in terms of altered metabolic sequences. In this web of reactions there are many common elements, even with cell types of quite diverse origins. It is perhaps not surprising, therefore, to find that several mechanisms of altered response, first discovered in microbial systems, were later found to apply to mammalian cells as well. For bacteria as well as for tumors, a number of generalized models have been proposed to cover the distinctive properties of drug-resistant cells (Davis and Maas,

1952; Davis, 1957; Law, 1956; Welch, 1959). Refractory responses, for example, could stem from specific alterations in cellular permeability, from the acquisition of mechanisms for increased destruction of the drug, or from the development of some means of converting the compound in question into an inactive form. Alternatively, competitive limitation of drug action might develop, based on increased concentrations of normal metabolites within a common reaction channel, from elevated activity within alternative metabolic pathways, or as the result of decreases in quantitative requirements for substrates related to a drug or its products. At the enzymatic level, drug effects could be decreased or eliminated by changes in activity as well as by simple deletion of the enzyme concerned, or stable alterations might develop in the relative affinity of enzymes for drugs as compared to a normal substrate. These suggestions by no means exhaust the list of possibilities, but serve to emphasize that drug resistance can be based on a wide variety of cellular changes.

A number of metabolic alterations have been actually identified within resistant cells. Perhaps the best known of these patterns relates to the decreased activity or elimination of enzymes required for incorporation of purine or pyrimidine antagonists into nucleotide form. The formation of fraudulent nucleotides from analogues such as 2,6-diaminopurine, 8-azaguanine, or 6-mercaptopurine has often been proposed as a basis for toxicity in sensitive cells. Evidence for a "lethal synthesis" of this type (Peters, 1952) is now extensive, and it appears that in most cases, transformation of purine or pyrimidine analogues to the nucleotide form must occur before growth inhibition is apparent (Handschumacher and Welch, 1960). This does not necessarily imply, however, that the mechanisms of toxicity lie in the eventual synthesis of defective or nonfunctional nucleic acids. Actually, only 6-thioguanine among a variety of antipurines that have been examined seems to be incorporated into the DNA of sensitive cells (Ellis and LePage, 1963). In at least some systems, interference by antimetabolites in nucleotide form results from competitive interference with specific enzymatic reactions that require nucleotide cofactors (Welch, 1959, 1961).

In tracing the modifications of purine metabolism within resistant cells, the early observations of Elion and her co-workers on *Lactobacillus casei* were suggestive. The experiments in question showed that mutants refractory to 2,6-diaminopurine or 6-mercaptopurine are characterized by a decreased utilization of one or more naturally occurring purines (Elion, Vanderwerff, Hitchings, Balis, Levin, and Brown, 1953; Elion, Singer, and Hitchings, 1954). Similar mutants in *Streptococcus faecalis* are also deficient in the ability to metabolize exogenous purines (Brockman, Sparks, and Simpson, 1957; Balis, Hylin, Coultas, and Hutchison,

1958a). Starting from this point, Brockman and his colleagues succeeded in correlating the metabolic block in resistant cells with specific enzymatic changes. In order to make clear their discoveries, it should perhaps be pointed out that the conversion of preformed purines to nucleotides takes place in a single step. In this transition, naturally occurring purines or their structural analogues combine with 5-phosphoribosyl-1-pyrophosphate (Kornberg, Lieberman, and Simms, 1955; Way and Parks, 1958). The reaction is catalyzed by a series of pyrophosphorylases, and it is these enzymes that represent a focal point of change within resistant cells. Working first with S. *faecalis* and later extending their studies to L-1210 mouse leukemic cells and other types of neoplasms, Brockman and his associates demonstrated that cells refractory to 8-azaguanine or 6-mercaptopurine are selectively deficient in pyrophosphorylases necessary to convert the analogues to the nucleotide form. Bacterial or tumor cells resistant to either antagonist can be shown to lack inosinic acid pyrophosphorylase and guanylic acid pyrophosphorylase or to possess these enzymes at lowered levels of activity. Adenylic acid pyrophosphorylase activity is unimpaired under the same conditions (Brockman, Bennett, Simpson, Wilson, Thomson, and Skipper, 1959; Brockman, Sparks, Simpson, and Skipper, 1959; Brockman, 1960; Brockman, Debavadi, Stutts, and Hutchison, 1961). On the other hand, a different pattern is seen in cells resistant to 2,6-diaminopurine, which is generally considered to be an adenine rather than a guanine antagonist. In a tumor variant of this type, Lieberman and Ove (1960) reported the absence of adenylic acid pyrophosphorylase activity, whereas other enzymes of the same series remained at levels comparable to those of sensitive cells. Thus the decrease or loss of pyrophosphorylases appears to confer resistance by specifically preventing the formation of toxic ribonucleotides from antipurine precursors.

In view of the correlations described, it might be assumed that graded reductions in appropriate pyrophosphorylases were responsible for differential levels of resistance to antipurines among a series of variant cell types. Such does not seem to be the case, however, for three sublines derived with 8-azaguanine from mouse lymphoma *P*-388, and which have been studied in some detail (Davidson, Bradley, Roosa, and Law, 1962; Brockman, Roosa, Law, and Stutts, 1962). These variants, representing clonal derivatives from a sensitive parental population, are 5, 20, and 2000 times, respectively, more resistant to 8-azaguanine. In view of this wide disparity in degree of resistance, it is surprising to find a common spectrum of enzyme changes. All three lines exhibit a 99 percent loss of inosinic-guanylic acid pyrophosphorylase activity, and in each case the level of adenylic acid pyrophosphorylase is unchanged. Caution is thus essential in evaluating the role of enzymatic changes as a basis for differential resistance in this system. While the possibility of differences in pyrophosphorylase activity below the 1 percent level cannot entirely be ruled out, it is perhaps more reasonable to look for other types of changes within the over-all pattern of resistance.

A related picture of enzyme changes has emerged from studies of resistance in bacteria and tumors to antipyrimidines. Refractory states in a number of instances have been linked with decreases in the enzymes presumably required for conversion of these analogues to an active form. A defect at the pyrophosphorylase level was observed by Brockman, Davis, and Stutts (1960) in mutants of *E. coli* resistant to 5-fluorouracil. Extracts from these cells, unlike those obtained from sensitive populations, failed to catalyze the reaction of uracil or 5-fluorouracil with 5-phosphoribosyl-1-pyrophosphate. Comparable changes have not yet been demonstrated in tumors. The conversion of pyrimidines to the nucleotide level, however, also proceeds by an alternative route. In this case, nucleosides are formed as an intermediate product, and the two-step sequence is catalyzed by a nucleoside phosphorylase and kinase, respectively. That the two-step pathway is implicated in resistance to 6-azauracil was suggested by Handschumacher (1957), who found that unresponsive mutants of *S. faecalis* are unable to utilize free uracil or to convert the analogue into nucleotide form. A block at the first stage seemed indicated, since the mutant cells were still sensitive to azauridine, although not to the free base. Pasternak, Fischer, and Handschumacher (1961) have subsequently shown that a block at the second stage of pyrimidine utilization can also occur. Using a strain of mouse leukemic cells that is particularly sensitive to azauridine, Pasternak and his collaborators administered the nucleoside directly and obtained variants that were 1500 times more resistant to the inhibitor in this form, although sensitivity to azauridylic acid remained unchanged.

Other experiments show that changes in the utilization of uracil and its analogues can be associated with decreased activity of specific enzymes within the pathway mentioned. Reichard, Sköld, and Klein (1959), and Klein (1961) have described such studies on mouse ascites tumors resistant to 5-fluorouracil. One subline of Ehrlich cells refractory to the analogue was nearly devoid of uridine phosphorylase and deoxyuridine phosphorylase activity. Another derived from *L*-1210 leukemic cells showed a decline of uridine kinase and uridine phosphorylase to 25 percent and 50 percent of the original levels, respectively. More recently, Reichard, Sköld, Klein, Révész, and Magnusson (1962) compared the enzymatic patterns of four variants obtained from Ehrlich ascites populations by treatment with 5-fluorouracil. All showed a progressive decrease in uridine kinase activity, beginning at about 8 to 10 passages and proceeding either by stepwise or continuous change. During the same period, the activity levels of uridine phosphorylase and of deoxyuridine phosphorylase and kinase remained essentially unaffected (Figure 6.10). Interestingly, in at least two of the tumors, refractory responses to 5-fluorouracil could be detected before any decline in uridine kinase took place. Additional means of resistance exist, therefore, and it may be that one of these is a change in properties of uridine kinase, rather than the activity level as such (see following section).

Although a deletion or specific decrease in enzyme activity appears to be the commonest correlate of drug resistance, increases may occur as well. Perhaps the best illustration of this pattern is to be seen in the development of resistance to amethopterin. The sensitive target for this analogue and for related compounds appears to be the enzyme folic acid reductase, which is essential for the conversion of folic acid into metabolically active derivatives (see Handschumacher and Welch, 1960). Amethopterin has a high affinity for folic acid reductase, forming a complex that is not easily reversible at pH 6.0, and which inhibits action by the enzyme completely (Werkheiser, 1961). Under these conditions,

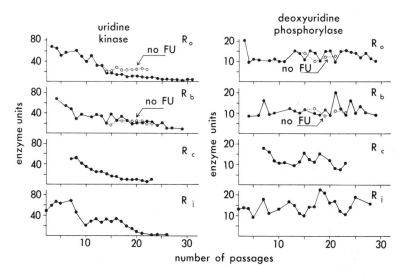

FIG. 6.10. Enzymatic changes in four lines of Ehrlich mouse ascites tumor cells during serial passage through animals treated with 5-fluorouracil. A steady decrease of uridine kinase is observed, beginning at about the eighth passage. Other enzymes, such as deoxyuridine phosphorylase, are unaffected, although considerable fluctuation in activity may occur. (Redrawn from Reichard, Sköld, Klein, Révész, and Magnusson, 1962. Copyright, University of Chicago Press.)

the onset of resistance might in principle signify either a shift in enzyme-analogue affinities or an increase in amount of enzyme. Apparently it is the latter that takes place commonly in transitions to a refractory state (Figure 6.11). This relationship is demonstrated particularly well in the clonal studies of Fischer (1961) on mouse leukemic cells in which stepwise elevations in resistance to amethopterin and in levels of folic acid reductase were observed. When first-step and second-step clones were compared, an exact correspondence appeared between the relative activity of folic acid reductase and the relative degree of resistance to inhibitor. Similarly, Hakala, Zakrzewski, and Nichol (1961) found that the activity of folic acid reductase rises in accordance with the time curve for the acquisition of resistance in populations of Sarcoma 180 cells. Human leukemias unresponsive to further treatment with folic acid analogues also have been shown to exhibit a high level of folic acid reductase (Bertino, Donohue, Gabrio, Silber, Alenty, Meyer, and Huennekens, 1962). It therefore appears that if the level of folic acid reductase increases to a sufficient extent, a residue is available for functional activity, and the cells become resistant to amethopterin even though the bulk of the enzyme is immobilized with inhibitor. While this is an at-

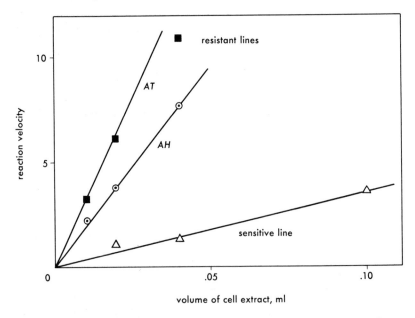

FIG. 6.11. Folic acid reductase activity in extracts from sensitive and resistant mouse Sarcoma 180 cells. Activity is proportional to the concentration of extract, with augmented levels for the two resistant lines studied, *AH* and *AT*. (Redrawn from Hakala, Zakrzewski, and Nichol, 1961.)

tractive explanation, other mechanisms for amethopterin resistance should not be excluded. The parallelism of resistance and folic acid reductase activity, for example, does not account for the extremely high levels of resistance to amethopterin (approximately 100,000-fold) which have in some instances been observed (Fischer, 1959), nor for the existence of "uptake" variants (Fischer, 1962).

Another example that can be cited to illustrate increased enzyme activity as a mechanism for drug resistance concerns the antagonist 2-deoxy-D-glucose. This compound is known to inhibit both glycolysis and cell growth by interfering with mechanisms for the phosphorylation and transport of sugars (Barban and Schulze, 1961). HeLa cell populations that are treated with deoxyglucose, however, develop refractory responses, and variants can be isolated with a tenfold increase in resistance to the inhibitor (Barban, 1962a). These accumulate 2-deoxyglucose-6-phosphate to a lesser degree and at a much slower rate than do sensitive cells. In cell-free extracts, the tempo of phosphorylation of analogue as well as other monosaccharides is 3 to 5 times less. An inhibitor for the hexokinase reaction thus seems to be present, and interestingly, this factor may be another enzyme, alkaline phosphatase. Activity levels of the latter are many times higher in resistant cells. It will be recalled that alkaline phosphatase activity in HeLa cells can also be augumented by treatment with prednisolone (see Chapter 3). This leads to the prediction that exposure of sensitive HeLa cells to prednisolone should incidentally confer resistance to 2-deoxy-D-glucose, and such a concept has been confirmed (Barban, 1962b). However, the probable identity of the inhibitor of hexokinase activity with alkaline phosphatase awaits definite proof by isolation and purification.

One of the most interesting mechanisms to be associated with drug resistance is the appearance in variant cells of genetically altered enzymes; that is, proteins with heritable differences from the original catalyst, the alterations being adaptive in the presence of inhibitor. Observations of this type were reported by Heidelberger and his co-workers, for example, during studies on populations of Ehrlich ascites cells treated with 5-fluorouracil (Heidelberger, Kaldor, Mukherjee, and Danneberg, 1960; Heidelberger, 1961). In both sensitive and resistant tumors of this type, the fluorinated analogue undergoes conversion into a deoxyribonucleotide. The latter, termed 5-fluoro-2-deoxyuridine monophosphate, or FUDRP, is a potent inhibitor of thymidylate synthetase and tends to block DNA synthesis by preventing the conversion of uracil to thymine via the addition of a methyl group at the carbon-5 position. Heidelberger showed that equivalent amounts of FUDRP were produced in the sensitive and resistant tumors under investigation, but when extracts containing thymidylate synthetase were compared, there was a 1000-fold greater specific inhibition by FUDRP for the sensitive line. Thus an alteration in substrate specificity of the enzyme seemed to have occurred, with a competitive shift from FUDRP in the direction of the corresponding uridylic acid derivative. Working with other lines of the Ehrlich ascites tumor resistant to 5-fluorouracil, Reichard, Sköld, Klein, Révész, and Magnusson (1962) were unable to demonstrate any difference in relative inhibition of thymidylate synthetase by FUDRP as compared to sensitive populations, and have reported Heidelberger's personal communication that the differential in his own resistant strain was eventually lost. But in a later paper, Sköld (1963) has reported that uridine kinase from resistant Ehrlich cells can be distinguished from the corresponding enzyme of sensitive cells by several physicochemical criteria. The relation of these changes to fluorouracil resistance needs further study.

The concept of genetically modified enzymes in resistant cells has received strong support from recent studies with bacteria. Wolf and Hotchkiss (1963), for example, compared cell-free extracts from several sulfanilamide-resistant mutants of pneumococci, and found differences in the spectrum of competitive inhibition with p-aminobenzoic acid analogues. They attributed this fact to hereditary alterations of affinity in the substrate binding groups of one enzyme in the folic acid synthesizing system. Similarly, Pato and Brown (1963) detected altered enzymes within two mutants of *E. coli* that were refractory to sulfathiazole. These enzymes, which are also active in the synthesis of folic acid, differ structurally from the corresponding wild type catalyst, and combine less readily with sulfonamides. To this general picture may be added the observations of Kalle and Gotts (1963) on a mutant of *Salmonella typhimurium* that shows resistance to 2,6-diaminopurine. In this case, the resistant strain does not lack adenylic pyrophosphorylase, and in fact enzyme preparations from mutant cells exhibit normal activity with adenine. However, although adenylic pyrophosphorylase from sensitive wild type cells converts diaminopurine to its ribonucleotide, the enzyme from mutant cells fails to do so. This strategic difference can be correlated with a number of other physical and chemical alterations that mark the enzyme in question as a new protein entity.

Several instances are known in which tumor resistance appears to depend on an increased destruction of inhibitor by the cells concerned. Sartorelli, LePage, and Moore (1958) observed that Ehrlich ascites cells refractory to 6-thioguanine degrade the analogue more rapidly to thiouric acid and other noninhibitory products than do sensitive cells. This differential may be a strategic primary factor in resistance within the populations studied, since both resistant and sensitive cells retained the capacity for converting 6-thioguanine to the nucleotide level. In a different system involving resistance to growth inhibition by the hormone cortisol, the emergence of variants with increased catabolic activity is seen even more clearly. Grosser, Sweat, Berliner, and Dougherty (1962) compared the metabolic patterns in a strain of human uterine fibroblasts, sensitive to growth inhibition by cortisol, with those of a variant subline resistant to this steroid at high concentrations. Neither the type nor proportions of conversion products differed in the two lines, but the over-all degradation of cortisol to less inhibiting forms was twice as rapid in resistant cells. Other factors, however, must enter into steroid resistance, since the differential actually observed between parental and variant strains in terms of growth inhibitions was approximately 250-fold.

The experiments of Jacobson have also been based on the assumed conversion of inhibitors to an inactive form (Jacobson, 1961). Over a period of years Jacobson has studied the effects of folic acid antagonists on cell division within cultures of chick embryonic tissues. Aminopterin or other 4-amino analogues of pteroylglutamic acid produce an immediate although temporary block in the mitotic activity of chick osteoblasts, and this effect can be prevented by the simultaneous administration of folinic acid, but not folic acid. Mitotic inhibition in the assay cultures can be eliminated, however, if the analogues to be added are given a preliminary incubation with certain types of normal and neoplastic cells. Jacobson and Cathie (1960a) have reported that mouse liver and cells from lymphoblastic leukemias were capable of inactivating aminopterin in this way, although normal lymphoblasts and lymphocytes of the mouse were unable to do so. The leukemic cells from 17 of 18 children also rapidly converted aminopterin to a form inactive for chick cells (Jacobson, 1961). Evidence has been presented that conversion of aminopterin to an inactive form for chick cells depends on a ring closure of the terminal glutamic acid (Jacobson and Cathie, 1960b). The presumed inactivation product has not actually been identified.

Jacobson (1961) has suggested in a more general discussion that the lack of response by many leukemias to folic acid analogues may signify inactivation at the outset by the mechanisms described. Experimental proof for this hypothesis is lacking, however, and alternative explanations for Jacobson's data must be considered. One of these follows from the fact that the effects of aminopterin can be bypassed by supplying the products of blocked reactions: thymidine, a utilizable purine, and glycine (Chapter 5). Conceivably, in Jacobson's experiments with chick cells, these derivatives might be supplied by incubates of normal or leukemic cells. In any event, a clear distinction should be drawn between the direct inactivation of inhibitors by naturally resistant cell types, if this occurs, and secondary resistance that results from the selection of variants with refractory responses. Thus there is no necessary conflict in principle between the model proposed by Jacobson and the demonstrably different changes that appear to implement resistance to folic acid analogues in other systems.

Until recently, changes in permeability of tumor cells were largely discounted as a basis for drug resistance. Mechanisms of this type have in fact been repeatedly excluded in specific studies on tumor resistance to such compounds as 8-azaguanine (Davidson, 1958), azauridine (Pasternak, Fischer, and Handschumacher, 1961), 5-fluorouracil (Heidelberger, 1961; Reichard, Sköld, Klein, Révész, and Magnusson, 1962), and azaserine (Anderson and Jacquez, 1962). Nevertheless, the well-known selectivity of cell membranes, the occurrence of active transport, and the existence in bacteria, at least, of permease systems (Chapter 2) all suggest potential mechanisms for the emergence of drug-resistant cells. There are increasing indications that resistance can indeed arise through such changes. One well-documented example has now been described for Ehrlich ascites cells (Paterson and Hori, 1962; Paterson, 1962). Working with a subline resistant to 6-mercaptopurine, Paterson showed, as others have done, that the refractory state is associated with failure to form nucleotide derivatives of the analogue. However, in the particular variant examined, this property was restricted to intact cells. Extracts of resistant cells were shown to contain a normal complement of pyrophosphorylases and adequate concentrations of phosphoribosylpyrophosphate; the synthesis of nucleotide derivatives from 6-mercaptopurine in cell-free preparations from resistant cells was indistinguishable from comparable processes in extracts of sensitive cells. Paterson therefore concluded that in the specific strain under study, resistance stems from a failure of 6-mercaptopurine to enter the tumor cell rather than from deficiencies in pyrophosphorylase activity that are known to occur in other variants of the same type. It may also be pointed out that resistance to amethopterin may in some instances arise through permeability changes. Fischer (1962) has described a variant clone of mouse leukemic cells that is refractory to amethopterin but shows no difference from sensitive populations, either in the level of folic acid reductase activity or in relative affinity between enzyme and analogue. Such cells appear to be "uptake" instead of "enzyme" variants, but are similarly stable when maintained in serial proliferation in the absence of inhibitor. There are no differences in nutritional requirements, growth rates, or tumor-inducing properties between the two classes of amethopterin variants, and both appear to represent heritable cell changes.

Taken as a whole, the metabolic modifications described in the foregoing discussion serve to illustrate the diversity of changes that may be correlated with drug resistance. The identification of cause-and-effect relationships here presents difficult problems. Clearly, some of the alterations noted may be secondary to the process or processes that define resistance per se in a given cell system. Aside from this fact, there is a growing body of evidence to show that even the primary mechanisms of resistance are often multiple. Considering that resistance may arise from changes that impinge at various points within a complex reaction system, a variety in means is understandable. The spectrum of cell types that may emerge is well illustrated by the studies of Balis, Hylin, Coultas, and Hutchison (1958b) on S. *faecalis*. Among a series of mutants resistant to 6-mercaptopurine, some were able to use the inhibitor by conversion as a source of natural purines. Another lacked one or more enzymes required for conversion of the analogue to nucleotides. A further mutant had acquired a greater ability for *de novo* synthesis of purines, and consequently a competitive basis for resistance to the antagonist. Judging from the literature summarized in the present discussion, a similar individuality must be expected for resistant variants arising within single tumor populations. Thus the concept of neoplasms as evolving mosaics of variant cell types receives strong support from studies of drug resistance, even though the genetic or epigenetic character of these changes remains to be clarified.

DEVELOPMENT OF DRUG
RESISTANCE IN CELL CULTURES

Owing to the simplicity with which drug resistance can be demonstrated in tumors, studies of this phenomenon have for the most part been carried out *in vivo*. In principle, however, the use of cell cultures offers much greater flexibility and opportunity in terms of experimental design. Within these isolated populations the necessary elements of selection can be applied to nonmalignant as well as to tumor-producing strains, and clonal analysis of population changes is simplified. The advantages of *in vitro* systems have not yet been fully utilized, but it is clear that the spectrum of adaptive responses to different compounds is a wide one. Among a variety of cell strains, variants have been isolated with resistance to folic acid antagonists (Vogt, 1959; Fischer, 1959, 1961, 1962; Aronow, 1959; Hakala, Zakrzewski, and Nichol, 1961; Herzenberg, 1962); antipurines (Lieberman and Ove, 1959a; Szybalski and Smith, 1959a; Szybalski, Szybalska, and Ragni, 1962; Harris and Ruddle,

1960; Harris, 1960; Tomizawa and Aronow, 1960; Kelley, Vail, Adamson, and Palmer, 1961); antipyrimidines (Morris and Fischer, 1960; Pasternak, Fischer, and Handschumacher, 1961; Roosa, Bradley, Law, and Herzenberg, 1962), and a miscellany of other agents such as steroids (Stone, 1962; Stone and Kang, 1962; Grosser, Sweat, Berliner, and Dougherty, 1962), antibiotics (Goldstein, Slotnick, and Journey, 1960), and even metallic ions (Daniel, Dingle, and Lucy, 1961). Up to the present time, all these variants have been obtained from what appear to be permanent cell strains, and information is still lacking as to whether primary diploid cells can develop resistance to specific drugs. An experimental decision on this point is complicated by the fact that primary strains are difficult to clone efficiently, and the presence of occasional variants in low frequency is not easily demonstrated. But at least within permanent cell lines, the onset of drug resistance by random variation is a common and reproducible phenomenon.

Analysis of Population Changes Several methods can be used to reveal the presence of drug-resistant variants within somatic cell lines. By exposing mass cultures of sensitive cells to suitably limiting concentrations of inhibitors, all but a small fraction of the initial population

FIG. 6.12. Drug-resistant colonies obtained by exposing a clonal population of pig kidney cells (strain *PK*-15) to antimetabolites for four weeks. (*A*) 8-azaguanine, 100 μg/ml. (*B*) Allylglycine, 1 mg/ml. (*C*) Aminopterin, 0.1 μg/ml. (From Harris and Ruddle, 1960. Copyright, University of Texas M. D. Anderson Hospital and Tumor Institute.)

may be destroyed, leaving the survivors to proliferate secondarily as resistant colonies, partially or completely unaffected by the selecting agent. This process can be illustrated by the experiments of Harris and Ruddle (1960), in which variants were derived from a strain of pig kidney cells (*PK*-15) by selection with 8-azaguanine, 2,6-diaminopurine, aminopterin, and the amino acid analogue allylglycine (Figure 6.12). Based on relative survival, the apparent incidence in this cell line of variants resistant to the inhibitors mentioned ranged from 1×10^{-4} to 1×10^{-6}. Drug-resistant populations can also be obtained by cyclic exposure to specific inhibitors, interspersed with recovery periods in agent-free medium. In this way, variant sublines are eventually derived that will grow progressively at drug concentrations lethal to the parental strain (Lieberman and Ove, 1959a). The modified responses of resistant cell strains may be conveniently expressed by a differential toxicity test (Figure 6.13). The level of drug required for 50 percent growth inhibition after a standard interval provides a useful reference index (Harris, 1961).

The frequency with which resistant variants arise within a given population is clearly a more fundamental parameter. By analogy with

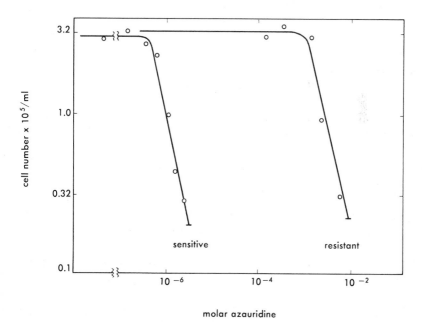

FIG. 6.13. Survival curves for sensitive and resistant lines of mouse *L*-5178Y leukemic cells exposed to azauridine in culture. (Redrawn from Pasternak, Fischer, and Handschumacher, 1961. Copyright, University of Chicago Press.)

microbial systems, such changes in cultures of somatic cells have commonly been expressed in terms of mutation rates. This procedure is convenient, but can be misleading if not properly qualified. As emphasized in Chapter 1, somatic mutation is still a purely descriptive term (see Luria, 1960). In the case of drug resistance, there is as yet insufficient evidence to determine where the locus of variation in somatic cells may be with any certainty, or even to demonstrate whether the underlying change is genetic or epigenetic. If resistant cells are referred to as "mutants," therefore, this usage should be taken to mean only that a random, heritable alteration in cellular characteristics has occurred.

Several experimental designs have been used to measure the appearance of resistant variants in sensitive populations of somatic cells; that is, mutation rates as defined above. Lieberman and Ove (1959b) employed fluctuation tests patterned closely on the Luria and Delbrück model. A permanent line of uncertain origin, but probably derived from strain L mouse cells, served as an assay system. From such populations, variants resistant to the antibiotic puromycin can be readily obtained by plating out appropriate numbers of cells in the presence of drug. The variance between individual cultures is small for replicate samples but large for strains maintained in parallel. These data, like those of Law, are thus consistent with a spontaneous origin of resistant variants. The same information can be treated by the equations of Luria and Delbrück to yield a quantitative expression for the rate of change. In this way, Lieberman and Ove obtained a value estimated at 3.6×10^{-6} mutations per cell per generation for the initial transition from sensitivity to resistance.

A second method for determining the rate of mutation from sensitivity to resistance within somatic cells can be termed a "clonal variance" test (Szybalski, 1959). In this procedure, sensitive populations are plated out so as to produce a large number of discrete colonies. Each of these in a sense can be regarded as equivalent to a unit culture within a standard fluctuation test. Thus resistant cells will appear in some but not all colonies. This fraction can be determined by applying selective agents after a known degree of cell multiplication, and a mutation rate can be calculated for the step in question. Where the differential elimination of sensitive colonies is sufficiently clear-cut, this method yields reproducible results and has the advantage of reducing the number of cultures required for scoring. Using the clonal variance test, Szybalski and Smith (1959b) measured the rate of mutation to resistance with 8-azaguanine in a clonal strain of cells derived from human bone marrow (Detroit $D98$). For the initial change from sensitivity, a rate of 5×10^{-4} mutations per cell per generation was obtained.

Still another method has been devised by Szybalski and his associates for a more precise determination of mutation rates in somatic cells, especially in the estimation of variations that occur only in low frequencies (Szybalski, Szybalska, and Ragni, 1962; Szybalski and Szybalska, 1962). This technique depends on "purifying" sensitive strains by the elimination of pre-existing resistant variants. Under such conditions, the frequency with which resistant cells arise in assay samples provides a direct index of the mutation rate. The selective removal of resistant cells from sensitive populations can be achieved by making use of differentials in nutritional or metabolic patterns. For example, the $D98$ strain, like other mammalian cells, does not ordinarily require preformed purines for growth *in vitro*, but can be made to do so if the functions of folic acid are blocked by amethopterin (Chapter 5). As noted previously, the addition of thymidine, glycine, and hypoxanthine permits a continuation of growth in such a system. Szybalski and his co-workers have found, however, that azaguanine-resistant cells require a significantly higher level of hypoxanthine under these conditions than do sensitive cells. By restricting the concentrations of hypoxanthine appropriately, a "purified" subline nearly free from pre-existing variants was derived, and the rate of mutation to azaguanine resistance subsequently was determined. The figure obtained, 1.6×10^{-4} per cell per generation, is in reasonably good agreement with the value previously estimated by means of the clonal variance method.

The stepwise character of transitions to resistance, seen frequently in tumors, has also been documented in detail for several cell systems *in vitro*. One-step patterns have been described by both Lieberman and Ove (1959a) and by Szybalski and Smith (1959a) for the emergence of variants with a relatively high level of resistance to 8-azaguanine (Figure 6.14). In the latter investigation the mutant line initially obtained ($D98/AG$) was still relatively sensitive to 8-azaguanosine, but variants arise within $D98/AG$ with a high level of resistance to the analogue in nucleoside form. From one of these, a second resistant line ($D98/AGR$) was established. The frequency of the change to AGR resistance appeared to be approximately 1.2×10^{-6} mutations per cell per generation (Szybalski, 1959). Since the AGR mutants could not be detected in the original sensitive population, Szybalski suggested that two sequential, obligatory, single-step mutations are required for the appearance of resistance to azaguanosine. Biochemical studies now permit the statement of these changes in more precise terms (Szybalski, Szybalska, and Brockman, 1961). Subline $D98/AGR$, resistant to 8-azaguanosine, displays a marked reduction of inosinic acid and guanylic acid pyrophosphorylase activities, but no change in adenylic acid

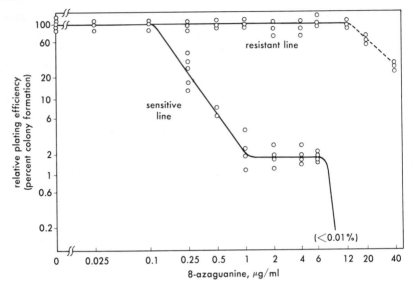

FIG. 6.14. Differential susceptibility to 8-azaguanine in sensitive and resistant lines of *D*98 human bone marrow cells. Survival curves are plotted on the basis of ability to form colonies from single cells. (After Szybalski and Smith, 1959a.)

pyrophosphorylase. By contrast, *D*98/*AG*, which is resistant to 8-azaguanine but not 8-azaguanosine, retains a normal complement of all pyrophosphorylase activities. This variant, however, clearly incorporates much less C^{14}-labeled azaguanine into nucleotide form than do sensitive cells. Thus the first-step variation, as illustrated by $D98S \rightarrow D98/AG$, appears to depend on some change preceding the actual conversion to nucleotides (for example, alteration in permeability or decreased ability for uptake of the inhibitor), whereas the subsequent transition to azaguanosine resistance is associated with a specific lowering in pyrophosphorylase activity.

In other cases, the development of resistance to single inhibitors within isolated populations appears to be an incremental process, coinciding with a typical multistep pattern. Thus Lieberman and Ove (1959a), in their investigations of resistance to puromycin, isolated four distinct cell types, all differing from one another in absolute levels of sensitivity to the antibiotic. These differences, which were relatively small, were thought to accumulate by mutations in tandem, although the frequency of occurrence of such changes was determined only for the last two members of this series. A similar picture can be made for resistance to amethopterin in isolated cultures of mouse leukemic cells (Fischer, 1959, 1961; Roosa, Bradley, Law, and Herzenberg, 1962; Herzenberg,

1962). In this system, Fischer has found that first-step variants arise from sensitive populations with a relatively low level of resistance to the inhibitor. For a series of 20 independently derived variant clones, the concentration of amethopterin required for 50 percent growth inhibition ranged from 1.5 to 4.8 times the level characteristic of the parental strain. By further selection within one of these lines, a second-step variant was obtained with a relative increased of 16-fold in level of resistance. Other resistant clones have now been isolated, and these in some instances require up to 100,000 times as much amethopterin for inhibition as does the sensitive precursor line of leukemic cells (Mathias and Fischer, 1962).

Clonal populations of resistant cells are, as a rule, relatively stable (Roosa, Bradley, Law, and Herzenberg, 1962), but reversions do occur in some instances. Fischer (1959) noted that two clones of mouse leukemic cells with low levels of resistance to amethopterin lost this characteristic when passed through mice, although the lines in question remained stable during serial passage in culture. Two other strains with high resistance declined from levels of 100,000-fold to 20,000-fold during animal transfer. That a similar process can occur during culture is suggested by the findings of Hakala, Zakrzewski, and Nichol (1961). In their experiments, two variant lines with resistance to amethopterin were obtained from mouse Sarcoma 180 cells. When these were maintained in culture without the analogue, resistance declined progressively to lower levels, reaching half the original value after one month (Figure 6.15). The mechanism of change, however, is not entirely clear. Uncloned populations were employed, and thus selective overgrowth by a few sensitive cells in the initially resistant populations could account for the decline observed. The investigations of Pasternak, Fischer, and Handschumacher (1961) are more explicit in this regard. In their experiments, a clonal line of cells refractory to azauridine was isolated, and the initial level of resistance declined when this population was propagated in medium free from inhibitor.

Other examples of reversion from resistance to sensitivity have been described by Harris and Ruddle (1960). In these experiments, a clonal population of pig kidney cells (PK-15) was exposed to 2,6-diaminopurine, and from the resistant strain ultimately obtained, eight clones were established from single cells plated in the presence of inhibitor. Subsequently these clonal sublines were maintained in analogue-free medium for 3 months, and tested at intervals for resistance. Four clones retained a high level of resistance without change during this period, three showed a decline by half or more in the concentration of drug required for 50 percent growth inhibition (ID_{50}), and in one clone, resistance was

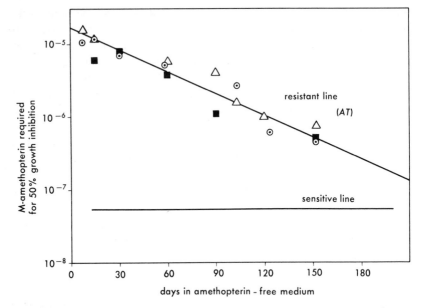

FIG. 6.15. Time curve for loss of resistance to amethopterin in a population of mouse Sarcoma 180 cells. The different symbols indicate data collected for sublines maintained in media containing ⊙ folic acid, △ folinic acid, and □ hypoxanthine, respectively. The rate at which resistance decreases is independent of the medium used. (After Hakala, Zakrzewski, and Nichol, 1961.)

lost completely at an early stage. In parallel experiments with clones resistant to 8-azaguanine, the drug response was unaltered for five lines over a 3-month period, while two clone strains showed progressive reversion toward sensitivity.

The most penetrating studies of reversion from resistance to sensitivity, however, are those of Szybalski and his collaborators (Szybalski, Szybalska, and Ragni, 1962; Szybalski and Szybalska, 1962). The experiments in question concern another variant of the D98 line, obtained from D98/AG populations by selection with 8-azahypoxanthine. The derivative strain, termed D98/AH, is highly resistant to this analogue and shows no detectable inosinic acid pyrophosphorylase (Szybalski, Szybalska, and Brockman, 1961). The D98/AH cells, moreover, cannot utilize the corresponding normal metabolite (hypoxanthine). They are thus unable to grow if *de novo* purine synthesis is blocked by amethopterin and hypoxanthine is provided as the sole purine source. Under such conditions, however, approximately 0.1 percent of cells from the D98/AH strain do give rise to colonies, and these prove to have regained a normal ability to utilize hypoxanthine. By applying methods to eliminate pre-existing variants from the $D98/AH$ strain, Szybalski and his co-workers have estimated the actual frequency of reversion at 3×10^{-6} mutations per cell per generation. The "revertants" are not identical in all respects with the ancestral $D98/AG$ cells. For example, they show a spectrum of sensitivity to various guanine and hypoxanthine analogues which lies between the $D98/AG$ and $D98/AH$ strains. More surprising, although inosinic acid pyrophosphorylase is again demonstrable in the revertant cells, the relative activity in cell-free preparations is only one-tenth that of $D98S$ or $D98/AG$ strains. Because of these differences, it seems unlikely that the revertants can be attributed to a simple process of back mutation. Szybalski has suggested that variants of this type might arise by a suppressor mechanism, although the nature of such changes remains to be determined.

One other question that arises is the possibility of interaction between sensitive and resistant cells in mass populations. Judging from the recent studies of Metzgar and Moskowitz (1963a, 1963b), this phenomenon may be a real one in some systems. In experiments with the Mox line (an apparent derivative of strain L mouse cells), these investigators found that over 50 percent of the clones isolated from stock cultures showed some degree of resistance to streptomycin. Nevertheless, mass populations of the stock strain appeared to be susceptible to the inhibitor, and the incidence of refractory variants within clones of sensitive cells was only one in 10^7. These divergent results were harmonized by the discovery that when two different strains of streptomycin-resistant cells are cultured together, the population ordinarily reacts to the drug as if sensitive. Of a series of 10 strains tested, nine appeared to be incompatible in this sense, while one proved to be partially independent in the expression of resistance. Complementation in some form is suggested by these findings, but the mechanisms that operate are still obscure.

Genetic and Epigenetic Mechanisms   The voluminous data that have been summarized in this chapter support the view that drug resistance in somatic cells arises by discrete and probably random changes rather than by a process of physiological adaptation. It is more difficult, however, to derive from these data a specific picture at the genetic level. Since drug resistance in microorganisms is demonstrably related to gene mutation, it has commonly been assumed that a similar association may apply within the cells of higher organisms. But direct evidence on this point has been hard to find. If, for example, drug resistance arises directly from point mutations, it should be possible to increase the spontaneous mutation rate by treating isolated cell strains with appropriate mutagens. In bacteria, it is well known that X irradiation, ultraviolet light, and a variety of chemical agents will markedly increase the frequency of mutations of all types, including those that confer resistance to specific drugs (Braun, 1953; Szybalski and Bryson, 1955; Jacob and Wollman, 1961). That mutations can be similarly induced in somatic cells during developmental stages is documented by experiments with embryos of *Drosophila* and other forms (see Chapter 1). The production of mutations within differentiated somatic cells, however, is less clearly established. Although Puck (1959) and others have frequently postulated that such changes can be induced directly within cell populations *in vitro*, there are no indications that any significant success has been achieved to date with specific genetic markers. In fact, Szybalski and Smith (1959b) observed that pretreatment of $D98$ cell populations with ultraviolet light selectively depresses the incidence of spontaneous variants with resistance to 8-azaguanine. More recently, a number of studies have been carried out with putative mutagens in the $D98$ system (Szybalski, Szybalska, and Ragni, 1962; Szybalski and Szybalska, 1962). The selective systems employed included mutations from $D98S \rightarrow D98/AG$ and $D98/AG \rightarrow D98/AH$ as well as reversions from the $D98/AH$ strain. No mutagenic effect could be substantiated for X-ray or ultraviolet irradiation or for a series of chemical agents that included nitrogen mustard, triethylene melamine, β-propiolactone, and halogen-substituted analogues of thymidine. Actually, the most striking effect, observed in about half of the cases, was a reduction in the rate of spontaneous mutation by 2- to 10-fold. The reason for this depression is still unknown, but it was shown not to depend on selective toxicity of the mutagens for mutant cell types.

Conceivably, the difficulty in demonstrating mutagenic effects within isolated somatic cells could lie in the recessive character of many, if not all, of the mutations that arise under these conditions. It will be recalled that resistance to streptomycin in *E. coli* behaves as a recessive marker within cells that contain the corresponding sensitive gene (Lederberg, 1951). If altered responses to drugs have a similar basis at the mammalian level, a direct expression of variation within diploid cells could be expected only in special cases (for example, for markers located on the X chromosome of male cells). Barring the occurrence of chromosome changes, mutations to drug resistance within the autosomes would require the rare coincidence of genetic change for both alleles in order to be detectable. Actually, even within euploid cells the possibility of crossing over must be considered (see Chapter 1), and in the permanent strains that have been used for studies on drug resistance, karyotypic changes are extensive (Chapter 4). An additional spectrum of possibilities can therefore be considered for the expression of recessive markers, that is, somatic segregation. Whether pre-existing in a heterozygous state or arising *de novo* by mutation, recessive determinants could be exposed by such processes as somatic crossing over, nondisjunction, or partial chromosome deletions. Each of these mechanisms might permit the appearance of drug resistance where this characteristic had previously been masked by the presence of a dominant sensitive allele.

The concept of recessive determinants, however, is difficult to reconcile with the fact that refractory variants can be obtained from polyploids or high aneuploids as well as from cells of near diploid karyotype. Assuming that mutation or segregation determines the expression of drug resistance, a lowered frequency of phenotypic alterations would be expected for cells that operate at a higher ploidy level. Owing to the necessity on the average for change or elimination of more than one allele at a given locus in high-ploid cells, the incidence of variants should decline. In actual fact, there seems to be comparatively little difference in the frequency of occurrence of drug resistance in high-ploid as compared to low-ploid cells. Where refractory variants are isolated as clonal derivatives from mixed populations, the proportion of high-ploid and low-ploid clones reflects roughly the proportion of such cells in the parental line (Harris and Ruddle, 1960). Evidently the appearance of resistant variants is frequent generally among cell strains with elevated chromosome numbers, judging from the data of Lieberman and Szybalski. It is, of course, true that the ploidy relationships for particular chromosomes can vary independently within cell populations, owing to the random nature of nondisjunction and other aberrations. Thus high chromosome number per se does not imply a multiplicity of alleles at all loci. Clearly, however, a large proportion of genetic loci are represented by more than two factors within high-ploid cells, even where a state of aneuploidy prevails. The over-all probability for the expression of recessives by somatic change would therefore seem to be less.

This line of reasoning leads to the suggestion that drug resistance in somatic cells may be a dominant or independently expressed character, with somatic segregation playing little if any significant role. The available evidence is inconclusive, however, and decisive experiments have yet to be performed. For this purpose clonal strains of haploid character would be particularly useful. If drug-resistant variants can be obtained from sensitive haploid populations, for example, the possibility of chromosomal change as an implementing mechanism would be effectively eliminated. Similarly, if recessive mutations are in fact the source of variation in this system, the frequency of expression should be significantly greater in haploid cells than in diploids or polyploids. A direct test of these predictions will necessitate the development of additional materials, since cell lines of haploid karyotype are not yet available from avian or mammalian sources. Haploid amphibian cells, however, have recently been established in culture (Freed, 1962), and may provide a means of assay. The ability of these populations to yield drug-resistant variants has not yet been determined.

According to an alternative genetic concept, drug resistance may arise through chromosomal rearrangements that lead to shifts in genic balance rather than mere exposure of mutant loci. This approach can be illustrated by the work of Vogt (1959), who suggested that most of the phenotypic variability of heteroploid cell populations can be attributed to changes in chromosome pattern. Using cultures of *HeLa* cells, she has attempted to show that altered phenotypes in this system are in general the result of altered karyotypes. Among the variants examined were three sublines refractory to amethopterin, two adapted to growth in horse or calf serum, and a number of other clones picked from standard medium on the basis of morphological differences. All these variants were found to show individuality in karyotype, including differences in modal chromosome numbers as well as the number of large metacentrics in modal cells. Vogt has interpreted these results to indicate a causal relationship between karyotype and phenotype. That instability in the karyotype of *HeLa* and other cell strains can contribute to cellular variation is certainly a reasonable assumption, but it is questionable that Vogt's results have demonstrated any simple or clear-cut association between these phenomena. At least some of the karyotypic individuality of her cell lines may be the result of nonselective changes accumulated at random within isolated populations (that is, genetic drift). This possibility needs further study, especially since chromosomal fluctuations may be facilitated by mitotic abnormalities in suboptimal media.

That variant karyotypes may accompany variant phenotypes without any necessary association is demonstrated in the investigations of Harris and Ruddle (1960). These experiments deal with the characteristics of clonal strains of resistant pig kidney cells, initiated from single cells plated in the presence of 8-azaguanine or 2,6-diaminopurine, respectively. Of seven near-diploid clones of pig kidney cells with resistance to 8-azaguanine, two showed conspicuous marker chromosomes while the others showed no gross differences from sensitive populations in terms of chromosome morphology or modal number. Over a period of 3 months, the latter group of clones maintained a high level of resistance to azaguanine, but in the lines with variant karyotypes, resistance declined significantly despite the uniform persistence of marker chromosomes in all cells. Within eight additional clones with resistance to 2,6-diaminopurine, no obvious changes were observed in chromosomal morphology. All these strains, however, were subdiploid, with modes at 32 or 35 chromosomes. This condition proved to be unstable in drug-free media, and marked heteroploid shifts occurred toward higher modal chromosome numbers. Despite this extensive remodeling of karyotype, there was no evidence for parallel changes in the pattern of drug resistance.

The lack of any consistent correlation between drug resistance and modifications in karyotype is also borne out by the experiments of other investigators. Hauschka (1958), in dealing with this problem, examined seven ascites tumors in mice which showed resistance to various antimetabolites, along with the sensitive precursor populations. Four of the resistant lines showed no structural or numerical deviations in chromosome patterns. Two that were resistant to amethopterin, for example, were indistinguishable from the sensitive parental type. Three other resistant tumors, however, showed clear shifts in karyotypic pattern, including new modal chromosomal numbers as well as the appearance of distinctive marker chromosomes. Similarly, Biesele, Biedler, and Hutchison (1959) developed variant strains of mouse L-1210 leukemic cells with resistance to 6-mercaptopurine, azaserine, mitomycin, and 5-fluorouracil; all failed to show any consistent deviation from the original karyotypic pattern. Biesele and his co-workers observed a large submetacentric chromosome in each of five sublines sensitive to amethopterin. The marker in question could not be found in resistant strains of the L-1210 tumor. However, a more comprehensive study showed that although the loss of this chromosome may be related to a rise in folic acid reductase, disappearance is not directly correlated with amethopterin resistance as such (Biedler, Schrecker, and Hutchison, 1963). In L-5178Y mouse leukemic cells resistant to amethopterin, Fischer (1961) was unable to find any gross chromosomal abnormalities. Both sensitive and resistant cells were near-diploids, with few if any detectable differences in karyotype.

The recent description of drug resistance in strain L mouse cells to 5-bromodeoxyuridine (Hsu and Somers, 1962) is particularly interesting because, in sensitive cells, this analogue induces selective breakage of chromosomes (Hsu and Somers, 1961) and is incorporated extensively into DNA in place of thymidine (Djordjevic and Szybalski, 1960). Paradoxically, the incidence of chromosomal breakage falls to normal within resistant strain L cells, although the uptake of 5-bromodeoxyuridine into cellular DNA within some variants continues unchecked. In this connection, it may be mentioned that resistant lines have also been isolated from populations of strain L cells that do not incorporate bromo-deoxyuridine into the cellular DNA. Here, the basis for resistance appears to be a deletion of the necessary enzyme, thymidine kinase (Kit, Dubbs, Piekarski, and Hsu, 1963). Regardless of the mechanism of change, however, no unique karyotypic differences can be found in populations resistant and sensitive to this analogue, respectively. Hsu and Somers found that some of the refractory sublines of strain L cells are as variable in chromosome pattern as the parental populations, suggesting that resistance in this case does not depend on the selection of stem cells with a distinctive karyotype. These observations, along with others cited previously, thus reinforce the prediction that karyotypic alterations are unlikely to be associated with specific cellular changes in most cases (Chapter 4). The fact seems to be that gross chromosomal patterns are a relatively insensitive index, if any, of genetic changes that may underlie the transition to drug resistance.

On the whole, it seems fair to say that although gene mutations or chromosomal alterations may be responsible for drug resistance in somatic cells, a convincing case has yet to be made for specific mechanisms. In bacteria, a similar impasse was eventually resolved by the development of techniques for the transfer of genetic information from cell to cell. Special interest thus centers on the possibility of communicating resistance or sensitivity between the units of somatic cell populations. Viruses offer a conceivable vector, since phage-mediated transfer of drug resistance within microorganisms is well known. The most promising agents for animal cells may be the Rous sarcoma and polyoma viruses, both of which can persist and multiply without causing mass destruction of somatic populations (Chapter 7). A number of experimental designs can, in principle, be utilized to test for transduction with these tumor viruses, but as yet no success has been reported in the transfer of drug resistance or other specific cell markers.

More effort has gone into attempts to demonstrate DNA-mediated transformation within tumors and isolated somatic cell strains. There are several reports that indicate that deoxyribonucleic acid can be incorporated into these cells from the surrounding medium. Sirotnak and Hutchison (1959), for example, found that soluble DNA prepared from *S. pneumoniae* is absorbed within a few minutes by L-1210 mouse cells, with the total amount taken up proportional to the external concentration. In other systems (for example, cultures of strain L mouse cells), soluble DNA does not enter in appreciable quantities. But if coacervates are prepared with DNA from bacterial or mammalian sources, extensive uptake of the particulates by phagocytosis occurs (Bensch and King, 1961). These observations indicate that at least the first in a series of events required for genetic transformation is feasible. Whether other necessary conditions remain to be defined is still unknown. Attempts to demonstrate the actual transfer of cell markers have either failed or yielded equivocal results. Typical of the unsuccessful efforts are the careful experiments of Mathias and Fischer (1962). For the work in question, DNA was extracted from strains of L-5178Y mouse leukemic cells known to be highly resistant to amethopterin. By tritium labeling, donor DNA could be shown to enter the cells in assay cultures, but the observed rate of mutation to amethopterin resistance remained unchanged. Evidently these negative results do not stem from a degradation of transforming DNA. No evidence was obtained for an extracellular deoxyribonuclease, and donor preparations of DNA were unaffected by incubation with extracts from assay cells.

That caution is needed in assessing ostensibly positive transformations is emphasized by the analytical studies of Bradley, Roosa, and Law (1962a, 1962b). Resistance to 8-azaguanine provided the marker in this case, and mouse lymphoma P-388 cells in culture were employed as an assay system. If sensitive P-388 cells are exposed to DNA extracts from a resistant line, they become regularly more refractory to 8-azaguanine when subsequently exposed to this inhibitor. Evidence that increased resistance is conferred as a heritable characteristic can be found in the fact that DNA-treated populations, even after serial subculture in the absence of both DNA and inhibitor, still prove to be refractory to 8-azaguanine when finally assayed. The impact of this result is lessened, however, by observations which indicate that the DNA used for treatment need not necessarily originate from refractory cells. In certain experiments, at least, the induction of a refractory response to 8-azaguanine can be achieved equally well through exposure of assay cultures to DNA prepared from sensitive P-388 populations. This anomalous finding may conceivably relate to another, and more clearly nonspecific, effect of DNA treatment that has been discovered by Bradley and his collaborators. By altering the original experimental pattern, DNA and inhibitor can be added simultaneously rather than sequentially to the assay cultures. Under these conditions, an increased frequency of resistant colonies is observed with all DNA preparations, regardless of whether the DNA comes from sensitive or resistant P-388 populations. Furthermore, the same result can be obtained with DNA from sensitive L-1210 mouse leukemic cells, or even with DNA from normal mouse liver or rat spleen. This generalized increase in resistance may conceivably depend on the release of adenine from DNA preparations. Adenine was found to antagonize growth inhibition by 8-azaguanine in the assay cultures.

Alternatively, Bradley and his co-workers suggest that DNA as such may exert a protective effect at the cell surface or in the interior of the cell. In summary, then, these experiments show that resistance in varying forms to azaguanine may be induced by DNA treatment, but it is not yet clear whether a true genetic transformation can be discerned among the web of nongenetic processes.

The experiments of Szybalski and his co-workers represent another effort to document genetic transformation in mammalian cells, involving here the various human $D98$ mutant strains mentioned earlier (Szybalski, Szybalska, and Ragni, 1962; Szybalski and Szybalska, 1962; Szybalska and Szybalski, 1962). Using DNA extracted with comparatively mild procedures, evidence has been sought for cell-to-cell transfer of specific markers. The chief finding of interest is a significant increase in variants capable of utilizing hypoxanthine when $D98/AH$ populations are treated with DNA from $D98S$ or $D98/AG$ cells. These potential transformants are reported to show a spectrum of sensitivity to guanine and hypoxanthine analogues that is typical of the donor strain rather than of the revertants which, as noted earlier, arise spontaneously in the $D98/AH$ line. The incidence of cells able to grow on hypoxanthine is proportional to the concentration of applied DNA, rising to frequencies of 1.2×10^{-4}, as compared to less than 2×10^{-7} in untreated populations. Apparently the effect obtained is a specific one. No increases in variants utilizing hypoxanthine are observed following addition of bacteriophage DNA, for example, or of DNA extracted from the $D98/AH$ recipient strain. On the other hand, digestion with deoxyribonuclease serves to abolish the activity of competent preparations.

These results, as obtained by Szybalski, again offer a parallel in certain respects to DNA-mediated transformations in microorganisms. Whether the analogy is in fact a valid one, however, remains to be determined. Although reversion to the utilization of hypoxanthine is demonstrably influenced by DNA extracts, the reverse step, $D98/AG \rightarrow D98/AH$, is not. Actually, Szybalski and his associates have been unable to demonstrate any transformations from sensitivity to drug resistance by DNA treatment, although preparations from donor strains refractory to azaguanine ($D98/AG$), azaguanosine ($D98/AGR$) and azahypoxanthine ($D98/AH$) have all been tried. Although these negative results can have various explanations, it seems evident that further study is needed to establish the nature and generality of the reversion phenomenon, on which indications of transformation in this system depend. The possibility of reversible changes in enzymatic activity by dedifferentiation and redifferentiation must be considered, and directed modulations may occur. These eventualities can be rigorously excluded only by proof that incorporation or replication of transforming DNA has definitely occurred in the host cell genome.

In actuality, the direct analogy of control systems for drug resistance in bacteria with those of somatic cells may be too facile a comparison (Klein, 1959, 1961). It does not take into account the possible intermediary role of epigenetic mechanisms in somatic systems, although the emergence of stable cell types by this means is a commonplace event in embryonic development. Drug resistance in somatic cells has usually been assumed to have a genetic rather than epigenetic basis, because variants arise at random and persist in the absence of a selective agent. Yet even within microorganisms, the characteristics of spontaneity and stability in cellular change do not necessarily imply any alteration in the basic information systems of the cell (Nanney, 1958; Ephrussi, 1958). Thus the possibility that drug resistance originates within epigenetic control systems that affect the stability of somatic differentiation cannot yet be ruled out.

Several provocative models suggest that the relation of epigenetic mechanisms to the onset of drug resistance in somatic cells deserves careful study. In a number of microbial systems, the expression of cell characters can be modified by exposure to base analogues, under conditions that do not involve incorporation into cellular DNA or the induction of genetic changes. Naono and Gros (1960) could show that alkaline phosphatase synthesized by *E. coli* in the presence of 5-fluorouracil displays an altered thermosensitivity; β-galactosidase formed under the same conditions is inactive although indistinguishable in amount and antigenic properties from the normal enzyme (Bussard, Naono, Gros, and Monod, 1960). Phenotypic reversion of mutant characters can also be demonstrated. Champe and Benzer (1962) showed that the ability to synthesize phosphatase may reappear in phosphatase-negative mutants of *E. coli* grown with 5-fluorouracil. This treatment also permits certain defective phage mutants to multiply in the *coli* host. Another instance of induced reversion has been described for *Neurospora* by Barnett and Brockman (1962). Adenine-requiring mutants grow poorly on minimal media lacking this compound, but can be stimulated to increase at a rate approximately 75 percent that of the wild type, by treatment with either 8-azaguanine or 5-fluorouracil. Conidia harvested from such cultures exhibit the original mutant character, however, indicating that the phenomenon in question is based on phenotypic changes rather than on back mutation.

The most convincing explanation of these findings stems from the viewpoint, now current, that messenger-RNA serves to convey genetic information in complementary form from DNA determinants to specific end systems within the cell (Brenner, Jacob, and Meselson, 1961). It follows from this concept that base pair substitution by analogues in messenger-RNA may garble the original transcription, leading to the formation of abnormal proteins, or may cancel out a variant code sequence that would otherwise give rise to a mutant phenotype. In either case, phenotypic changes could be expected against an intact background genome (Champe and Benzer, 1962). The broader significance of these epigenetic phenomena for other types of cellular variation, especially in somatic systems, is not immediately apparent. Certainly the temporary character of phenotypic changes in the examples cited above is in keeping with the ephemeral nature of messenger-RNA in microbial cells. But the occurrence of differentiation in somatic units may lead to the appearance of epigenetic information systems with a much higher degree of continuity than messenger-RNA as such (see Chapter 3, pp. 161–162). If these directive mechanisms are subject to spontaneous or induced changes on a random basis, the final expression of genetic instructions (for example, patterns of response to particular inhibitors) might be altered more permanently, as if by gene mutation. These speculations in an epigenetic vein are discussed in more detail in Chapter 7 (pp. 422–432); their merit can be determined only by experimental tests. But since the exact origin of resistance to drugs in somatic cells remains obscure, it may be useful to search for new approaches rather than to continue merely with a preconception of genetic mechanisms from microbial systems.

OTHER TYPES OF ACQUIRED RESISTANCE *IN VITRO*

As an enlargement of this discussion directed primarily toward drug reactions, the existing literature on adaptive responses to other types of environmental agents is briefly reviewed. The experimental data are not yet extensive, but there are reports of increased tolerance to supranormal temperatures within isolated cell populations as well as sublines with modified susceptibility to radiation injury. Variants are also known which exhibit acquired resistance to infection with specific viruses. In none of these experimental systems have implementing mechanisms at the cellular level yet been determined, and the information available at the present time is thus preliminary in character.

Adaptation for growth at elevated temperatures has been examined extensively with bacteria, particularly in thermophilic species that are genetically endowed for survival in hot springs and other unfavorable environments. Those forms with temperature optima at more moderate levels, however, are capable in general of limited adjustments only for growth at higher temperatures, whether by mutation or physiological adaptation (Clegg and Jacobs, 1953). Among somatic cell populations, the only systematic analysis of this phenomenon has been that of Selawry, Goldstein, and McCormick (1957). Three strains of human tumor cells (*HeLa, HEP-2, J96*) were maintained in culture, and their reactions to elevated temperatures were variously determined. These lines grow more vigorously at 38° C than at 37° C, but show inhibition to a varying extent at higher temperatures, with 100 percent cell death in all cases for populations maintained at 42° C. Short periods of exposure to temperatures of 42° to 46° C are followed by cell injury and recovery, after which the same procedure can be repeated. In this way, thermotolerant sublines were obtained from all three strains of cells by cyclic exposure at 42° C, followed by recovery and growth at 36° C (Figure 6.16). When assayed at elevated temperatures, the derivative strains survived for longer periods than did the original cell lines. Above 42° C, resistant and sensitive populations tend to converge more closely in their response to heat treatment. The basis for thermotolerance in this system is unknown, but it does not seem to stem from physiological adaptation alone.

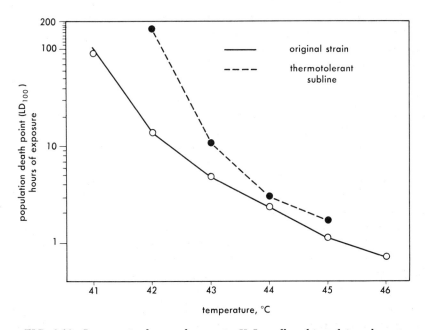

FIG. 6.16. Increase in thermotolerance in *HeLa* cells subjected in culture to repeated heat application. (After Selawry, Goldstein, and McCormick, 1957. Copyright, University of Chicago Press.)

Selawry and his colleagues maintained three thermotolerant sublines for 3 months at 36° C and found that resistance to elevated temperatures was unimpaired. These facts indicate that heritable differences exist between sensitive and resistant sublines, although the origin of this differential is not clear. Since the original strains were uncloned, it is possible that the thermotolerant sublines originated merely by selection of more resistant cell types from an initially heterogeneous population. Additional experiments will be required to determine whether thermotolerance, like drug resistance, can arise by random change within strains of single cell origin.

Radiation resistance is a more familiar phenomenon, particularly in microbial cells. The investigations of Witkin (1947) on E. coli served to open up this field of study. She showed that mutants which are relatively resistant to the lethal effects of both ultraviolet light and X irradiation arise spontaneously within sensitive populations. In this system, high doses of ultraviolet illumination markedly increase the frequency of mutations to radiation resistance. Experimental designs must thus distinguish between selective and mutagenic effects by the same agent. Witkin also made the important observation that resistance to radiation damage may be associated with altered responses to certain antibiotics. Cross resistance can in fact be demonstrated with a number of drugs, particularly radiomimetic compounds such as nitrogen mustard or azaserine (Bryson, 1948; Curry and Greenberg, 1962). These facts suggest that resistance depends on an altered response to chemical agents formed or liberated during exposure to irradiation. Cytological studies on E. coli indicate that resistant cells possess mechanisms for improved recovery from radiation damage rather than any invulnerability to primary injury (Payne, Hartman, Mudd, and Phillips, 1956).

From a genetic standpoint, the radioresistant mutants that have been obtained from E. coli represent a heterogeneous group (Witkin, 1947; Hill and Simson, 1961). The individuality of particular substrains is expressed by differences in the spectrum of response to radiation and chemical agents, suggesting that resistance may arise from a number of independent changes at various loci within the genome. The interpretation of these studies is complicated by the fact that responses to radiation are markedly influenced by environmental factors (de Serres, 1961). Wide differences in experiments with both sensitive and resistant cells can result from variations in oxygen tension, pH, temperature, composition of the culture medium, and previous history of the cell population. For this reason, it may be difficult to compare different investigations on radiation resistance unless they are done under identical conditions.

There have been no studies of resistance to ultraviolet light as such within somatic cell populations, although Szybalski and Smith (1959b) noted that strain *D*98/*AG*, with established resistance to 8-azaguanine, was also less susceptible to the lethal effects of ultraviolet radiation. Interest has, however, focused on a phenomenon of opposite character, that is, the induction of radiosensitivity. Szybalski and his colleagues have shown that the incorporation of halogenated analogues in place of thymidine within the DNA molecule renders somatic cell populations extremely sensitive to radiation treatment. In *D*98 cells, for example, up to 45 percent of the thymidine can be replaced by 5-bromodeoxyuridine without loss of viability, the cultures continuing to grow unhindered by the presence of analogue. But if these chemically modified cells are exposed to either ultraviolet light or X irradiation, destruction occurs at dose levels far below those ordinarily required for lethal damage in the parental strain (Djordjevic and Szybalski, 1960; Erikson and Szybalski, 1961). It is possible that this interesting effect reflects a greater instability of cellular DNA, owing to stresses set up by the presence of bromodeoxyuridine, but it is reversible. If cells that have incorporated bromodeoxyuridine are maintained in analogue-free medium, sensitivity to ultraviolet rapidly returns to normal as the analogue is diluted out in successive cell divisions. Thus these shifts in radiosensitivity seem to depend on purely physiological changes within the population as a whole, rather than on the selective growth of variants with heritable alterations in cell properties.

Resistance to X irradiation is a common experience in the treatment of tumors, but has usually been ascribed to secondary effects (for example, vascular or stromal changes) rather than to the altered reactions of variant cell types. This may well be true at the clinical level, but several observations now indicate that variants with modified responses to X irradiation can be detected even within cell cultures of clonal origin. Whitfield and Rixon (1960a) exposed strain *L* mouse cells (clone 929) to a single dose of 1000 r, and from the survivors isolated a colony with four to five times the survival of the parental population when irradiated at a similar level (Figure 6.17). The variant subline proved to be stable in serial proliferation and showed an undiminished radioresistance after more than 350 cell generations (Rixon and Whitfield, 1960). It is not immediately evident whether resistance in this case was induced directly by exposure to X irradiation or whether refractory cells originally present arose by spontaneous variation at some previous point in the history of clone 929. Other radioresistant sublines have been isolated from strain *L* by Rhynas and Newcombe (1960). In no case, however, has it been possible to select out stepwise variants with higher multiplicities of

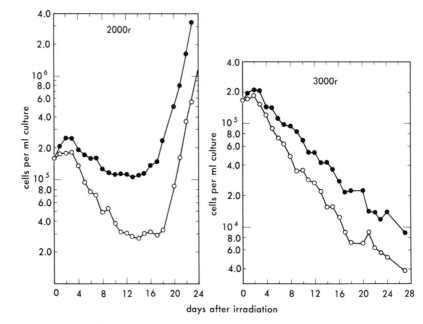

FIG. 6.17. Radioresistance in cultures of strain *L* mouse cells. *Open circles:* stock cells, previously unirradiated. *Solid circles:* subline derived from surviving remnants of population exposed earlier to X irradiation at 1000 r. When given an assay dose of 2000 r (*left diagram*) the radioresistant line shows lower mortality and more rapid return to a logarithmic growth pattern. After 3000 r (*right diagram*), neither sensitive nor radioresistant lines recover, but mortality is delayed in populations of the latter. (Redrawn from Whitfield and Rixon, 1960a.)

resistance by repeated exposures to X irradiation. The physiological basis for these modified responses is still unknown, but resistance does not depend on increases in catalase activity, glycolytic changes, or altered rates of oxygen consumption (Whitfield and Rixon, 1960b).

As in the case of drug resistance, the question has arisen whether refractory responses to X irradiation in *L* cells can be correlated with changes in karyotypic pattern. Rhynas and Newcombe (1960) found that several resistant lines had a lower average chromosome number and wider modal variation than did the parental strain. Approximately 98 percent of the resistant cells lacked a prominent metacentric chromosome, which occurred in nearly all cells from sensitive populations. Whitfield and Rixon (1961) followed this same marker and noted a progressive selection for cells lacking the large metacentric element within populations recovering from X-ray treatment. It is not possible to generalize from this limited sample, but judging from the parallel studies on radiosensitivity that were described in Chapter 4, a broader spectrum of radioresistant strains is likely to yield variants with no detectable chromosomal deviations as well as those that show alterations in some form. If karyotypic changes do in fact signal a primary mechanism in the transition to refractory states, a ploidy effect might be expected. So far there is no evidence that this is the case. Rhynas and Newcombe (1960) found polyploid cells in both sensitive and radioresistant lines of strain *L*, with no apparent differences in their relative frequency.

To round out this inventory of acquired resistance to extrinsic agents, brief mention should be made of modified responses at the cellular level to viral infection. In bacteria, phage resistance (Chapter 2) is a familiar phenomenon that has formed the basis for many genetic studies. In such a system, resistance appears most commonly to stem from a change in the host cell surface, so that adsorption of virus does not occur (Garen and Kozloff, 1959). The variant property may be specific for one or more phages, and resistance to several types may develop by sequential mutations. Refractory responses to viruses can also develop within populations of isolated animal cells, as Vogt and Dulbecco (1958) first showed in a *HeLa*-poliovirus system. Starting with a clonal strain of host cells, cultures were exposed to massive doses of virus, with a repetition of the same treatment when the survivors had increased sufficiently in number. After five such cycles, the population assumed a fusiform instead of polygonal cell morphology. By treatment with poliomyelitis antiserum to cure the existing infection, a subline apparently free from virus was eventually obtained. In subsequent assays, this variant showed a markedly greater ability to survive exposure to poliovirus than did the original parent strain (Figure 6.18).

Other investigators have likewise succeeded in isolating clonal sublines from permanent cell strains with heritable differences in sensitivity to polioviruses (Leidy, Sprunt, Redman, and Alexander, 1959; Darnell and Sawyer, 1959, 1960; Chessin and Hirschhorn, 1961). For the most part, these studies have been performed with uncloned parental populations, but the experiments of Vogt and Dulbecco, described above, leave little doubt that variations in viral susceptibility can develop within lines derived from a single cell. The acquisition of resistance to Newcastle disease virus (Cieciura, Marcus, and Puck, 1957) as well as to ECHO viruses (Nakano, 1959) has also been reported for *HeLa* populations, while Rapp (1960) has isolated a number of sublines from human *HEP*-2 cells that vary in response to infection with measles virus. Very little attention has yet been given to the cellular mechanisms of resistance in these systems, although one such analysis has been de-

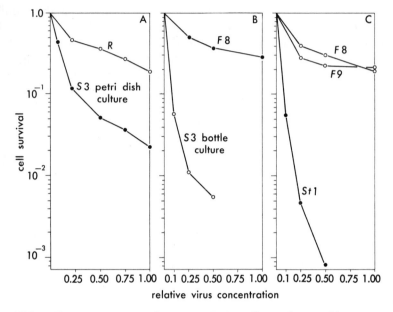

FIG. 6.18. Resistance to poliovirus in *HeLa* cell populations. The assays measure fractional survival in the presence of increasing multiplicities of virus. (*A*) Survival curves for stock S3 *HeLa* cells and a resistant subline, *R*. (*B*) Comparative survival of S3 and F8, a clonal derivative of the resistant line. (*C*) Maximum differential between clonal derivatives F8 and F9 from the resistant line, and St1, representing a clonal isolate of sensitive cells from the stock S3 *HeLa* population. (Redrawn from Vogt, 1958. Copyright, Wistar Institute Press.)

scribed by Darnell and Sawyer (1960) for poliovirus in *HeLa* cells. Unlike the pattern observed with phage, the adsorption and penetration of poliovirus takes place with equal facility in sensitive and resistant strains. Significantly, however, resistance in *HeLa* cells disappears if poliovirus RNA, rather than intact virus, is used for infection. Thus the basis of resistance in this case may lie in an impaired release of viral nucleic acid within the host cell. It is likely that other mechanisms may serve as well to implement acquired resistance to viral agents in animal cells. One of these may be the selective production of interferons, now known to arise in various systems from cell-virus interactions (Isaacs and Lindenmann, 1957; Bader, 1962; Wagner, 1963a, 1963b; Henle, 1963). It appears that interferons, which act to inhibit or repress viral synthesis in varying degree, are basic proteins of relatively low molecular weight. These agents cannot be identified with viral or normal cellular components as such. They may be formed as special products by infected cells, under the inductive influence of viruses (Wagner, 1963b). The role of interferons in natural resistance to viral infections, and in the acquisition of refractory states, offers a broad field for study.

■ References

ALEXANDER, P., and STACEY, K. A. 1958. Comparison of the changes produced by ionizing radiations and by the alkylating agents: Evidence for a similar mechanism at the molecular level. Ann. N. Y. Acad. Sci., **68**: 1225–1237.

ANDERSON, E. P., and JACQUEZ, J. A. 1962. Azaserine resistance in a plasma-cell neoplasm without change in active transport of the inhibitor. Cancer Res., **22**: 27–37.

ARONOW, L. 1959. Studies on drug resistance in mammalian cells. I. Amethopterin resistance in mouse fibroblasts. J. Pharmacol. Exptl. Therap., **127**: 116–121.

AUERBACH, C. 1958. Radiomimetic substances. Radiation Res., **9**: 33-47.

BADER, J. P. 1962. Production of interferon by chick embryo cells exposed to Rous sarcoma virus. Virology, **16**: 436–443.

BALIS, M. E., HYLIN, V., COULTAS, M. K., and HUTCHISON, D. J. 1958a. Metabolism of resistant mutants of *Streptococcus faecalis*. II. Incorporation of exogenous purines. Cancer Res., **18**: 220–225.

BALIS, M. E., HYLIN, V., COULTAS, M. K., and HUTCHISON, D. J. 1958b. Metabolism of resistant mutants of *Streptococcus faecalis*. III. The action of 6-mercaptopurine. Cancer Res., **18**: 440–444.

BARBAN, S. 1962a. Studies on the mechanism of resistance to 2-deoxy-D-glucose in mammalian cell cultures. J. Biol. Chem., **237**: 291–295.

BARBAN, S. 1962b. Induced resistance to 2-deoxy-D-glucose in cell cultures. Biochim. et Biophys. Acta, **65**: 376–377.

BARBAN, S., and SCHULZE, H. O. 1961. The effects of 2-deoxyglucose on the growth and metabolism of cultured human cells. J. Biol. Chem., **236**: 1887–1890.

BARNETT, W. E., and BROCKMAN, H. E. 1962. Induced phenotypic reversion by 8-azaguanine and 5-fluorouracil. Bioch. Biophys. Res. Comm., **7**: 199–203.

BEALE, G. H. 1954. The genetics of *Paramecium aurelia*. Cambridge: The University Press. 179 pp.

BENSCH, K. G., and KING, D. W. 1961. Incorporation of heterologous deoxyribonucleic acid into mammalian cells. Science, **133**: 381–382.

BERTINO, J. R., DONOHUE, D. R., GABRIO, B. W., SILBER, R., ALENTY, A., MEYER, M., and HUENNEKENS, F. M. 1962. Increased level of dihydrofolic reductase in leucocytes of patients treated with amethopterin. Nature, **193**: 140–142.

BIEDLER, J. L., SCHRECKER, A. W., and HUTCHISON, D. J. 1963. Selection of chromosomal variant in amethopterin-resistant sublines of leukemia L1210 with increased levels of dehydrofolate reductase. J. Natl. Cancer Inst., 31: 575–601.

BIESELE, J. J., BIEDLER, J. L., and HUTCHISON, D. J. 1959. The chromosomal status of drug resistant sublines of mouse leukemia L-1210. In: Genetics and Cancer, pp. 295–307. Austin: University of Texas Press.

BISHOP, A. 1959. Drug resistance in protozoa. Biol. Revs., 34: 445–500.

BRADLEY, T. R., ROOSA, R. A., and LAW, L. W. 1962a. Antagonism by deoxyribonucleic acid extracts of the growth inhibitory effects of 8-azaguanine on mammalian cells in culture. Nature, 195: 304–305.

BRADLEY, T. R., ROOSA, R. A., and LAW, L. W. 1962b. Transformation studies with mammalian cells in culture. J. Cellular Comp. Physiol., 60: 127–137.

BRAUN, W. 1953. Bacterial genetics. Philadelphia: W. B. Saunders Company, 238 pp.

BRENNER, S., JACOB, F., and MESELSON, M. 1961. An unstable intermediate carrying information from genes to ribosomes for protein synthesis. Nature, 190: 576–581.

BROCKMAN, R. W. 1960. A mechanism of resistance to 6-mercaptopurine: Metabolism of hypoxanthine and 6-mercaptopurine by sensitive and resistant neoplasms. Cancer Res., 20: 643–653.

BROCKMAN, R. W., BENNETT, L. L., JR., SIMPSON, M. S., WILSON, A. R., THOMSON, J. R., and SKIPPER, H. E. 1959. A mechanism of resistance to 8-azaguanine. II. Studies with experimental neoplasms. Cancer Res., 19: 856–869.

BROCKMAN, R. W., DAVIS, J. M., and STUTTS, P. 1960. Metabolism of uracil and 5-fluorouracil by drug-sensitive and by drug-resistant bacteria. Biochim. et Biophys. Acta, 40: 22–32.

BROCKMAN, R. W., DEBAVADI, C. S., STUTTS, P., and HUTCHISON, D. J. 1961. Purine ribonucleotide pyrophosphorylases and resistance to purine analogues in Streptococcus faecalis. J. Biol. Chem., 236: 1471–1479.

BROCKMAN, R. W., ROOSA, R. A., LAW, L. W., and STUTTS, P. 1962. Purine ribonucleotide pyrophosphorylase activity and resistance to purine analogs in P-388 murine lymphocytic leukemia. J. Cellular Comp. Physiol., 60: 65–84.

BROCKMAN, R. W., SPARKS, M. C., and SIMPSON, M. S. 1957. A comparison of the metabolism of purines and purine analogs by susceptible and drug-resistant bacterial and neoplastic cells. Biochim. et Biophys. Acta, 26: 671–672.

BROCKMAN, R. W., SPARKS, M. C., SIMPSON, M. S., and SKIPPER, H. E. 1959. Decreased ribonucleotide pyrophosphorylase activity of Streptococcus faecalis and L-1210 leukaemia resistant to purine antagonists. Biochem. Pharmacol., 2: 77–79.

BRYSON, V. 1948. The effects of nitrogen mustard on Escherichia coli. J. Bacteriol., 56: 423–433.

BRYSON, V. 1962. Antibiotics: Practical and experimental aspects. Survey Biol. Progr., **4**: 345–440.

BRYSON, V., and DEMEREC, M. 1950. Patterns of resistance to antimicrobial agents. Ann. N. Y. Acad. Sci., **53**: 283–289.

BRYSON, V., and SZYBALSKI, W. 1955. Microbial drug resistance. Advan. Genet., **7**: 1–46.

BURCHENAL, J. H. 1955a. Folic acid antagonists. Am. J. Clin. Nutr., **3**: 311–320.

BURCHENAL, J. H. 1955b. Discussion of paper by L. W. Law. *In: Origins of Resistance to Toxic Agents*, p. 342. M. G. Sevag, R. D. Reid, and O. E. Reynolds, eds. New York: Academic Press, Inc.

BURCHENAL, J. H., BENDICH, A., BROWN, G. B., ELION, G. B., HITCHINGS, G. H., RHOADS, C. P., and STOCK, C. C. 1949. Preliminary studies on the effect of 2,6-diaminopurine on transplanted mouse leukemia. Cancer, **2**: 119–120.

BURCHENAL, J. H., ROBINSON, E., JOHNSTON, S. F., and KUSHIDA, M. N. 1950. The induction of resistance to 4-amino-N^{10}-methyl-pteroylglutamic acid in a strain of transmitted mouse leukemia. Science, **111**: 116–117.

BUSSARD, A., NAONO, S., GROS, F., and MONOD, J. 1960. Effets d'un analogue de l'uracile sur les propriétiés d'une protéine enzymatique synthétisée en sa présence. Compt. Rend. Acad. Sci., **250**: 4049–4051.

CAVALLI, L. L., and MACCACARO, G. A. 1952. Polygenic inheritance of drug-resistance in the bacterium *Escherichia coli*. Heredity, **6**: 311–331.

CAVALLI-SFORZA, L. L., and LEDERBERG, J. 1956. Isolation of pre-adaptive mutants in bacteria by sib selection. Genetics, **41**: 367–381.

CHAMPE, S. P., and BENZER, S. 1962. Reversal of mutant phenotypes by 5-fluorouracil: an approach to nucleotide sequences in messenger-RNA. Proc. Natl. Acad. Sci., **48**: 532–546.

CHESSIN, L. N., and HIRSCHHORN, K. 1961. Virus resistance and sensitivity in cultured human synovial cells as a possible genetic marker. Exptl. Cell Res., **23**: 138–144.

CIECIURA, S. J., MARCUS, P. I., and PUCK, T. T. 1957. The use of X-irradiated HeLa cell giants to detect latent virus in mammalian cells. Virology, **3**: 426–427.

CLARKE, D. A., PHILIPS, F. S., STERNBERG, S. S., and STOCK, C. C. 1954. Effects of 6-mercaptopurine and analogs on experimental tumors. Ann. N. Y. Acad. Sci., **60**: 235–243.

CLARKE, D. A., PHILIPS, F. S., STERNBERG, S. S., STOCK, C. C., ELION, G. B., and HITCHINGS, G. H. 1953. 6-mercaptopurine: Effects in mouse sarcoma 180 and in normal animals. Cancer Res., **13**: 593–604.

CLEGG, L. F. L., and JACOBS, S. E. 1953. Environmental and other aspects of adaptation in thermophiles. *In: Adaptation in Micro-organisms*, pp. 306–325. R. Davies and E. F. Gale, eds. Cambridge: The University Press.

COLE, R. J., and DANIELLI, J. F. 1963. Nuclear-transfer studies on induced increases in streptomycin resistance of *Amoeba proteus*. J. Protozool., **10**: 124–129.

CURRY, J., and GREENBERG, J. 1962. Filament formation in radioresistant mutants of *Escherichia coli* S after treatment with ultraviolet light and radio-mimetic agents. J. Bacteriol., **83**: 38–42.

DANIEL, M. R., DINGLE, J. T., and LUCY, J. A. 1961. Cobalt-tolerance and mucopolysaccharide production in rat dermal fibroblasts in culture. Exptl. Cell Res., **24**: 88–105.

DARNELL, J. E., JR., and SAWYER, T. K. 1959. Variation in plaque-forming ability among parental and clonal strains of HeLa cells. Virology, **8**: 223–229.

DARNELL, J. E., JR., and SAWYER, T. K. 1960. The basis for variation in sus-ceptibility to poliovirus in HeLa cells. Virology, **11**: 665–675.

DAVIDSON, J. D., 1958. Permeability of resistant L-1210 leukemia cells to 8-azaguanine and 6-mercaptopurine. Proc. Am. Assoc. Cancer Res., **2**: 290–291.

DAVIDSON, J. D., BRADLEY, T. R., ROOSA, R. A., and LAW, L. W. 1962. Purine nucleotide pyrophosphorylases in 8-azaguanine-sensitive and resistant P-388 leukemias. J. Natl. Cancer Inst., **29**: 789–803.

DAVIS, B. D. 1957. Physiological (phenotypic) mechanisms responsible for drug resistance. *In: Drug Resistance in Micro-organisms,* pp. 165–182. G. E. W. Wolstenholme and C. M. O'Connor, eds. Boston: Little, Brown & Company.

DAVIS, B. D., and MAAS, W. K. 1952. Analysis of the biochemical mechanism of drug resistance in certain bacterial mutants. Proc. Natl. Acad. Sci., **38**: 775–785.

DEAN, A. C. R., and HINSHELWOOD, C. 1953. Observations on bacterial adapta-tion. *In: Adaptations in Micro-organisms,* pp. 21–45. R. Davies and E. F. Gale, eds. Cambridge: The University Press.

DEAN, A. C. R., and HINSHELWOOD, C. 1957. Aspects of the problem of drug resistance in bacteria. *In: Drug Resistance in Micro-organisms,* pp. 4–29. G. E. W. Wolstenholme and C. M. O'Connor, eds. Boston: Little, Brown & Company.

DEMEREC, M. 1945. Production of staphylococcus strains resistant to various concentrations of penicillin. Proc. Natl. Acad. Sci., **31**: 16–24.

DEMEREC, M. 1948. Origin of bacterial resistance to antibiotics. J. Bacteriol., **56**: 63–74.

DEMEREC, M. 1951. Studies of the streptomycin-resistance system of mutations in *E. coli.* Genetics, **36**: 585–597.

DEMEREC, M. 1957. Genetic aspects of drug resistance. *In: Drug Resistance in Micro-organisms,* pp. 47–63. G. E. W. Wolstenholme and C. M. O'Con-nor, eds. Boston: Little, Brown & Company.

DESERRES, F. J. 1961. Some aspects of the influence of environment on the radiosensitivity of micro-organisms. *In: Microbial Reaction to Environ-ment,* pp. 196–216. G. G. Meynell and H. Gooder, eds. Cambridge: The University Press.

DJORDJEVIC, B., and SZYBALSKI, W. 1960. Genetics of human cell lines. III. In-corporation of 5-bromo- and 5-iododeoxyuridine into the deoxyribonucleic acid of human cells and its effect on radiation sensitivity. J. Exptl. Med., 112: 509–531.

DRABBLE, W. T., and HINSHELWOOD, C. 1961. Development of resistance to streptomycin by *Bact. lactis aerogenes* (*Aerobacter aerogenes*). I. The role of mutation and of physiological adaptation. Proc. Roy. Soc. (London) Ser. B, 154: 449–462.

DUSCHINSKY, R., PLEVEN, E., and HEIDELBERGER, C. 1957. The synthesis of 5-fluoropyrimidines. J. Am. Chem. Soc., 79: 4559–4560.

EHRLICH, P. 1907. Chemotherapeutische Trypanosomen-Studien. Berlin. klin. Wochschr., 310: 341–344.

ELION, G. B., SINGER, S., and HITCHINGS, G. H. 1954. Microbiological effects of 6-mercaptopurine. Ann. N. Y. Acad. Sci., 60: 200–206.

ELION, G. B., VANDERWERFF, H., HITCHINGS, G. H., BALIS, M. E., LEVIN, D. H., and BROWN, G. B. 1953. Purine metabolism of a diaminopurine-resistant strain of *Lactobacillus casei*. J. Biol. Chem., 200: 7–16.

ELLIS, D. B., and LePAGE, G. A. 1963. Biochemical studies of resistance to 6-thioguanine. Cancer Res., 23: 436–443.

EPHRUSSI, B. 1958. The cytoplasm and somatic cell variation. J. Cellular Comp. Physiol., 52(Suppl. 1): 35–53.

ERIKSON, R. L., and SZYBALSKI, W. 1961. Molecular radiobiology of human cell lines. I. Comparative sensitivity to X-rays and ultraviolet light of cells containing halogen-substituted DNA. Biochem. Biophys. Res. Commun., 4: 258–261.

FARBER, S., DIAMOND, L. K., MERCER, R. D., SYLVESTER, R. F., JR., and WOLFF, J. A. 1948. Temporary remissions in acute leukemia in children produced by folic acid antagonist, 4-aminopteroylglutamic acid (aminopterin). New Engl. J. Med., 238: 787–793.

FISCHER, G. A. 1959. Nutritional and amethopterin-resistant characteristics of leukemic clones. Cancer Res., 19: 372–376.

FISCHER, G. A. 1961. Increased levels of folic acid reductase as a mechanism of resistance to amethopterin in leukemic cells. Biochem. Pharmacol., 7: 75–77.

FISCHER, G. A. 1962. Defective transport of amethopterin (methotrexate) as a mechanism of resistance to the antimetabolite in L-5178Y leukemic cells. Biochem. Pharmacol., 11: 1233–1234.

FREED, J. J. 1962. Continuous cultivation of cells derived from haploid *Rana pipiens* embryos. Exptl. Cell Res., 26: 327–333.

GAREN, A., and KOZLOFF, L. M. 1959. The initiation of bacteriophage infection. *In: The Viruses*, Vol. 2, pp. 203–236. F. M. Burnet and W. M. Stanley, eds. New York: Academic Press, Inc.

GILLHAM, N. W. 1963a. The nature of exceptions to the pattern of uniparental inheritance for high level streptomycin resistance in *Chlamydomonas reinhardi*. Genetics, 48: 431–439.

GILLHAM, N. W. 1963b. Transmission and segregation of a non-chromosomal factor controlling streptomycin resistance in diploid   *Chlamydomonas*. Nature, 200: 294.

GILLHAM, N. W., and LEVINE, R. P. 1962. Studies on the origin of streptomycin resistant mutants in *Chlamydomonas reinhardi*. Genetics, **47**: 1463–
1474.

GILMAN, A., and PHILIPS, F. S. 1946. The biological actions and therapeutic
applications of the β-chloroethyl amines and sulfides. Science, **103**: 409–
415.

GOLDSCHMIDT, E. P., MATNEY, T. S., and BAUSUM, H. T. 1962. Genetic
analyses of mutations from streptomycin dependence to independence in
Salmonella typhimurium. Genetics, **47**: 1475–1487.

GOLDSTEIN, M. N., SLOTNICK, I. J., and JOURNEY, L. J. 1960. *In vitro* studies
with HeLa cell lines sensitive and resistant to actinomycin D. Ann. N. Y.
Acad. Sci., **89**: 474–483.

GROSSER, B. I., SWEAT, M. L., BERLINER, D. L., and DOUGHERTY, T. F. 1962.
Comparison of cortisol metabolism by two variants of cultured fibroblasts.
Arch. Biochem. Biophys., **96**: 259–264.

HAAS, V. H., and STEWART, S. E. 1956. Sparing effect of A-methopterin and
guanazolo in mice infected with virus of lymphocytic choriomeningitis.
Virology, **2**: 511–516.

HAKALA, M. T., LAW, L. W., and WELCH, A. D. 1956. Inhibitory activity of
6-azauracil, 6-uracil methyl sulfone, and related compounds on the growth
of mouse lymphomas and sarcoma 180. Proc. Am. Assoc. Cancer Res.,
2: 113.

HAKALA, M. T., ZAKRZEWSKI, S. F., and NICHOL, C. A. 1961. Relation of folic
acid reductase to amethopterin resistance in cultured mammalian cells.
J. Biol. Chem., **236**: 952–958.

HANDSCHUMACHER, R. E. 1957. Studies of bacterial resistance to 6-azauracil
and its riboside. Biochim. et Biophys. Acta, **23**: 428–430.

HANDSCHUMACHER, R. E., and WELCH, A. D. 1960. Agents which influence
nucleic acid metabolism. *In: The Nucleic Acids*, Vol. 3, pp. 453–526.
E. Chargaff and J. N. Davidson, eds. New York: Academic Press, Inc.

HARADA, K., SUZUKI, M., KAMEDA, M., and MITSUHASHI, S. 1960. On the drug-
resistance of enteric bacteria. 2. Transmission of the drug-resistance among
Enterobacteriaceae. Japan. J. Exptl. Med., **30**: 289–299.

HARRIS, M. 1960. Specificity and cross-reactions in a strain of pig kidney cells
resistant to 2,6-diaminopurine. Exptl. Cell Res., **21**: 439–442.

HARRIS, M. 1961. Evaluation of drug resistance in cell cultures by differential
toxicity tests. J. Natl. Cancer Inst., **26**: 13–18.

HARRIS, M., and RUDDLE, F. H. 1960. Growth and chromosome studies on drug
resistant lines of cells in tissue culture. *In: Cell Physiology of Neoplasia*,
pp. 524–546. Austin: University of Texas Press.

HARTMAN, P. E. 1957. Transduction: A comparative review. *In: A Symposium
on the Chemical Basis of Heredity*, pp. 408–467. W. D. McElroy and
B. Glass, eds. Baltimore: The Johns Hopkins Press.

HASHIMOTO, K. 1960. Streptomycin resistance in *Escherichia coli* analyzed by
transduction. Genetics, **45**: 49–62.

HAUSCHKA, T. S. 1958. Correlation of chromosomal and physiologic changes in tumors. J. Cellular Comp. Physiol., **52**(Suppl. 1): 197–233.

HEIDELBERGER, C. 1961. Nucleic acid synthesis and mechanism of action of fluoropyrimidines. *In: Biological Approaches to Cancer Chemotherapy*, pp. 47–58. R. J. C. Harris, ed. New York: Academic Press, Inc.

HEIDELBERGER, C., GHOBAR, A., BAKER, R. K., and MUKHERJEE, K. L. 1960. Studies on fluorinated pyrimidines. X. *In vivo* studies on tumor resistance. Cancer Res., **20**: 897–902.

HEIDELBERGER, C., GRIESBACH, L., CRUZ, O., SCHNITZER, R. J., and GRUN-BERG, E. 1958. Fluorinated pyrimidines. VI. Effects of 5-fluorouridine and 5-fluoro-2'-deoxyuridine on transplanted tumors. Proc. Soc. Exptl. Biol. Med., **97**: 470–475.

HEIDELBERGER, C., KALDOR, G., MUKHERJEE, K. L., and DANNEBERG, P. B. 1960. Studies on fluorinated pyrimidines. XI. *In vitro* studies on tumor resistance. Cancer Res., **20**: 903–909.

HENLE, W. 1963. Interference and interferon in persistent viral infections of cell cultures. J. Immunol., **91**: 145–150.

HERZENBERG, L. A. 1962. I. Steps toward a genetics of somatic cells in culture. II. Maternal isoimmunization as a result of breeding in the mouse. J. Cellular Comp. Physiol., **60**(Suppl. 1): 145–157.

HILL, R. F., and SIMSON, E. 1961. A study of radiosensitive and radioresistant mutants of *Escherichia coli* strain B. J. Gen. Microbiol., **24**: 1–14.

HIRONO, I. 1955. Some properties of Yoshida sarcoma cells resistant to methyl-bis-(β-chlorethyl)-amine N-oxide. Proc. Soc. Exptl. Biol. Med., **88**: 147–149.

HOTCHKISS, R. D. 1951. Transfer of penicillin resistance in pneumococci by the desoxyribonucleate derived from resistant cultures. Cold Spring Harbor Symp. Quant. Biol., **16**: 457–461.

HSU, T. C., and SOMERS, C. E. 1961. Effect of 5-bromodeoxyuridine on mammalian chromosomes. Proc. Natl. Acad. Sci., **47**: 396–403.

HSU, T. C., and SOMERS, C. E. 1962. Properties of L cells resistant to 5-bromodeoxyuridine. Exptl. Cell Res., **26**: 404–410.

HUMPHREYS, S. R., VENDITTI, J. M., MANTEL, N., and GOLDIN, A. 1956. Observations on a leukemic cell variant in mice. J. Natl. Cancer Inst., **17**: 447–457.

ISAACS, A., and LINDENMANN, J. 1957. Virus interference. I. The interferon. Proc. Roy. Soc. (London) Ser. B., **147**: 258–267.

JACKSON, H. 1954. The development of resistance in the Walker carcinosarcoma to the action of triethylene melamine. Brit. J. Cancer, **8**: 336–345.

JACOB, F., and WOLLMAN, E. L. 1961. Sexuality and the genetics of bacteria. New York: Academic Press, Inc. 374 pp.

JACOBSON, W. 1961. Biological aspects of chemotherapy with folic acid antagonists. *In: Biological Approaches to Cancer Chemotherapy*, pp. 149–166. R. J. C. Harris, ed. New York: Academic Press, Inc.

JACOBSON, W., and CATHIE, I. A. B. 1960a. The inactivation of folic acid antagonists by normal and leukaemic cells. Biochem. Pharmacol., **5**: 130–142.

JACOBSON, W., and CATHIE, I. A. B. 1960b. The nature of aminopterin inactivated by normal and leukaemic tissues. Biochem. Pharmacol., **5**: 143–156.

JOLLOS, V. 1921. Experimentelle Protistenstudien. I. Untersuchungen über Variabilität und Vererbung bei Infusorien. Arch. Protistenk., **43**: 1–222.

KALLE, G. P., and GOTTS, J. S. 1963. Genetic alteration of adenylic pyrophosphorylase in *Salmonella*. Science, **142**: 680–681.

KARNOFSKY, D. A. (ed.) 1958. Comparative clinical and biological effects of alkylating agents. Ann. N. Y. Acad. Sci., **68**: 657–1266.

KARNOFSKY, D. A., and CLARKSON, B. D. 1963. Cellular effects of anticancer drugs. Ann. Rev. Pharmacol., **3**: 357–428.

KELLEY, G. G., VAIL, M. H., ADAMSON, D. J., and PALMER, E. A. 1961. The isolation and propagation of human epidermoid carcinoma cells resistant to 6-mercaptopurine. Am. J. Hyg., **73**: 231–235.

KIDDER, G. W., DEWEY, V. C., PARKS, R. E., JR., and WOODSIDE, G. L. 1949. Purine metabolism in *Tetrahymena* and its relation to malignant cells in mice. Science, **109**: 511–514.

KIT, S., DUBBS, D. R., PIEKARSKI, L. J., and HSU, T. C. 1963. Deletion of thymidine kinase activity from L cells resistant to bromodeoxyuridine. Exptl. Cell Res., **31**: 297–312.

KLEIN, G. 1959. Variation and selection in tumor cell populations. Can. Cancer Conf., **3**: 215–240.

KLEIN, G. 1961. Population changes and drug resistance in tumors. *In: Biological Approaches to Cancer Chemotherapy*, pp. 210–217. R. J. C. Harris, ed. New York: Academic Press, Inc.

KLEIN, G. 1963. Genetics of somatic cells. *In: Methodology in Mammalian Genetics*, pp. 407–468. W. J. Burdette, ed. San Francisco: Holden-Day, Inc.

KLEIN, G., and KLEIN, E. 1957. The evolution of independence from specific growth stimulation and inhibition in mammalian tumour-cell populations. Symp. Soc. Exptl. Biol., **11**: 305–328.

KORNBERG, A., LIEBERMAN, I., and SIMMS, E. S. 1955. Enzymatic synthesis of purine nucleotides. J. Biol. Chem., **215**: 417–427.

LAM, G. T., and SEVAG, M. G. 1955. Mechanism of the development of resistance to streptomycin. II. Biochemical differences of replica colonies. J. Bacteriol., **69**: 184–187.

LAW, L. W. 1951a. Observations on properties of leukemic cells resistant to folic acid antagonists. J. Natl. Cancer Inst., **11**: 849–865.

LAW, L. W. 1951b. Response of a resistant variant of leukemic cells to an antagonist of pteroylglutamic acid. Proc. Soc. Exptl. Biol. Med., **77**: 340–344.

LAW, L. W. 1951c. Resistance in leukemic cells to a guanine analog, 8-azaguanine. Proc. Soc. Exptl. Biol. Med., **78**: 499–502.

LAW, L. W. 1952a. Origin of the resistance of leukaemic cells to folic acid antagonists. Nature, **169**: 628–629.

LAW, L. W. 1952b. Mechanisms of resistance and dependence in growth of leukemic cells. Tex. Repts. Biol. Med., **10**: 571–597.

LAW, L. W. 1953. Resistance in leukemic cells to an adenine antagonist, 6-mercaptopurine. Proc. Soc. Exptl. Biol. Med., **84**: 409–412.

LAW, L. W. 1954a. Studies on transformations in leukemic cells of the mouse. J. Natl. Cancer Inst., **15**: 817–834.

LAW, L. W. 1954b. Studies on transformations to resistance and dependence in leukemic cells. *In: Origins of Resistance to Toxic Agents,* pp. 268–286. M. G. Sevag, R. D. Reid, and O. E. Reynolds, eds. New York: Academic Press, Inc.

LAW, L. W. 1956. Differences between cancers in terms of evolution of drug resistance. Cancer Res., **16**: 698–716.

LAW, L. W. 1958. Some aspects of drug resistance in neoplasms. Ann. N. Y. Acad. Sci., **71**: 976–993.

LAW, L. W., and BOYLE, P. J. 1950. Development of resistance to folic acid antagonists in a transplantable lymphoid leukemia. Proc. Soc. Exptl. Biol. Med., **74**: 599–602.

LAW, L. W., and DUNN, T. B. 1951. Effects of a filtrable, self-propagating contaminant on a transplantable acute lymphoid leukemia in mice. J. Natl. Cancer Inst., **11**: 1037–1055.

LAW, L. W., TAORMINA, V., and BOYLE, P. J. 1954. Response of acute lymphocytic leukemias to the purine antagonist 6-mercaptopurine. Ann. N. Y. Acad. Sci., **60**: 244–250.

LEDERBERG, J. 1950. The selection of genetic recombinations with bacterial growth inhibitors. J. Bacteriol., **59**: 211–215.

LEDERBERG, J. 1951. Streptomycin resistance: A genetically recessive mutation. J. Bacteriol., **61**: 549–550.

LEDERBERG, J. 1957. Discussion following paper by A. C. R. Dean and C. Hinshelwood. *In: Drug Resistance in Micro-organisms,* pp. 24–29. G. E. W. Wolstenholme and C. M. O'Connor, eds. Boston: Little, Brown & Company.

LEDERBERG, J., and LEDERBERG, E. M. 1952. Replica plating and indirect selection of bacterial mutants. J. Bacteriol., **63**: 399–406.

LEIDY, G., SPRUNT, K., REDMAN, W., and ALEXANDER, H. E. 1959. Sensitivity of populations of clonal lines of HeLa cells to polioviruses. Proc. Soc. Exptl. Biol. Med., **102**: 81–85.

LEVENBERG, B., MELNICK, I., and BUCHANAN, J. M. 1957. Biosynthesis of the purines. XV. The effect of aza-L-serine and 6-diazo-5-oxo-L-norleucine on inosinic acid biosynthesis *de novo.* J. Biol. Chem., **225**: 163–176.

LIEBERMAN, I., and OVE, P. 1959a. Isolation and study of mutants from mammalian cells in culture. Proc. Natl. Acad. Sci., **45**: 867–872.

LIEBERMAN, I., and OVE, P. 1959b. Estimation of mutation rates with mammalian cells in culture. Proc. Natl. Acad. Sci., **45**: 872–877.

LIEBERMAN, I., and OVE, P. 1960. Enzyme studies with mutant mammalian cells. J. Biol. Chem., **235**: 1765–1768.

LURIA, S. E. 1960. Viruses, cancer cells, and the genetic concept of virus infection. Cancer Res., **20**: 677–688.

MAGILL, G. B., MYERS, W. P. L., REILLY, H. C., PUTNAM, R. C., MAGILL, J. W., SYKES, M. P., ESCHER, G. C., KARNOFSKY, D. A., and BURCHENAL, J. H. 1957. Pharmacological and initial therapeutic observations on 6-diazo-5-oxo-L-norleucine (DON) in human neoplastic disease. Cancer, **10**: 1138–1150.

MANDEL, H. G. 1955. Some aspects of the metabolism of 8-azaguanine. *In: Antimetabolites and Cancer*, pp. 199–218. C. P. Rhoads, ed. Washington: Am. Assoc. Advan. Sci.

MANDEL, H. G. 1959. The physiological disposition of some anticancer drugs. Pharmacol. Revs., **11**: 743–838.

MATHIAS, A. P., and FISCHER, G. A. 1962. Transformation experiments with murine lymphoblastic cells (L-5178Y) grown in culture. Biochem. Pharmacol., **11**: 69–78.

METZGAR, D. P., JR., and MOSKOWITZ, M. 1963a. Studies on the effect of streptomycin on mammalian cells in culture. I. Isolation of resistant strains. Exptl. Cell Res., **30**: 379–387.

METZGAR, D. P., JR., and MOSKOWITZ, M. 1963b. Studies on the effect of streptomycin on mammalian cells in culture. II. Effect on mixtures of sensitive and resistant strains. Exptl. Cell Res., **30**: 388–392.

MINER, R. W. (ed.) 1954. 6-mercaptopurine. Ann. N. Y. Acad. Sci., **60**: 183–508.

MORRIS, N. R., and FISCHER, G. A. 1960. Studies concerning inhibition of the synthesis of deoxycytidine by phosphorylated derivatives of thymidine. Biochim. et Biophys. Acta, **42**: 183–184.

NAKANO, M. 1959. The development of variants of HeLa cells possessing resistance against the cytopathogenic effect of ECHO viruses. Japan. J. Med. Sci. Biol., **12**: 79–97.

NANNEY, D. L. 1958. Epigenetic control systems. Proc. Natl. Acad. Sci., **44**: 712–717.

NAONO, S., and GROS, F. 1960. Synthèse par *E. coli* d'une phosphatase modifiée en présence d'un analogue pyrimidique. Compt. Rend. Acad. Sci., **250**: 3889–3891.

NEWCOMBE, H. B. 1955. Spontaneous and induced mutations to drug resistance in *Escherichia coli*. *In: Origins of Resistance to Toxic Agents*, pp. 4–19. M. G. Sevag, R. D. Reid, and O. E. Reynolds, eds. New York: Academic Press, Inc.

NEWCOMBE, H. B., and HAWIRKO, R. 1949. Spontaneous mutation to streptomycin resistance and dependence in *Escherichia coli*. J. Bacteriol. **57**: 565–572.

NEWCOMBE, H. B., and NYHOLM, M. H. 1950. The inheritance of streptomycin resistance and dependence in crosses of *Escherichia coli*. Genetics, **35**: 603–611.

NICHOL, C. A. 1957. Studies on resistance to folic acid antagonists. *In: The Leukemias: Etiology, Pathophysiology, and Treatment*, pp. 583–604.

J. W. Rebuck, F. H. Bethell, and R. W. Monto, eds. New York: Academic Press, Inc.

OAKBERG, E. F., and LURIA, S. E. 1947. Mutations to sulfonamide resistance in *Staphylococcus aureus*. Genetics, **32**: 249–261.

PARKS, R. E., JR. 1963. Cancer chemotherapy with purine antimetabolites. *In: Biochemical Frontiers in Medicine*, pp. 245–273. H. Busch, ed. Boston: Little, Brown & Company.

PASTERNAK, C. A., FISCHER, G. A., and HANDSCHUMACHER, R. E. 1961. Alterations in pyrimidine metabolism in L-5178Y leukemia cells resistant to 6-azauridine. Cancer Res., **21**: 110–117.

PATERSON, A. R. P. 1962. Resistance to 6-mercaptopurine. II. The synthesis of thioinosinate in a 6-mercaptopurine-resistant subline of the Ehrlich ascites carcinoma. Can. J. Bioch. Physiol., **40**: 195–206.

PATERSON, A. R. P., and HORI, A. 1962. Resistance to 6-mercaptopurine. I. Biochemical differences between the Ehrlich ascites carcinoma and a 6-mercaptopurine-resistant subline. Can. J. Bioch. Physiol., **40**: 181–194.

PATO, M. L., and BROWN, G. M. 1963. Mechanisms of resistance of *Escherichia coli* to sulfonamides. Arch. Biochem. Biophys., **103**: 443–448.

PAYNE, J. I., HARTMAN, P. E., MUDD, S., and PHILLIPS, A. W. 1956. Cytological analysis of ultraviolet-irradiated *Escherichia coli*. III. Reactions of a sensitive strain and its resistant mutants. J. Bacteriol., **72**: 461–472.

PETERING, H. G. 1952. Folic acid antagonists. Physiol. Revs., **32**: 197–213.

PETERS, R. A. 1952. Lethal synthesis. Proc. Roy. Soc. (London) Ser. B., **139**: 143–170.

POTTER, M. 1958. Variation in resistance patterns in different neoplasms. Ann. N. Y. Acad. Sci., **76**: 630–642.

POTTER, M., and LAW, L. W. 1957. Studies of a plasma-cell neoplasm of the mouse. I. Characterization of neoplasm 70429, including its sensitivity to various antimetabolites with rapid development of resistance to azaserine, DON, and N-methylformamide. J. Natl. Cancer Inst., **18**: 413–441.

PUCK, T. T. 1959. Quantitative studies of mammalian cells *in vitro*. Rev. Mod. Phys., **31**: 433–448.

RAPP, F. 1960. Observations of measles virus infection of human cells. III. Correlation of properties of clones of H.Ep.-2 cells with their susceptibility to infection. Virology, **10**: 86–96.

RAVEN, R. W. (ed.) 1959. Cancer. Vol. 6. Part X: Chemotherapy, pp. 1–342. London: Butterworth and Company.

RAVIN, A. W. 1961. The genetics of transformation. Advan. Genet., **10**: 61–163.

REICHARD, P., SKÖLD, O., and KLEIN, G. 1959. Possible enzymatic mechanism for the development of resistance against fluorouracil in ascites tumors. Nature, **183**: 939–941.

REICHARD, P., SKÖLD, O., KLEIN, G., RÉVÉSZ, L., and MAGNUSSON, P. 1962. Studies on resistance against 5-fluorouracil. I. Enzymes of the uracil pathway during development of resistance. Cancer Res., **22**: 235–243.

RHYNAS, P. O. W., and NEWCOMBE, H. B. 1960. A heritable change in radiation resistance of strain L mouse cells. Exptl. Cell Res., **21**: 326–331.

Rixon, R. H., and Whitfield, J. F. 1960. Comparison of the effects of ultraviolet light on multiplication of normal and X-ray resistant mouse cells. Exptl. Cell Res., **20**: 220–222.

Roosa, R. A., Bradley, T. R., Law, L. W., and Herzenberg, L. A. 1962. Characterization of resistance to amethopterin, 8-azaguanine, and several fluorinated pyrimidines in the murine lymphocytic neoplasm, P-388. J. Cellular Comp. Physiol., **60**: 109–126.

Sager, R. 1954. Mendelian and non-Mendelian inheritance of streptomycin resistance in *Chlamydomonas reinhardi*. Proc. Natl. Acad. Sci., **40**: 356–363.

Sager, R. 1955. Inheritance in the green alga *Chlamydomonas reinhardi*. Genetics, **40**: 476–489.

Sager, R. 1960. Genetic systems in *Chlamydomonas*. Science, **132**: 1459–1465.

Sager, R. 1961. Chromosomal and non-chromosomal determinants in *Chlamydomonas*. Pathologie-Biologie (Paris), **9**: 760–761.

Sager, R. 1962. Streptomycin as a mutagen for nonchromosomal genes. Proc. Natl. Acad. Sci., **48**: 2018–2026.

Sager, R., and Ishida, M. R. 1963. Chloroplast DNA in *Chlamydomonas*. Proc. Natl. Acad. Sci., **50**: 725–730.

Sager, R., and Ramanis, Z. 1963. The particulate nature of nonchromosomal genes in *Chlamydomonas*. Proc. Natl. Acad. Sci., **50**: 260–268.

Sager, R., and Tsubo, Y. 1961. Genetic analysis of streptomycin-resistance and dependence in *Chlamydomonas*. Z. Vererbungslehre, **92**: 430–438.

Sager, R., and Tsubo, Y. 1962. Mutagenic effects of streptomycin in *Chlamydomonas*. Arch. Mikrobiol., **42**: 159–175.

Sartorelli, A. C., and LePage, G. A. 1958. The development and biochemical characterization of resistance to azaserine in a TA3 ascites carcinoma. Cancer Res., **18**: 457–463.

Sartorelli, A. C., LePage, G. A., and Moore, E. C. 1958. Metabolic effects of 6-thioguanine. I. Studies on thioguanine-resistant and sensitive Ehrlich ascites cells. Cancer Res., **18**: 1232–1239.

Schnitzer, R. J. 1963. Drug resistance in chemotherapy. *In: Experimental Chemotherapy*, Vol. 1, pp. 81–128. R. J. Schnitzer and F. Hawking, eds. New York: Academic Press, Inc.

Schnitzer, R. J., and Grunberg, E. 1957. Drug resistance of microorganisms. New York: Academic Press, Inc. 395 pp.

Selawry, O. S., Goldstein, M. N., and McCormick, T. 1957. Hyperthermia in tissue-cultured cells of malignant origin. Cancer Res., **17**: 785–791.

Sevag, M. G. 1955. Protein molecule resistance to microbicides, mutations, and related problems. *In: Origins of Resistance to Toxic Agents*, pp. 370–408. M. G. Sevag, R. D. Reid, and O. E. Reynolds, eds. New York: Academic Press, Inc.

Sirotnak, D. J., and Hutchison, D. J. 1959. Absorption of deoxyribonucleic acid by mouse lymphoma cells. Biochim. et Biophys. Acta, **36**: 246–248.

Skipper, H. E., Bennett, L. L., Jr., and Law, L. W. 1952. Effects of A-methopterin on formate incorporation into the nucleic acids of susceptible and resistant leukemic cells. Cancer Res., **12**: 677–679.

SKÖLD, O. 1963. Studies on resistance against 5-fluorouracil. IV. Evidence for an altered uridine kinase in resistant cells. Biochim. et Biophys. Acta, **76**: 160–162.

SNEATH, P. H. A. 1955. Proof of the spontaneity of a mutation to penicillinase production in *Bacillus cereus*. J. Gen. Microbiol., **13**: 561–568.

STONE, D. 1962. Selection of Hela cell sublines resistant to steroids from a HeLa cell strain sensitive to the growth inhibitory influences of desoxy-corticosterone, progesterone, and testosterone. Endocrinology, **71**: 233–237.

STONE, D., and KANG, Y. S. 1962. Differences in chromosome stemlines of a strain of HeLa cells inhibited in growth by certain steroids, and of steroid-resistant sublines selected from the sensitive strain. Endocrinology, **71**: 238–243.

SUGUIRA, K., and STOCK, C. C. 1955. IV. Effect of O-diazoacetyl-L-serine (azaserine) on growth of various mouse and rat tumors. Proc. Soc. Exptl. Biol. Med., **88**: 127–129.

SZYBALSKA, E. H., and SZYBALSKI, W. 1962. Genetics of human cell lines. IV. DNA-mediated heritable transformation of a biochemical trait. Proc. Natl. Acad. Sci., **48**: 2026–2034.

SZYBALSKI, W. 1959. Genetics of human cell lines. II. Method for determination of mutation rates to drug resistance. Exptl. Cell Res., **18**: 588–591.

SZYBALSKI, W., and BRYSON, V. 1952. Genetic studies on microbial cross resistance to toxic agents. I. Cross resistance of *Escherichia coli* to fifteen antibiotics. J. Bacteriol., **64**: 489–499.

SZYBALSKI, W., and BRYSON, V. 1953. One step resistance to isoniazid and sodium p-aminosalicylate. J. Bacteriol., **66**: 468–469.

SZYBALSKI, W., and BRYSON, V. 1955. Origin of drug resistance in microorganisms. *In: Origins of Resistance to Toxic Agents*, pp. 20–41. M. G. Sevag, R. D. Reid, and O. E. Reynolds, eds. New York: Academic Press, Inc.

SZYBALSKI, W., and SMITH, M. J. 1959a. Genetics of human cell lines. I. 8-azaguanine resistance, a selective "single-step" marker. Proc. Soc. Exptl. Biol. Med., **101**: 662–666.

SZYBALSKI, W., and SMITH, M. J. 1959b. Effect of ultraviolet light on mutation to 8-azaguanine resistance in a human cell line. Federation Proc., **18**: 336.

SZYBALSKI, W., and SZYBALSKA, E. H. 1962. Approaches to the genetic analysis of mammalian cells. Drug sensitivity as a genetic marker. Univ. of Mich. Med. Bull., **28**: 277–293.

SZYBALSKI, W., SZYBALSKA, E. H., and BROCKMAN, R. W. 1961. Biochemical basis of sequential mutations toward resistance to purine analogs in human cell lines. Proc. Am. Assoc. Cancer Res., **3**: 272.

SZYBALSKI, W., SZYBALSKA, E. H., and RAGNI, G. 1962. Genetic studies with human cell lines. Natl. Cancer Inst. Monogr., **7**: 75–89.

TIMMIS, G. M. 1961. Antagonists of purine and pyrimidine metabolites and of folic acid. Advan. Cancer Res., **6**: 369–401.

TOMIZAWA, S., and ARONOW, L. 1960. Studies on drug resistance in mammalian cells. II. 6-mercaptopurine resistance in mouse fibroblasts. J. Pharmacol. Exptl. Therap., **128**: 107–114.

VOGT, M. 1958. A genetic change in a tissue culture line of neoplastic cells. J. Cellular Comp. Physiol., **52**(Suppl. 1): 271–285.

VOGT, M. 1959. A study of the relationship between karyotype and phenotype in cloned lines of strain HeLa. Genetics, **44**: 1257–1270.

VOGT, M., and DULBECCO, R. 1958. Properties of a HeLa cell culture with increased resistance to poliomyelitis virus. Virology, **5**: 425–434.

WAGNER, R. R. 1963a. Cellular resistance to viral infection, with particular reference to endogenous interferon. Bacteriol. Revs., **27**: 72–86.

WAGNER, R. R. 1963b. The interferons: cellular inhibitors of viral infection. Ann. Rev. Microbiol., **17**: 285–296.

WATANABE, T. 1963. Infective heredity of multiple drug resistance in bacteria. Bacteriol. Revs., **27**: 87–115.

WATANABE, T., and FUKASAWA, T. 1961a. Episome-mediated transfer of drug resistance in *Enterobacteriaceae*. I. Transfer of resistance factors by conjugation. J. Bacteriol., **81**: 669–678.

WATANABE, T., and FUKASAWA, T. 1961b. Episome-mediated transfer of drug resistance in *Enterobacteriaceae*. II. Elimination of resistance factors with acridine dyes. J. Bacteriol., **81**: 679–683.

WATANABE, T., and FUKASAWA, T. 1961c. Episome-mediated transfer of drug resistance in *Enterobacteriaceae*. III. Transduction of resistance factors. J. Bacteriol., **82**: 202–209.

WAY, J. L., and PARKS, R. E. 1958. Enzymatic synthesis of 5'-phosphate nucleotides of purine analogues. J. Biol. Chem., **231**: 467–480.

WELCH, A. D. 1959. The problem of drug resistance in cancer chemotherapy. Cancer Res., **19**: 359–371.

WELCH, A. D. 1961. Some metabolic approaches to cancer chemotherapy. Cancer Res., **21**: 1475–1490.

WERKHEISER, W. C. 1961. Specific binding of 4-amino folic acid analogues by folic acid reductase. J. Biol. Chem. **236**: 888–893.

WHITFIELD, J. F., and RIXON, R. H. 1960a. Radiation resistant derivatives of L strain mouse cells. Exptl. Cell Res., **19**: 531–538.

WHITFIELD, J. F., and RIXON, R. H. 1960b. Some properties of radiation resistant derivatives of L strain mouse cells. Exptl. Cell Res., **20**: 242–244.

WHITFIELD, J. F., and RIXON, R. H. 1961. Distinctive chromosome markers of normal and radioresistant derivatives of L strain mouse cells. Exptl. Cell Res., **23**: 412–415.

WITKIN, E. M. 1947. Genetics of resistance to radiation in *Escherichia coli*. Genetics, **32**: 221–248.

WOLF, B., and HOTCHKISS, R. D. 1963. Genetically modified folic acid synthesizing enzymes of pneumococcus. Biochemistry, **2**: 145–150.

WOLSTENHOLME, G. E. W., and O'CONNOR, C. M. (eds.) 1957. Drug resistance in micro-organisms. Boston: Little, Brown & Company. 352 pp.

ZINDER, N. D., and LEDERBERG, J. 1952. Genetic exchange in *Salmonella*. J. Bacteriol., **64**: 679–699.

Carcinogenesis
in vitro

Neoplastic transformation is plainly a problem in cellular ecology, one in which the outcome is to be measured in terms of population dynamics. In this shifting transition, there can be little doubt that the intact organism forms an essential frame of reference. It does not follow, however, that the inception of tumors is dependent on systemic changes, and in fact, all available evidence points to neoplastic conversion as a localized series of cellular events. Carcinogenesis thus seems to be a phenomenon well suited to analysis in isolated cell systems, provided assays of appropriate specificity can be devised. Many cell properties known to alter commonly on neoplastic transformation can be considered as indices; for example, changes in morphology, karyotype, growth behavior, or metabolic pattern. Various of these have proved useful in the monitoring of transitional stages, but their causal relation to carcinogenesis *in vitro,* as *in vivo,* remains to be defined. The only indubitable proof that neoplastic conversion has occurred in an isolated population is the demonstration by implantation in appropriate hosts that the cells in question can grow progressively and bring about death of the organism. Failure to do so does not necessarily mean that the cells are "normal" or incapable of malignant growth under other conditions, but a positive result is unambiguous and unmistakable.

TUMOR PRODUCTION WITH CELL STRAINS

The criteria for malignant transformation have not to date been fulfilled for any primary cell strains in serial propagation. But in a number of well-defined instances, permanent lines have acquired a

375

reproducible tumor-producing ability, as revealed by injection into appropriate hosts. For mouse cells, at least, the incidence of neoplastic change appears to be relatively high *in vitro,* and it is possible that most of these populations may become potentially malignant if maintained in serial culture for a sufficient length of time. There are no clear indications that malignant transformations are similarly prevalent in permanent cell lines from other species, but in the absence of inbred animals for assay in many of these, a direct test is difficult.

Transformation in Long-Term Culture The actual demonstration that neoplastic conversion can take place in isolated systems stems from the discoveries of Gey, Earle, and their collaborators more than two decades ago. These works represent a milestone in cancer research, and their significance has been heightened by the realization that no known carcinogen need be added to the culture system. It follows that the tendency of untreated populations to acquire tumor-producing properties in long-term culture must be carefully examined as a background for neoplastic transformations *in vitro* mediated more directly by the addition of viruses or other extrinsic agents.

Gey's experiments were first reported in 1941 and dealt with changes that occurred during serial propagation in a population of rat cells. These studies have subsequently been described in more detail (Firor and Gey, 1945; Gey, Gey, Firor, and Self, 1949; Gey, 1955). The cell strains in question had been isolated from adult subcutaneous areolar tissue, and after 4 months of cultivation, Gey observed an increased incidence of abnormal mitoses in one subline, with wide variation in the size and appearance of individual cells. On inoculating these cells into young rats, progressively growing tumors were obtained in a number of instances. The neoplasms arising from injections were sarcomas of differing cytological character and growth behavior. They increased progressively in size, metastasized, and could be serially transplanted in other animals of the same genotype. Morphological variations were also observed in another subline of the original rat cell strain after more than two years in culture. In this case, the altered cells showed a reduced mutual cohesion, rounded up, and tended to digest the plasma coagulum. They consistently produced tumors in inoculation into the inbred animals of origin, although none were obtained from the unaltered parental strain. Gey was unable to account for the neoplastic conversions observed, but he was inclined to stress the prolonged exposure of cells in culture to heterologous proteins in the nutrient medium as a causative factor. No known contact with chemical carcinogens or viral agents had occurred during the experimental period, and the remote possibility of stray gamma radiation from another investigation in the same laboratory was discounted.

Rat cells were also employed for studies on carcinogenesis *in vitro* by Goldblatt and Cameron (1953). Using a strain of fibroblasts derived from a five-day-old animal, these investigators exposed the cells to alternating anaerobic and aerobic conditions. The experimental design consisted of replacing the air phase in culture with nitrogen at regular intervals. In the course of two years, neoplastic transformations occurred on two occasions in the line treated with nitrogen, and these changes were confirmed by injecting cultures into animals of the strain of origin. No tumors were obtained from cultures maintained continuously in air, although the significance of this finding was lessened by the failure to use an inbred stock of rats for assay purposes. But numerous attempts to overcome a conceivable histocompatibility barrier did not result in takes with control cell populations. These measures included the use of X-irradiated or cortisone-treated hosts as well as inoculation into the anterior chamber of the eye as a favored location (Chapter 8). Goldblatt and Cameron had initiated this study on the assumption that neoplastic change might be favored by chronic exposure of cell populations to an environment poor in oxygen. However, the number of malignant conversions observed in their study is obviously too small to permit generalizations on this point. Whether tumors would eventually have developed with the control strain, after a longer period of culture, or from a broader sample of untreated cells is unknown, although the results of others make this a possibility.

Experiments with mouse cells have provided a more comprehensive picture of the neoplastic transformations that occur within untreated cells during long-term culture. Here, the carefully documented studies of Earle and his collaborators have established a wealth of descriptive information. Interestingly, this program began with a quite different objective, that of following the cellular changes which accompany the induction of tumors by chemical carcinogens (Earle and Voegtlin, 1938, 1940). For this purpose, strains of fibroblasts were established from the abdominal musculature of adult C_3H mice, with methylcholanthrene applied at graded levels to a spectrum of sublines in plasma culture. There was a partial inhibition of growth on addition of the carcinogen, but despite this initial toxicity, it proved possible to maintain treated populations in serial culture. Three strains were exposed to methylcholanthrene at 1 μg/ml for long periods, and all developed marked alterations in cell morphology and growth patterns. The cells in these cultures were short and compact, unlike the long, slender cells with terminal processes that had predominated in earlier passages. A marked tendency for lateral cohesion could be noted among the altered cells, giving the outgrowth zone a dense and compact character. Such changes appeared to be progressive with increasing exposure to methylcholanthrene, and tended to persist even when the addition of carcinogen was discontinued. They were most conspicuous in a strain that had been treated for over 200 days.

Recognizing the need to correlate degree of alteration with the ability of treated cells to produce tumors in mice, Earle initiated a second and larger experiment on carcinogenesis *in vitro* (Earle, 1943, 1944). A strain of mouse fibroblasts derived from adult subcutaneous tissue provided starting material, and was maintained in plasma culture without carcinogen for a preliminary period of 200 days. Thereafter, sublines were treated with methylcholanthrene at 1 μg/ml for intervals varying from 6 to 406 days, and were subsequently continued without further exposure in a stock medium consisting of chicken plasma with a supernatant containing horse serum, chick embryonic extract, and balanced saline. Typical morphological alterations similar to those observed earlier were noted in sublines of cells exposed to methylcholanthrene. Among the several strains, Earle found the degree of morphological alteration to be correlated with the duration of treatment with carcinogen, and these changes were especially marked in the subline exposed for the maximal period of 406 days (Figure 7.1). However, two lines maintained as control strains began to undergo morphological change several months after all the carcinogen-treated sublines had become altered. This observation seemed puzzling, since rigorous precautions had been taken throughout to avoid contaminating the control populations with trace amounts of methylcholanthrene. Nevertheless, these cultures eventually resembled the carcinogen-treated strains, although the degree of morphological alteration was not so great.

Equally unexpected were the results obtained when control and experimental cultures were injected into C_3H mice, using subcutaneous, intramuscular, and other routes (Earle and Nettleship, 1943; Nettleship and Earle, 1943). Two principal assays were carried out, one over a period of 3 months to a year after the beginning of carcinogen treatment, and a second at approximately two years, well beyond the longest periods of exposure to methylcholanthrene. Essentially similar results were obtained on both occasions, aside from quantitative variation. Contrary to what might have been predicted, there was a generally inverse correlation between increasing duration of exposure to carcinogen, with consequent heightening of morphological changes on the one hand, and ability to produce tumors on the other. All strains tested gave rise to tumors, but the highest proportion of positive inoculations (86

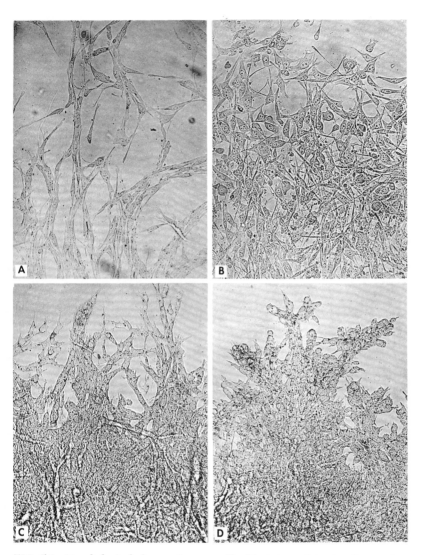

FIG. 7.1. Morphological changes in mouse fibroblasts treated *in vitro* for varying periods with methylcholanthrene. All photographs made of marginal areas at the glass interface of plasma cultures. (A) Strain D (untreated with carcinogen) after 5 years in culture. (B) Strain N (treated initially with methylcholanthrene at 1 μg/ml for 184 days) after nearly 5 years in culture. (C) An earlier culture of strain N, photographed after 2 years in culture. (D) Strain O (treated initially with methylcholanthrene at 1 μg/ml for 406 days) after 2 years in culture. (From Earle, Schilling, and Shelton, 1950.)

and 100 percent in the two tests, respectively) were obtained with one of the control populations. By contrast, the incidence of tumors obtained with methylcholanthrene-treated cells diminished sharply, and in the case of strains exposed for the two longest periods, amounted to only 7 and 2 percent, respectively.

Despite some unexplained discrepancies, these results showed clearly that the degree of morphological alteration of carcinogen-treated populations *in vitro* is not correlated with the ability to produce tumors on return to the intact organism, except in a negative sense. Curiously, the highly variant populations obtained by prolonged exposure to methylcholanthrene seemed to have a greatly reduced ability for autonomous proliferation when tested *in vivo*. But these and other tumors arising from injection of cell strains were unquestionably malignant. They emerged as typical sarcomas at the site of injection within a few days or weeks, and enlarged progressively to kill the host. Although the cells exposed for long periods to methylcholanthrene gave rise to only a few neoplasms on inoculation into C_3H mice, the tumors that did appear were more anaplastic and pleomorphic than those obtained from control strains or from strains treated with carcinogen for shorter intervals.

The paradoxes and uncertainties in these experimental findings led to a new round of investigation, reported eventually by Sanford, Earle, Shelton, Schilling, Duchesne, Likely, and Becker (1950). One of the objectives of these studies was to determine whether or not trace contamination of control cultures by methylcholanthrene could explain the neoplastic conversions previously noted in supposedly untreated cultures. To this end, eight strains of fibroblasts were isolated independently from the abdominal muscle of C_3H mice and were exposed after one month of culture to methylcholanthrene at minimal levels. Among various series, this concentration ranged from 0.001 to 0.22 $\mu g/ml$, and was applied continuously for a 21-day period. During 4 to 18 months of subsequent culture in carcinogen-free medium, tumors were obtained in assays from treated cells as well as from paired control cultures of identical origin. There was little if any significant difference in malignant potential between the two. In further tests, five series were exposed for 21 days to methylcholanthrene at dosages ranging from 0.00008 to 0.08 $\mu g/ml$. Over a period of 13 months, a total 319 of these cultures were injected into C_3H mice and only three tumors were obtained, one each from different experimental groups. During the same interval, four of 238 mice inoculated with untreated cultures developed sarcomas. Thus there is no evidence that exposure to methylcholanthrene at low levels increases the tendency of isolated cell strains to produce sarcomas on reinoculation, over and above the number obtained with untreated control cells.

A second objective in this study by Sanford and her co-workers was to explore more closely the relation between morphological alteration and neoplastic change. Even though long-continued modification seems to reduce the malignancy potential of isolated cells, this does not rule out the possibility that the initial onset of tumor-producing properties is characteristically accompanied by morphological alterations in less extreme form. Among the various lines examined for this purpose, some exhibited changes identical to those described earlier by Earle. But others persisted for long periods, with morphological characteristics similar to those of freshly isolated fibroblasts. In general, no perceptible differential could be found in the morphology of cells exposed to low levels of methylcholanthrene and those carried without carcinogen. Tumors were obtained from strains showing no morphological change as well as from those with variant patterns (Figure 7.2). It follows that though visible alterations in appearance or growth form may be frequently seen within cells in long-term culture, there is no necessary correlation between these transitions and the acquisition of malignant potential.

Further experiments have served to define in more detail the characteristics of this reaction system. Sanford, Likely, and Earle (1954), in reporting additional instances of transformation in mouse cells, showed that the ability to produce sarcomas can arise in cultures of fibroblasts maintained exclusively on a cellophane or glass substrate, as well as in those carried continuously within a plasma matrix. Parenthetically, in relation to the work of others, it is also worth noting that in these studies by Earle's group, the cell populations concerned were maintained without antibiotics and were transferred routinely by mechanical means rather than by trypsin treatment. Small variations in culture management seem accordingly not to be implicated in the phenomenon under study. Nor is neoplastic conversion *in vitro* restricted to a single cell type. Although transformation of fibroblasts to sarcoma-producing cells has proved convenient for experimental study, it does not represent the only system available. The formation of tumors following the injection of cultures originating from mouse liver cells has been reported by Evans, Hawkins, Westfall, and Earle (1958), and tumors have been obtained by Rothfels, Kupelwieser, and Parker (1963) with cultures of kidney, skin, and lung (see below). Whether transformation of cell populations in either epithelial or fibroblast strains can be modulated by nutritional factors remains to be seen. As yet, there have been no observations of malignant conversion *in vitro* in the absence of serum

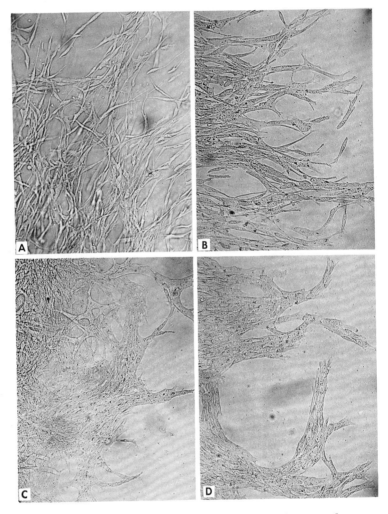

FIG. 7.2. Lack of correlation between morphological changes and tumor-producing ability in isolated strains of mouse fibroblasts. (*A–B*) Normal pattern of fibroblast growth at glass interface of plasma cultures. Strains shown are in 17th and 34th passage, respectively. Population *A* produced a transplantable sarcoma on injection. (*C–D*) Altered patterns of growth in fibroblasts carried for 17 and 31 passages, respectively. Population *C* produced a sarcoma on injection. (From Sanford, Earle, Shelton, Schilling, Duchesne, Likely, and Becker, 1950.)

protein (Evans, 1961). However, the difficulty may lie more in the inability of primary populations to grow in the chemically defined nutrients presently available (see Chapter 5) than in any inherent lack of potential for neoplastic transformation in a protein-free medium.

From these well-documented investigations, the capacity of untreated cell populations in culture to undergo neoplastic transformation can now scarcely be questioned. No evidence of an overt carcinogen as the mediating agent has ever been found, but the suggestion has frequently been made that chronic exposure to heterologous proteins in the nutrient medium may induce or select for variants with tumor-producing ability (Sanford, Earle, Shelton, Schilling, Duchesne, Likely, and Becker, 1950). It has been difficult to test this concept directly, owing to the practical problem of providing homologous media for mouse cells in sufficient quantity to permit large-scale experiments.

An unequivocal answer has finally issued from a quite different quarter, that is, culture of cell populations *in vivo* (Shelton, Evans, and Parker, 1963). These experiments deal with the propagation of subcutaneous tissue from C_3H mice within diffusion chambers bounded by Millipore filter membranes. The intact units are inserted into the peritoneal cavity of isologous hosts, a procedure that isolates the implants from direct contact with the tissues of the host while maintaining free diffusion of noncellular components, including serum proteins. Shelton and her co-workers found that the experimental cell populations proliferated luxuriantly for long periods in this environment, producing sheets of tissue in which the cells were bound together by a matrix of collagenous fibers. As a rule, the implants were transferred to new chambers at monthly intervals during a total period of 856 days. In some instances, however, the cells were left in a quiescent intact state without subculture for intervals ranging up to 378 days. Two sublines of cells were also established *in vitro* by explanting chamber populations at 385 and 450 days, respectively.

All these experimental populations were assayed for malignant change by intraocular and intramuscular injection into C_3H mice. The inoculation of chamber tissue at intervals during the first 18 months of continuous cultivation *in vivo* did not yield any tumors, but after 23 months, rapidly growing sarcomas were obtained from these cells in 76 percent of the intraocular tests and essentially 100 percent of the intramuscular assays. Interestingly, the onset of tumor-producing ability seems to occur at approximately the same time, whether chamber populations are maintained in a state of rapid proliferation by serial transfer or are allowed to remain quiescent as an intact system. Furthermore, there is little difference in the process of neoplastic conversion among sublines of cells isolated from chambers after varying periods and subsequently maintained *in vitro*, except for a possible shortening of the latent period.

Shelton and her collaborators did observe prominent morphological alterations within the serially transferred chamber cells after about 18 months *in vivo*. The secretion of extracellular materials appeared to decline, and perhaps as a result, the cells formed tightly packed masses, often floating freely in the chamber fluid. In agreement with previous findings, however, no correlation could be established between the time of appearance of morphological changes and the development of tumor-producing ability. These experiments are notable for demonstrating that malignant change can occur simultaneously in sublines of a population that are propagated under quite different physiological conditions. They also show that untreated mouse fibroblasts in isolated systems can undergo neoplastic transformation even when maintained in a completely isologous environment. This demonstration seems to rule out the concept of heterologous proteins as an essential factor for the parallel transformations that take place *in vitro*.

The cycle of experiments summarized above has come full circle with the recent investigations of Berwald and Sachs (1963). In this work, the focus has returned to the induction of cellular changes by chemical carcinogens in isolated populations. Since monolayers rather than plasma cultures can now be used as a reaction system, it is possible to re-examine the original studies of Earle in more quantitative fashion. For these initial efforts, Berwald and Sachs employed primary populations of mouse and golden hamster cells, to which carcinogens were variously added. In confirmation of Earle's findings, they observed morphological alterations in cultures treated with methylcholanthrene for periods as short as 2 to 3 days. A similar phenomenon occurred in populations treated with 3,4-benzpyrene, but no changes took place upon the addition of urethane. The lack of visible effects in this case does not have an obvious explanation, since urethane is a well-known carcinogen *in vivo*. Possibly, a metabolic conversion may be necessary for the action of urethane, or perhaps cell types responsive to urethane do not proliferate in the cultures chosen for test.

However, the most important finding of Berwald and Sachs was the observation that alterations produced by methylcholanthrene or benzpyrene represent focal transformations (like virus-induced changes to be discussed in detail later in the present chapter). Chemically transformed cells within their assay system could be recognized by differences in appearance from normal cells, as well as by a partial loss of contact inhibition. Owing to these alterations, the variant cells pile up in the form of discrete colonies, while adjacent areas of the monolayer remain unaffected. Significantly, transformation seems to occur as readily when small numbers of cells are plated as in mass populations. Over-all, the incidence of conversion ranged from 5 to 26 percent for benzpyrene, with the exact level dependent in part on the duration and amount of exposure to carcinogen. Thus, the transformation process seems to be inductive in nature, rather than a selection by chemical agents of a pre-existing variant cell type.

Here, then, is an experimental system that may aid in bridging the gap between the appearance of tumorigenic potential within untreated cultures, and the known facts of carcinogenesis with chemical agents in the whole organism. It should perhaps be emphasized that the time interval in the work of Berwald and Sachs was relatively short, and whether the changes observed are identical to those that arise more slowly in untreated cultures is still unknown. There is also the question whether morphological alterations induced by methylcholanthrene or benzpyrene represent in any simple sense an indicator of neoplastic conversion. Judging from the lack of correlation between morphological shifts and tumorigenic potential in untreated cultures, and similar discrepancies in experiments with polyoma virus (see p. 417), reservations on this point must be entertained. The results of reinjecting chemically altered cells into animals—yet to be performed—may provide the necessary information.

In their experimental studies, Berwald and Sachs, like Earle, made no observation of chromosomal patterns during the initial period of transitional change. However, it will be recalled (Chapter 4) that Levan and Biesele (1958) did make such an investigation, using cultures of embryonic mouse skin maintained as monolayers in serial culture. In this case, aneuploidy and the ability to produce tumors successively appeared, but there was no close correlation in the timing of these processes. A somewhat similar picture can be seen in the experiments of Rothfels, Kupelwieser, and Parker (1963), who carried out karyotypic analysis and malignancy tests with mouse cells on a larger scale. As described earlier (see pp. 173–176), these investigators established primary strains from adult C_3H mouse skin, lung, and kidney. Ultimately a number of aneuploid permanent lines were obtained, of which at least 15 have produced tumors in the host of origin, including cells from all three of the organ types. Tumors have not been obtained in any instance with trypsinized cell suspensions from fresh tissue, nor from primary diploid populations in serial cultures.

This dichotomy makes it improbable that the tumors which have arisen can be attributed to the presence of polyoma virus or a similar agent.

Inasmuch as the transition from primary diploid cells to heteroploid strains is clear-cut in this material (Chapter 3), a well-defined onset of malignant transformation might also be expected. However, the observations of Rothfels and his co-workers indicate that the acquisition of tumor-producing ability is a gradual rather than abrupt process. When cell populations that have newly emerged as heteroploid lines are tested, tumors are rarely produced. If they do appear, survival times for the host are relatively long. Later, the incidence of tumor production rises, as does the relative virulence of individual neoplasms.

That transitions to aneuploidy *in vitro* do not necessarily confer neoplastic properties is also shown by the experiments of Barski and Cassingena (1963). These investigators isolated cell strains from the lung tissue of $C_{57}BL$ mice, a source chosen because the incidence of spontaneous lung tumors in this inbred line is very low. One of the cultured populations was maintained in subculture by trypsin treatment, another by mechanical dispersal, and the two populations diverged markedly in morphological pattern. However, a noticeable acceleration of growth rate took place in each line after a few months, and both were found to be hypotetraploid in chromosome pattern at 142 days. No tumors were obtained in repeated tests of the aneuploid population maintained by mechanical dispersion up to a total of 436 days of culture, but the trypsin-treated line produced tumors when first tested at 184 days, and regularly thereafter. Although this difference correlates with a disparity in transfer technique, it should be noted that Earle and his collaborators have repeatedly observed neoplastic conversion of mouse cell lines in the absence of trypsin; in some of these experiments, the latent period before acquisition of malignant potential has been relatively short (Evans, 1961). The more important point emphasized here is that aneuploidy does not *ipso facto* result in malignant transformation.

Up to the present time, only a few studies have been performed on carcinogenesis within untreated cell cultures other than those of murine origin. Yerganian and his co-workers have reported on inoculation studies with Chinese hamster cells (Yerganian, Leonard, Gagnon, and Gagnon, 1961). They were unable to produce tumors in isologous hosts by the inoculation of primary diploid populations. Transplantable fibrosarcomas arose from injection of some aneuploid lines, although others failed to yield tumors. The tumorigenic strains all showed structural changes in chromosome pattern as well as numerical deviation. Cells from the Syrian hamster have also been assayed recently for spontaneous neoplastic change (Defendi, Lehman, and Kraemer, 1963). The results are of particular interest in relation to virus studies (pp. 416–417). In this case, populations that closely resembled primary diploid cells in appearance and general characteristics proved nevertheless to be uniformly malignant on assay. This finding was less surprising when chromosome studies showed all strains in question to be aneuploid.

In summary, the acquisition of malignant properties by cells in untreated cultures presents an intriguing but blurred picture in terms of causal relationships. Cell strains with aneuploid patterns have produced tumors on injection, but other cell strains with altered karyotype have failed to do so. Malignant transformations have occurred in the absence as well as in the presence of morphological alterations in cell lines, in populations transferred by mechanical dispersion in addition to those propagated by trypsin treatment, and in a completely isologous environment as well as in media containing sera and tissue extracts foreign to the cells in question.

In seeking for common denominators not to be readily discounted, it may be that the focus on possible carcinogens in the culture environment is misplaced. Conceivably, the long-term cultivation of dissociated cells in isolated systems merely establishes conditions for the expression of an intrinsic neoplastic change. It is perhaps significant that in each case where neoplastic conversion has occurred in cultured cells, the populations in question have been maintained for extended periods on a foreign substrate: glass, cellophane, or a Millipore filter membrane. Even for strains carried in a plasma matrix, this generalization holds, since growth in this case occurs in part at the glass interface. The facilitating action of plastics and other inert materials on tumor formation *in vivo* has been previously described (Chapter 1). There can be little doubt that the effect is an indirect one, since glass cover slips or plastic films elicit tumors on implantation, but the same materials as powders fail to do so (see Alexander and Horning, 1959; Oppenheimer, Willhite, Danishefsky, and Stout, 1961). Further evidence is found in the experiments of Goldhaber (1961), who has demonstrated that the initiation of tumors by the implantation of Millipore filters is a function of pore size rather than the membrane material as such.

Just why the disposition of apparently inert substrates in large expanses should facilitate carcinogenesis is far from clear. Whether the effect is based on contact with a foreign surface or on a partial isolation of cells that otherwise form a continuous system must be determined. However, the implications of this finding for neoplastic conversion in untreated cell cultures are interesting. It is true that within the intact organism, tumors form only if a fibrous capsule develops in conjunction with the foreign materials. But according to Alexander and Horning (1959), neoplasms do not always arise in direct association with the foreign implant. In addition, the occasional appearance of such tumors as rhabdomyosarcomas indicates that more than a mere conversion of inflammatory cells is involved. Regardless of the exact explanation, the Oppenheimer phenomenon is provocative, since attention is directed to the minimum essentials for spontaneous transformation within the cell as such, rather than on the action of an extrinsic agent. If the analogy to carcinogenesis *in vitro* is justified, cell cultures offer a means of pursuing this analysis with a new series of experimental variables.

Growth of Cells in Heterologous Hosts   The basic questions of when and if cell populations in culture take on malignant properties have been examined more widely in recent years through the use of heterologous assay systems. In general, cells and tissues are unable to grow progressively in hosts of another species, but proliferation may be facilitated if the animals are pretreated with X irradiation or cortisone (Toolan, 1954). The effectiveness of these procedures stems from a weakening of the immune responses that ordinarily cause rejection of foreign grafts (Chapter 8). Means for the conditioning of animal hosts were first devised to permit the laboratory propagation of human tumors as experimental material. Later, the same methods came into extensive use in attempts to evaluate the neoplastic or nonneoplastic character of cell strains obtained from normal tissues and maintained for varying periods *in vitro*.

The first assays of cell lines for tumor production in heterologous hosts were performed with the Chang lines of human cells (Moore, Southam, and Sternberg, 1956; Moore, 1957). In maintaining these populations as stock strains, Moore noted that after 40 to 50 serial transfers, all lines had assumed the variable appearance now known to characterize permanent cell lines in general. Differences were recorded in cell size, appearance, and colonial patterns. When such altered populations were injected subcutaneously into conditioned rats or into human volunteers, nodules developed at the site of implantation, and on microscopic examination, these growths in some respects resembled malignant tumors. The findings of Moore were extended by Coriell, McAllister, Wagner, Wilson, and Dwight (1958), who injected the Chang lines intraperitoneally into weanling rats pretreated with X ray and cortisone. The incidence of intraperitoneal tumors obtained ranged from 40 to 80 percent when these tests were made, although implantation of the same cell lines 1½ years earlier had given completely negative results (Coriell, McAllister, and Wagner, 1957). A number of cell strains supposedly derived from normal tissues of other species also gave rise to tumors in conditioned rats (McAllister and Coriell, 1959). No tumors were obtained in rats injected with freshly isolated monkey kidney cells.

Similar results with the inoculation of a spectrum of cell lines into rats were reported by Moore (1958) and by Fogh and Hok (1958).

Such observations have suggested that most if not all cell strains maintained in serial culture might be potentially malignant in an appropriate assay system. This suspicion can be reinforced by circumstantial evidence derived from the histological study of "normal" human and animal cell lines after extended periods of culture (Leighton, Kline, Belkin, Legallais, and Orr, 1957; Leighton, 1957). These populations frequently show features associated with the microscopic patterns of malignant tumors *in vivo*, including an increased incidence of mitotic abnormalities, a heightened nucleocytoplasmic ratio, hyperchromaticism, and wide variations in cell size. Despite this persuasive evidence, however, there are good indications that the analogy has been overdrawn. Certainly, injection into heterologous hosts does not produce evidence that primary diploid strains of human origin are capable of producing malignant tumors (Hayflick and Moorhead, 1961). Such findings are consistent with the experiments described earlier, in which all primary cells derived from mice, Chinese hamsters, and Syrian hamsters failed to elicit neoplasms in the hosts of origin. Even if the characteristics of permanent cell strains alone are considered, there is reason to doubt whether the altered and variable properties of these populations can be equated in any simple sense with malignant change. From the experiments that have been outlined in the preceding section, it should be apparent that for mouse cells at least, morphological alteration as such does not signify tumor-producing ability. It is unlikely that the cells of other organisms (for example, man) differ significantly in this regard.

An additional element of uncertainty in the assays reported with cell lines in heterologous hosts lies in the fact that much of this work was performed during a period when the hazard of cellular contamination between established strains was not yet realized (Chapter 3). Thus the literature contains some observations that are very likely artifacts. For example, Coriell, McAllister, Wagner, Wilson, and Dwight (1958) were unable to distinguish by transplantation behavior in rats between *HeLa* cells on the one hand, and *ERK* cells (supposedly of rabbit origin) or *SCH* cells (of putative derivation from a cynomolgus monkey) on the other. The similarity is more readily understood in the light of subsequent studies, which show that certain sublines, at least, of *ERK* and *SCH* cells show human properties and are in fact almost certainly *HeLa* (Brand and Syverton, 1962). Since no measures were taken to secure the actual identity of the cell lines used in the earlier transplantation assays, the validity of the results obtained is problematical.

Lastly, it should be pointed out that some investigators believe that distinctions can be made by appropriate assay between cell lines originating from neoplastic and nonneoplastic tissues, respectively, despite the resemblances that the two types of population may exhibit in serial culture. The Syrian hamster has been utilized by Foley and Handler (1957, 1958) for this purpose, taking advantage of the relatively mild response to foreign grafts in the cheek pouch of the animal (Chapter 8). A number of cell lines derived from normal and malignant tissues of various species were assayed in this way. Untreated animals were used, as well as those conditioned with X ray and cortisone, and the number of cells inoculated was systematically varied. Initial growth was obtained in unconditioned hosts from all lines tested when the inoculum exceeded 1×10^6 cells, but at 1×10^4 cells, only the cell strains originating from malignant sources gave rise to detectable increases. In pretreated hosts, the same differential was observed, although the absolute numbers of cells required for growth was less and some tumors were established from malignant sources with as little as ten cells.

The hamster appears to be an especially favorable host for demonstrating these quantitative distinctions in terms of dose-response. However, other changes are observed in heterologous transplants that support the rationale of the assay more effectively (Foley and Handler, 1958; Foley, Handler, Adams, and Craig, 1962). Tumors derived from cell lines of malignant origin characteristically become vascularized and grow progressively in hamsters. They often fill the cheek pouch, and are frankly invasive in character. Although these growths may eventually become necrotic and are reabsorbed, especially in unconditioned hosts, the nodules obtained can be transplanted serially if removed before necrosis sets in. Such a picture is in marked contrast to the sequence of events that, with few exceptions, is noted when cell lines originating from normal tissues are inoculated in the hamster cheek pouch. In this case, the growths obtained are not invasive, do not increase progressively in size, and regress rapidly, persisting for a few days only. None of these nodules can be transplanted to other hamsters, even when removed before necrosis develops. Essentially the same result is obtained if the host is pretreated with cortisone, or if very large numbers of cells of normal origin are inoculated. According to Foley, behavioral differences in heterologous hosts, even more than the ability to grow temporarily from inocula of a given size, seem by and large to distinguish cell lines of malignant and normal origin.

On the basis of these findings, it may be reasonable to conclude that although cell lines of normal and malignant origin frequently tend to converge in appearance under common conditions of culture, basic differences in growth potential can still be demonstrated in many cases within the intact organism. Thus malignancy is not a necessary concomitant of growth in long-term culture. From this standpoint, the relatively high frequency of malignant conversion in long-term cultures of mouse fibroblasts may be misleading, if generalized without further evidence to cover other cell types and systems of different species origin. Neoplastic transformation in many of these may take place far less frequently. Nevertheless it would be an oversimplification to regard permanent cell strains, even where nontumorigenic, as the simple equivalent of "normal" cells. Such populations are perhaps more nearly analogous to the elements of a preneoplastic lesion. They are plainly altered as the result of transitional changes *in vitro,* and have no exact counterpart in the cells and tissues of the intact organism.

It seems fair to say that the implantation of cell strains into heterologous hosts has not as yet resolved any basic problems, but at least the significance of bioassays for malignancy has become more apparent. Clearly, temporary growth as such is an inadequate criterion for establishing the validity of neoplastic change. In one sense, this merely reaffirms a conclusion reached earlier from the transplantation of embryonic rudiments into older animals. It has long been known that such implants under appropriate conditions can give rise to large growths of chaotic structure. Although these embryomata may for a time progressively enlarge in size, they eventually stabilize or regress, and do not in general show invasiveness or other characteristics of neoplastic change (Willis, 1935; Harris, 1942; Greene, 1955). Such observations underline the point made in beginning the present discussion; namely, that malignancy can be reliably inferred by transplantation only if the test cells proliferate reproducibly in assay hosts to a lethal end point.

ANALYSIS OF VARIATION IN TUMORIGENIC LINES

Cell populations that have acquired neoplastic properties *in vitro* may undergo a further remodeling in serial culture. These sequential changes are analogous to the progressions of primary or transplanted tumors within the intact organism. Nevertheless, variation as seen in tumorigenic lines does not differ from the patterns observed for permanent cell strains that lack an overt neoplastic potential. The similarity is perhaps not surprising, since the selective advantage, if any, of variations in either system must be judged in terms of increased efficiency for growth in long-term culture. However, the ability to produce neoplasms in the host of origin does not necessarily remain constant in tumorigenic strains during such progressions *in vitro*. There is no obvious mechanism to ensure that this potential for performance within the animal body must be reinforced or held invariant during long-term cultivation. Modulation, adaptation, or heritable changes may take place in accordance with patterns of selection that bear no immediate relation to factors regulating growth in the intact organism. Thus antigenic changes might limit the ability of isolated populations to produce tumors *in vivo*. Or metabolic conditioning of cells could take place in certain culture media, with a corresponding change in virulence when these strains were implanted into assay hosts. There is now good evidence that such changes in tumor-producing ability do occur, and these trends form the subject matter of the following sections.

Fluctuations in Tumor Induction That cell populations may be so altered by exposure to carcinogens as to impair their ability to produce tumors was suggested by the original experiments of Earle and his collaborators (Earle and Nettleship, 1943). As previously noted, there seemed to be a negative correlation between the frequency of tumor production and the duration of treatment *in vitro* with methylcholanthrene. Particularly after long exposure, the cells yielded very few tumors on injection, and the populations in culture were markedly altered in appearance. Evidently such changes are far-reaching, for the neoplasms that did arise were characterized by a variable and highly aberrant cell picture. Conceivably, the low efficiency of tumor production with these cells, as compared to controls, might be the consequence of antigenicity for the host, induced by carcinogen treatment. It is now known that tumors arising in mice from the application of methylcholanthrene exhibit new and individualized antigens (Chapter 8). These may be immunologically reactive even within the primary autochthonous host (Klein, Sjögren, Klein, and Hellström, 1960). However, in order to explain Earle's data on this basis, it would be necessary to assume that the degree of antigenic modification is proportional to the period of treatment *in vitro* with methylcholanthrene. No information on this point is yet available, and other explanations remain to be explored.

The continuity of tumor-producing capacity in populations of proved malignancy was examined by Earle, Shelton, and Schilling (1950), as a sequel to the main body of experiments performed earlier. Over a period of 4½ years, cell strains that had been exposed to methylcholanthrene, together with the untreated controls, were injected in groups of assay mice on several occasions. Sarcomas were obtained regularly from each cell strain, but the general incidence of tumors for all series eventually declined (Figure 7.3). After three years, the untreated control

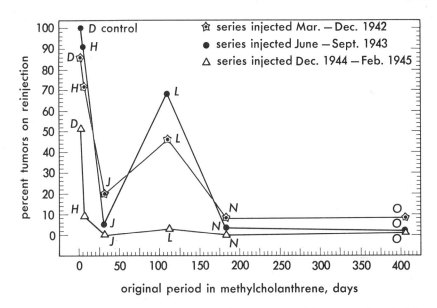

FIG 7.3. Decline in tumor-producing ability within Earle's series of methylcholanthrene-treated cultures when maintained in serial passage. Strains D, H, J, L, N,
and O were initiated originally in 1941 and were treated at that time with methylcholanthrene at 1 μg/ml for 0, 6, 32, 111, 184, and 406 days, respectively. (After
Earle, Shelton, and Schilling, 1950.)

strain D gave only 50 percent neoplasms after injection, although in
previous assays the frequency had reached 86 to 100 percent. Even
fewer tumors were produced by strains exposed to methylcholanthrene
for short periods, and for those that had been treated for long intervals,
the incidence was nearly zero.

Although most of these lines were eventually closed out, one of the
treated populations, strain L, was maintained in culture along with its
single cell derivative, NCTC-929. After a total of ten years *in vitro*, clone
929 cells were again assayed for tumor production (Sanford, Hobbs, and
Earle, 1956). Sarcomas on this occasion were obtained in 15 percent
of untreated C_3H mice, but when the animals were conditioned with
X irradiation to inhibit possible immune reactions, the incidence rose to
64 percent. This suggestion of antigenic divergence was reinforced by
the fact that an injection of NCTC-929 cells in untreated hosts could
now effectively prevent the development of tumors from another inoculation of the same kind (Sanford, Merwin, Hobbs, Fioramonti, and Earle,
1958). The difference had arisen at least in part, within a known period.
In 1943, soon after strain L had been established, the cells grew pro-

gressively in the form of a translucent mass when placed within transparent chambers in C_3H mice. Five years later, when strain L cells were again examined in transparent chambers, there was an initial phase of vascularization and growth for a few days, followed by opacity and eventual regression of the implant (see Algire, Chalkley, and Earle, 1950). Whatever the character of this immunological differential between the cell line and homologous host, Sanford, Hobbs, and Earle (1956) showed that it could be minimized or eliminated by animal passage of the corresponding tumors. Of 18 sarcomas that arose from the implantation of clone 929 into C_3H mice, at least two were capable of serial growth after the second passage in 100 percent of mice of this strain, although no growth took place in other mouse strains.

Decline in the tumor-producing capacity of cells maintained in continuous culture has also been described by other workers, and it is apparent that this phenomenon is not unique to the strains mentioned above. For example, Dawe, Potter, and Leighton (1958) followed changes in the malignancy of a reticulum-cell sarcoma cultivated for extended intervals *in vitro*. The tumor in question had been induced earlier by methylcholanthrene in a $DBA/2$ mouse, and was subsequently converted to the ascites form. Over a period of 3 to 11 months *in vitro*, the ascites tumors arising from injection of these cells showed a marked decrease in virulence, and after the 11-month interval, inocula of 10^6 cells in mice rarely gave rise to neoplastic growth. Similarly, Hsu (1960) observed the tumor-producing ability of cultures established from the Novikoff rat hepatoma to attenuate in serial transfer, and de Bruyn and Hansen-Melander (1962) found that certain sublines of the MB mouse lymphosarcoma, but not others, lost the ability to produce tumors after prolonged cultivation *in vitro*. Although Hsu suggested that the decline in tumor production might be associated with chromosome alterations, de Bruyn and Hansen-Melander could find no relation between gross karyotypic changes and degree of malignancy (see also Chapter 4).

Clonal Diversification in Serial Culture Several interpretations might be placed on the changing potential for malignant growth within populations maintained continuously in culture. One obvious possibility is that of genetic drift within the group of host animals used for tumor assay. It is well known from studies on mice and other inbred animals that if two groups of a homogeneous population are isolated, they soon diverge as substrains through a disparate accumulation of random mutations and other heritable changes. Thus genetic instability in host background might conceivably complicate assays for malignancy, where these are performed with cells isolated for long periods *in vitro*. In practice, however, this possibility can be largely discounted in the systems under study. When clonal analysis is applied to variation in the tumorigenic properties of mouse cell strains, it appears that most, if not all, of the differences observed can be attributed to changes in the cultured cells rather than in the assay hosts.

The investigations of Sanford and her collaborators demonstrate in more specific form how tumor-producing potential can vary within sublines descended from a single cell. These experiments began with the intention of comparing the ability of clonal sublines to undergo neoplastic transformation (Sanford, Likely, and Earle, 1954). For this purpose, a new population of fibroblasts was isolated from C_3H mouse subcutaneous tissue, having no relation to strain L or other cell lines initiated in the course of earlier investigations. During a preliminary culture period of 3 months, this strain produced no tumors on assay with C_3H hosts. Eventually a clone was isolated as the progenitor for several sublines, two of which were continued in serial culture. Although similar in appearance originally, these populations diverged morphologically over 20 months of separate culture (Figure 7.4). Both eventually produced tumors on inoculation into mice but with characteristic differences in frequency. As previously noted (see Chapter 4), one substrain after nearly two years of culture produced sarcomas in 97 percent of untreated C_3H mice, whereas the other yielded tumors in only 1 percent of these animals. Consequently these populations can be conveniently referred to as high-line and low-line cells, respectively.

The fact that sublines derived from a clonal population can display so different a tumorigenic potential is intriguing. In searching for an explanation, one might assume as a first approximation that Sanford's low-line cells had become distinct antigenically from the C_3H hosts and had elicited an immune response, whereas the high-line cells did not. Indeed, Sanford, Likely, and Earle (1954) observed that if C_3H mice were pretreated with X irradiation, the incidence of sarcomas with low-line cells rose from 1 to 44 percent. Moreover, after one passage in irradiated hosts, tumors derived from low-line cells grew uniformly in all C_3H mice without further pretreatment. However, when the concept of differential changes in antigenicity was tested directly, both high-line and low-line cells were found to induce immunity in C_3H hosts (Sanford, Merwin, Hobbs, Fioramonti, and Earle, 1958).

A more convincing explanation for the distinction in tumorigenic potential of these cell strains has been found in their growth behavior within the assay hosts. High-line and low-line cells multiply at the same rate *in vitro*, but not when placed for observation within transparent chambers in C_3H mice (Sanford, Merwin, Hobbs, Fioramonti, and Earle, 1958). In this environment the high-line cells proliferate vigorously

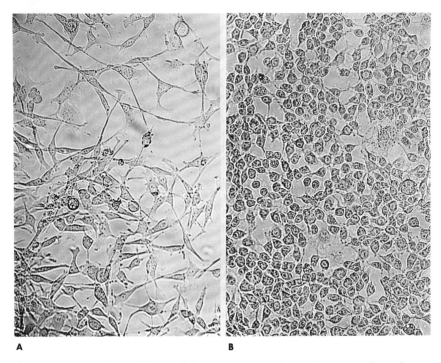

A   B

FIG. 7.4. Morphology of low and high sarcoma-producing lines, both derived originally from the same single cell from mouse subcutaneous tissue. (*A*) Subclone of
high-line cells 597 days after single-cell isolation. (*B*) Low-line clone, 538 days after
isolation. The distinctive difference in appearance from high-line cells is consistently
observed in culture. (From Sanford, Merwin, Hobbs, Young, and Earle, 1959.)

from the outset, stimulating conspicuous engorgement and ingrowth
of nearby blood vessels. Low-line cells are not incapable of bringing
about a vascular response, but they divide less rapidly on implantation
and a hyperemia fails to develop at an early stage in the adjacent host
tissues. These observations correlate well with the longer latent period
required for the appearance of palpable neoplasms after intramuscular
inoculation of low-line populations. It appears, therefore, that although
both cell types are antigenic in C_3H mice, the high-line cells override
the host response by developing to a mass population before immune
reactions can be marshaled effectively, whereas low-line cells fail to do
so in most cases. A problem in semantics thus arises: Do the experimental findings represent a differential in malignancy, virulence, or
transplantability between the two strains? If these concepts are defined
in operational terms, little if any distinction can be made in such a model
system.

Whatever its formal designation, tumorigenic potential, even within a single strain, is subject to experimental modification. It can, for example, be enhanced or depressed by varying the culture medium used to propagate the cells prior to assay (Sanford, Merwin, Hobbs, Young, and Earle, 1959). The discovery of this fact was made incidentally. Hoping to facilitate the isolation of subclones from high-line and low-line cells for further study, Sanford replaced the embryo extract-serum mixture, employed earlier, with a semisynthetic nutrient. The latter consisted of a chemically defined medium, NCTC-109 (Evans, Bryant, McQuilkin, Fioramonti, Sanford, Westfall, and Earle, 1956; McQuilkin, Evans, and Earle, 1957), fortified with 10 percent horse serum. Unexpectedly, this shift opened up a new perspective on the differences in tumor-producing ability of cell strains. For, when high-line and low-line cells were cultivated for an extended period in the new medium, progressively growing sarcomas were obtained from practically 100 percent of implants, regardless of strain. The rise in tumorigenic potential appeared to be a gradual one, extending over several months after transfer to the semisynthetic nutrient. Using the same technique, Sanford and her collaborators also elevated the sarcoma-producing ability of strain L mouse cells, after many years in culture, from nearly zero to approximately 50 percent. Thus the phenomenon appears to be a general one.

No immediate explanation can be provided for the increased capacity of cell populations to give rise to tumors after propagation in certain culture media. However, several possibilities have been ruled out for practical purposes (Sanford, Merwin, Hobbs, Young, and Earle, 1959). For example, the increased incidence of tumors from low-line cells is not mediated by any loss of antigenicity for the assay host, nor by an improved ability to elicit vascular responses, and there are no indications that pretreatment affects the rate of proliferation within cell populations that are inoculated into mice. In view of these findings, Sanford suggested that cells with increased resistance to reactions by the host appear or become dominant as a result of multiplication in appropriate culture media. More efficient growth by these variants in the presence of immune responses could account for the rise in tumor incidence. She points out the analogy that exists with the problem of virulence in bacteria. In this case, it is well known that strains of pathogenic bacteria maintained *in vitro* may undergo attenuation for appropriate hosts; that alterations in virulence may accompany changes in culture conditions, and that growth *in vivo* may restore high virulence in attenuated strains (Dubos, 1945).

The similarity in end result suggests that augmentation in tumorigenic potential by cultural pretreatment and by animal passage may have a common basis. Such a view is supported by data on the properties of low-line cells before and after growth in tumor form (Sanford, Merwin, Hobbs, and Earle, 1959). In these experiments, hybrid hosts ($C_3H \times BALB/c$) were used to secure the identity of the donor population. Neoplasms arising from such hybrids were freely transplantable in similar hosts or in C_3H mice, but not in animals of $BALB/c$ origin. Thus the possibility of a secondary malignant transformation in the host stroma could be effectively ruled out. The derivative tumors showed an enhanced ability to grow as a result of animal passage. Nevertheless they were still capable of immunizing C_3H mice against low-line cells that had been maintained in the older embryo extract-serum medium. The same immunity, however, was ineffective against an implant of cells that had been cultivated in semisynthetic medium, or against an inoculum from a low-line tumor after animal passage. Apparently, therefore, low-line cells that acquire a high tumorigenic potential are in fact more refractory to the immune responses of the host, while retaining intact their antigenicity.

What processes actually occur in the appearance of these populations with a higher tumor-producing capacity? Immunoselection, it would seem, offers the most immediate mechanism for enhancement by animal passage. Even if refractory variants occur only in low frequency within the original inoculum, they should ultimately emerge by selection in the face of adverse host reactions. However, this explanation may be misleading, since equally resistant populations can arise indirectly *in vitro* without exposure to the final selection screen. It may be that resistance here is primarily a modulative phenomenon, dependent on a shift in surface properties or metabolic pattern. Such changes might take place in response to certain substrates present in the *mileu interieur* of the host, or alternatively, to particular components in the culture medium. Consistent with this view is the fact that increases in tumor-producing capacity are not irreversible. Sanford and her co-workers found that high tumorigenic potential may persist for a time in low-line cells that are re-established in an embryo extract-serum medium, but not indefinitely. Testing such populations by periodic reinjection, they found that a heightened production of tumors could be demonstrated in part for several months, but that this was almost obliterated in one strain after eight months of culture. However, whether such reversion is accomplished by modulation or through variation and selection remains to be determined.

It is noteworthy that a variety of markers persist without change in cells that are enhanced in tumorigenic potential by experimental treatment. The modifications conferred by animal passage or growth conditions in culture thus seem to be limited, if strategic in nature. For example, low-line and high-line cells that have come to grow at the same frequency in assay hosts continue to display characteristic differences in cell morphology and tumor architecture, as well as the disparity in latent periods and vascular reactions incident to establishment in mice. Metabolic differentials may likewise persist unchanged, as illustrated in studies of glycolytic activity by Woods, Sanford, Burk, and Earle (1959). In this case, it can be demonstrated by manometric techniques that the anaerobic glycolysis of high-line cells is several fold greater than that of low-line cells.

Initially, the possibility existed that this difference might account for the relative tumor-producing activity of the two cell strains (see Warburg, 1956). However, such a view is untenable in the light of more recent experiments. These show that high-line and low-line cells that are brought to the same tumorigenic potential nevertheless differ as before in glycolytic pattern (Sanford, Westfall, Woods, and Earle, 1959). Within the strains in question, the tempo of anaerobic glycolysis seems, therefore, to relate more to the duration of the latent period required for the development of palpable neoplasms than to the over-all potential for tumor production (Sanford, 1958). A similar association can be demonstrated for several enzymes concerned with the oxidative degradation of glucose. Hexokinase, glucose-6-phosphate dehydrogenase, and phosphogluconate dehydrogenase are all noticeably elevated in high-line as compared to low-line cells, and this differential holds even when the stock populations are maintained regularly in semisynthetic nutrient (Scott, Pakoskey, and Sanford, 1960).

The essential independence of most enzymatic changes from tumorigenic potential within these populations can be further illustrated by certain progressions known to have occurred within high-line strains *in vitro* (Westfall, Peppers, Evans, Sanford, Hawkins, Fioramonti, Kerr, Hobbs, and Earle, 1958; Sanford, Westfall, Chu, Kuff, Covalesky, Dupree, Hobbs, and Earle, 1961). Originally, both high-line and low-line strains showed arginase activity at a barely detectable level, in contrast to permanent strains established from mouse liver, where higher values for arginase may provide a characteristic marker. But when a clone of cells was later isolated from a high-line tumor, two sublines from this population unexpectedly showed arginase activities of 20 and 400 times that of the parent strain. Other characteristics of high-line cells, including frequency of tumor production, were not significantly altered by the onset of these changes. The sublines in question have subsequently proved to have greatly elevated levels of β-glucuronidase activity as well. However, the relative increase differs for the two strains and does not coincide with the degree of change in arginase activity. In these neoplastic populations derived from a single cell, the progression of unit characters in the sense of Foulds (1954) is illustrated particularly well. It is evident that the capacity for tumor production in assay hosts varies independently of numerous other characteristics in the system under study.

VIRUSES AS CARCINOGENS IN
ISOLATED POPULATIONS

If neoplastic transformations *in vitro* are approached through the action of specific carcinogens rather than by the analysis of changes in untreated cells, the tumor-producing viruses as a group offer most promising experimental designs. No other type of carcinogenic agent provokes so direct and immediate a neoplastic response, and for no other class of carcinogens are the possibilities of interaction with cellular mechanisms so extensive. There is, moreover, a provocative conceptual background for studies in this area. Lysogenic states in bacteria, episomes, and genetic control by virus of host cell characters (Chapter 2) all contribute models of possible relevance in carcinogenesis. The questions posed by these analogies are primary issues. Can neoplastic conversion, for example, be mediated by an integration of virus into the replicating information systems of somatic cells? Or is carcinogenesis with tumor viruses based on cellular modification by some more indirect means? Analysis of such problems can be pursued effectively in isolated cell populations, where a variety of parameters affecting the cell-virus relationship may be manipulated individually.

Several *in vitro* systems have been developed for the study of tumorigenic viruses. Extensive information is available on the action of Rous sarcoma virus in monolayers of chick cells and on the effects of polyoma virus in mouse or hamster cultures. Both agents give rise to striking changes, which have been frequently discussed and reviewed (Stanley, 1958; Luria, 1960; Dulbecco, 1960a, 1963; Gross, 1961; Kaplan, 1962; Prince, 1962a; Kohn, 1963; Habel, 1963). A number of other viruses have been shown to convert isolated cell populations into tumor-producing strains. Among viruses of the avian leukosis complex (Beard, 1957), transformation has been achieved with the myeloblastosis agent (Beaudreau, Becker, Bonar, Wallbank, Beard, and Beard, 1960; Baluda and Goetz, 1961) as well as by others, which will be mentioned in subsequent discussions. The oncogenic effects of simian vacuolating virus

(SV_{40}) in hamsters have already been outlined in Chapter 4, and are summarized in more detail in a paper by Eddy (1962). It is now clear that hamster cells which are exposed directly to SV_{40} *in vitro* may produce neoplasms if reintroduced into the corresponding host (Rabson and Kirschstein, 1962; Shein, Enders, Levinthal, and Burket, 1963). Similarly, certain adenoviruses of human origin can elicit tumors when inoculated into hamsters, and may well bring about neoplastic conversion in isolated populations (Trentin, Yabe, and Taylor, 1962; Huebner, Rowe, and Lane, 1962). Other potential systems for study *in vitro* include the morphological changes induced in isolated populations by bovine papilloma virus (Black, Hartley, Rowe, and Huebner, 1963), as well as the still undefined effects of mouse leukemogenic viruses and mammary agents in cell cultures. As yet, proof of neoplastic transformation *in vitro* by use of these factors is lacking,

Transformations with Rous Sarcoma Virus Although the Rous agent in chickens was the first tumor-producing virus to be discovered (Chapter 1), little understanding of its effects was gained for some years, owing to the lack of a simple quantitative assay. In 1938, Keogh adapted the chick chorioallantoic membrane for this purpose. Viral concentrations were estimated from the number of tumors that arose as focal growths, following inoculation of eggs with infectious samples. The chorioallantoic assay was refined further by Rubin (1957) and used to measure the production of virus by Rous sarcoma cells in monolayer culture. These experimental populations were not maintained permanently *in vitro*, but instead were passed at weekly intervals by serial transfer in young chicks. Virus appeared in cultures at a slow but steady rate. Most of the cells seemed to produce virus, but they were not destroyed in the process and continued to release infectious particles for a considerable period of time. Rubin concluded, therefore, that the production of Rous sarcoma virus is compatible with growth and cell division, a view that has been confirmed by more rigorous tests with single isolated cells (Temin and Rubin, 1959).

Eventually, Rubin and Temin developed a direct assay for Rous sarcoma virus *in vitro*, based on morphological changes that occur reproducibly under certain conditions of culture. This work takes its origin from experiments by Halberstaedter, Doljanski, and Tenenbaum (1941), who had observed that if chick fibroblasts are exposed to Rous virus in tissue culture, altered cells may appear which closely resemble those arising directly from an explanted Rous tumor. Later, Manaker and Groupé (1956) showed that discrete foci of altered cells can be obtained in monolayers of normal chick cells, provided the virus is added in suitable dilution. Working from these observations, Rubin and Temin devised techniques for a quantitative assay and used the method for determination of virus as well as the registration of Rous virus-infected cells (Rubin and Temin, 1958; Temin and Rubin, 1958; Rubin, 1959). Second-passage cultures from whole chick embryos provided standardized assay populations, and to these were added diluted aliquots of virus, or infected cells, in an agar overlay. In both cases, characteristic foci appeared, consisting of grapelike clusters of rounded refractile elements against a background of unmodified normal cells. A series of initial tests indicated that the number of foci was a linear function of free virus within the countable range. However, of the cells added from populations containing Rous virus, only about 10 percent registered as infective centers. These facts at first seemed to indicate that only a small proportion of cells are susceptible to infection with the Rous agent at any one time, the balance remaining virus-free. But further studies have shown that most, if not all, cells to which Rous virus is added in sufficient concentration can actually become infected (Rubin, 1960a). Apparently there is merely a low probability during the initial period following infection that a given cell will form a focus on transfer to an assay culture. The percentage of cells that register as infective centers rises sharply if plating is delayed for a day or two.

The morphologically altered elements that arise through interaction between the Rous virus and chick embryo monolayers have been referred to directly as Rous sarcoma cells by Rubin and other investigators. Several types of evidence can be offered to support this identification. On the one hand, focal cells from virus-infected populations are identical in appearance to the rounded, basophilic cells that are seen in cultures prepared directly from Rous tumors (Tenenbaum and Doljanski, 1943). The transformed cells also show a behavioral change which has been described as characteristic of sarcoma cells; namely, the loss of contact inhibition (see Rubin, 1961; Abercrombie and Heaysman, 1953; Abercrombie, Heaysman, and Karthauser, 1957; Abercrombie, 1962). Within focal areas of change, the cells pile up in disorganized fashion rather than remain in an intact layer. Finally, there is convincing proof that cultures containing cells transformed by Rous virus can actually produce sarcomas on inoculation into chickens (Morgan and Andrese, 1962). At first sight, such tests would seem ambiguous, since tumors might be initiated by action of associated virus on the host tissues as well as through direct growth of the introduced cells (Dulbecco, 1960a). This contingency was covered in the experiments of Morgan and Andrese by using male donor cells and female assay hosts. The neoplasms that arose exhibited predominantly the male pattern of sex chromatin. Interestingly, when serially transferred, these tumors seem to undergo gradual conversion to the host cell type through secondary viral inductions (see also Pontén, 1962). A limited transplantability of Rous sarcoma cells can thus be inferred. However, in the experimental design employed, elimination of donor cells is complicated by the occurrence of homograft reactions in noninbred hosts (Chapter 8).

While morphological conversion appears to be characteristic of cells infected with Rous sarcoma virus, it is subject to modulation in accordance with extrinsic factors. The development of foci can be suppressed, for example, without interfering with the capacity of cells in culture to produce infectious virus. Such a finding emerged through effects to improve the assay medium (Rubin, 1960c). As an aid to cell growth, fetal calf serum was substituted for ordinary calf serum. This seemingly minor variation in procedure served to block morphological alterations completely in populations infected with low concentrations of Rous virus. Inhibition could also be demonstrated with high concentrations of ordinary calf serum, although if the latter was added at the customary 10 percent level, foci of altered cells appeared as usual. The lack of morphological changes was not associated with a decrease in the number of cells undergoing infection. Furthermore, the rate of virus production in cultures containing fetal calf serum proved similar to that of populations maintained in the standard assay medium during the first four or five days *in vitro*. The basis for these effects has not been definitely determined, but Rubin suggests that the morphological conversion induced by Rous virus can be suppressed through products elaborated by unmodified cells in certain nutrient media.

If cellular transformations resulting from interaction with Rous sarcoma virus are not expressed under all cultural conditions, it is perhaps not surprising that some investigators have been unable to observe alterations with the Rous agent in the manner described. For example, Sanford, Likely, Bryan, and Earle (1952) carried out an extensive series of experiments with Rous sarcoma virus in cultures of chick cells. Although multiplication of virus and the production of tumors was demonstrated for these populations, the characteristic morphological conversions described by Rubin did not take place. Similarly, Prince (1962b) could not detect significant morphological transformations in cultures of chick and turkey fibroblasts to which the Rous agent was added, although the majority of cells were demonstrably virus producers. In this case, the discrepancy was eventually explained when tryptose phosphate broth, an ingredient regularly used by Rubin, was added to the culture medium. The modified nutrient then supported morphological changes effectively, with the majority of cells in virus-treated populations undergoing transformation to basophilic round cells. Prince also showed that the extent and type of alteration in cell form which follows infection with Rous virus is conditioned by the physiological state of experimental populations.

The causal relation, if any, between morphological changes and the assumption of malignant properties remains to be determined (Prince, 1962a, 1962b). In this connection, the sequence morphological alteration → loss of contact inhibition → malignancy offers an attractive concept. The possibility must be considered, however, that the correlation of these processes is purely coincidental. No proof exists as yet that infected but untransformed cells (for example, in populations in which morphological conversion has been suppressed) are any less tumorigenic. These uncertainties ought to be resolved. Unfortunately, it seems difficult to do so by simple inoculation, since the production of tumors by cells unmodified *in vitro* might signify merely that a transformation had occurred during the assay procedure.

It may be that morphological changes induced by the Rous agent are chiefly significant in modifying the cell surface for virus production (Rubin, 1961). This view developed originally from observations which showed that cells in an advanced stage of infection with Rous virus have a higher probability of forming morphologically altered foci (Rubin, 1960a). More direct information has come from studies with fluorescent antibody techniques (Vogt and Rubin, 1961, 1962). By this means, it can be shown that maturation of infectious particles takes place at the cell surface. Large amounts of viral antigen are released from the periphery of cells showing the characteristic, rounded form. Thus morphologic conversion might be regarded as a consequence of virus production, and the two processes could be linked together. However, since transformation is now known to occur equally well in cells that contain the Rous agent but do not form infectious virus (see later discussion), this interpretation must be abandoned. If morphological changes have any functional implication for viral synthesis, it would seem to lie merely in preparation of the cell surface for the assembly process which ordinarily follows.

In this unfolding vista of reactions, a new variable was introduced by the discovery that other agents of the avian leukosis complex can interfere with infection and growth of Rous virus in chick cell cultures (Rubin 1960d; Friesen and Rubin, 1961). Thus, occasional embryos are found that yield cells difficult to infect with Rous virus *in vitro*. If supernatant fluids from these cultures are added to populations of known sensitivity to Rous virus, the latter become equally resistant to infection, and a stable resistance-inducing factor (RIF) can be readily propagated. No cytopathic changes can be detected when chick cells are infected *in vitro* with RIF. The production of RIF is assayed quantitatively by determining the capacity of culture fluids to interfere with cell alteration by Rous virus under standard conditions. For this purpose, serial dilutions of media containing RIF are added to chick cell monolayers. After a cycle of growth to allow for multiplication of RIF within the experimental populations, the latter are challenged with Rous virus, and the appearance of foci is used as a measure of susceptibility or resistance.

The nature of the resistance-inducing factor was at first unknown, but subsequent investigation has established an identity between RIF and avian lymphomatosis virus (Friesen and Rubin, 1961). Viral agents of a generally similar character can be obtained either by direct isolation from chickens with lymphomatosis or from asymptomatic embryos in the manner described. The active factor resembles or is identical with Rous sarcoma virus in many physicochemical properties. On the other hand, the two can be separated by serological means as well as through clear differences in pathogenicity. The mechanism by which RIF prevents infection by Rous virus in cell cultures is not known with certainty. However, interferon can be demonstrated in populations infected with RIF, and it has been suggested that exclusion is based on production of this factor (Bader, 1962).

Other agents of the avian leukosis complex also interact with Rous sarcoma virus. This list includes avian myeloblastosis virus, which produces characteristic morphological changes when added alone to chick cells *in vitro* (Baluda and Goetz, 1961). Because of a close affinity with Rous virus, the myeloblastosis agent can be titrated by an interference technique similar to that used with RIF (Rubin, Cornelius, and Fanshier, 1961). Still another member of the avian leukosis group has recently been discovered in crude stocks of the Rous agent. This factor is referred to as Rous-associated virus or RAV (Rubin and Vogt, 1962). RAV is quite similiar to Rous sarcoma virus in immunological properties and can be separated from the latter only because where the two are found together, RAV occurs in higher titre. When such preparations are diluted beyond the end point of infectivity for Rous agent, a transmissible agent can be obtained in pure form by inoculating susceptible cultures. Like RIF, from which it is distinguished serologically, RAV does not give rise to cytopathic changes *in vitro*. RAV fails to produce sarcomas on inoculation into chicks, but an erythroblastosis can be induced by intravenous injection, indicating the relationship of this factor to other viruses within the avian leukosis complex.

The relative avirulence of both RAV and RIF at the cellular level accounts for the frequent presence of avian lymphomatosis virus in healthy chick embryos (Burmester, 1957). This circumstance has made possible an analysis of host-virus relationships, with results that are of general significance. One area of work deals with the epidemiology of the RIF agent (Rubin, Cornelius, and Fanshier, 1961). In surveying a flock of birds with a relatively high level of visceral lymphomatosis, these workers observed two types of individuals. Some exhibited conspicuous viremia without detectable neutralizing antibody. Others were free of viremia, but displayed high levels of antibody. Since it is known that visceral lymphomatosis can be transmitted by the egg (see Burmester, 1957), breeding tests were performed. These demonstrated that infection can arise as a congenital condition, but only with the female as a source. Practically all the progeny derived from viremic hens proved to contain RIF when the embryos were assayed in cell culture by the Rous-virus interference technique. The viremic roosters failed uniformly to transmit the lymphomatosis virus to their offspring. A clue to this disparity may lie in the stripping of most cytoplasmic systems from the mature sperm. If the virus had a cytoplasmic location, it could then be lost from the sperm while persisting in the egg. By implication, therefore, the RIF agent does not seem to be transmitted in association with the host cell genome or other nuclear component.

The pattern of congenital transmission with RIF does not immediately make clear why some birds exhibit a persisting viremia and others do not. An explanation can be found in the phenomenon of immunological tolerance, using concepts that originated in the study of transplant systems (Chapter 8). Briefly, congenital infection with RIF seems to confer acceptance of the viral agent by suppressing an immune response (Rubin, 1962a, 1962b). The production of virus occurs in quantity at an early stage and specifically prevents the formation of neutralizing antibody by the developing immune system. Such individuals remain susceptible to the effects of virus, however, and the persisting viremia may eventually be expressed in the symptoms of lymphomatosis, which develops as usual at a late stage. Those birds that display neutralizing antibody can be assumed to have escaped congenital infection. Here, contact with the virus appears to have occurred only after immunological competence in the host had been established. The viral agent then serves to elicit the synthesis of neutralizing antibodies rather than to suppress their formation.

A similar duality of response applies to hosts infected with Rous sarcoma virus. In this case, it is not possible to induce tolerance directly during early stages of development, since the Rous agent causes death in a short time if introduced into young animals. However, the Rous-associated virus (RAV) may be inoculated into chick embryos for this purpose, since RAV and Rous sarcoma virus cross-react immunologically. When the pretreated birds after hatching are challenged with Rous virus, tumors arise and grow reproducibly and progressively, their viral content consistently maintained at a high level (Rubin, 1962c, 1962d; Rubin and Hanafusa, 1963). By contrast, tumors produced in chicks without RAV injection follow a more familiar pattern. Growth is less regular and some tumors may regress; marked infiltration of host leukocytes occurs; and the titre of Rous sarcoma virus declines or may even fall below detectable levels. Clearly, then, the production of infectious virus can be conditioned by immunological responses, although there is no evidence that the decline or elimination of viral synthesis alters the properties of established tumors.

The central problem in carcinogenesis with the Rous agent concerns the exact form of association that develops between virus and target cell. At an earlier time, there were repeated suggestions that viral and host cell genomes might be linked in a manner directly or indirectly analogous to the lysogenic state in bacteria (Rubin, 1957, 1959; Rubin and Temin, 1958; Dulbecco, 1960a, 1960b; Prince, 1960). In a search for possible parallels with lysogeny, Rubin and Temin (1958, 1959a, 1959b) carried out a series of radiation studies on virus-infected cells. The motivation for this work came from reports that temperate phages in bacteria are more resistant to ultraviolet light than are virulent phages. Such a difference has been attributed to the integration that develops in the case of prophage with the bacterial genome, since this might permit a repair of radiation injury (Stent, 1958). An analogous pattern seemed possible when preliminary experiments showed that Rous sarcoma virus is ten times more resistant to ultraviolet light than is the cytocidal Newcastle disease virus.

Following this lead further, Rubin and Temin obtained data that seemed to conform to the temperate bacteriophage model. The capacity of chick cell cultures to initiate the formation of Newcastle disease virus proved to be comparatively resistant to X irradiation, and this finding was confirmed for another cytocidal virus, the agent for vesicular stomatitis. However, the ability of such populations to produce Rous sarcoma virus seemed to be inactivated with low doses of X irradiation. The effect was particularly striking, since doses required to suppress virus formation coincided with the level of irradiation that inhibited cell division and colony formation. A logical construction of these data was the assumption of a common radiosensitive target for the properties studied, arising from a close association or actual incorporation of Rous virus within the cellular genome. Unfortunately, this interpretation was vitiated by later studies, which showed that with high multiplicities of infection, the synthesis of Rous virus can take place in chick cells even after X irradiation at levels many times the dose needed to inhibit cell division and colony formation (Rubin, 1960b). Thus, although the radiation data may have an intrinsic interest, they no longer offer supporting evidence for an integration concept.

There are other problems to be faced in drawing an analogy between the classic picture of lysogeny in bacteria and the observed relationship between Rous virus and infected cells. One of these is the fact that Rous virus contains RNA rather than DNA (Bather, 1957) With rare exceptions (Loeb and Zinder, 1961), bacteriophages belong to the class of DNA viruses. Another difficulty is the fact that while populations infected with the Rous agent and with lysogenic bacteria both display a low rate of virus production, the mechanics of this process are entirely different in the two cases. In populations of cells that form infectious Rous virus, practically all cells liberate the mature agent in small amounts, continuing meanwhile to grow and divide (Rubin, 1957) The production of virus cannot be increased further in these cells by exposure to ultraviolet light or X irradiation (Rubin and Temin, 1959b) In lysogenic bacteria, the spontaneous release of virus takes place in "bursts" from a small number of cells within the total population, and these cells are destroyed in the process. The remainder of the cells can respond with massive virus production, however, if exposed to ultra violet light or other agents (Chapter 2).

Perhaps the most significant objection to the assumption that the Rous genome is incorporated directly into the genetic apparatus of the host is an indirect inference. This arises out of the mode of transmission previously described for the closely related RIF. It will be recalled that passage of RIF takes place reproducibly through the egg but not at all through the sperm. This observation is difficult to explain, if in fact a close association of viral and host cell genomes does occur. Actually, the contrary seems to be indicated by direct visualization of viral antigen and mature virus with fluorescent antibody techniques. Such studies suggest that the RNA chicken tumor viruses as a group are confined to the cytoplasm (Vogt and Rubin, 1961). Considering all available evidence it seems questionable that bacterial lysogeny as such can provide a useful framework of explanation for RNA tumorigenic agents (Rubin 1961).

But if genetic integration as provirus seems unlikely, there is still the possibility that the Rous genome may persist in continuity with the host cell in some more indirect form. One such carrier state has now been reported (Rubin and Hanafusa, 1963). The evidence on which this conclusion rests derives in part from the study of noninfective tumors; that is, those induced by the Rous agent, but which fail later to yield infectious virus. These neoplasms fall into two categories. One group consists of tumors arising in immunologically competent animals that have received relatively high doses of Rous sarcoma virus. As noted previously, the titre of infectious virus in this case may gradually decline or disappear, but the trend is associated with host reactions to the foreign antigen. The content of Rous virus does not diminish within birds made tolerant by pretreatment with RAV. A quite different picture is presented by the so-called low-dose noninfective tumors (Bryan, Calnan, and Moloney, 1955; Prince, 1959). These are neoplasms arising in young or old birds after inoculation of Rous virus in limiting dilutions. Many of the resulting tumors seem to lack infectious virus from the outset. None can be obtained by extraction, and even if the tumor cells are cultivated in monolayers or on the chorioallantoic membrane of chick embryos, the Rous agent fails to be released in detectable form.

An explanation for the anomalies of noninfective Rous tumors has come from the examination of cell populations infected *in vitro* with minimal doses of the Rous agent (Hanafusa, Hanafusa, and Rubin, 1963). Inasmuch as the only virus stock available for this purpose was known to contain RAV as well as Rous virus per se, efforts were made to separate the two experimentally. The inoculum was adjusted to give only one or two foci of altered cells per plate, and RAV antiserum was incorporated into the culture medium to increase the probability of solitary infections with Rous sarcoma virus. The transformed cells within foci, probably clonal in origin, were isolated and added to uninfected chick monolayers. As cultivation continued, they preserved their characteristic appearance and multiplied in relative number. But when tested for virus production, over 80 percent of the sublines containing altered cells failed to form RAV or Rous sarcoma virus. In instances where Rous virus did appear, RAV was invariably produced also. This suggested that RAV might be strategic for the production of Rous sarcoma virus in an infective form, and confirmation was readily forthcoming. Even in populations that had failed to yield Rous virus after many passages, synthesis could be induced directly by adding RAV. Additional experiments have revealed that a similar induction can be obtained with RIF, avian myeloblastosis virus, and presumably with other agents of the avian leukosis complex.

The results of these experiments have been interpreted as demonstrating that the Rous sarcoma agent is a defective virus, which requires the complementary action of a "helper" virus such as RAV to complete the formation of infective particles. This possibility had been suggested earlier by Prince (1959) on a speculative basis, and the general concept is a familiar one in bacteriophage studies. Numerous examples exist of temperate phages with specific blocks for the replication or assembly of infectious particles. The production of these agents can be induced by appropriate superinfection with a phage not bearing the same deficiency (Jacob and Wollman, 1961). From such data, it is reasonable to assume that the helper virus supplies genetic determinants that are missing in the primary infective agent, owing to a substitution of bacterial genes (Chapter 2). Defectiveness in bacteriophage systems is thus strategic for gene transfer and seems in fact to be a prerequisite for transduction (Luria, 1962).

The implications of defectiveness for the Rous sarcoma virus are as yet unexplored. In this case, the deficiency can scarcely represent the incorporation of genetic information from the host cell in the usual sense, since the Rous agent presumably contains no DNA. However, a substitution of chick RNA may have occurred. Conceivably, this might facilitate a functional association with cytoplasmic systems for the continued production of viral RNA in a steady-state pattern. That only the Rous genome is perpetuated under these conditions is suggested by the complete absence of viral antigen in cells arising from solitary infection, when these are examined by fluorescent antibody techniques. Such populations are nevertheless capable of producing sarcomas of the usual type if injected into chickens, and the derivative neoplasms also remain free of viral antigen unless induction occurs (Rubin, personal communication).

Of particular interest in these studies is the clear indication that the Rous agent can produce stable modifications in host cells that do not depend on the overt synthesis of mature virus; for example, morphological changes, or the ability to grow as tumors. In terms of end result, this process bears a formal similarity to lysogenic conversion in bacteria; that is, the acquisition of new cellular properties or the modification of existing ones as a consequence of viral entry (Luria, 1959). It is well known, for example, that populations infected with temperate bacteriophages may undergo changes in colonial form, antigenic transformation, or other heritable changes (see Jacob and Wollman, 1961; Kohn, 1963). The cell-virus association in the Rous sarcoma seems to have little in common with lysogeny; virogenic conversion, if it occurs, may therefore require unique effector mechanisms. The consequences of conversion in microbial systems, however, may offer suggestive clues. The synthesis of new proteins, for example, is a frequent sequel to phage infections. A similar induction could render animal viruses tumorigenic if the protein in question served to trigger an unlimited cell proliferation. For such a hypothesis, the experiments of Mueller, Kajiwara, Stubblefield, and Rueckert (1962) may have a special interest. Their evidence, based on inhibitor studies, supports the concept that localized changes involving protein synthesis are required to initiate the replication of DNA in mammalian cells. If this interpretation is valid, a virus-induced protein of appropriate character might provide the mitotic stimulant for continuing malignant growth.

Polyoma-mediated Conversions   The interactions that occur *in vitro* between somatic cells and tumor viruses have also been explored through extensive experiments with the polyoma agent. Like Rous sarcoma virus, polyoma produces demonstrable effects in cell cultures, and can be readily propagated within isolated cell populations. The multiplication of infectious virus was first described with primary cultures of monkey kidney cells (Stewart, Eddy, Gochenour, Borgese, and Grubbs, 1957). Optimal yields, however, are obtained only in a homologous system, and monolayers prepared from mouse embryonic cells are convenient for this purpose (Eddy, Stewart, Young, and Mider, 1958). If such populations are infected with polyoma, synthesis and release of virus in large amounts take place. The cell-free supernatants elicit a wide variety of neoplasms on injection into newborn mice, hamsters, and other laboratory animals (Chapter 1).

The multiplication of polyoma virus in monolayers of mouse embryonic cells is accompanied by characteristic cytopathic changes (Eddy, Stewart, and Berkeley, 1958). In suitable multiplicities of infection, these cytocidal effects are localized in the form of plaques, which can be employed for purposes of assay (Dulbecco and Freeman, 1959). Attempts have also been made to purify stock strains of the polyoma agent by serial isolation from solitary plaques in low-level infections. The derivative viral lines exhibit an unchanged capacity for inducing a wide variety of tumors in experimental animals. This suggests that polyoma virus in pure form possesses a broad spectrum of tumorigenic action and that the diverse effects obtained are not the expression of mixed viral types (Eddy and Stewart, 1959). Polyoma variants do exist, however, and can be recognized by differences in plaque size as well as by other characteristics, including relative oncogenicity in appropriate hosts (Medina and Sachs, 1960; Gotlieb-Stematsky and Leventon, 1960). These distinctions in virulence have been thought by some workers to correlate with the level of interferon produced by host cells in response to individual strains of the infective agent (Allison, 1961; Friedman, Rabson, and Kirkham, 1963).

One of the most significant features of polyoma virus is the occurrence of DNA as the sole nucleic acid component (DiMayorca, Eddy, Stewart, Hunter, Friend, and Bendich, 1959; Smith, Freeman, Vogt, and Dulbecco, 1960; Weil, 1962). Polyoma thus seems a priori to offer a more promising prospect for integration with the host cell genome than does the Rous agent or other RNA-containing viruses. Of interest is the topographic association that does develop between polyoma virus and the nuclei of infected mouse cells. Electron micrographs show that extensive numbers of particles may occur within the nucleus (Bernhard, Febvre, and Cramer, 1959). Also, if the progress of polyoma infection in mouse embryonic cells is monitored by fluorescent antibody techniques, virus-specific antigen appears first in the nuclear region (Henle, Dienhardt, and Rodriguez, 1959). These observations are significant in tracing the sequence of events during viral entry and in the subsequent production of infectious particles. They do not necessarily imply, however, that any interaction occurs at a genetic level. It is well known that a number of noncarcinogenic viruses may also multiply in the cell nucleus. There is no indication in such instances that integration with the genetic apparatus of the host takes place.

Much of the experimental interest in polyoma virus centers on the remarkable transformation of cell properties that can be observed within populations treated *in vitro* with this agent. The changes in question were first documented in mass cultures by Vogt and Dulbecco (1960). Using monolayers prepared from Syrian hamster and mouse embryos, these investigators added polyoma virus and maintained the treated populations for extended periods. Cytopathic changes occurred initially within the mouse cell lines, but tapered off during serial transfer. The hamster cells remained free from cytopathic changes from the outset. In both types of cultures, however, cell proliferation was stimulated and morphologically altered cells eventually appeared. These grew in densely interwoven networks and came to dominate the experimental population. When the variant hamster lines were inoculated into newborn animals of the same species, tumors arose at the site of inoculation and grew progressively. No virus could be detected in the hamster populations except for a brief period following infection. In cultures of mouse cells, quantities of virus were released initially, but the titre declined as the populations became transformed in appearance and growth characteristics. Nevertheless, a persistent release of virus occurred in the mouse cell cultures. This was eventually traced to the residual propagation of infection by a small fraction of the population, with other cells free from viral agent in an infectious form (Dulbecco and Vogt, 1960).

Observations similar to those of Vogt and Dulbecco were reported by Sachs and his colleagues (Sachs and Medina, 1961; Medina and Sachs, 1961; Sachs, 1962), who also succeeded in producing tumors with hamster cells transformed by polyoma virus *in vitro*. Noting the tendency of variant cells to pile up in irregular layers, Sachs suggested that, as in the Rous sarcoma system, the induction of malignancy by polyoma virus includes a release from contact inhibition within the transformed populations. A contrasting impression is gained from the experiments of Sanford, Dunn, Covalesky, Dupree, and Earle (1961). No special morphological changes or elevation of growth rates were observed by these workers in a clone of mouse salivary gland cells treated with polyoma, despite the fact that neoplastic conversion was effected rapidly and reproducibly by exposure to the viral agent. The failure of visible transformations to develop in this system has not been explained. It is conceivable, however, that, as in experiments with Rous virus, alterations in morphology may be suppressed or conditioned by extrinsic factors. To exclude other interpretations, it should be emphasized that Sanford and her co-workers used hybrid hosts for assays, and they examined the transplantability of derivative neoplasms. The data obtained show clearly that the tumors in question originated from cultured cells and not from a host reaction to virus introduced at the same time.

It is curious that transformation by polyoma virus occurs much more rapidly with hamster strains than in mouse cell populations, and no explanation can yet be provided for this difference. However, the experiments of Weisberg (1963a, 1963b) have eliminated a number of possibilities. Seemingly, the cytocidal effects of polyoma virus on mouse cells are modulated by transient physiological differences, and the survivors do not represent a unique class of mutants. There is no evidence that interferon production accounts for the long delay of several weeks before transformed cells can be detected in mouse embryo cultures, nor can phenotypic lag or a destructive interaction between polyoma virus and variant cells be invoked. Other possibilities remain to be tested; for example, the assumption that transformation stems from a rare spontaneous event superimposed on a special state of physiological competence. In that case, polyoma virus might interfere to a greater extent in metabolism of the surviving mouse cells, as compared to hamster cells, thus reducing the proportion of the population susceptible to random change.

The modifications imposed by polyoma virus can be described in more quantitative terms if conversion is dealt with at the level of individual cells rather than mass populations. Plating techniques for a clonal analysis of the transformation phenomenon were first devised by

Stoker and his collaborators (Stoker and Macpherson, 1961; Macpherson and Stoker, 1962; Stoker, 1962a; Stoker and Abel, 1962). In general, these methods involve the addition of polyoma virus to the target populations while in suspension form, after which the treated cells are plated in small numbers in a nutrient medium. Hamster cultures are convenient for study, since in this case the transformation process is uncomplicated by cytocidal changes. In such a system, transformation by polyoma virus is expressed by the appearance of altered cells in discrete colonies, which contrast sharply with the unmodified population in appearance and growth characteristics. Assuming that these foci represent clonal variants, the frequency of transformation can be estimated as a function of population size and plating efficiency. For their initial studies, Stoker and Macpherson (1961) employed cultures of cells isolated directly from hamster embryos or from primary hamster strains in early transfer. With these materials the incidence of transformed colonies is proportional to virus dose at low concentrations. At higher multiplicities of infection, a ceiling is soon reached. The majority of cells remain unmodified, and the proportion of those transformed does not in any case appear to exceed 1 percent.

Subsequent studies by Stoker and his colleagues have been pursued with an improved assay system, devised by substituting a permanent strain of hamster cells as the reactive substrate for polyoma virus (Macpherson and Stoker, 1962; Stoker and Abel, 1962). The line in question, designated *BHK*-21, was derived from cultures of neonatal hamster kidney that had acquired an elevated growth rate during serial transfer. The altered strain displays an increased cloning efficiency, but in general appearance and architectural pattern the populations are similar to freshly isolated kidney cells. A number of clonal sublines were isolated from the *BHK*-21 strain, and have been compared in susceptibility to modification by polyoma virus. The incidence of transformation remains low in these single-cell derivatives, and the numerical frequencies are not greatly different from those obtained on mass populations freshly isolated from hamster kidney. Expressed as a function of the total cells plated, the frequency of transformation in nine experiments with a single clone ranged from 0.8 to 5.7 percent, with a mean value of 2.7 (Stoker and Abel, 1962).

The basis for variation in this model system is not yet entirely clear. Freshly isolated populations represent complex and changing mixtures, and if the data were based solely on these materials, the observed low rate of transformation could result from the selection of one or more cell types present as a small fraction of the initial population. However, since the frequency of transformation is similar in cloned and uncloned populations, it is evident that selection alone is an inadequate explanation. A hypothesis of random mutation plus selection by the viral agent also presents difficulties, since the observed frequency of variants (10^{-2}) within clonal sublines treated with virus is far greater than the spontaneous occurrence, if any, of transformed colonies in control cultures not exposed to the polyoma agent (not over 10^{-5}). Thus transformation is most reasonably construed as an inductive phenomenon. The relative inefficiency of this process may in part represent physiological variability.

Although the rate of transformation is not affected by prior growth history of cell populations, the frequency can be increased if feeder layers are employed in assays, a procedure that also leads to a rise in plating efficiency (Stoker and Abel, 1962). Interestingly, the functional differences that limit transformation do not seem to involve any differential susceptibility to viral entry. Fraser and Gharpure (1962) have shown with fluorescent antibody techniques that essentially all cells in BHK-21 populations ingest large quantities of polyoma virus antigen when exposed to the virus in culture. However, only a small proportion of cells show nuclear staining, in contrast to the very generalized occurrence of antigen in the cytoplasm. The frequency of nuclear involvement is of the same order of magnitude as the incidence of transformation, but whether the two have more than a coincidental correlation remains to be seen. Attempts to increase the frequency of transformation by prior exposure of hamster cells to X irradiation have met with some success, although the absolute proportion of altered cells remains low (Stoker, 1963b). The basis for this effect is not yet known.

Considerable attention has been given to the variant properties of cells transformed *in vitro* by polyoma virus as possible implementing mechanisms in the transition to malignancy. The differentials that arise can be seen particularly well by comparing transformed and nontransformed substrains derived from a single clonal population (Macpherson and Stoker, 1962; Macpherson, 1963). The variants grow in nonoriented patterns, have an elevated glycolysis, and exhibit a higher plating efficiency than unmodified cells. Populations transformed by polyoma virus are also characterized by chromosomal instability, although alterations in karyotype may not appear immediately (Chapter 4). Furthermore, it is now clear that polyoma-mediated conversions lead to the appearance of a new cellular antigen that is not associated with the viral agent as such (Habel, 1962; see also Chapter 8). Transformation thus involves a spectrum of changes in addition to the characteristic alterations in morphology and growth behavior by which conversion was first recognized. It is the latter, however, that have provided a principal focus in the study of neoplastic change.

According to Vogt and Dulbecco (1962b, 1963), the assumption of altered morphology and growth patterns proceeds in two stages within cultures of hamster cells treated with polyoma virus. These investigators isolated small groups of cells at an early period from focal areas of morphological change and examined the population structure of the resulting cultures by clonal analysis. Some of the derivative colonies grew in single layers, differing only from normal hamster cells in a random orientation and refringent appearance of the cells. Other clones proliferated more vigorously, with the piling up of cells to form dense nodules. Only the latter gave rise to tumors in high frequency when injected into hamsters. Since cells of the dense type were observed to arise as variants within clones of the thin variety, Vogt and Dulbecco suggested that carcinogenesis in this system may follow a sequential progression. The initial morphological alteration, as seen in thin clones, could be viewed as a primary consequence of tumor virus action. At the same time, chromosomal instability is induced, and this might provide for further progression in cell properties, culminating in frank malignancy. The possibility was recognized, however, that chromosomal aberrations may be a consequence rather than a cause of progression in the transformed cells (see also Chapter 4).

A somewhat different impression of morphological change in polyoma-treated cells is gained from the reports of Stanners and his colleagues (Stanners, Till, and Siminovitch, 1963; Stanners, 1963). These investigators compared the properties of 47 transformed lines, all derived by cloning from populations of hamster embryo cells previously exposed to polyoma virus. The transformed lines in general showed differences in morphology and behavior from normal hamster cells, but they could not be assigned to alternative or contrasting categories. In terms of colonial morphology, the variant strains presented a broad spectrum. For any single line, distinctions in form seemed to be heritable in serial transfer, although in some instances modifications appeared secondarily. A total of 37 transformed strains were assayed for tumorigenic potential by inoculation into hamster hosts; all gave rise to malignant, rapidly growing tumors. Parallel injections were also performed with morphologically unmodified hamster cells, but in no instances were neoplasms produced.

Morphological alteration has provided an attractive model for carcinogenesis with polyoma virus, and despite occasional cautions (see Dawe, Law, Morgan, and Shaw, 1962), there has been a general tendency to equate transformation in cell appearance and growth pattern with the process of neoplastic conversion. It has been difficult to avoid the impression that the two were in fact identical in *BHK*-21 populations, since here, too, tumors seemed to occur only when transformed cells were inoculated into hamsters (Macpherson and Stoker, 1962). The stock strain appeared to retain a diploid complement and oriented growth pattern without change for long periods, and even clones of cells derived from cultures containing polyoma virus did not yield neoplasms unless a morphological transformation had occurred (Stoker, 1962b). The significance of these findings, however, has been lessened by the demonstration of Defendi, Lehman, and Kraemer (1963) that *BHK*-21 substrains, at least under some conditions, can produce malignant neoplasms in high frequency without morphological transformation *in vitro* or even without exposure to polyoma virus. There seems to be no outward sign of change in the tumorigenic cultures, although an appreciable fraction of the cells were found to contain an extra chromosome, apparently as a trisomic condition. These populations continue to proliferate as intact monolayers, with the well-defined orientation of cells that has been characteristic of the *BHK*-21 strain from the outset. The latter observations are of particular interest, since they tend to cast doubt on the concept that neoplastic conversion depends on a loss of contact inhibition. Other investigators have also obtained tumors with untreated *BHK*-21 cells (see Macpherson, 1963), and it seems apparent that this line must be classified as neoplastic in character.

It should not be too surprising to find that neoplastic conversion can occur without an overt morphological change in hamster cells, inasmuch as this observation had already been made with long-term strains of mouse cells (Sanford, Earle, Shelton, Schilling, Duchesne, Likely, and Becker, 1950). Such experiments emphasize again that although morphological alteration is a frequent accompaniment of the transition to malignancy in isolated cell populations, the relationship is not a necessary or invariant one. More interesting is the observation of Defendi and his colleagues that *BHK*-21 cells of proved tumorigenic potential can still undergo morphological transformation by polyoma virus in typical fashion. If the transformed derivatives are tested by injection into hamsters, their capacity for tumor production is found to be identical to that of unmodified cells. Evidently, then, morphological conversion by polyoma virus is not to be identified strictly with the transition from normal to malignant states. In the populations under study, at least, transformation seems clearly to be an epiphenomenon, unrelated to the earlier assumption of neoplastic properties by the stock strain.

The mechanism of cell-virus interaction in the polyoma system has occasioned wide interest and extensive speculation (see Dulbecco and

Vogt, 1962; Sachs, 1962; Prince, 1962a; Stoker, 1962a, 1963; Kohn, 1963). Is carcinogenesis with the polyoma agent mediated by integration with the host cell genome, by a directed process of mutagenesis, or by the modification of epigenetic control mechanisms? The initial studies on transformation *in vitro* seemed consistent with a model based on bacterial lysogeny (Vogt and Dulbecco, 1960; Dulbecco and Vogt, 1960). In this context, stress was laid on the disappearance of virus from transformed cells, both in mouse and hamster cultures. Except for the early period of infection, polyoma virus cannot ordinarily be recovered from hamster populations, and even in mouse cell lines, clones are obtained that seem to be virus-free. Vogt and Dulbecco found the transformed cells of either type to be resistant to superinfection, a feature that is particularly characteristic of lysogenic bacteria carrying a temperate phage in an integrated form.

Although the initial occurrence of cell destruction may favor the resistant variants in mouse cell cultures by simple selection, the acquisition of resistance to superinfection in hamster cultures is less readily explained on this basis. However, resistance to superinfection does not seem to be a consistent outcome of neoplastic conversion by polyoma virus, if consideration is extended to tumors arising *in vivo*. Among such neoplasms, there is a spectrum ranging from resistance to complete sensitivity if the tumors are explanted and challenged in culture with polyoma virus. The range of susceptibility appears to be identical when polyoma tumors are compared to those of nonviral origin (Hellström, Hellström, Sjögren, and Klein, 1960; Hellström and Hellström, 1962; Hellström, Hellström, and Sjögren, 1962).

If the behavior of temperate bacteriophages offers a significant model for the polyoma system, it should be possible to induce the production of virus within tumor cells that appear to be agent-free. Failure to do so was reported by Habel and Silverberg (1960). Their experiments were performed with a tumor induced in hamsters by polyoma virus and which ceased to release virus after serial transplantation. Although the neoplasm in question was treated *in vivo* in an indirect fashion by X irradiation, cortisone treatment, and starvation of the host, and although cultures of the tumor were exposed to X irradiation and ultraviolet light, no indications of virus production or release were obtained. These findings have been supported by the careful and precise studies of Vogt and Dulbecco (1962a) on cell populations transformed *in vitro*. Major efforts in particular were made to secure virus release from a clone of mouse cells in which polyoma virus could no longer be detected. A number of treatments were tried, including several known to induce the formation of mature phage in lysogenic bacteria: X irradiation, exposure to mitomycin, deprivation of thymine by administration of aminopterin, and different conditions of starvation. None of these procedures resulted in the appearance of infective virus when cell extracts or supernatants were added to sensitive indicator cultures. A similar range of treatments, extended to include additional drugs and ultraviolet irradiation, failed to induce the release of virus from transformed hamster cells. Even when persistently infected populations of mouse cells were employed, it did not prove possible to increase the production of polyoma virus above the original low level.

Reasoning that viral antigen, if not mature virus, might be formed by negative strains of polyoma tumor cells, Vogt and Dulbecco continued their investigation by the use of fluorescent antibody techniques. However, no synthesis of polyoma antigens could be demonstrated visually, nor was there any evidence that cell extracts could bind specific antibody when incubated with rabbit polyoma immune serum. Finally, all attempts to extract an infectious DNA from the negative lines proved fruitless. The products failed to cause cytopathic changes or to induce morphological transformation when added to cultures of indicator cells. In sum, these experiments offer no analogies to the behavior of temperate bacteriophage, and do not support the concept that polyoma can exist in proviral form. While an induction process cannot be ruled out completely in tumor cells that appear to lack infectious virus, this possibility has become increasingly remote (Dulbecco and Vogt, 1962).

Left unresolved by these findings is the question whether polyoma virus actually disappears from cells that become negative after transformation or whether the viral genome is merely integrated with the cell in some more novel form. It has been suggested, for example, that polyoma DNA might become an integral part of tumor chromosomes rather than replicating as an accessory or proviral factor (Dulbecco and Vogt, 1962). Although the failure to recover polyoma with the DNA extracted from cells that appear to be virus-free militates against this hypothesis, it is difficult to perform a decisive test experimentally. A more obvious suggestion, made plausible by recent discoveries with the Rous sarcoma, is that polyoma may be propagated in continuity with the host cell as a defective virus. There is little support, however, for this idea. Unlike the Rous model, it has not been possible to induce mouse tumors with the polyoma agent under conditions that yield neoplasms free of infectious virus from the outset. Moreover, no evidence for the existence of helper viruses has been found.

Particularly convincing are the phenomena of superinfection in transformed populations that no longer release virus. If these cells are exposed to a polyoma variant differing in properties from the strain employed originally, only virus of the superinfecting type is produced (Dulbecco and Vogt, 1962). Other concepts of cell-virus interaction must therefore be considered; especially those that do not require the indefinite persistence of polyoma within transformed cells. It is conceivable, for example, that polyoma virus may act as a selective mutagen by imposing specific lesions on the host cell genome (Stoker, 1963). Alternatively, a change in the functional state of the cell can be envisioned which, though induced by polyoma virus, could persist in its absence (Dulbecco and Vogt, 1962). The merit of these speculations can only be judged by experimental tests.

In concluding the present discussion, it is important to note the remarkable similarities that exist between polyoma virus and simian vacuolating virus (SV_{40}) as tumorigenic and transforming agents. Both multiply in the host cell nucleus, giving rise to DNA-containing particles of comparable size and architectural pattern (Melnick, 1962). Host age in each case is a prime factor in conditioning the development of tumors when the viruses are injected into experimental animals. SV_{40}, like polyoma, produces sarcomas in newborn hamsters but not in animals over 3 months old (Girardi, Sweet, and Hilleman, 1963). A further similarity lies in the ability of SV_{40} to produce both cytopathic and proliferative effects in cell cultures, and morphological transformation takes place as well. The exact pattern of expression depends on the target population. When SV_{40} is added to primary cultures from human tissues, for example, there is an initial sequence of cytopathic changes followed by the emergence of pleomorphic cells, which grow rapidly and in dense array. Morphological alterations are obtained, which may include the appearance of epithelioid cells even within strains of fibroblasts. Virus continues to be released by the variant populations, but strains free from infectious particles may occur secondarily (Shein and Enders, 1962; Rabson, Malmgren, O'Conor, and Kirschstein, 1962; Pontén, Jensen, and Koprowski, 1963).

Morphological changes also take place in cultures of hamster cells exposed to SV_{40}, although cytopathic effects are not observed at any stage (Rabson and Kirschstein, 1962; Black and Rowe, 1963a; Shein, Enders, Levinthal, and Burket, 1963). Infectious virus can be isolated from these populations initially, but appears to be absent or present only in trace amounts after an extended period of subculture. So far, the question of induction has received only superficial study. There have been several reports suggesting that SV_{40} can be conserved in a subviral form within hamster tumors or cell lines that seem to be virus-free (Sabin and Koch, 1963; Gerber, 1963; Black, Rowe, and Cooper, 1963). In these instances, a renewed output of virus can be demonstrated by special techniques (for example, the plating of test cells on cercopithecus monkey kidney monolayers). Direct proof is still lacking, however, that the mature virus appearing secondarily is actually regenerated from a subviral unit that had been integrated in some fashion with the host cell.

Several sequelae of infection with SV_{40} are shared in common with polyoma-treated populations. The transformed cells in both cases are characterized by karyotypic instability, leading to the onset of aneuploidy in variable form (see Chapter 4 for details). In this respect, Rous sarcoma cells offer a clear contrast, for as a rule the latter are essentially diploid, with no detectable alterations in chromosome structure (Pontén, 1963). This difference may perhaps be significant, for while the capacity of Rous sarcoma cells for indefinite proliferation has sometimes been questioned, it is increasingly clear that both SV_{40} and polyoma can cause prompt conversion of primary strains into permanent cell lines (Jensen, Koprowski, and Pontén, 1963; Black and Rowe, 1963b; Todaro, Wolman, and Green, 1963; Todaro, Nilausen, and Green, 1963). The transition in question may be induced with SV_{40} in cultures of human as well as animal cells. It is particularly striking, and occurs with considerable rapidity, when primary strains of human fibroblasts in a declining phase of growth are used as a reaction system. A closer examination of these virus-induced changes may thus shed new light on problems relating to the spontaneous origin of permanent cell lines (Chapter 3).

A final point of similarity is the fact that neoplasms induced with SV_{40}, like polyoma tumors, contain a new cellular antigen (Defendi, 1963; Habel and Eddy, 1963; Koch and Sabin, 1963). The techniques of transplantation immunity afford a sensitive means for detecting these factors, and their nature will be considered in more detail in Chapter 8. The new antigens are foreign to the host cells, yet they cannot be identified with viral components as such. A process of virogenic conversion may be indicated, since all neoplasms elicited with SV_{40} exhibit the same novel antigen, whereas a different but equally characteristic factor is found in common among polyoma tumors. Whether the same phenomenon applies to all tumorigenic viruses remains to be seen, although this possibility has been suggested (Habel and Eddy, 1963). New cellular antigens have been reported within leukemic cells in several systems (see pp. 496–497). On the other hand, the immunological individuality of Rous sarcoma cells is well known, but the host response here could be merely a reaction to persisting virus as such (Rubin, 1962d). However, if in fact the polyoma and SV_{40} models are representative, the induction of new antigens may be a distinctive hallmark of transformation by tumor viruses. The specificity of these markers could then be used for recognition of the inducing agent.

EPIGENETIC MECHANISMS IN
NEOPLASTIC CHANGE

Genetic concepts have come increasingly to occupy a central position in discussions of neoplastic conversion at the cellular level. This emphasis seems particularly well justified in the case of tumor viruses, where heritable changes in target cells follow the entry of a novel information system. As previous discussions have made clear, it is tempting to assume that the mechanism of viral transformation depends on some alteration of the genetic apparatus of the host, perhaps by an integration of new determinants into the cellular genome. However, attempts thus far to demonstrate the validity of this hypothesis have not been notably successful. While the negative findings by no means exclude genetic modifications in virus-infected cells, there is an obvious need to keep other explanations in mind for the action of tumor viruses and, by implication, for carcinogens in general (Dulbecco and Vogt, 1962; Stoker, 1963). One alternative to be considered is the possibility that neoplastic conversion, like developmental change, stems from epigenetic modifications against a constant cellular genome. From this standpoint, induction by tumor viruses might be equivalent, for example, to the incorporation of subviral units in a new cytoplasmic steady state. Transformations by the Rous agent, and perhaps by other RNA viruses, are most readily harmonized with such assumptions. There is no evidence that DNA viruses fit into the same mold, but this might be so if a complementary RNA derivative, rather than viral DNA, were perpetuated in virus-free cells. Under these circumstances it would be understandable that Rous sarcoma virus can be induced to reappear from a noninfectious subviral form, while it is difficult or impossible to accomplish the same result with polyoma virus.

The idea that carcinogens may act by epigenetic means is far from novel. There have been repeated suggestions that neoplastic transformation can proceed through changes imposed directly on cytoplasmic organelles, with the expression of aberrant properties in the form of malignant growth (Graffi and Bielka, 1959). Implicit in these theories is the concept that at least some variations can arise and be perpetuated within somatic cells despite the presence of unmodified genetic determinants for the marker in its original form. Such assumptions raise a more general question: To what extent is the maintenance of phenotypic expression in somatic systems dependent on a continuous flow of information from the cellular genome? No conclusive answer can be given to this important question, and the pertinent data are still fragmentary. It appears, however, that wide differences may exist between individual markers with respect to the immediacy of gene control (Davidson, Allfrey, and Mirsky, 1963).

Transplantation isoantigens can perhaps be singled out to illustrate cellular characteristics that seem to require continuous gene action for phenotypic expression. As will be indicated in more detail in Chapter 8, these markers are shared in common by the cells of a given individual or by series of individuals within an inbred strain. They can be demonstrated at early stages in development, and tend to persist within isolated cells in culture. The genetic loci that control the production of isoantigens in mice are known in some detail. With this background it is possible to design experiments that demonstrate the occasional loss of specific isoantigens from heterozygous tumor cells and to show that the events concerned are consistent with a process of somatic crossing over (Chapter 8). Here, then, the removal of a specific genetic determinant is followed by a disappearance of the corresponding antigens, and continuous gene control can accordingly be inferred.

How widely this pattern may apply to other characteristics within the cellular phenotype remains to be seen. On a somewhat different basis, immediate gene control has been postulated for the biosynthetic mechanisms leading to the production of acid mucopolysaccharides in a permanent line of connective tissue cells (Davidson, Allfrey, and Mirsky, 1963; Davidson, 1963). In this case, evidence for direct gene regulation is based on a sharp decline in product formation following the administration of actinomycin D, an agent known to block the synthesis of most, if not all, cell RNA. A similar fall in the production of acid mucopolysaccharides was found by Davidson and his collaborators to take place in the presence of puromycin, which inhibits protein synthesis. Taken together, the two observations suggest that synthesizing enzymes in this system are elaborated at a high rate to compensate for turnover, and that enzyme formation requires continuous activation from the cellular genome in the form of a messenger-type RNA.

Direct gene control can thus be visualized for some cellular properties, but it is equally clear that for others, the relationship is less immediate. In the mammalian organism, for example, hemoglobin synthesis continues to take place in developing erythrocytes for some time after loss of the cell nucleus. During this interval, the cells are known as reticulocytes. They differ from mature red cells in the possession of a basophilic network rich in RNA. An explanation consistent with these facts is that final specialization of red cells depends on long-lived RNA of a template type, rather than on the continuous flow of information from nuclear genes during the biosynthetic process (see Brachet, 1960).

The relay function of RNA control systems is suggested even more clearly by the classic example of differentiation in anucleate fragments of *Acetabularia* (see Hämmerling, 1963; Brachet, 1960). This simple organism, a unicellular alga, can readily be separated into parts containing or lacking a nucleus, respectively. The anucleate fragments have a remarkable capacity for survival, and may last for several months. During this period, regeneration of characteristic morphological structures can occur, there is net protein synthesis, and the formation of specific enzymes takes place. Obviously, the maintenance and direction of synthetic processes here do not require the presence of a nucleus. As in the reticulocyte, the simplest explanation is that RNA formed originally in the intact cell persists in a functional state, and can direct morphogenetic changes for a considerable period. Such an interpretation is supported by the observation that actinomycin D inhibits growth and morphogenesis more strongly in nucleated than in anucleate halves of *Acetabularia* (Brachet and Denis, 1963). The experimental picture is complicated to some extent by the apparent occurrence of DNA within the chloroplasts of *Acetabularia* (as in those of *Chlamydomonas;* see p. 315). However, chloroplasts are known to have a remarkable degree of autonomy, and it has been suggested that chloroplast DNA may function only in the synthesis of chloroplastic RNA or protein, and not in processes of morphogenesis for the cell as a whole (Baltus and Brachet, 1963).

Still another example of gene-delegated control within microorganisms is worth mentioning. This concerns the so-called "metagons" of *Paramecium aurelia,* the existence of which has been revealed by the studies of Gibson and Beale (1962, 1963). Metagons appear to be RNA-containing particulates, synthesized as a result of primary gene action in *Paramecium.* They represent an intermediate link in the phenotypic expression of certain genetic traits; for example, the well-known killer characteristics of certain strains. As noted in Chapter 2, this feature depends on the presence of unique plasmids termed kappa particles, or other agents of a similar character. These particulates may be symbiotic bacteria, but an appropriate genetic background in the host is necessary for their persistence. The genes in question seem to function by the production of specific metagons, which in turn are indispensable for maintenance of the symbionts. The complexities of this system need not be detailed further, but the point to be emphasized is that if the killer genes are replaced experimentally with normal alleles, there is no immediate loss of the killer potential. Not until the existing metagons are diluted out in succeeding divisions (approximately 18 fissions are necessary) does the new genetic background become manifest.

Within the present climate of cytogenetic opinion, it is understandable that emphasis should be given to the persistence of information-type RNA or its derivatives in any discussion dealing with the expression and maintenance of cell characters by indirect means. But preformed structure may also play an important if accessory role in providing for the continuity of phenotypic patterns (see Sonneborn, 1963). As many authors have pointed out, structural specificity doubtless serves to modulate the flow, localization, and action of gene products. However, morphological organization also represents a secondary information system, and the degree of self-sufficiency that some structural units have is remarkable. A good example of this phenomenon can be seen in the studies made by Sonneborn and his collaborators on the cortical morphology of *Paramecium*. The surface organelles of this animal form a well-differentiated pattern, but are also subject to occasional modification. For example, "doublet" paramecia with supernumerary structures in the cortex may arise after exposure to antiserum, or natural "grafts" can occur by the transfer of cortical pieces between individuals during abnormal conjugation. Such alterations in cortical morphology are unusually stable. The variant patterns remain unchanged during binary fission, conjugation with normal animals, alterations of macronuclear features, and shifts in cytoplasmic background. Cortical specificity thus is self-propagating in *Paramecium;* it seems to require neither direct nor indirect genetic instruction from determinants located elsewhere in the cell.

These illustrations may be specialized in character, but there is no reason to believe that diversity in the control of phenotype is a unique feature of microorganisms. On the contrary, it seems likely that phenotypic stability in all cells results from a combination of gene-directed, gene-relay, and gene-independent mechanisms. At the somatic level, this concept may be particularly useful in viewing the outcome of cellular differentiation. Thus, control systems with varying degrees of decentralization may govern the specialized characteristics that emerge during morphogenesis by primary gene action. Some properties of somatic cells may be maintained exclusively by epigenetic means, without further transmission of information from the cellular genome, once the developmental period is complete (see Kaplan, 1962). Such an assumption is consistent with the common occurrence of dedifferentiation in cell cultures (Chapter 3), since epigenetic mechanisms are likely to respond more directly to extrinsic conditions. As has been previously suggested, the regression or loss of cell characters in this fashion might even be permanent in those cases where peripheral control systems were not readily regenerated by primary gene action. Several implications may be drawn from the foregoing hypothesis concerning possible mechanisms of neoplastic change. If the differentiated properties of somatic cells are not uniformly under immediate gene control, it is easier to project cellular modification in epigenetic terms. Random changes may take place within specific control systems; alternatively, variation could be imposed as a directed process by external agents, including tumor viruses. The significant feature in either case might be the perpetuation of phenotypic alteration at the cellular level, owing to a central failure by the corresponding genes to reassert the original pattern. Conceivably, some epigenetic variations might provide a direct basis for malignant change; for example, the elaboration of mitotic triggers or other novel products of biosynthesis. Alternatively, the gradual or abrupt modification of epigenetic control systems might cut off the production of specific gene repressors, by which a more primitive metabolism is blocked during morphogenesis in favor of more specialized patterns. In this case, the reactivation of growth and proliferation could be expected to follow a disorganized (that is, neoplastic) course.

If carcinogenesis is assumed to proceed along epigenetic pathways, one may conclude that tumor nuclei need not differ at the outset from their nonneoplastic counterparts, even if changes do set in secondarily. Indirectly, support for this inference can be found in the occurrence of some primary neoplasms with intact diploid patterns (Chapter 4), but a definite test would require the actual transplantation of tumor nuclei. Preliminary studies of this type have been reported by King and McKinnell (1960), who employed the techniques described in Chapter 1 to probe the developmental potential of nuclei within a frog kidney tumor. The neoplasm in question, referred to as the Lucké adenocarcinoma, occurs regularly in certain natural populations of *R. pipiens* (Lucké, 1934) and can be propagated serially in frogs by intraocular transplantation (Schlumberger and Lucké, 1949). There is circumstantial evidence, although no direct proof, that this tumor is virus-induced. Conspicuous acidophilic inclusions occur in about 50 percent of the tumor nuclei (Lucké, 1938), and viruslike particles are to be found in electron micrographs of both nucleus and cytoplasm (Fawcett, 1956). Transmission of the tumor has also been reported with cell-free filtrates (Duryee, 1956, 1960). However, it is possible that this treatment merely accelerates the rate of tumor development, since the incidence of kidney neoplasms among control animals and frogs receiving injections comes finally to the same end point (Rafferty, 1963a). Furthermore, infective spread of a tumor-inducing agent does not seem to occur between individuals of *R. pipiens,* either in the laboratory or under natural conditions (Rafferty, 1963b).

Cytologically, neoplasms of the Lucké type may have a comparatively normal chromosome complement, if the limited studies of Di Berardino, King, and McKinnell (1963) are representative. In the karyotypic analysis of a single tumor and its derivatives, some maintained for over two years in serial transfer, Di Berardino and her collaborators found remarkably few departures from the standard diploid pattern. Only 3 percent of all tumor cells examined showed numerical changes, and although structural alterations were somewhat more frequent, they were nonspecific in character. These observations suggest that the Lucké adenocarcinoma may be an especially favorable material for exploring the potential of nuclei from neoplastic cells.

In their pioneering investigation, King and McKinnell (1960) transferred tumor nuclei to enucleated eggs of R. *pipiens*, using primary neoplasms of the frog kidney or intraocular transplants as donor sources. Particularly with the primary tumors, it proved difficult to dissociate the cells completely without damage, and the incidence of mitosis was relatively low. Groups of tumor cells were therefore transplanted in some instances to the recipient eggs, although transfers of single nuclei were made as well. Only one nucleus in any event seemed to function when development of the egg took place. The exploratory experiments that were performed do not yet reveal clearly what the developmental potential of nuclei from the Lucké tumor may be. However, it appears that many of these can participate normally in cleavage and blastula formation if implanted into enucleated eggs. The most distinctive findings were obtained by implanting groups of 10 to 20 cells from primary kidney tumors. About one-third of a total of 142 eggs inoculated in this fashion underwent genuine cleavage and formed normal blastulae. The individual blastomeres each contained a single nucleus and were normal in size and shape. Most of these embryos were arrested at the blastula stage, but a few formed partial or complete gastrulae. One exceptional embryo, the cells of which appeared to be tetraploid, developed into an abnormal postneurula. The histological picture of this individual showed numerous anomalies, but partial organogenesis was evident in the appearance of hindbrain, notochord, foregut, pericardial cavity, and other embryonic structures. Cleavage and blastula formation were also obtained by the transfer of one or more nuclei from intraocular tumors, although none of the embryos developed beyond an early gastrula stage.

In considering these interesting observations, the question arises whether stromal rather than tumor cell nuclei might be responsible for the effects obtained. Such an explanation has not been ruled out conclusively, but does not seem likely because cleavage and blastula formation have yet to be induced by nuclei taken directly from normal adult tissues. The use of nuclear markers (Chapter 1) may eventually provide a more adequate control. The reasons for developmental arrest in eggs receiving tumor nuclei are not known in detail, but do not necessarily differ from those that limit the differentiation of eggs inoculated with normal nuclei. In limited karyotypic studies, King and McKinnell did find ring chromosomes in the blastomeres of embryos initiated with nuclei from an intraocular tumor transplant. Similar aberrations, however, have been seen in some embryos receiving implants of normal endodermal nuclei (King and Briggs, 1956). Moreover, it will be recalled that alterations of the cytoplasmic milieu by nitrogen mustard or by brief exposure of normal nuclei to a foreign cytoplasm are also capable of inducing a persisting karyotypic instability on nuclear transfer (Chapter 4). It may be that a comparable alteration in nucleocytoplasmic balance underlies the appearance of chromosome changes in the implanted Lucké tumor nuclei, since few if any aberrations were observed within the corresponding neoplasms *in vivo*.

Final proof that tumor formation can be mediated by epigenetic mechanisms would be the demonstration that cellular transformation and the acquisition of neoplastic properties are potentially reversible by a process of modulative change. There are no indications that such a phenomenon can occur generally, particularly in those tumors that have undergone karyotypic change. However, the possibility of reversal under special conditions needs to be examined. If the continuity of neoplastic states depends on epigenetic variation perpetuated against one or more inactive determinants in the cellular genome, it seems possible that modulation might be achieved by inducing a renewed transfer of information. In this case, a process of intracellular regeneration could be envisioned, by which the variant epigenetic control systems might be replaced by those appropriate to a more normal cellular phenotype. The apparent irreversibility of malignant change for tumors in general would then reflect merely the inability of most somatic cells to undergo a renewal of morphogenetic activity in the manner described. However, the remodeling of epigenetic patterns by primary gene action is a distinctive feature of embryonic or other pluripotent cell types. Thus the question of reversibility in neoplastic conversion can perhaps be explored most profitably with tumors that arise from cells of broad morphogenetic or regenerative capacity.

Several models can be offered to support the concept of malignant transformation as a modulative change. Of these, the most interesting are to be found among the tumors of plants, especially the so-called crown gall neoplasms (see Braun, 1961a, 1961b, 1962). Plant and animal tumors have frequently been looked upon as intrinsically distinct, and significant differences can be found (see Kupila, 1963). However, at a cellular level, the similarities in behavior are striking. Tumors of both kinds consist of variant cells that multiply as autonomous units, not subject to growth control by the organism concerned; in each, the disorganization of structure and function may be conspicuous. Crown gall, more specifically, is a neoplastic growth that occurs in various higher plants as a result of infection with a specific bacterium, *Agrobacterium tumefaciens*. A tumor-inducing principle is released, and while the exact identity of this factor remains unknown, there are a number of indications that a virus or viruslike agent may be concerned (see Braun, 1962). The continued presence of bacteria is unnecessary for maintenance of the neoplastic state. Sterile derivatives of the primary tumor can be isolated, and these can be propagated in culture or as transplants with unchanged properties.

The induction of crown gall tumors follows a pattern that is consistent with an assumption of epigenetic change. A preliminary wounding of the host plant serves to condition the reacting system and is essential for a neoplastic response. Interestingly, the growth characteristics of tumors that arise depend on the stage during the conditioning period when the tumor-inducing principle is introduced. In the succulent *Kalanchoë daigremontiana*, for example, rapidly growing and fully autonomous neoplasms are obtained only if the tumor-inducing principle is presented at about 60 hours in the normal healing cycle. More slowly growing tumors are obtained by induction at 40 or 80 hours, while at 30 to 34 or 90 to 96 hours, the resulting neoplasms are small and benign. Cyclic changes in responsiveness are also noted in crown gall formation with other plants. There is a similar gradation in neoplastic conversion at different points in the wound-healing cycle. A series of nutritional studies carried out with cell cultures shows further that growth autonomy in these neoplasms is paralleled by an increasing independence of exogenous growth factors (Braun, 1958, 1962). Thus the transformation of a normal plant cell into a crown gall tumor cell seems to proceed by the unblocking of biosynthetic systems for the elaboration of essential metabolites not formed by normal cells (Braun, 1961a, 1961b).

Crown gall tumors in general show no tendency for reversion to a nonneoplastic state, even when maintained for extended periods in culture or by serial transplantation. In some plant species such as tobacco, however, crown galls can be obtained that exhibit the properties of a teratoma; that is, highly abnormal stems and leaves are formed by the tumor cells *in vitro* or within grafts on host plants. These aberrant morphogenetic tendencies are seen in clonal cultures as well as in the uncloned parent neoplasm, demonstrating that individual teratoma cells are pluripotent (Braun, 1959). Spectacular results can be achieved if teratoma masses derived from a single cell are forced into rapid growth, as may be done by serial grafting to the stems of healthy tobacco plants. Braun (1951, 1959) has shown in this case that the aberrant stems and leaves appearing first are succeeded by shoots with a more typical pattern of development. Eventually, complete plants are formed, which flower, produce fertile seed, and are normal in every respect. Here, then, the reversal of neoplastic change seems to be effectively demonstrated. Recovery at the cellular level is symbolized by the fact that cells from the reconstituted normal tissues will no longer grow in simplified culture media that are quite adequate for propagation of the precursor teratoma. Braun has suggested that the rapid tempo of growth in the teratoma grafts may result in the dilution and eventual elimination of a more slowly replicating cytoplasmic factor, which in turn is assumed to be responsible for the neoplastic state. However, this argument would seem to apply with equal force to fast growing crown galls of the unorganized type, in which there never is any sign of reversion. The restriction of recovery to the pluripotent teratoma cells suggests that the fundamental process may be a renewal of primary gene action in the presence of appropriate morphogenetic stimuli, leading to an intracellular replacement of the variant effector systems.

No similarly striking examples can be offered for the reversibility of neoplastic change in animal cells, which generally lack the morphogenetic potential found in the meristematic tissues of higher plants. There may be a partial parallel, however, in the so-called teratocarcinomas, which can be defined as malignant neoplasms containing derivatives of all three embryonic germ layers (Pierce, 1961). For the most part, these rare and unusual tumors originate in or near the ovaries or testes, and are thought to arise from primitive germ cells or misplaced blastomeres. Those derived from the testis tend to be particularly malignant. Typically, teratocarcinomas present a great variety of tissue types, all in disorganized array. Nervous tissue, muscle, cartilage, bone, hair follicles, tooth buds, and many other recognizable structures may occur. This broad morphological spectrum is perpetuated indefinitely during serial transfer (see also Abell and Holtz, 1963).

In terms of organization, the teratocarcinoma presents a number of interesting problems. Do the various parts proliferate in parallel, or do they originate from a common precursor? Can malignancy be ascribed to one cell type, or is this characteristic associated with the tumor as a whole? Some of these questions have been considered experimentally by Pierce and his co-workers in studies of a transplantable teratocarcinoma of the mouse (Pierce, Dixon, and Verney, 1960; Pierce, 1961). The tumor in question originated as a spontaneous growth within the testis, and can be propagated as a polycystic mass in which at least 12 structural components occur. Scattered groupings of undifferentiated and atypical cells are found throughout, and these distinctive elements are referred to as embryonal carcinoma cells. Pierce and his co-workers have analyzed the population dynamics of this complex neoplasm in a novel way. By injecting thick suspensions of the tumor into the peritoneal cavity of mice, he obtained large numbers of free-floating structures, termed embryoid bodies because of their remarkable resemblance to the developmental stages of normal ova. Initially, only two or three tissue types could be found within these cystic units: an outer layer of visceral yolk-sac cells, an inner layer of mesenchyme, and in some cases, aggregates of embryonal carcinoma cells embedded in the mesenchymal network.

The developmental potential of neoplastic embryoids has been examined in some detail by subcutaneous grafting (Pierce, Dixon, and Verney, 1960). About one-third contain embryonal carcinoma cells at the outset, and the same proportion of transplants give rise to typical teratocarcinomas. Other implants disappear or develop as simple entodermally lined cysts, in which embryonal carcinoma cells are invariably missing. Circumstantial evidence thus points toward the latter as multipotential elements, capable of broad morphogenetic activity; yet retaining, when undifferentiated, the malignant behavior so characteristic of the intact complex.

There is no evidence that the developmental products of these unique stem cells are neoplastic in the usual sense. The entodermal cysts in which embryonal carcinoma cells could not be detected were found to contain a number of different components, including nodules of cartilage, brain, glands, muscle, and other specialized derivatives. But none of these exhibited a progressive growth potential, and the cysts consistently developed as benign masses. One gains the impression, therefore, that embryonal carcinoma cells as such are not seen in these cysts because a complete differentiation into specialized end products occurs. If this is so, it would appear that morphogenesis in teratocarcinomas, as in crown gall teratomas, can obliterate the epigenetic patterns on which tumorous manifestations may depend. The two systems may differ primarily in the degree of organotypic regulation that can be achieved and the completeness with which neoplastic components undergo differentiation.

If malignant cells arising from embryonic sources can in some instances be converted to nonneoplastic tissues, it is reasonable to look for a similar histogenesis in tumors derived from adult tissues that may have persisting developmental potentials. The urodele amphibia in particular are noted for their extensive regenerative ability, and this fact may account for the remarkable findings of Seilern-Aspang and Kratochwil (1962, 1963). These workers induced epithelial tumors in the European newt, *Triturus cristatus,* by subcutaneous injections of methylcholanthrene and other carcinogenic hydrocarbons. The neoplasms that appeared arose in multicentric fashion from mucous glands of the skin. Subsequently, they coalesced to form massive growths, enlarging by expansion as well as by invasion of contiguous host tissues. The malignant quality of these tumors seems well established by a pattern of infiltrating and destructive growth (extending in some cases into the peritoneal cavity), by the frequent occurrence of metastases to other parts of the body, and by the numerous deaths of experimental animals which resulted from these complications. Yet, in many cases, the neoplastic process was terminated by a conspicuous tumor regression. The basis of this phenomenon appeared to be a differentiation of tumor cells into normal, nonmalignant tissues. Within expansively growing tumors, neoplastic elements were replaced by pigment cells, cornified layers, mucous glands, and typical integumental epithelium. Infiltrating projections of tumor took on the characteristics of fibrous connective tissue. The inductive factors are unknown, and the mechanisms of such morphogenetic transformations remain an open problem. However, the suggestion seems obvious that neoplastic conversion here, as in certain other systems, may be a reversible process.

Tumor modulation may thus provide a strategic testing ground for genetic and epigenetic concepts of neoplastic change. In this area, the techniques of cell culture could be particularly fruitful. Except in plants, morphogenetic processes within tumors have not been examined by clonal analysis, nor have the malignancy potentials of individual components in complex neoplasms been compared directly. Conceivably, morphogenetic expression by neoplastic stem cells might become more reproducible if these elements were subjected to an appropriate conditioning *in vitro*. The possibility of shifting the pattern of neoplastic proliferation to one of organized growth by the induction or reassertion of primary gene action is an attractive concept, if only on a speculative basis. As such, it deserves to be explored more widely with neoplastic populations that may be uniquely suited to this study.

■ References

ABELL, M. R., and HOLTZ, F. 1963. Testicular neoplasms in infants and children. I. Tumors of germ cell origin. Cancer, **16**: 965–981.

ABERCROMBIE, M. 1962. Contact-dependent behavior of normal cells and the possible significance of surface changes in virus-induced transformation. Cold Spring Harbor Symp. Quant. Biol., **27**: 427–431.

ABERCROMBIE, M., and HEAYSMAN, J. E. M. 1953. Observations on the social behavior of cells in tissue culture. I. Speed and movement of chick heart fibroblasts in relation to their mutual contacts. Exptl. Cell Res., **5**: 111–131.

ABERCROMBIE, M., HEAYSMAN, J. E. M., and KARTHAUSER, H. M. 1957. Social behavior of cells in tissue culture. III. Mutual influence of sarcoma cells and fibroblasts. Exptl. Cell Res., **13**: 276–291.

ALEXANDER, P., and HORNING, E. S. 1959. Observations on the Oppenheimer method of inducing tumors by subcutaneous implantation of plastic films. *In: Carcinogenesis. Mechanisms of Action*, pp. 12–25. G. E. W. Wolstenholme and M. O'Connor, eds. Boston: Little, Brown & Company.

ALGIRE, G. H., CHALKLEY, H. W., and EARLE, W. R. 1950. Vascular reactions of normal and malignant tissues *in vivo*. III. Vascular reactions of mice to fibroblasts treated *in vitro* with methylcholanthrene. J. Natl. Cancer Inst., **11**: 555–579.

ALLISON, A. C. 1961. Interference with, and interferon production by, polyoma virus. Virology, **15**: 47–51.

BADER, J. P. 1962. Production of interferon by chick embryo cells exposed to Rous sarcoma virus. Virology, **16**: 436–443.

BALTUS, E., and BRACHET, J. 1963. Presence of deoxyribonucleic acid in the chloroplasts of *Acetabularia mediterranea*. Biochim. et Biophys. Acta, **76**: 490–492.

BALUDA, M. A., and GOETZ, I. E. 1961. Morphological conversion of cell cultures by avian myeloblastosis virus. Virology, **15**: 185–199.

BARSKI, G., and CASSINGENA, R. 1963. Malignant transformation *in vitro* of cells from $C_{57}BL$ mouse normal pulmonary tissue. J. Natl. Cancer Inst., **30**: 865–883.

BATHER, R. 1957. The nucleic acid of partially purified Rous No. 1 sarcoma virus. Brit. J. Cancer, **11**: 611–619.

BEARD, J. W. 1957. Etiology of avian leukosis. Ann. N. Y. Acad. Sci., **68**: 473–486.

BEAUDREAU, G. S., BECKER, C., BONAR, R. A., WALLBANK, A. M., BEARD, D., and BEARD, J. W. 1960. Virus of avian myeloblastosis. XIV. Neoplastic response of normal chicken bone marrow treated with the virus in tissue culture. J. Natl. Cancer Inst., **24**: 395–415.

BERNHARD, W., FEBVRE, H. L., and CRAMER, R. 1959. Mise en évidence au microscope électronique d'un virus dans les cellules infectées *in vitro* par l'agent du polyome. Compt. Rend. Acad. Sci., **249**: 483–485.

BERWALD, Y., and SACHS, L. 1963. *In vitro* transformation with chemical carcinogens. Nature, **200**: 1182–1184.

BLACK, P. H., HARTLEY, J. W., ROWE, W. P., and HUEBNER, R. J. 1963. Transformation of bovine tissue culture cells by bovine papilloma virus. Nature, **199**: 1016–1018.

BLACK, P. H., and ROWE, W. P. 1963a. Transformation in hamster kidney monolayers by vacuolating virus, SV-40. Virology, **19**: 107–108.

BLACK, P. H., and ROWE, W. P. 1963b. SV-40 induced proliferation of tissue culture cells of rabbit, mouse, and porcine origin. Proc. Soc. Exptl. Biol. Med., **114**: 721–727.

BLACK, P. H., ROWE, W. P., and COOPER, H. L. 1963. An analysis of SV 40-induced transformation of hamster kidney tissue *in vitro*. II. Studies of three clones derived from a continuous line of transformed cells. Proc. Natl. Acad. Sci., **50**: 847–854.

BRACHET, J. 1960. The biological role of ribonucleic acids. Amsterdam: Elsevier Publishing Company. 144 pp.

BRACHET, J., and DENIS, H. 1963. Effects of actinomycin D on morphogenesis. Nature, **198**: 205–206.

BRAND, K. G., and SYVERTON, J. T. 1962. Results of species-specific hemagglutination tests on "transformed," nontransformed, and primary cell cultures. J. Natl. Cancer Inst., **28**: 147–157.

BRAUN, A. C. 1951. Recovery of crown-gall tumor cells. Cancer Res., **11**: 839–844.

BRAUN, A. C. 1958. A physiological basis for autonomous growth of the crown-gall tumor cell. Proc. Natl. Acad. Sci., **44**: 344–349.

BRAUN, A. C. 1959. A demonstration of the recovery of the crown-gall tumor cell with the use of complex tumors of single-cell origin. Proc. Natl. Acad. Sci., **45**: 932–938.

BRAUN, A. C. 1961a. Plant tumors as an experimental model. Harvey Lectures, **56**: 191–210. New York: Academic Press, Inc.

BRAUN, A. C. 1961b. The plant tumor cell as an experimental tool for studies on the nature of autonomous growth. Can. Cancer Conf., **4**: 89–98.

BRAUN, A. C. 1962. Tumor inception and development in the crown gall disease. Ann. Rev. Plant Physiol., **13**: 533–558.

BRYAN, W. R., CALNAN, D., and MOLONEY, J. B. 1955. Biological studies on the Rous sarcoma virus. III. The recovery of virus from experimental tumors in relation to initiating dose. J. Natl. Cancer Inst., **16**: 317–335.

BURMESTER, B. R. 1957. Routes of natural infection in avian lymphomatosis. Ann. N. Y. Acad. Sci., **68**: 487–495.

CORIELL, L. L., McALLISTER, R. M., and WAGNER, B. M. 1957. Criteria for determining malignancy in tissue-culture cell lines in the albino rat. Spec. Publ. N. Y. Acad. Sci., **5**: 341–350.

CORIELL, L. L., McALLISTER, R. M., WAGNER, B. M., WILSON, S. R., and DWIGHT, S. A. 1958. Growth of primate and nonprimate tissue culture cell lines in X-irradiated and cortisone-treated rats. Cancer, **11**: 1236–1241.

DAVIDSON, E. H. 1963. Heritability and control of differentiated function in cultured cells. J. Gen. Physiol., **46:** 983–998.

DAVIDSON, E. H., ALLFREY, V. G., and MIRSKY, A. E. 1963. Gene expression in differentiated cells. Proc. Natl. Acad. Sci., **49:** 53–60.

DAWE, C. J., LAW, L. W., MORGAN, W. D., and SHAW, M. G. 1962. Morphological responses to tumor viruses. Federation Proc., **21:** 5–14.

DAWE, C. J., POTTER, M., and LEIGHTON, J. 1958. Progressions of a reticulum-cell sarcoma of the mouse *in vivo* and *in vitro*. J. Natl. Cancer Inst., **21:** 753–781.

DE BRUYN, W. M., and HANSEN-MELANDER, E. 1962. Chromosome studies in the MB mouse lymphosarcoma. J. Natl. Cancer Inst., **28:** 1333–1354.

DEFENDI, V. 1963. Effect of SV_{40} virus immunization on growth of transplantable SV_{40} and polyoma tumors in hamsters. Proc. Soc. Exptl. Biol. Med., **113:** 12–16.

DEFENDI, V., LEHMAN, J., and KRAEMER, P. 1963. "Morphologically normal" hamster cells with malignant properties. Virology, **19:** 592–598.

DI BERARDINO, M. A., KING, T. J., and McKINNELL, R. G. 1963. Chromosome studies of a frog renal adenocarcinoma line carried by serial intraocular transplantation. J. Natl. Cancer Inst., **31:** 769–789.

DiMAYORCA, G. A., EDDY, B. E., STEWART, S. E., HUNTER, W. S., FRIEND, C., and BENDICH, A. 1959. Isolation of infectious deoxyribonucleic acid from SE polyoma-infected tissue cultures. Proc. Natl. Acad. Sci., **45:** 1805–1808.

DUBOS, R. J. 1945. The bacterial cell in its relation to problems of virulence, immunity and chemotherapy. Cambridge: Harvard University Press, 460 pp.

DULBECCO, R. 1960a. Induction of tumors *in vitro* with viruses. Natl. Cancer Inst. Monogr., **4:** 355–361.

DULBECCO, R. 1960b. A consideration of virus-host relationship in virus-induced neoplasia at the cellular level. Cancer Res., **20:** 751–761.

DULBECCO, R. 1963. Transformation of cells *in vitro* by viruses. Science, **142:** 932–936.

DULBECCO, R., and FREEMAN, G. 1959. Plaque production by the polyoma virus. Virology, **8:** 396–397.

DULBECCO, R., and VOGT, M. 1960. Significance of continued virus production in tissue cultures rendered neoplastic by polyoma virus. Proc. Natl. Acad. Sci., **46:** 1617–1623.

DULBECCO, R., and VOGT, M. 1962. Is there an integrated virus genome in virus-induced neoplastic cells? *In: The Molecular Basis of Neoplasia,* pp. 475–482. Austin: University of Texas Press.

DURYEE, W. R. 1956. Seminar on transmission studies on renal adenocarcinoma of the frog. J. Franklin Inst., **261:** 377–379.

DURYEE, W. R. 1960. Nuclear physiology in adenocarcinoma of the amphibia. *In: Cell Physiology of Neoplasia,* pp. 501–523. Austin: University of Texas Press.

EARLE, W. R. 1943. Production of malignancy *in vitro*. IV. The mouse fibroblast cultures and changes seen in the living cells. J. Natl. Cancer Inst., 4: 165–212.

EARLE, W. R. 1944. A summary of certain data on the production of malignancy *in vitro*. In: *A. A. A. S. Research Conference on Cancer*, pp. 139–153. Washington: American Association for the Advancement of Science.

EARLE, W. R., and NETTLESHIP, A. 1943. Production of malignancy *in vitro*. V. Results of injections of cultures into mice. J. Natl. Cancer Inst., 4: 213–228.

EARLE, W. R., SCHILLING, E. L., and SHELTON, E. 1950. Production of malignancy *in vitro*. X. Continued description of cells at the glass interface of the cultures. J. Natl. Cancer Inst., 10: 1067–1102.

EARLE, W. R., SHELTON, E., and SCHILLING, E. L. 1950. Production of malignancy *in vitro*. XI. Further results from reinjection of *in vitro* cell strains into strain C_3H mice. J. Natl. Cancer Inst., 10: 1105–1113.

EARLE, W. R., and VOEGTLIN, C. 1938. The mode of action of methylcholanthrene on cultures of normal tissues. Am. J. Cancer, 34: 373–390.

EARLE, W. R., and VOEGTLIN, C. 1940. A further study of the mode of action of methylcholanthrene on normal tissue cultures. U.S. Public Health Rep., 55: 303–322.

EDDY, B. E. 1962. Tumors produced in hamsters by SV_{40}. Federation Proc., 21: 930–935.

EDDY, B. E., and STEWART, S. E. 1959. Physical properties, and hemagglutinating and cytopathogenic effects of the SE polyoma virus. Can. Cancer Conf., 3: 307–324.

EDDY, B. E., STEWART, S. E., and BERKELEY, W. 1958. Cytopathogenicity in tissue cultures by a tumor virus from mice. Proc. Soc. Exptl. Biol. Med., 98: 848–851.

EDDY, B. E., STEWART, S. E., YOUNG, R., and MIDER, G. B. 1958. Neoplasms in hamsters induced by mouse tumor agent passed in tissue culture. J. Natl. Cancer Inst., 20: 747–761.

EVANS, V. J. 1961. The culture of long-term strains in protein-free chemically defined medium. Path. et Biol. (Paris), 9: 578–580.

EVANS, V. J., BRYANT, J. C., McQUILKIN, W. T., FIORAMONTI, M. C., SANFORD, K. K., WESTFALL, B. B., and EARLE, W. R. 1956. Studies of nutrient media for tissue cells *in vitro*. II. An improved protein-free chemically defined medium for long-term cultivation of Strain L-929 cells. Cancer Res., 16: 87–94.

EVANS, V. J., HAWKINS, N. M., WESTFALL, B. B., and EARLE, W. R. 1958. Studies on culture lines derived from mouse liver parenchymatous cells grown in long-term tissue culture. Cancer Res., 18: 261–266.

FAWCETT, D. W. 1956. Electron microscope observations on intracellular viruslike particles associated with the cells of the Lucké renal adenocarcinoma. J. Biophys. Biochem. Cytol., 2: 725–742.

FIROR, W. M., and GEY, G. O. 1945. Observations on the conversion of normal into malignant cells. Ann. Surg., 121: 700–703.

FOGH, J., and HOK, K. A. 1958. Tumor production in x-ray- and cortisone-treated rats given injections of human cells in continuous cultivation. Cancer Res., **18:** 692–697.

FOLEY, G. E., and HANDLER, A. H. 1957. Differentiation of "normal" and neoplastic cells maintained in tissue culture by implantation into normal hamsters. Proc. Soc. Exptl. Biol. Med., **94:** 661–664.

FOLEY, G. E., and HANDLER, A. H. 1958. Tumorigenic activity of tissue cell cultures. Ann. N. Y. Acad. Sci., **76:** 506–512.

FOLEY, G. E., HANDLER, A. H., ADAMS, R. A., and CRAIG, J. M. 1962. Assessment of potential malignancy of cultured cells: Further observations on the differentiation of "normal" and "neoplastic" cells maintained *in vitro* by heterotransplantation in Syrian hamsters. Natl. Cancer Inst. Monogr., **7:** 173–204.

FOULDS, L. 1954. The experimental study of tumor progression: a review. Cancer Res., **14:** 327–339.

FRASER, K. B., and GHARPURE, M. 1962. Immunofluorescent tracing of polyoma virus in transformation experiments with BHK-21 cells. Virology, **18:** 505–507.

FRIEDMAN, R. M., RABSON, A. S., and KIRKHAM, W. R. 1963. Variation in interferon production by polyoma virus strains of differing oncogenicity. Proc. Soc. Exptl. Biol. Med., **112:** 347–349.

FRIESEN, B., and RUBIN, H. 1961. Some physiochemical and immunological properties of an avian leucosis virus (RIF). Virology, **15:** 387–396.

GERBER, P. 1963. Tumors induced in hamsters by simian virus 40: persistent subviral infection. Science, **140:** 889–890.

GEY, G. O. 1941. Cytological and cultural observations on transplantable rat sarcomata produced by the inoculation of altered normal cells maintained in continuous culture. Cancer Res., **1:** 737.

GEY, G. O. 1955. Some aspects of the constitution and behavior of normal and malignant cells maintained in continuous culture. Harvey Lectures, **50:** 154–229. New York: Academic Press, Inc.

GEY, G. O., GEY, M. K., FIROR, W. M., and SELF, W. O. 1949. Cultural and cytologic studies on autologous normal and malignant cells of specific *in vitro* origin. Conversion of normal into malignant cells. Acta Unio Intern. Contra Cancrum, **6:** 706–712.

GIBSON, I., and BEALE, G. H. 1962. The mechanism whereby the genes M_1 and M_2 in *Paramecium aurelia*, stock 540, control growth of the mate-killer particles. Genet. Res., **3:** 24–50.

GIBSON, I., and BEALE, G. H. 1963. The action of ribonuclease and 8-azaguanine on mate-killer paramecia. Genet. Res., **4:** 42–54.

GIRARDI, A. J., SWEET, B. H., and HILLEMAN, M. R. 1963. Factors inducing tumor induction in hamsters by vacuolating virus, SV_{40}. Proc. Soc. Exptl. Biol. Med., **112:** 662–667.

GOLDBLATT, H., and CAMERON, G. 1953. Induced malignancy in cells from rat myocardium subjected to intermittent anaerobiosis during long propagation *in vitro*. J. Exptl. Med., **97:** 525–552.

GOLDHABER, P. 1961. The influence of pore size on carcinogenicity of subcutaneously implanted Millipore filters. Proc. Am. Assoc. Cancer Res., 3: 228.

GOTLIEB-STEMATSKY, T., and LEVENTON, S. 1960. Studies on the biological properties of two plaque variants isolated from SE polyoma virus. Brit. J. Exptl. Pathol., 41: 507–519.

GRAFFI, A., and BIELKA, H. 1959. Probleme der experimentellen Krebsforschung. Leipzig: Akademische Verlagsgesellschaft. Geest and Portig K.-G. 560 pp.

GREENE, H. S. N. 1955. Compatibility and non-compatibility in tissue transplantation. In: *Biological Specificity and Growth,* pp. 177–194. E. G. Butler, ed. Princeton: Princeton University Press.

GROSS, L. 1961. Oncogenic viruses. New York: Pergamon Press, Inc. 393 pp.

HABEL, K. 1962. Polyoma tumor antigen in cells transformed *in vitro* by polyoma virus. Virology, 18: 553–558.

HABEL, K. 1963. Malignant transformation by polyoma virus. Ann. Rev. Microbiol., 17: 167–178.

HABEL, K., and EDDY, B. E. 1963. Specificity of resistance to tumor challenge of polyoma and SV$_{40}$ virus-immune hamsters. Proc. Soc. Exptl. Biol. Med., 113: 1–4.

HABEL, K., and SILVERBERG, R. J. 1960. Relationship of polyoma virus and tumor *in vivo.* Virology, 12: 463–476.

HALBERSTAEDTER, L., DOLJANSKI, L., and TENENBAUM, E. 1941. Experiments on the cancerization of cells *in vitro* by means of Rous sarcoma agent. Brit. J. Exptl. Pathol., 22: 179–187.

HÄMMERLING, J. 1953. Nucleo-cytoplasmic relationships in the development of *Acetabularia.* Intern. Rev. Cytol., 2: 475–498.

HANAFUSA, H., HANAFUSA, T., and RUBIN, H. 1963. The defectiveness of Rous sarcoma virus. Proc. Natl. Acad. Sci., 49: 572–580.

HARRIS, M. 1942. Differentiation and growth of gastrular anlagen implanted homoplastically into tadpoles of *Hyla regilla.* Univ. Calif. Publ. Zoöl., 51: 41–86.

HAYFLICK, L., and MOORHEAD, P. S. 1961. The serial cultivation of human diploid cell strains. Exptl. Cell Res., 25: 585–621.

HELLSTRÖM, I., and HELLSTRÖM, K. E. 1962. Variations in the sensitivity to polyoma virus in cultures of polyoma tumors and other neoplasms. Exptl. Cell Res., 26: 608–611.

HELLSTRÖM, I., HELLSTRÖM, K. E., and SJÖGREN, H. O. 1962. Further studies on superinfection of polyoma-induced mouse tumors with polyoma virus *in vitro.* Virology, 16: 282–306.

HELLSTRÖM, I., HELLSTRÖM, K. E., SJÖGREN, H. O., and KLEIN, G. 1960. Superinfection of polyoma-induced mouse tumors with polyoma virus *in vitro.* Exptl. Cell Res., 21: 255–259.

HENLE, G., DEINHARDT, F., and RODRIGUEZ, J. 1959. The development of polyoma virus in mouse embryo cells as revealed by fluorescent antibody staining. Virology, 8: 388–391.

Hsu, T. C. 1960. Reduction of transplantability of Novikoff hepatoma cells grown *in vitro* and the consequent protecting effect to the host against their malignant progenitor. J. Natl. Cancer Inst., **25**: 927–935.

Huebner, R. J., Rowe, W. P., and Lane, W. T. 1962. Oncogenic effects in hamsters of human adenovirus types 12 and 18. Proc. Natl. Acad. Sci., **48**: 2051–2058.

Jacob, F., and Wollman, E. L. 1961. Sexuality and the genetics of bacteria. New York: Academic Press, Inc. 374 pp.

Jensen, F., Koprowski, H., and Pontén, J. A. 1963. Rapid transformation of human fibroblast cultures by simian virus 40. Proc. Natl. Acad. Sci., **50**: 343–348.

Kaplan, H. S. 1962. Possible mechanisms of virus carcinogenesis. Federation Proc., **21**: 1–4.

Keogh, E. V. 1938. Ectodermal lesions produced by the virus of Rous sarcoma. Brit. J. Exptl. Pathol., **19**: 1–9.

King, T. J., and Briggs, R. 1956. Serial transplantation of embryonic nuclei. Cold Spring Harbor Symp. Quant. Biol., **21**: 271–290.

King, T. J., and McKinnell, R. G. 1960. An attempt to determine the developmental potentialities of the cancer cell nucleus by means of transplantation. *In: Cell Physiology of Neoplasia*, pp. 591–617. Austin: Univ. Texas Press.

Klein, G., Sjögren, H. O., Klein, E., and Hellström, K. E. 1960. Demonstration of resistance against methylcholanthrene-induced sarcomas in the primary autochthonous host. Cancer Res., **20**: 1561–1572.

Koch, M. A., and Sabin, A. B. 1963. Specificity of virus-induced resistance to transplantation of polyoma and SV_{40} tumors in adult hamsters. Proc. Soc. Exptl. Biol. Med., **113**: 4–12.

Kohn, A. 1963. Possible integration of viral nucleic acid into the genome of animal cells. Progr. Med. Virol., **5**: 169–218.

Kupila, S. 1963. Crown gall as an anatomical and cytological problem. A review. Cancer Res., **23**: 497–509.

Leighton, J. 1957. Contributions of tissue culture studies to an understanding of the biology of cancer: A review. Cancer Res., **17**: 929–941.

Leighton, J., Kline, I., Belkin, M., Legallais, F., and Orr, H. C. 1957. The similarity in histologic appearance of some human "cancer" and "normal" cell strains in sponge-matrix tissue culture. Cancer Res., **17**: 359–363.

Levan, A., and Biesele, J. J. 1958. Role of chromosomes in cancerogenesis, as studied in serial tissue culture of mammalian cells. Ann. N. Y. Acad. Sci., **71**: 1022–1053.

Loeb, T., and Zinder, N. D. 1961. A bacteriophage containing RNA. Proc. Natl. Acad. Sci., **47**: 282–289.

Lucké, B. 1934. A neoplastic disease of the kidney of the frog, *Rana pipiens*. Am. J. Cancer, **20**: 352–379.

Lucké, B. 1938. Carcinoma in the leopard frog: Its probable causation by a virus. J. Exptl. Med., **68**: 457–468.

Luria, S. E. 1959. Viruses as determinants of cellular functions. Can. Cancer Conf., 3: 261–270.

Luria, S. E. 1960. Viruses, cancer cells, and the genetic concept of virus infection. Cancer Res., 20: 677–688.

Luria, S. E. 1962. Bacteriophage genes and bacterial functions. Science, 136: 685–692.

Macpherson, I. 1963. Characteristics of a hamster cell clone transformed by polyoma virus. J. Natl. Cancer Inst., 30: 795–815.

Macpherson, I., and Stoker, M. 1962. Polyoma transformation of hamster cell clones—an investigation of genetic factors affecting cell competence. Virology, 16: 147–151.

Manaker, R. A., and Groupé, V. 1956. Discrete foci of altered chicken embryo cells associated with Rous sarcoma virus in tissue culture. Virology, 2: 838–840.

McAllister, R. M., and Coriell, L. L. 1959. Tumorigenicity of tissue culture cells. Cancer Res., 19: 1040–1041.

McQuilkin, W. T., Evans, V. J., and Earle, W. R. 1957. The adaptation of additional lines of NCTC Clone 929 (Strain L) cells to chemically defined protein-free medium NCTC 109. J. Natl. Cancer Inst., 19: 885–907.

Medina, D., and Sachs, L. 1960. The *in vitro* formation of a stable cell-virus association with polyoma virus. Virology, 10: 387–388.

Medina, D., and Sachs, L. 1961. Cell-virus interactions with the polyoma virus: the induction of cell transformation and malignancy *in vitro*. Brit. J. Cancer, 15: 885–904.

Melnick, J. L. 1962. Papova virus group. Science, 135: 1128–1130.

Moore, A. E. 1957. Tumor formation by cultured cells derived from normal and cancerous tissues. Spec. Publ. N.Y. Acad. Sci., 5: 321–329.

Moore, A. E. 1958. Tumorigenic activity of cultures. Ann. N. Y. Acad. Sci., 76: 497–505.

Moore, A. E., Southam, C. M., and Sternberg, S. S. 1956. Neoplastic changes developing in epithelial cell lines from normal persons. Science, 124: 127–129.

Morgan, H. R., and Andrese, A. P. 1962. Comparative studies in Rous sarcoma with virus, tumor cells and chick embryo cells transformed *in vitro* by virus. III. Malignancy *in vivo* of cells transformed *in vitro* by virus. J. Exptl. Med., 116: 329–336.

Mueller, G. C., Kajiwara, K., Stubblefield, E., and Rueckert, R. R. 1962. Molecular events in the reproduction of animal cells. I. The effect of puromycin on the duplication of DNA. Cancer Res., 22: 1084–1090.

Nettleship, A., and Earle, W. R. 1943. Production of malignancy *in vitro*. VI. Pathology of tumors produced. J. Natl. Cancer Inst., 4: 229–248.

Oppenheimer, E. T., Willhite, M., Danishefsky, I., and Stout, A. P. 1961. Observations on the effects of powdered polymer in the carcinogenic process. Cancer Res., 21: 132–134.

Pierce, G. B., Jr. 1961. Teratocarcinomas, a problem in developmental biology. Can. Cancer Conf., 4: 119–137.

PIERCE, G. B., JR., DIXON, F. J., JR., and VERNEY, E. L. 1960. Teratocarcinogenic and tissue-forming potentials of the cell types comprising neoplastic embryoid bodies. Lab. Invest., 9: 583–602.

PONTÉN, J. 1962. Homologous transfer of Rous sarcoma by cells. J. Natl. Cancer Inst., 29: 1147–1159.

PONTÉN, J. 1963. Chromosome analysis of three virus-associated chicken tumors: Rous sarcoma, erythroleukemia, and RPL12 lymphoid tumor. J. Natl. Cancer Inst., 30: 897–921.

PONTÉN, J., JENSEN, F., and KOPROWSKI, H. 1963. Morphological and virological investigation of human tissue cultures transformed with SV_{40}. J. Cellular Comp. Physiol., 61: 145–154.

PRINCE, A. M. 1959. Quantitative studies on Rous sarcoma virus. IV. An investigation of the nature of "non-infective" tumors induced by low doses of virus. J. Natl. Cancer Inst., 23: 1361–1381.

PRINCE, A. M. 1960. Quantitative studies on Rous sarcoma virus. VI. Clonal analysis of *in vitro* infections. Virology, 11: 400–424.

PRINCE, A. M. 1962a. Tumor virus: cell relationships. A critical survey of findings in the polyoma system. Progr. Med. Virol., 4: 208–258.

PRINCE, A. M. 1962b. Factors influencing the determination of cellular morphology in cells infected with Rous sarcoma virus. Virology, 18: 524–534.

RABSON, A. S., and KIRSCHSTEIN, R. L. 1962. Induction of malignancy *in vitro* in newborn hamster kidney tissue infected with simian vacuolating virus (SV_{40}). Proc. Soc. Exptl. Biol. Med., 111: 323–328.

RABSON, A. S., MALMGREN, R. A., O'CONOR, G. T., and KIRSCHSTEIN, R. L. 1962. Simian vacuolating virus (SV_{40}) infection in cell cultures derived from adult human thyroid tissue. J. Natl. Cancer Inst., 29: 1123–1145.

RAFFERTY, K. A., JR. 1963a. Effect of injected frog-kidney tumor extracts on development of tumors under promoting conditions. J. Natl. Cancer Inst., 30: 1103–1113.

RAFFERTY, K. A., JR. 1963b. Spontaneous kidney tumors in the frog: rate of occurrence in isolated adults. Science, 141: 720–721.

ROTHFELS, K. H., KUPELWIESER, E. B., and PARKER, R. C. 1963. Effects of X-irradiated feeder layers on mitotic activity and development of aneuploidy in mouse-embryo cells *in vitro*. Can. Cancer Conf., 5: 191–223.

RUBIN, H. 1957. The production of virus by Rous sarcoma cells. Ann. N. Y. Acad. Sci., 68: 459–472.

RUBIN, H. 1959. Special interactions between virus and cell in the Rous sarcoma. *In: Virus Growth and Variation,* pp. 171–184. A. Isaacs and B. W. Lacey, eds. Cambridge: The University Press.

RUBIN, H. 1960a. An analysis of the assay of Rous sarcoma cells *in vitro* by the infective center technique. Virology, 10: 29–49.

RUBIN, H. 1960b. Growth of Rous sarcoma virus in chick embryo cells following irradiation of host cells or free virus. Virology, 11: 28–47.

RUBIN, H. 1960c. The suppression of morphological alterations in cells infected with Rous sarcoma virus. Virology, 12: 14–31.

RUBIN, H. 1960d. A virus in chick embryos which induces resistance *in vitro* to infection with Rous sarcoma virus. Proc. Natl. Acad. Sci., **46**: 1105–1119.

RUBIN, H. 1961. Influence of tumor virus infection on the antigenicity and behavior of cells. Cancer Res., **21**: 1244–1253.

RUBIN, H. 1962a. Conditions for establishing immunological tolerance to a tumor virus. Nature, **195**: 342–345.

RUBIN, H. 1962b. Response of cell and organism to infection with avian tumor viruses. Bacteriol. Revs., **26**: 1–13.

RUBIN, H. 1962c. The immunologic basis for non-infective tumors and regressions in the Rous sarcoma. Ann. N. Y. Acad. Sci., **101**: 181–185.

RUBIN, H. 1962d. The immunological basis for non-infective Rous sarcomas. Cold Spring Harbor Symp. Quant. Biol., **27**: 441–452.

RUBIN, H., CORNELIUS, A., and FANSHIER, L. 1961. The pattern of congenital transmission of an avian leukosis virus. Proc. Natl. Acad. Sci., **47**: 1058–1069.

RUBIN, H., and HANAFUSA, H. 1963. Significance of the absence of infectious virus in virus-induced tumors. *In: Viruses, Nucleic Acids, and Cancer*, pp. 508–525. Baltimore: The Williams and Wilkins Company.

RUBIN, H., and TEMIN, H. M. 1958. Infection with the Rous sarcoma virus *in vitro*. Federation Proc., **17**: 994–1003.

RUBIN, H., and TEMIN, H. M. 1959a. Radiation studies on lysogeny and tumor viruses. *In: Radiation Biology and Cancer*, pp. 359–381. Austin: Univ. Texas Press.

RUBIN, H., and TEMIN, H. M. 1959b. A radiological study of cell-virus interaction in the Rous sarcoma. Virology, **7**: 75–91.

RUBIN, H., and VOGT, P. K. 1962. An avian leukosis virus associated with stocks of Rous sarcoma virus. Virology, **17**: 184–194.

SABIN, A. B., and KOCH, M. A. 1963. Evidence of continuous transmission of non-infectious SV_{40} viral genome in most or all SV_{40} hamster tumor cells. Proc. Natl. Acad. Sci., **49**: 304–311.

SACHS, L. 1962. The *in vitro* analysis of malignancy induced by polyoma virus. *In: Tumor Viruses of Murine Origin*, pp. 380–394. G. E. W. Wolstenholme and M. O'Connor, eds. Boston: Little, Brown & Company.

SACHS, L., and MEDINA, D. 1961. *In vitro* transformation of normal cells by polyoma virus. Nature, **189**: 457–458.

SANFORD, K. K. 1958. Clonal studies on normal cells and on their neoplastic transformation *in vitro*. Cancer Res., **18**: 747–752.

SANFORD, K. K., DUNN, T. B., COVALESKY, A. B., DUPREE, L. T., and EARLE, W. R. 1961. Polyoma virus and production of malignancy *in vitro*. J. Natl. Cancer Inst., **26**: 331–357.

SANFORD, K. K., EARLE, W. R., SHELTON, E., SCHILLING, E. L., DUCHESNE, E. M. LIKELY, G. D., and BECKER, M. M. 1950. Production of malignancy *in vitro*. XII. Further transformations of mouse fibroblasts to sarcomatous cells. J. Natl. Cancer Inst., **11**: 351–375.

SANFORD, K. K., HOBBS, G. L., and EARLE, W. R. 1956. The tumor-producing capacity of Strain L mouse cells after 10 years *in vitro*. Cancer Res., **16:** 162–166.

SANFORD, K. K., LIKELY, G. D., BRYAN, W. R., and EARLE, W. R. 1952. The infection of cells in tissue culture with Rous sarcoma virus. J. Natl. Cancer Inst., **12:** 1317–1343.

SANFORD, K. K., LIKELY, G. D., and EARLE, W. R. 1954. The development of variations in transplantability and morphology within a clone of mouse fibroblasts transformed to sarcoma-producing cells *in vitro*. J. Natl. Cancer Inst., **15:** 215–237.

SANFORD, K. K., MERWIN, R. M., HOBBS, G. L., and EARLE, W. R. 1959. Influence of animal passage on a line of tissue culture cells. J. Natl. Cancer Inst., **23:** 1061–1077.

SANFORD, K. K., MERWIN, R. M., HOBBS, G. L., FIORAMONTI, M. C., and EARLE, W. R. 1958. Studies on the difference in sarcoma-producing capacity of two lines of mouse cells derived *in vitro* from one cell. J. Natl. Cancer Inst., **20:** 121–145.

SANFORD, K. K., MERWIN, R. M., HOBBS, G. L., YOUNG, J. M., and EARLE, W. R. 1959. Clonal analysis of variant cell lines transformed to malignant cells in tissue culture. J. Natl. Cancer Inst., **23:** 1035–1059.

SANFORD, K. K., WESTFALL, B. B., CHU, E. H. Y., KUFF, E. L., COVALESKY, A. B., DUPREE, L. T., HOBBS, G. L., and EARLE, W. R. 1961. Alterations in morphology, arginase, and β-glucuronidase within a clone of mouse tumor cells *in vitro*. J. Natl. Cancer Inst., **26:** 1193–1219.

SANFORD, K. K., WESTFALL, B. B., WOODS, M. W., and EARLE, W. R. 1959. Metabolic variations within a clone of mouse fibroblasts transformed to neoplastic cells *in vitro*. Acta Unio Intern. Contra Cancrum, **15:** 675–679.

SCHLUMBERGER, H., and LUCKÉ, B. 1949. Serial intraocular transplantation of frog carcinoma for fourteen generations. Cancer Res., **9:** 52–60.

SCOTT, D. B. M., PAKOSKEY, A. M., and SANFORD, K. K. 1960. Analysis of enzymatic activities of clones derived from variant cell lines transformed to malignant cells in tissue culture. J. Natl. Cancer Inst., **25:** 1365–1379.

SEILERN-ASPANG, F., and KRATOCHWIL, K. 1962. Induction and differentiation of an epithelial tumour in the newt (*Triturus cristatus*). J. Embryol. Exptl. Morphol., **10:** 337–356.

SEILERN-ASPANG, F., and KRATOCHWIL, K. 1963. Die experimentelle Aktivierung der Differenzierungspotenzen enarteter Zellen. Wien. klin. Wochschr., **19:** 337–346.

SHEIN, H. M., and ENDERS, J. F. 1962. Transformation induced by simian virus 40 in human renal cell cultures. I. Morphology and growth characteristics. Proc. Natl. Acad. Sci., **48:** 1164–1172.

SHEIN, H. M., ENDERS, J. F., LEVINTHAL, J. D., and BURKET, A. E. 1963. Transformation induced by simian virus 40 in newborn Syrian hamster renal cell cultures. Proc. Natl. Acad. Sci., **49:** 28–34.

SHELTON, E., EVANS, V. J., and PARKER, G. A. 1963. Malignant transformation of mouse connective tissue grown in diffusion chambers. J. Natl. Cancer Inst., **30:** 377–391.

Smith, J. D., Freeman, G., Vogt, M., and Dulbecco, R. 1960. The nucleic acid of polyoma virus. Virology, **12**: 185–196.

Sonneborn, T. M. 1963. Does preformed cell structure play an essential role in cell heredity? *In: The Nature of Biological Diversity*, pp. 165–221. J. M. Allen, ed. New York: McGraw-Hill Book Company, Inc.

Stanners, C. P. 1963. Studies on the transformation of hamster embryo cells in culture by polyoma virus. II. Selective techniques for the detection of transformed cells. Virology, **21**: 464–476.

Stanners, C. P., Till, J. E., and Siminovitch, L. 1963. Studies on the transformation of hamster embryo cells in culture by polyoma virus. I. Properties of transformed and normal cells. Virology, **21**: 448–463.

Stanley, W. M. 1958. Relationships between cancer and viruses. A.M.A. Arch. Internal Med., **102**: 939–947.

Stent, G. S. 1958. Mating in the reproduction of bacterial viruses. Advan. Virus Res., **5**: 95–149.

Stewart, S. E., Eddy, B. E., Gochenour, A. M., Borgese, N. G., and Grubbs, G. E. 1957. The induction of neoplasms with a substance released from mouse tumors by tissue culture. Virology, **3**: 380–400.

Stoker, M. 1962a. Studies on transformation by polyoma virus *in vitro*. *In: Tumour Viruses of Murine Origin*, pp. 365–379. G. E. W. Wolstenholme and M. O'Connor, eds. Boston: Little, Brown & Company.

Stoker, M. 1962b. Characteristics of normal and transformed clones arising from BHK 21 cells exposed to polyoma virus. Virology, **18**: 649–651.

Stoker, M. 1963a. Neoplastic transformation by polyoma virus and its wider implications. Brit. Med. J., **1**: 1305–1311.

Stoker, M. 1963b. Effect of X-irradiation on susceptibility of cells to transformation by polyoma virus. Nature, **200**: 756–758.

Stoker, M., and Abel, P. 1962. Conditions affecting transformation by polyoma virus. Cold Spring Harbor Symp. Quant. Biol., **27**: 375–386.

Stoker, M., and Macpherson, I. 1961. Studies on transformation of hamster cells by polyoma virus *in vitro*. Virology, **14**: 359–370.

Temin, H. M., and Rubin, H. 1958. Characteristics of an assay for Rous sarcoma virus and Rous sarcoma cells in tissue culture. Virology, **6**: 669–688.

Temin, H. M., and Rubin, H. 1959. A kinetic study of infection of chick embryo cells *in vitro* by Rous sarcoma virus. Virology, **8**: 209–222.

Tenenbaum, E., and Doljanski, L. 1943. Studies on Rous sarcoma cells cultivated *in vitro*. 2. Morphological properties of Rous sarcoma cells. Cancer Res., **3**: 585–603.

Todaro, G. J., Nilausen, K., and Green, H. 1963. Growth properties of polyoma virus-induced hamster tumor cells. Cancer Res., **23**: 825–832.

Todaro, G. J., Wolman, S. R., and Green, H. 1963. Rapid transformation of human fibroblasts with low growth potential into established cell lines by SV_{40}. J. Cellular Comp. Physiol., **62**: 257–265.

Toolan, H. W. 1954. Transplantable human neoplasms maintained in cortisone-treated laboratory animals: H.S. #1; H. Ep. #1; H. Ep. #2; H. Ep. #3; and H. Emb. Rh. #1. Cancer Res., **14**: 660–666.

TRENTIN, J. J., YABE, Y., and TAYLOR, G. 1962. The quest for human cancer viruses. Science, **137**: 835–841.

VOGT, M., and DULBECCO, R. 1960. Virus-cell interaction with a tumor-producing virus. Proc. Natl. Acad. Sci., **46**: 365–370.

VOGT, M., and DULBECCO, R. 1962a. Studies on cells rendered neoplastic by polyoma virus: the problem of the presence of virus-related materials. Virology, **16**: 41–51.

VOGT, M., and DULBECCO, R. 1962b. Properties of cells transformed by polyoma virus. Cold Spring Harbor Symp. Quant. Biol., **27**: 367–374.

VOGT, M., and DULBECCO, R. 1963. Steps in the neoplastic transformation of hamster embryo cells by polyoma virus. Proc. Natl. Acad. Sci., **49**: 171–179.

VOGT, P. K., and RUBIN, H. 1961. Localization of infectious virus and viral antigen in chick fibroblasts during successive stages of infection with Rous sarcoma virus. Virology, **13**: 528–544.

VOGT, P. K., and RUBIN, H. 1962. The cytology of Rous sarcoma virus infection. Cold Spring Harbor Symp. Quant. Biol., **27**: 395–405.

WARBURG, O. 1956. On the origin of the cancer cell. Science, **123**: 309–314.

WEIL, R. 1962. The subviral infective agent from polyoma virus. Cold Spring Harbor Symp. Quant. Biol., **27**: 83–87.

WEISBERG, R. A. 1963a. Virus multiplication and cell killing in polyoma-infected mouse embryo cultures. Virology, **21**: 658–660.

WEISBERG, R. A. 1963b. Delayed appearance of transformed cells in polyoma virus-infected mouse embryo cultures. Virology, **21**: 669–671.

WESTFALL, B. B., PEPPERS, E. V., EVANS, V. J., SANFORD, K. K., HAWKINS, N. M., FIORAMONTI, M. C., KERR, H. A., HOBBS, G. L., and EARLE, W. R. 1958. The arginase and rhodanese activities of certain cell strains after long cultivation in vitro. J. Biophys. Biochem. Cytol., **4**: 567–570.

WILLIS, R. A. 1935. Experiments on the intracerebral implantation of embryo tissues in rats. Proc. Roy. Soc. (London) Ser. B., **117**: 400–412.

WOODS, M. W., SANFORD, K. K., BURK, D., and EARLE, W. R. 1959. Glycolytic properties of high and low sarcoma-producing lines and clones of mouse tissue-culture cells. J. Natl. Cancer Inst., **23**: 1079–1088.

YERGANIAN, G., LEONARD, M. J., GAGNON, B. S., and GAGNON, H. J. 1961. Chromosomes of the Chinese hamster Cricetulus griseus. II. Onset of malignant transformation in vitro and the appearance of the X_1 chromosome. Path. et Biol. (Paris), **9**: 533–541.

Individuality
in transplant
systems

chapter

8

The implantation of tumors or normal tissues as grafts introduces cells that may differ in genetic origin from those of the host in which they come to reside. Organisms that carry such transplants are thus chimeras at the cellular level; that is, composites of unlike parts. In man and higher animals, however, grafts genetically dissimilar to the host are rarely viable for long periods. The basis for this phenomenon is a challenging problem. Aside from its practical significance in surgery and medicine, the tendency for rejection of alien cells limits the experimental usefulness of transplant systems. Graft-host antagonism has accordingly been the subject of intensive study, and the questions that arise are fundamental ones. What, for example, are the devices that signal individuality at the cellular level among homologous units of the same type? By what means is self-recognition assured for native cell populations, as opposed to the discrimination of cells foreign to the host? Histocompatibility in this sense has provided a meeting ground for genetics, immunology, and cell biology. Cellular specificity, it seems, is a function of identification antigens, which are in turn genetically determined. Where the antigenic patterns of graft and host are nonmatching, a series of rejection mechanisms may be triggered, leading ultimately to elimination of the foreign cells. Much of the work on tissue transplantation in recent years has been devoted to a delineation of these patterns as well as to possible means for bypassing or suppressing the immune responses.

Individuality differentials in transplant systems, however, do not in all cases constitute a fixed and unchanging distinction between graft and host. In transplantable tumors, at least, the histocompatibility requirements for particular neoplasms may alter during serial passage. Transitions of this type constitute immunological progressions, dependent on antigenic changes in the transplanted cells or on the resistance of these cells to immune reactions by the host. The mechanisms of such alterations are little known. A multiplicity of means may conceivably exist, involving alternatively (1) the addition or subtraction of antigenic components within transplant cells, (2) changes in character or strength of induced host responses, and (3) increased resistance by tumor cells to rejection mechanisms. So far, only the first of these possibilities has been explored systematically. Like other markers, the spectrum of cellular antigens can be made subject to variation and selection under appropriate conditions. Tumors may be assayed for growth in hosts of known genetic background, and both gain and loss of antigenic components have in this way been documented experimentally. Whether normal tissue cells are similarly capable of isoantigenic variation is still unknown. Conceivably, immunological progressions in both neoplastic and nonneoplastic cells may be analyzed by culture methods *in vitro,* although experiments of this type are only beginning. Such a prospect is particularly attractive, since the genetic determinants for histocompatibility are known more precisely than for any other somatic cell markers, and their phenotypic expressions can be assayed with serological methods of high resolving power.

HISTOCOMPATIBILITY AND HOST-GRAFT ANTAGONISM

There is a large and rapidly expanding literature on the several aspects of tissue transplantation that have received particular study within recent years. It is not the purpose of the present discussion to review these developments *in extenso,* particularly since a number of excellent accounts are now available. Comprehensive coverage may be found, for example, in general papers by Snell (1953, 1957a, 1957b, 1957c, 1963), Gorer (1956), Medawar (1958a, 1958b, 1959a), Ebert (1959), Lawrence (1959a), Merrill (1959), Owen (1959, 1960), and Billingham and Silvers (1963). A number of symposia have also been devoted to problems of tissue grafting and histocompatibility (Rogers, 1955, 1958, 1962; Converse, 1957, 1960; Albert and Medawar, 1959; Lawrence, 1959b; Wolstenholme and O'Connor, 1960; Christoffanini and Hoecker, 1962; Wolstenholme and Cameron, 1962). In addition, several books now deal systematically with problems of tissue and organ transplantation (Peer, 1955, 1959, Woodruff, 1960; Billingham and Silvers, 1961). To these various sources, reference may be made for detailed ac-

counts of particular transplant systems. As an introduction to developments in depth, however, it may be useful to provide an abbreviated
and more general picture. The account that follows is intended to
highlight the main features of transplant systems, especially those that
define the immunological relations of donor cells in a foreign host.

A few preliminary comments can be made concerning the typical
course of host-graft associations and the principal variables that may
affect this relationship. A most significant parameter is the genetic
differential that separates donor and recipient animals. On this basis a
distinction is commonly made among autografts, homografts, and heterografts. Autografting may be defined as the transfer of tissues or organs
from one site to another within the same individual. In this case, the
adjustments that occur subsequently depend upon the tissues chosen as
well as on the operative procedure. Skin or cartilage, for example, heal
in promptly and retain their characteristic architectural patterns. More
extensive changes may occur in other types of autografts. Transplants
of muscle become vascularized, but atrophy in the absence of a nerve
supply, whereas grafts of kidney to a heterotopic location degenerate if
unable to carry on secretory functions. On the other hand, fragments of
ovary, thyroid, or adrenal are capable of extensive regeneration, even
when placed at sites other than the normal position of these organs.

Autografts may thus have a variable fate, but cellular or humoral
rejection mechanisms are invariably lacking with transplants of this type.
The same can be said for transfers made between two individuals whose
genetic constitution is in common. Identical twins fall under this heading, and skin grafts or other transplants between the two individuals
behave as autografts. A somewhat similar situation is encountered in the
transplantation of tumors or normal tissues between the animals of a
highly inbred strain. Such implants have usually been termed isografts.
Alternatively, these may be referred to as syngeneic grafts, a designation
favored by some workers (Gorer, Loutit, and Micklem, 1961). To the
extent that inbreeding has produced genetically uniform stocks, isogenic
(or syngeneic) transplants succeed routinely.

A quite different sequence of events follows the transfer of normal
or neoplastic cells between unrelated individuals of the same species.
The implant in this case is termed a homograft (or an allogeneic graft,
according to the terminology of Gorer), and at first is indistinguishable
from the cells of the host. Healing-in occurs normally with skin homografts, for example, and there is an initial ingrowth of vascular sprouts
and supporting stroma from adjacent tissues. After a few days, however,
the histological appearance of such a homotransplant changes abruptly.
Inflammation sets in, accompanied by the accumulation of histiocytes

and especially cells of a lymphoid nature in or around the graft. Eventually, the blood vessels supplying the transplant become engorged and tend to rupture or become blocked. As a result of these and other less obvious rejection mechanisms, skin homografts ordinarily become necrotic within a week or two and are sloughed off, to be replaced largely by scar tissue. Other types of homotransplants, for example, ovary, may in some instances persist for longer periods, but ultimately they tend to disappear or undergo gradual replacement by the corresponding cells and tissues of the host (see Figure 8.1).

As a rule, homografts survive only temporarily, regardless of whether the transfer of tissues is made by free grafting or by direct anastomosis of cut blood vessels with those of the host. It is equally immaterial whether tissue fragments or intact organs are implanted. Actually, neither vascular nor stromal responses are crucial for the rejection of homografts, since ascites cells proliferating freely in body cavities are eliminated as readily as solid grafts, if genetic differences exist between graft and host. It is of interest that the success of parabiotic unions between two animals is also determined by genetic factors. If postoperative healing occurs satisfactorily, surgically united pairs of mice or other laboratory animals may be compatible indefinitely, where derived from the same inbred strain. By contrast, parabionts of unlike genotype are rarely viable except for short periods, and sickness or decline of one or both partners appears to be analogous to homograft incompatibility.

Transplants made between two species of animals are referred to as heterografts, and are ordinarily destroyed promptly. In this case, the host response is clearly abnormal from the outset. Vascularization is scanty or lacking, the provision of stroma tends to be deficient, and there is little evidence for an initial period of complete host acceptance as seen with homografts. After a few days, pronounced cellular and humoral rejection mechanisms come into play. These do not differ greatly from responses described for homografts, but appear earlier, and destruction is more intense.

This generalized sketch of the natural history of transplants within alien hosts must be immediately qualified in several important respects. Homografts placed in embryos or newborn animals instead of adults may remain indefinitely. Host reactions do not develop against these grafts, and a state of tolerance is established, which extends in later stages to other transplants of the same genotypic constitution. Similarly, host responses can be suppressed to some extent by X irradiation, antimetabolites, and other experimental agents. These modulations of graft-host associations will be discussed in more detail in subsequent sections. In addition may be mentioned a number of more specialized exceptions

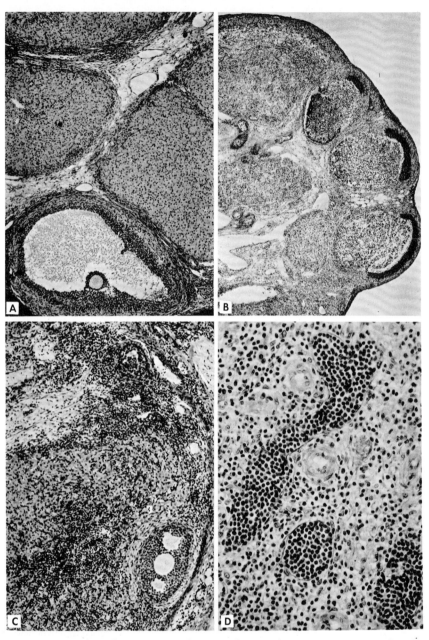

FIG. 8.1. Histological appearance of ovarian homografts in rats. (*A*) Typical well-preserved homograft, 3 months after transplantation into an ovariectomized host. (*B*) Homograft 24 hours after implantation. The transplant is avascular, with a peripheral shell of living cells surrounding a necrotic interior. (*C*) Lymphocytic infiltration of a graft that had undergone regeneration; seen at 1 month following transplantation. (*D*) Interior of homograft in advanced state of destruction, 1 month after transplantation. Note vessels engorged with lymphocytes. (From Harris and Eakin, 1949. Copyright, Wistar Institute Press.)

to the rule that alien grafts do not persist in a genetically dissimilar host. The faculty of corneal transplants to succeed, even when made between unrelated donors, is well known, and apparently depends on the fact that this tissue does not have a direct vascular supply. Even skin homografts fail to elicit the usual rejection responses, or are insusceptible to them, when placed within pockets of the host cornea, provided blood vessels do not penetrate the implant (Billingham and Boswell, 1953). A somewhat similar situation holds true for cartilage. In this case, the absence of vascularity, plus physical isolation of chondrocytes by enveloping matrix, may account for the persistence of homografts for extended periods (Loeb, 1926; Craigmyle, 1958).

Certain locations within the body are apparently more favorable than others for the survival of homografts. Among these are the anterior chamber of the eye, brain, and testis (see Woodruff, 1960). Such sites are believed to be "immunologically privileged"; that is, immune responses to alien grafts are elicited there less readily, or rejection of foreign cells is less effective. The fluid-filled anterior chamber of the eye, for example, may provide some degree of immunological isolation, as shown by the fact that homografts or even heterografts of tumors that fail subcutaneously can sometimes grow progressively in this favored location (Greene, 1942, 1955). A somewhat similar condition holds for the cheek pouch of the Syrian hamster, where a layer of loosely packed areolar tissue acts as a partial barrier between graft and host (Billingham, Ferrigan, and Silvers, 1960). It has been suggested that grafts confined within the brain may be less prone to elicit rejection mechanisms, perhaps owing to the absence of lymphatics within nervous tissue (Medawar, 1948). The relative superiority of the testis as a site for transplantation may in turn stem from the fact that there are no nearby lymph nodes on the drainage from this organ (Russell, 1961).

Transplants that are capable of vigorous proliferation may in some cases, even as homografts, grow progressively for limited periods. This phenomenon is frequently observed in the transplantation of tumors, and indeed, some neoplasms are capable of indefinite growth across histocompatibility barriers. Examination of these nonspecific tumors falls under the heading of tumor progression, however, and can best be deferred at this point. Most tumors behave more typically as homografts within transplant systems. They may show a variable initial proliferation in the alien host, sometimes forming extensive masses, but as a rule they later regress and disappear. The capacity for temporary growth as homografts is, however, not confined to tumors. Embryonic primordia may also be capable of an extensive proliferation and enlargement when implanted into older hosts. As mentioned previously (Chapter 7), however, these eventually become static or are resorbed (Loeb, 1945; Harris, 1942).

Some adult tissues may also show limited growth as homografts. In rats, for example, homotransplants of ovary may persist in a functional state for a number of months in some cases, forming large proliferating masses in spite of demonstrable cellular reactions and other host responses (Harris and Eakin, 1949). In an analysis of this phenomenon, Billingham and Parkes (1955) showed that ovarian grafts are capable of surviving in the presence of genetic differentials that lead to the destruction of skin grafts, but they fail to do so if placed within rats in which skin grafts have already regressed. In mice, the transplantation behavior of ovary and skin is in general more similar (Krohn, 1959). If, however, the genetic differences between donor and host are not great, ovarian grafts in mice may also survive for long periods, even though skin grafts between animals of the same strains are regularly destroyed (Linder, 1961). In this case, cellular reactions by the host can be observed within the ovarian homografts. But skin transplants from the donor strain, if subsequently placed on such mice, fail to precipitate a rejection of the ovarian implant. Instead, these skin grafts, as a rule, persist indefinitely. This unexpected finding may find an explanation in the phenomena of enhancement and tolerance, topics that will be considered in a later part of the present chapter.

ANALYSIS OF HOMOGRAFT REACTIONS

The mechanics of host-graft incompatibility have been clarified principally by analyzing the responses that lead to the rejection of tissue homografts. Early concepts of these processes were dominated by the views of Loeb (see Loeb, 1945). Over a period of years, he and his collaborators amassed an extensive array of observations on the histological changes that occur in tissue grafts within hosts of unlike genetic constitution. On the basis of this information, Loeb proposed the theory of organismal differentials, which laid stress on a local interaction between the alien graft and surrounding fluids of the host. Specific substances ("differentials") diffusing out of the transplant were assumed to be changed into toxins by direct contact with the adjacent body fluids. These toxins were thought to initiate lymphocytic infiltration and stromal encapsulation by chemotactic means, and in some cases, to injure the graft directly by diffusing back into the transplanted cells. This point of view, however, was difficult to reconcile with the known ability of explanted cells to grow in sera or tissue extracts derived from another species. Direct tests *in vitro* showed, in fact, that tissue cells from rats, mice, and chick embryos could be cultivated as composites for long periods without sign of injury (Harris, 1943).

Evidence for Immune Responses The suggestion that immune mechanisms are instrumental in the removal of foreign grafts was made at an early time by Schöne (1912) and other workers in the field of tissue transplantation. Such an assumption was, however, rejected by Loeb (1945), who stated at length his belief that antigen-antibody reactions were not directly concerned with the destruction of homografts of normal adult tissues. A key point in the argument was Loeb's inability to demonstrate an accelerated reaction to successive homografts of thyroid and other tissues placed in experimental animals (Loeb, 1930, 1945). The fallacy in this reasoning was finally exposed by Medawar in an incisive series of investigations. He showed that acquired resistance to homografts can be readily demonstrated if successive transfers are made from the same individual donor, a restriction in experimental design that Loeb had failed to observe. Medawar's studies were concerned primarily with skin, and involved a careful comparison of autografts with homografts and of primary transplants (first set) with repeated transplants (second set) into the same host (Gibson and Medawar, 1943; Medawar, 1944, 1945, 1946a, 1946b). If, for example, two homografts of skin are made in tandem from one rabbit to another, the reaction of the host to the second transplant becomes markedly altered. Characteristic hyperplastic changes in the graft epidermis fail to develop under these conditions, the breakdown in vascular supply is precocious, and sloughing occurs at an early stage. Various criteria can be used to express this differential in quantitative terms. Perhaps the simplest indicator is the median survival time (MST), which, like an LD_{50} in drug assays, can be used to contrast the viability of primary and secondary homografts, respectively (Billingham, Brent, Medawar, and Sparrow, 1954). In general, discovery of the "second-set" phenomenon in the transplantation of normal tissues was a most significant development and one that opened up the homograft problem on a broad new front. From the resulting profusion of studies, it has become clear that the rejection of foreign grafts is definitely based on immunological processes rather than on a mere local reaction between the transplant and surrounding tissue fluids.

If the assumption of central mechanisms in the elimination of foreign cells is granted, a question of prime importance is whether graft rejection hinges on the effects of circulating antibodies, on the localized action of host cells in direct association with the transplant, or on both. This problem was first approached effectively by studies on the transmission of resistance to homografts from one host to another. Working with mice, Mitchison (1954) inoculated a lymphosarcoma into animals of an unrelated inbred strain, where regression of the homotransplants eventually occurred. The acquisition of resistance (that is, transplantation immunity) could be demonstrated by the prompt rejection within these mice of another implant of the same kind. Using the accelerated breakdown of test grafts as a criterion, Mitchison then attempted to transmit immunity to normal mice by means of serum, peritoneal exudate, and lymph nodes from resistant animals. Pretreatment with immune serum or peritoneal exudate were found not to affect the growth of assay grafts. But the inoculation of lymph nodes that drained the tumor in resistant hosts did serve to confer an effective immunity. Such mice promptly rejected tumor homotransplants, much as if growth and regression of a primary implant had previously occurred. In further experiments of the same kind, Mitchison (1955) extended his findings to a number of other host-tumor combinations. In these, the ability of activated lymph nodes to transfer selective immunity was consistently observed.

While Mitchison's experiments were, for convenience, conducted with tumors, the investigations of Billingham, Brent, and Medawar (1954) soon showed that cellular resistance is an integral part of the "second-set" response to homografts of skin and other normal tissues. In *CBA* mice, for example, primary grafts of *A*-strain skin have a median survival time of 11.0 ± 0.3 days, whereas for secondary transplants, the corresponding figure is 6 days or less. This accelerated pattern of response can be duplicated by transferring lymph nodes from hosts with *A* strain grafts to other *CBA* mice, and also by splenic implants, or even by blood-borne leukocytes present in the buffy coat (Billingham, Silvers, and Wilson, 1962). Only living cells appear to serve in this role. Killed lymph nodes, for example, are ineffective as a means of transferring an established state of resistance, as are massive doses of immune serum. The transmission of resistance to homografts thus appeared to differ from passively acquired immunity as this concept is ordinarily understood; that is, resistance brought into being by the inoculation of preformed antibody. For this reason, Billingham and his collaborators coined the term adoptively acquired immunity, to emphasize that resistance in the cases studied is conferred by introducing immunologically activated cells, which persist in chimeric combination with the tissues of an isogenic host.

The concept of adoptively acquired immunity assumes that lymphoid cells with selective ability for the destruction of foreign cells act directly on the targets to which they have previously been sensitized. Experimental confirmation of this thesis has been obtained by *in vivo* experiments with cell populations in diffusion chambers. A simple unit for the purpose may be fashioned by sealing the two sides of a plastic ring with a Millipore filter or other membrane of controlled porosity (Algire, Weaver, and Prehn, 1954). Grafts of normal or neoplastic tissues can be enclosed in the chamber thus created, after which the entire unit is implanted into a suitable host, usually in the peritoneal cavity. By selection of an appropriate membrane porosity, the implants can be isolated from physical contact with lymphocytes or other cellular mechanisms of the host while retaining a comparatively free exchange of extracellular fluids. Under these circumstances, homografts as a rule persist without damage by the foreign host (Prehn, Weaver, and Algire, 1954). Selective destruction of the implants can be demonstrated, however, if suspensions of spleen are introduced into the Millipore chambers along with the target cells (Weaver, Algire, and Prehn, 1955; Algire, Weaver, and Prehn, 1957). No reaction to the homografted cells is observed if the spleen cells are derived from untreated mice isogenic with the host. But if the spleen cell donors are immunized by a preliminary inoculation of target tissues, sensitization takes place. When spleen cells from such animals are introduced into diffusion chambers, the corresponding homotransplants are promptly destroyed.

Histocompatibility Loci and Isoantigens Strong evidence supports the concept that immunologically activated cells in direct association with homografts can effectively bring about their destruction. The question of whether humoral antibodies also participate in homograft reactions has been more difficult to approach directly. Information on this point has accumulated only gradually and mainly as a by-product of genetic studies. The latter were concerned initially with the hereditary basis for tumor transplantation. A number of empirical "laws" were formulated for the transfer of tumors between inbred strains, largely through the investigations of Little and his collaborators (Little, 1941). These showed, for example, that if two different strains are crossed, a tumor from either parental line will grow in 100 percent of the F_1 hybrids, but as a rule, only in a fraction of the F_2 generation, or in backcrosses to the original lines. Data of this kind suggested that the transplantability of tumors is determined by a series of dominant genetic determinants, which were eventually designated histocompatibility genes (Snell, 1948).

Methods were initially lacking, however, for the recognition and characterization of individual loci. This gap was filled by the important discovery that histocompatibility genes produce specific antigens, which can be assayed by serological techniques (Gorer, 1937). In earlier work,

Gorer had established the existence of a specific factor, Antigen II, on the erythrocytes and tissue cells of A-strain mice. Subsequently, he proved that the presence of this antigen within the host is essential for the progressive growth of A-strain tumor cells as transplants. Mice lacking Antigen II rejected the tumor, and isoantibodies appeared in the serum, specifically directed against the antigenic factor in question. These observations suggested the existence of genetic factors that determine the appearance of isoantigens, which are in turn the basis for tissue specificity in homograft reactions. The correctness of this view has since been amply verified by many different lines of evidence.

The genetic analysis of histocompatibility loci was greatly facilitated by the discovery of markers with which genes affecting transplantation are linked. In 1948, Gorer, Lyman, and Snell demonstrated a linkage between the factor determining Antigen II and the locus for fused tail (Fu), a prominent skeletal anomaly in mice. Since the animals bearing Antigen II were invariably susceptible to A-strain tumors, while those without it were resistant, the determinant governing both these characteristics was named H-2, the first histocompatibility locus to be specifically identified. Subsequent studies showed that H-2 is also closely linked with brachy, or short tail (T), and that crossing over between H-2 and Fu or T can be observed (Snell, 1952; Allen, 1955). These accompanying mutant genes are part of a linkage group that lies in the ninth chromosome of the mouse, thus definitely localizing the H-2 system.

As crosses were made between various inbred strains of mice, the presence of multiple alleles at the H-2 locus soon became apparent (Snell, Smith, and Gabrielson, 1953; Snell, 1953). Strain A, for example, can be designated H-$2^a/H$-2^a. Individuals of the $C_{57}BL$ strain are homozygous for H-2^b whereas $BALB/c$ mice are H-2^d (Gorer, 1961). At least 18 distinct H-2 alleles have now been discovered in the course of typing more than 50 inbred strains (Snell, 1963). The detailed analysis of these and other histocompatibility alleles has stemmed principally from the production of so-called isogenic resistant (IR) lines (Snell, 1948, 1958b). These represent an attempt to obtain matched strains that are genotypically identical except for contrasting alleles at a single genetic locus. Snell approached the problem by hybridizing mice of two inbred strains, followed by serial backcrosses to one of the parental lines (see Figure 8.2). The resulting animals in alternate generations were inoculated with a tumor from the backcross strain, and serial backcrossing continued only with offspring from mice which continued to reject the assay implant. In this way after approximately 14 generations of brother-sister mating, the derivative IR lines should in principle differ

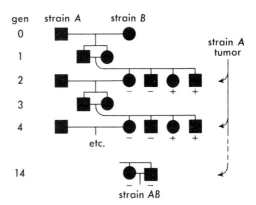

FIG. 8.2. Method for the production of isogenic resistant (IR) lines of mice. Minus (−) indicates that animal survived tumor implant; plus (+), that it succumbed to implant. The effect of the crosses is to introduce a histocompatibility gene from strain B onto a strain A background. (Redrawn from Snell, 1958b.)

only at a single histocompatibility locus from the corresponding backcross strain, with which they are therefore said to be coisogenic.

Numerous IR lines were initiated by Snell through crosses between different inbred strains of mice, and the findings have been summarized in some detail (Snell, 1957c, 1958b, 1963; Snell and Stevens, 1961). By performing linkage tests with the marker short-tail (T), about 30 out of an initial group of 38 IR lines were found to depart from the corresponding coisogenic strain by a difference at the H-2 locus. The remaining IR lines appeared to differ in one or more histocompatibility genes other than H-2. By crosses made between lines with the same H-2 allele, these non-H-2 differences have been examined in more detail. Two histocompatibility loci proved to be linked with markers in the first chromosome, such as albinism (c). These genes have been designated H-1 and H-4, and are separable, respectively, by approximately 24 percent crossing over (Snell and Stevens, 1961). Similarly, another histocompatibility gene, termed H-3, is linked to agouti (A), an identifying marker that is known to occur in the fifth linkage group of the mouse (Figure 8.3). Multiple alleles appear to exist at all these loci, and a number have already been demonstrated for H-1 and H-3. In addition, a histocompatibility gene appears to be located in the Y chromosome of the mouse. Male skin, or tumor grafts from males, are rejected when transferred to females within a number of inbred strains (Eichwald and Silmser, 1955; Eichwald, Silmser, and Weissman, 1958; Hauschka, Grinnell, Meagher, and Amos, 1959). In strains where this occurs, transplants from female to male, or between two individuals of the same sex, are invariably free from an adverse reaction. Endocrine factors can apparently be ruled out as a basis for this response. That determination of the male antigen is associated with the Y chromosome as such is clear from the experiments of Celada and Welshons (1963). Using mice of exceptional

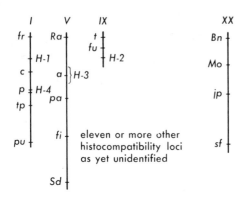

FIG. 8.3. Chromosome map of the mouse, showing in part those linkage groups in which histocompatibility loci have been identified. The histocompatibility factor of Eichwald and Silmser (1955) is on the Y chromosome, which is not shown because it carries no other known loci. (Redrawn from Snell, 1963.)

chromosomal constitution, they have shown that XO females lack the antigen, whereas XXY males possess it. Whether the male antigen appears by the action of an independent locus in the Y chromosome, or merely emerges as a consequence of sexual differentiation, remains to be seen. Unlike other histocompatibility loci, the male factor does not appear to exist in the form of multiple alleles, and is not strain-specific.

It is probable that numerous other genetic loci for histocompatibility in the mouse remain to be identified. Their demonstration is complicated by the fact that marked differences exist in the "strength" of individual histocompatibility genes (Counce, Smith, Barth, and Snell, 1956; Berrian and McKhann, 1960; Snell, 1963). H-2 can be regarded as a "strong" locus in the sense that tumors or normal cells showing an allelic difference from the host are ordinarily rejected as transplants. By contrast, differences at H-1, H-3, or H-4 can be overridden relatively easily by tumors. To show the effect of these "weak" loci, it may be necessary to pre-immunize the host (Snell, 1958a). Other histocompatibility loci may not reach even this threshold of expression, and new techniques are likely to be required for their demonstration. What the total number of histocompatibility genes in the mouse may be is unknown, but early studies on tumor transplantation suggested that a considerable number of independently segregating factors were involved (Little, 1941). This conclusion has been supported by the more recent experiments of Barnes and Krohn (1957) with skin grafts. Here, the percentage of successful skin transplants in F_2 hybrids between inbred strains suggest that not less than 14 different loci may participate. A similar complex of histocompatibility genes may be expected for other organisms, although information on this point is still meager. The investigation of Billingham, Hodge, and Silvers (1962) indicates a figure of approximately 15 genes for the rat, of which at least three are "strong" loci. The Syrian hamster offers a somewhat contrasting picture. In this case, the experimental data on interstrain homograft responses can be explained by assuming no more than three histocompatibility loci (Billingham, Sawchuck, and Silvers, 1960). Whether this reflects a greater stability of histocompatibility genes in the Syrian hamster, or merely the fact that many loci are too "weak" to be manifest experimentally, remains to be determined.

Histocompatibility systems can thus be viewed as independent groups of genetic determinants, operating with varying strength at specific loci. The true complexity of this pattern, however, can be appreciated only by examining with serological methods the products of a single locus, such as H-2. For this purpose, the coisogenic strains of Snell offer material of ideal specificity. With a series of IR strains, antisera can be produced selectively against the products of each H-2 allele. The development of improved technical methods by Gorer and Mikulska (1954) has been an important factor in characterizing the spectrum of specific isoantigens. Using dextran and human serum to enhance reactions *in vitro*, they showed that agglutination of mouse erythrocytes by specific isoantisera can be regularly obtained, whereas earlier tests in saline alone had frequently given negative or inconclusive results.

The systematic analysis of the H-2 locus by hemagglutination techniques has been pursued by a number of investigators, notably Hoecker, Counce, and Smith (1954); Hoecker (1956); Amos, Gorer, and Mikulska (1955); Gorer and Mikulska (1959); Gorer (1959, 1961); and Pizarro, Hoecker, Rubinstein, and Ramos (1961). These studies have shown that the H-2 locus determines a complex array of hemagglutinogens, similar to the Rhesus system in man. The tendency for these isoantigens to appear is inherited as a unit. For any given member of the multiple alleles that may be present at the H-2 site, a specific group of serologically discrete antigens may thus be demonstrated (Figure 8.4). If the latter are designated by capital letters, H-2^a, for example, corresponds to $ACDEFHJKMNY$. Similarly, the antigenic code for H-2^b is D^bEFK^bNV, and for H-2^k ACD^kEHKY (Gorer, 1961). The list of known isoantigens associated with the H-2 locus is already an extensive one, with some 26 distinct components identified among the products of the 18 or more alleles that have been studied to date (Snell, 1963). Further search is likely to reveal an even greater spectrum of differences.

These isoantigens, it should be pointed out, are not restricted to erythrocytes. Hemagglutinogens can be demonstrated on the cells from all tissues, and lymphoid or tumor cells are relatively high in absorbing power when assayed with specific isoantisera. Histocompatibility genes behave ordinarily as codominants, and F_1 hybrids between two inbred

H-2 symbol	antigens present	typed strains of mice
a	ACDEFHJKMNY	A, AKR.K
b	D^bEFK^{b}NV	C_{57}BL, LP,STA
d	CDE^{d}FHJMN	BALB/c, DBA/$_2$
k	ACD^{k}EHKY	CBA,C$_3$H C_{57}BR, C_{58},AKR,STB
q	CEFMQ	DBA/$_1$

FIG. 8.4. A partial listing of histocompatibility alleles at the H-2 locus in the mouse, together with the spectrum of accompanying antigens that have been demonstrated by serological methods. (Data from Gorer, 1961.)

lines differing at the H-2 locus show all the hemagglutinogens associated with each allele. This fact makes clear why skin grafts or tumor transplants can be made freely from either parental line into F_1 hybrids, but not vice versa. Apparently the absence of host antigens from skin or tumor cells is innocuous, but all antigens of the graft must be matched in the host, for compatibility to occur. Some exceptions to the acceptance of parental cells in F_1 hybrids have been reported (Celada and Welshons, 1962), suggesting that recessive histocompatibility genes may conceivably exist. The possibility must be considered, however, that these discrepancies result merely from dosage effects; that is, a heightened antigenic output by homozygous cells.

The question of whether the H-2 system of isoantigens represents the products of a single gene or of a series of closely linked determinants is not yet definitely settled. The occurrence of true mutations at the H-2 locus has not been authenticated, and supposedly mutant types described earlier are now believed to stem from residual heterozygosity in some inbred strains (Gorer, 1961). Crossing over does take place within the H-2 locus, however, and in some instances the reciprocal products with complementary antigenic patterns have been recovered (Gorer and Mikulska, 1959; Pizarro, Hoecker, Rubinstein, and Ramos, 1961). In recent discussions, the H-2 locus has been characterized as a cluster of pseudoalleles representing a functional unit or gene (Pizarro, Hoecker, Rubinstein, and Ramos, 1961; Snell, 1963). This conclusion is based on the fact that the H-2 antigens are inherited as a block and appear simultaneously in the maturing individual. There is, however,

ANALYSIS OF HOMOGRAFT REACTIONS

no evidence as yet for a *cis-trans* position effect within the *H*-2 locus, although this phenomenon has formed the basis for identifying pseudo-alleles in a number of other genetic systems (Pontecorvo, 1958).

The chemical nature of histocompatibility isoantigens has been difficult to ascertain, in part because the factors in question are not readily separated from other components in the cell. Early suggestions included the possibility that DNA proteins or mucopolysaccharides of the blood group type might function in this role (see below). The participation of deoxyribonucleic acid or ribonucleic acid fractions now seems to be ruled out (Hašková, Hrubešová, and Medawar, 1958; Castermans, 1961), and active preparations with little or no associated carbohydrate have been obtained. Several investigations indicate that extracts containing histocompatibility antigens can be obtained by methods designed to isolate cell membranes. These fractions show a variable but consistent activity by several criteria, and the responsible agents in all cases appear to be lipoproteins (Davies, 1962a, 1962b; Haenen-Severyns, Vrancken-Paris, Lejeune, Castermans, and Dieu, 1962; Kandutsch and Stimpfling, 1963; Manson, Foschi, and Palm, 1963; see also Snell, 1963). The chemical characterization of these isoantigens as a class thus seems to be in prospect, but the nature of the specificities that separate the individual factors serologically is as yet untouched.

A logical prediction from the fact that isoantigens occur on tissue cells generally is that homografts from cells of all types should elicit antibodies, provided a threshold antigenic stimulus is furnished to an immunologically competent host. This expectation is clearly fulfilled for tumor transplants, and the formation of humoral antibodies is equally characteristic of animals with skin homografts (Amos, Gorer, Mikulska, Billingham, and Sparrow, 1954; Gorer, 1955; Terasaki, McClelland, Cannon, and Longmire, 1961). Quantitative differences, however, are observed in the antibody titre elicited by homografts of various types. Tumors characteristically call forth a much stronger response than do skin grafts, for example, presumably because the enlarging tumor mass subjects the host to a more extensive dose of antigen (Snell, 1963).

The serological manifestations of histocompatibility alleles have been studied primarily by hemagglutination, but other techniques can be used as well. Complement fixation, red cell lysis, and cytotoxic effects may all be observed with appropriate materials (see Gorer, 1956; 1961; Snell, 1963; Möller and Möller, 1962b). By an adaptation of the fluorescent antibody technique, it is even possible to visualize directly the specific accumulation of isoantibodies at the surface of normal or tumor cells that bear the corresponding antigens (Möller, 1961). Cytotoxic isoantibodies in particular have received considerable attention as a possible direct mechanism for homograft destruction. Complement is required for the activity of these factors (Gorer, 1956; Winn, 1960a). The apparently irregular occurrence of cytotoxins in murine systems may reflect in part the fact that complement is usually absent from unsupplemented mouse serum when tested *in vitro* (Gorer, 1961). Not all cell types, however, are susceptible to damage or destruction by cytotoxic antibodies. Leukemias and lymphoid elements as a rule are sensitive, but the cells from solid tumors and most normal tissues tend to be resistant (Snell, 1957a; 1963; Winn, 1960b). Such differences in susceptibility to cytotoxins appear to depend more on surface density of isoantigens than on tissue variation per se (Möller and Möller, 1962a). These investigators compared the amount of hemagglutinin absorbed by different suspensions of cells that varied in the average diameter of individual cells but were adjusted to the same aggregate surface area. The data obtained show that the concentration on individual cells of isoantigenic receptors varies, as measured by the relative ability of each preparation to bind hemagglutinins. The amounts absorbed by particular cell types showed a high correlation with cytotoxic sensitivity.

In this light, the susceptibility of lymphocytes as compared to other cells may stem from a minimal surface area, with consequent high density of antigenic sites. Möller and Möller (1962b) as well as Winn (1962) have suggested that cytotoxic damage is enhanced by antibody groupings that are closely associated, since interaction with complement is more complete under these conditions. A further implication from the data presented is the possibility that cytotoxins and hemagglutinins may be actually the same isoantibodies, demonstrated merely by two different techniques. This view receives additional support from the experiments of Jensen and Stetson (1961), who observed a direct parallelism in the hemagglutinating and cytotoxic properties of isoimmune sera. The number of serologically discrete factors in histocompatibility reactions is thus not necessarily identical with the methods used to demonstrate them, although the degree to which a unitary concept may apply is uncertain.

Cellular and Humoral Mechanisms On the basis of the evidence described, the existence of humoral antibodies in animals bearing homografts may be regarded as well established. Likewise, the experiments summarized earlier clearly define the participation of cellular reactions in this system. The exact relation of these two mechanisms in the homograft response as a whole represents a continuing problem. From one standpoint, the data available could be interpreted as indicating a duality of rejection patterns for homotransplants, with cellular and humoral mechanisms operating in variable combination for any given target system. The effectiveness of purely humoral factors can be documented by the studies of Gorer and his collaborators on certain leukemias (Gorer and Amos, 1956; Gorer, 1956). Using the $C_{57}BL$ lymphoma EL-4, they were able to prevent the growth of tumor cells in alien strains by simultaneous injection of immune serum. The protection afforded is purely passive, since the same hosts, if challenged later with EL-4 cells alone, show a primary response. Direct inhibition by humoral factors can also be observed with other leukemic tumors in homologous hosts (Amos and Day, 1957; Gorer, 1961). When histological studies are made, they reinforce the impression that the rejection of leukemic cells as homografts takes place by a humoral response. A conspicuous exudation of plasma can be seen around local implants, rather than the early infiltration by host cells (Gorer, 1958).

For homografts of solid tissues such as skin, and for nonleukemic tumors, the passive administration of immune serum is without inhibitory effect (Billingham and Brent, 1956; Brent and Medawar, 1961). In fact, enhanced growth and survival may occur instead (Gorer and Kaliss, 1959), and this phenomenon will be considered in greater detail in the following section. There is thus little indication that circulating antibody plays a significant role in the destruction of skin or other solid tissue homografts (Billingham and Silvers, 1961; Snell, 1963). In these systems, the host response appears to be one that is based on direct cellular reactions to the transplant rather than on circulating humoral agents. While various explanations for this pattern can be provided, the specific hypothesis that has found most favor is the concept of homograft responses as delayed hypersensitivity reactions of the tuberculin type (Medawar, 1958a, 1958b, 1959a; Lawrence, 1959a).

Not all investigators are in accord on the exact mechanism of tuberculin hypersensitivity (Karush and Eisen, 1962), but this reaction has in the past been looked upon as a prototype for immunity based on purely cellular reactions. Circulating antibody is not demonstrable by ordinary methods in animals that have been sensitized by infection with tuberculosis organisms, or in those that have acquired a similar elevated response from injections of cell-free extracts (for example, tuberculin). In these animals, but not in untreated hosts, the topical administration of tuberculin results in the formation of a characteristic lesion. The changes in question are localized in character and appear only after a delay of many hours. Histologically, an abundant infiltration of lymphoid cells can be observed in well-developed lesions. Cellular effectors thus seem to be predominant in the tuberculin reaction, and the circumscribed changes may be viewed as simulating a homograft response to host elements that are "made foreign" by coating with specific antigen (Lawrence, 1959a). This concept is illustrated by the diagrams shown in Figure 8.5.

The concept of delayed hypersensitivity as the basis for homograft reactions has received further support from the experiments of Billingham, Brent, and Medawar (1958), and Brent, Brown, and Medawar (1959). These investigations showed that a tuberculinlike reaction can be elicited in rabbits or guinea pigs that have been sensitized to homografts by the intradermal injection of cell-free antigens from the corresponding donor. In addition to this direct response, a localized reaction can be demonstrated by reversing the procedure; that is, by inoculating lymphoid cells from sensitized hosts into the skin of the original donors. Such observations reinforce the view that cell-bound rather than freely circulating antibody is the mediating factor in the destruction of skin or other solid tissue homografts under ordinary conditions. The exact mechanism of interaction between host cells and target cells is still unknown. Suggestions have included the possibilities that immunologically activated sites may exist on the surface of lymphoid cells or that antibody can be released locally in the presence of specific antigen (Berrian and Brent, 1958).

The antithesis between cellular and humoral concepts of homograft responses eventually reached a focal point in the concept of T-antigens and H-antigens (Medawar, 1959a, 1959b). According to this hypothesis, two groups of products were assumed to be formed by each of the various histocompatibility alleles. One type, the T-antigens, were thought to call forth transplantation immunity by activating immunologically competent elements in the host, which could then react specifically with homografts on a localized cellular basis. The formation of humoral

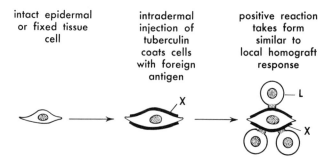

FIG. 8.5. Analogy between tuberculin and homograft reactions. X = foreign antigen; L = sensitized lymphocyte. (After Lawrence, 1959a.)

factors, on the other hand, was attributed to specific stimulation of antibody-forming cells by H-antigens, this constituting a parallel series of effects that bore no necessary relation to transplantation immunity as such.

Initially, several types of evidence seemed to give provisional support to this dualistic concept of isoantigens. The early observations of a number of investigators had suggested that transplantation immunity could be elicited only with living cells. Eventually, however, Billingham, Brent, and Medawar (1956c) succeeded in preparing a cell-free extract with capacity to sensitize appropriate assay hosts; that is, to call forth a "second-set" reaction to skin homografts. The transplantation antigens in these preparations seemed to accompany the nuclei or nuclear fractions in the isolation procedures and were suppressed by treatment with deoxyribonuclease. On the basis of these findings, the reasonable inference was drawn that T-antigens might be deoxyribonucleoproteins. Such a concept was particularly attractive, since mammalian erythrocytes as nonnucleated cells appeared incapable of eliciting transplantation immunity when inoculated into appropriate hosts. The red cell might therefore be regarded as the bearer of H-antigens, but not T-antigens, because a voluminous array of serological studies makes clear that erythrocytes can stimulate the production of humoral isoantibodies as well as react with them.

Later investigations, however, have not supported this general thesis. Among others, Hašková, Hrubešová, and Medawar (1958) have shown that DNA is not an essential component of preparations known to induce transplantation immunity. The association of transplantation antigens with DNA proteins in early experiments appears to have been merely fortuitous, reflecting perhaps some action by the latter as a carrier in extraction procedures (Billingham, Brent, and Medawar, 1958). On the other hand, the immunity elicited by erythrocytes is not uniquely different from that produced by tissue cells. Barrett (1958) has shown in at least one case that red cells will induce a clear-cut tumor resistance. Some H-2 components have proved difficult to demonstrate on mouse red cells, but there is no evidence for the absence of any group of antigens *en bloc*. In all probability, the feeble immunizing power of erythrocytes for skin grafts reflects merely the low surface density of isoantigens on these cells, a feature that can be visualized directly by fluorescent antibody techniques (Möller, 1961).

Other distinctions between H-antigens and T-antigens were based on reports that humoral and transplantation immunity did not follow the same time course of development (Mitchison and Dube, 1955) and that extracts known to contain transplantation antigens did not seem to stimulate the production of isoantibodies (Hildemann and Medawar, 1959). Neither of these assertions can now be supported. The disparity in appearance of humoral and transplantation immunity has been shown by Gorer, Mikulska, and O'Gorman (1959) to hinge on technical problems. If sufficient care is taken to assure optimal sensitivity in serological tests, the acquisition of both types of immunity can be demonstrated to proceed concurrently. The most decisive evidence bearing on this problem, however, is that of Brent, Medawar, and Ruskiewicz (1961). These investigators have performed an apparently definitive study on the development of humoral and transplantation immunity. Skin grafts between A-strain and CBA or C_3H mice were employed as an assay system, and improved procedures were used to extract immunizing antigens. Under these conditions, both humoral and transplantation immunity could be elicited by one cell-free preparation, and the two activities proceeded in parallel through extraction procedures. It did not prove possible to demonstrate a duality of antigens by differential susceptibility of factors within the extracts to various physical and chemical agents. These careful experiments clearly imply that the notion of H-antigens and T-antigens has outlived its usefulness. In recent discussions, the duality of histocompatibility factors has been abandoned in favor of the concept that the factors which elicit humoral and transplantation immunity are identical (Snell, 1963; Möller and Möller, 1962b; Stetson, 1963).

A similar unification of conceptual patterns for effector mechanisms in homograft responses may be in prospect. Dissimilar reactions for the elimination of several classes of target cells have been assumed by Gorer (1961) and others, but the need for plural mechanisms seems less clear-cut than formerly. To an increasing extent, the varying aspects of graft rejection can be related to the release of isoantibodies by immunologically activated and probably lymphoid elements. Whether this process is termed cellular or humoral seems to depend more on the characteristics of the target cells and their proximity to sources of isoantibody than on qualitative differences in the rejection phenomenon.

As a model, skin grafts appear to illustrate such a concept particularly well. The elimination of skin transplants here seems to take place ordinarily by means of direct cellular intervention by the host. This does not necessarily imply any freedom from the effects of humoral factors, however, except on a quantitative basis. If, for example, the effective titre of immune serum is raised locally by subcutaneous injection in the neighborhood of skin homografts, an accelerated rejection may occur (Kretschmer and Pérez-Tamayo, 1961). Similarly, if suspensions of epidermal cells are incubated for an extended period in specific isoantiserum, their capacity for growth when replaced in the original donor is impaired or abolished (Billingham and Sparrow, 1954).

Other experiments suggest that although the rejection of skin homografts *in vivo* usually involves a close association with immunologically active cells, direct proximity is not absolutely required. This finding emerges from the investigations of Najarian and Feldman (1962a), in which skin grafts were transferred between mice of *CBA* and *A* strains. Adoptive transfers were made of sensitized lymphoid cells from the immune animals, using donors that had previously been injected with tritiated thymidine to label the elements to be transferred. These cells produced the expected acceleration in rejection of skin grafts when placed within the assay hosts. But despite a patent "second-set" response, labeled lymphoid cells were only rarely observed at the rejection site. The adoptively transferred elements were not eliminated, for labeled lymphoid cells could readily be found in the host spleen and lymph nodes, and the implantation of solid donor lymph nodes in a direct proximity to the graft gave no evidence of allergic destruction. These results are in fact reminiscent of those reported by Mitchison and Dube (1955) for transplants of the *SAI* tumor in mice. On that occasion, acriflavine dyes were used to label the lymphoid cells of sensitized donors for adoptive transfer. As in the present experiments, however, no significant accumulation of marked elements could be observed at the homograft site.

The simplest explanation of these findings seems to be the concept that even for skin rejection, lymphoid cells can operate to some extent while at a distance from the graft; that is, through the release of humoral isoantibodies. Najarian and Feldman (1962a) have supported this view additionally by chamber experiments with mice, in which sensitized lymphoid cells were enclosed in Millipore units for adoptive transfer. If direct proximity of these elements with skin transplants were essential for graft rejection, it might be expected that the homograft response would be blocked. Such does not appear to be the case, however. Najarian and Feldman found that competent lymphoid cells within Millipore units can bring about a clear-cut "second-set" response to skin homografts in untreated animals, although injections of immune serum alone do not. Evidently this is not an isolated finding. In rabbits (Kretschmer and Pérez-Tamayo, 1962) and in guinea pigs (Najarian and Feldman, 1963), immunity to skin homografts can also be passively conferred by activated lymphoid cells contained within Millipore chambers. The results of these investigations stand in contrast to parallel studies performed with the same techniques on tuberculin sensitivity in guinea pigs (Najarian and Feldman, 1961). In the latter system a conspicuous accumulation of labeled lymphoid cells definitely does occur within the characteristic lesions, and when sensitized cells are enclosed in Millipore units, the tuberculin reaction does not take place.

None of these observations are necessarily in conflict with the concept that the rejection of skin grafts under ordinary circumstances is a local rather than a humoral phenomenon (Billingham and Silvers, 1961). They do suggest that the analogy to hypersensitivity reactions may be less direct than originally envisioned, and bring into question particularly the necessity for any direct contact between host elements and target cells. It appears that even for solid tissue grafts, the essential event in regression may be the release of isoantibodies, a process that is especially effective in the immediate neighborhood of alien cells but which can occur at some distance from the graft as well. From this standpoint, humoral and cellular distinctions may represent merely varying emphases within a single modality of homograft responses, a possibility that has been recognized many times in previous discussions (Medawar, 1959a; Lawrence, 1959a; Brent, Brown, and Medawar, 1959).

Tolerance and Enhancement   The dimensions of compatibility in transplant systems extend well beyond the phenomenon of graft rejection as such, for elimination by humoral or cellular mechanisms is not an inevitable consequence of antigenic differences between donor and host. This fact first became apparent through the discovery of means whereby animals can be rendered tolerant or unresponsive toward genetically disparate cells and tissues. The methods available are specialized, and it does not follow that general success in the free transfer of homografts is imminent. But the resulting analysis of tolerance has opened up a new vista of fundamental studies at the cellular level. The conditions that attend the induction of tolerance to foreign cells have provided a series of model systems that are useful in assessing the development and nature of immune responses in general.

Immunological tolerance in the sense just indicated is a specific phenomenon; that is, responsiveness is selectively altered toward antigenic stimuli of one or more types. As such, it must be distinguished from the generalized suppression of antibody formation, which follows exposure to various agents known to weaken or reduce the capacity for immune reactions as a whole. It is recognized, for example, that X irradiation suppresses antibody production in sublethal doses, and therefore it is not surprising to find that, in irradiated animals, the homograft response may be slowed or abrogated in part (Woodruff, 1960). Similarly, the administration of ACTH or corticosteroids may provide some lessening of the reaction to homotransplants (Billingham, Krohn, and Medawar, 1951; Medawar, 1959a), presumably as a result of the selective destruction of lymphocytes known to accompany administration of these agents in effective doses. A variety of experiments shows further that antipurines, folic acid antagonists, and antimetabolites of other types can ameliorate to a degree the effects of homograft reactions (see Schwartz, 1963; Hitchings and Elion, 1963). Lastly, it may be pointed out that if the thymus is removed from mice or other animals at the time of birth, the potential for graft rejection and for immune responses in general is curtailed. Conceivably, the thymus in young animals might provide precursor elements that mature and migrate to other sites as immunologically competent cells (Miller 1962; Miller, Marshall, and White 1962). However, more recent studies seem to show clearly that the essential role of the thymus is a humoral one (Osaba and Miller, 1964). These various investigations need not be considered in detail; the results indicate in sum that homograft reactions can be diminished by procedures that interfere with, or attenuate the output of, antibodies in a nonspecific way.

The selective inhibition of immune responses is a phenomenon of greater intrinsic interest. That such a result could be obtained in young animals was predicted on theoretical grounds by Burnet and Fenner (1949) as part of their general concept of how immunological specificity is established in the developing individual. On the basis of a sequential transition to immunological maturity, they reasoned that an early exposure to a foreign antigen should leave the corresponding cells and their descendants incapable of reacting to the same stimulus when presented subsequently. In this sense, tolerance could be viewed as an induced extension of the self-recognition thought to develop in each individual from the exposure of immunologically maturing cells to antigens originating elsewhere in the body.

Indirectly, experimental support for these speculations about tolerance was already available. Owen (1945) had examined the erythrocytic patterns of twin cattle embryos and had noted that, for the most part, these were chimeras; that is, where the two individuals differed in blood cell type, each twin possessed circulating erythrocytes of the two kinds. Since cattle twins have long been known to be synchorial, the origin of the chimeric blood pattern could be readily inferred as a consequence of vascular exchanges via the common placental circulation. The persistence of erythrocyte chimerism beyond the embryonic period, however, was more difficult to account for, since red cells have a finite existence within the blood stream. The explanation is now known to lie in the exchange of stem cells via the embryonic circulation. The latter then are tolerated rather than rejected in the corresponding twin. From precursors derived in this way are produced the erythrocytes that differ in antigenic pattern from those native to the host.

Owen's results are clear-cut in retrospect, but it was the outstanding investigations of Billingham, Brent, and Medawar (1953, 1955, 1956a) that first showed immunological tolerance to be a definite and easily reproducible phenomenon. Following the lead developed in embryos, these investigators found that mosaicism in erythrocytic patterns is accompanied by acceptance in most cases of skin grafts between the resulting twin cattle (Billingham, Lampkin, Medawar, and Williams, 1952). Attention was then directed to other systems. As a means of achieving the same effect experimentally, *CBA* mouse embryos were inoculated, while still *in utero*, with suspensions of cells derived by mincing adult organs of strain *A* mice. The injections were made by inserting a syringe through the maternal body wall, a procedure that fortunately did not prevent normal birth and development of the embryos. Eight weeks after birth, mice pretreated in this way were grafted with adult *A*-strain skin. The homotransplants remained viable for long periods and in some cases survived indefinitely. In untreated *CBA* controls, the *A*-strain skin grafts were rejected promptly. Thus, far from sensitizing the embryonic *CBA* hosts, the initial injection of *A*-strain cells actually conferred a state of compatibility toward subsequent transplants of the same kind. To describe this remarkable shift in host response, Billingham and his collaborators proposed the term "actively acquired tolerance," a state that seemed to represent the exact inverse of actively acquired immunity in other animals.

That homograft acceptance could be obtained by exposure of embryonic hosts to the corresponding donor cells was demonstrated independently by Hašek and his collaborators (Hašek, 1953a, 1953b; Hašek, Lengerová, and Hraba, 1961). In this case, chick embryos were brought into parabiotic union. These individuals subsequently failed to produce antibodies against one another when inoculated with partner blood. Skin grafts were also accepted when transferred between the two parabionts, although in control chicks, analogous transplants were promptly rejected.

The main outlines of tolerance as a biological phenomenon were established by Billingham, Brent, and Medawar in the strategic initial experiments mentioned above. Studies with a variety of laboratory animals, including rats, rabbits, and chicks, soon showed that acceptance of homografts can be induced generally among young animals by pretreatment at an early stage (Figure 8.6). In all such cases, the acquisition of tolerance proved to be highly selective, and was directed only toward cells genotypically identical with those used for primary inoculation. No

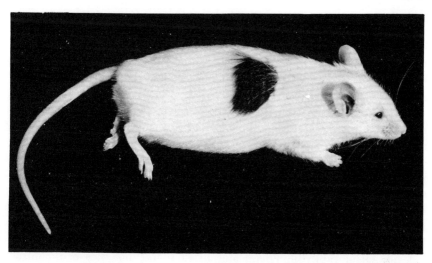

FIG. 8.6. Acquired tolerance in mice. Photograph shows a *CBA* skin homograft that had been transplanted 50 days previously to a specifically tolerant *A*-strain host. The graft has regenerated a dense crop of hairs. (From Billingham and Silvers, 1961. Copyright, Wistar Institute Press.)

indications of tissue specificity were observed. Tolerance could be elicited with a variety of normal tissues, although the efficiency of induction varied with different cell types. Tolerance could even be produced toward normal tissues by pretreatment with tumor cells, and vice versa. Other observations showed clearly that the change in response pattern was not an all-or-nothing phenomenon. A continuous gradation could be noted among individual animals, ranging from complete acceptance of homografts derived from a specific donor source to only slightly delayed rejection of the same cells.

Perhaps most important among the early findings of Billingham and his collaborators was the discovery that tolerance toward homografts can be summarily abolished if an adoptive transfer is made of immunologically competent cells from an isogenic but nontolerant animal (Billingham, Brent, and Medawar, 1955). If, for example, tolerant *CBA* mice bearing *A*-strain skin are inoculated with lymphoid cells from an untreated *CBA* mouse, the *A*-strain graft is promptly rejected in a typical primary homograft reaction. Further, if sensitized lymphoid cells are used (that is, from an adult *CBA* mouse that has previously rejected a transplant of *A*-strain tissues), the elimination of *A*-strain skin in the tolerant host takes the form of a "second-set" reaction. These results highlight the fact that tolerance is based on an inability to respond to the foreign graft, rather than any inhibition of effector mechanisms. The introduction of immunologically competent elements leads to a normal homograft reaction in the tolerant animal, even though the host's own cells appear incapable of participating. Billingham and his associates thus reached the conclusion that tolerance results from a central inhibition of immunologic response to specific antigens, a view that can now be even more strongly supported.

Although the first demonstrations of tolerance were performed with embryos, subsequent studies showed that neonatal animals can be used as a more convenient test object. Woodruff and Simpson (1955) succeeded in conferring tolerance on newborn rats by the subcutaneous inoculation of adult spleen cells. Billingham and Brent (1957a, 1957b) were not able to induce tolerance in newborn mice by the subcutaneous administration of spleen cells, but did have considerable success with intraperitoneal injection. Intravenous inoculation, however, proved to be an even better method. By devising a technique for injection via the anterior facial vein, Billingham and Brent found that they could introduce large numbers of spleen cells to the circulating blood of newborn animals. When 4 to 10 million *CBA* spleen cells were administered in this way to *A*-strain mice within 24 hours of birth, nearly all animals proved to be tolerant toward *CBA* skin grafts in subsequent assays. The superiority of the intravenous procedure over other routes of administration apparently hinges on the rapid distribution of spleen cells to immunologically active sites within the host; for example, to lymph nodes, where the induction of tolerance can take place directly.

Animals that become fully tolerant by intravenous injection are effectively converted into permanent chimeras, as Billingham and Brent (1957b, 1959) showed with the aid of a test devised originally by Mitchison (1956a). As an illustration, lymph nodes or spleen can be removed from an adult *A*-strain mouse which had been rendered tolerant at the neonatal stage by inoculation with *CBA* spleen cells. The excised organs are made into suspension and are injected into a normal adult *A* mouse. Four or five days later, the latter is challenged with a *CBA* skin graft. Chimerism is manifest if the assay host shows a "second-set" reaction. This altered response is indicative of prior contact with *CBA* antigens and, by inference, with the presence of *CBA* cells within the spleen preparations introduced for assay purposes. Many tests of this kind show that young animals made tolerant by inoculation of spleen cells always become chimeras. The persistence of donor cells in direct association with immunologically active tissues of the host is thus an important factor in accounting for stability and continuity of the tolerant state.

The use of spleen or lymphoid cells to induce tolerance soon led to a complication hitherto not encountered in transplantation studies, and which can be termed a "graft-against-the-host" reaction (see Simonsen, 1962). This reversal in the ordinary direction of homograft responses is now known to occur in several immunological systems, and in each case the host tissues are incapable of eliminating the donor cells. If the latter are immunologically competent, they are thus able to react within the host to antigens that are not produced by the donor genotype. Particularly where a state of tolerance is induced by the implant, a full expression of this potential antagonism can become manifest. Such conditions obtain when homologous adult spleen cells are transferred into newborn mice. The resulting disturbances in this system have been examined in detail by Billingham and Brent (1957b, 1959). The syndrome of changes that occur within affected animals has been aptly termed "runt disease" by these investigators, and involves severe interference with growth and development (Figure 8.7). The individuals thus produced are stunted and poor in appearance. They are also susceptible to infection and mortality from other causes. Histologically, there is a marked involution of lymphoid tissues together with pathological changes of other types in the body organs. The use of neonatal animals that can readily become tolerant obviously facilitates the occurrence of this graft-versus-host reaction, but a state of complete passivity in the host is apparently not required. If spleen cells presensitized to the host strain are introduced into adult mice, loss of weight, pathological changes in body organs, and other indications of runt disease may soon develop (Najarian and Feldman, 1962b). Where newborn mice are used as test objects, the incidence and severity of the runting syndrome varies among various donor-recipient combinations. The most pronounced reactions are obtained where donor cells differ from the host at the H-2 locus (Jutila and Weiser, 1962).

The investigations of Simonsen on hemolytic disease and splenomegaly in chick embryos, it may be emphasized, paralleled these studies on runting in mice. Actually, the concept of graft-against-the-host responses had been outlined by this investigator in an early paper (Simonsen, 1953), but convincing evidence of the phenomenon in question was obtained only with a different experimental system (Simonsen, 1957). In this work, chick embryos were inoculated intravenously with homologous cells derived from adult chicken spleen or the buffy coat of peripheral blood. A severe hemolytic anemia subsequently developed in these individuals, who usually died within a week or two after hatching. Postmortem examinations revealed pathological changes in the spleen, liver, thymus, and bone marrow In particular, the spleens were markedly

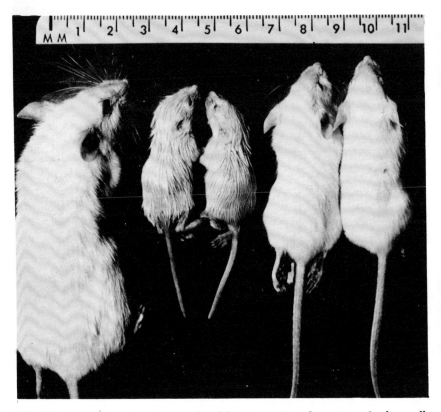

FIG. 8.7. Runt disease in mice, produced by intraperitoneal injection of spleen cells from an unrelated strain. The photograph shows a mother and litter of runted and normal offspring. Note the characteristic "oily" coats of the two animals in which runting was induced with homologous immune cells. (From Jutila and Weiser, 1962.)

enlarged, leading Simonsen to suggest that a colonization of this organ by donor cells had occurred. The correctness of this interpretation was verified through the cytological studies of Biggs and Payne (1959). Using the sex chromosome of the chicken as a marker, these investigators were able to identify male spleen cells after inoculation into female recipients. In the enlarged host spleens, nearly half of the dividing cells were found to be of donor origin.

Splenomegaly of this type can be produced by nearly pure preparations of homologous blood lymphocytes, but not by monocytes or mature thymocytes (Terasaki, 1959). It occurs in mammals as well as birds. The enlargement that takes place seems clearly a part of the graft-versus-host response, since no splenic increase occurs if spleen cells are inoculated from isogenic donors (Simonsen, 1957). Contrary to original expectations, however, the proliferation of host elements appears to be the principal mechanism involved in enlargement (Howard, Michie, and Simonsen, 1961). The specific stimulus for hyperplasia in the host spleen has not yet been identified.

Graft-versus-host reactions figure prominently in still another context. This relates to the use of hemopoietic tissues for replacement therapy in patients or animals that have been subjected to ionizing radiations. It is well known that hemopoietic cells are more sensitive to radiation damage than are other cell types, and this has resulted in attempts to ameliorate the syndrome of primary radiation sickness by injections of spleen, bone marrow, and other tissues. A considerable restoration can often be achieved, provided the individuals have not received total body exposures greatly in excess of the minimal lethal dose. This encouraging result has led to many studies on radiation protection through replacement therapy, the details of which may be found in several comprehensive reviews (Koller, Davies, and Doak, 1961; Christoffanini, 1962; Congdon, 1962). In the development of this field, a number of possible mechanisms were considered originally to account for the recovery from primary radiation sickness in animals that had received injections of hemopoietic tissues. A humoral or cell-free factor contributed by unirradiated cells seemed possible; even donor deoxyribonucleoprotein was suggested by some workers. None of these suggestions has been confirmed. On the contrary, there is now strong evidence that animals that recover from primary radiation sickness by spleen or bone marrow injections are cellular chimeras, with hemopoietic tissues repopulated by the donor elements. Particularly convincing are the chromosome studies performed by Ford and his collaborators (Ford, Hamerton, Barnes, and Loutit, 1956; Ford, Ilbery, and Loutit, 1957). In these experiments, spleen cells possessing a conspicuous marker chromosome were injected into irradiated mice of normal karyotype. When the dividing cells from bone marrow, spleen, and lymph nodes were later examined, all showed the identifying donor tag. If the dose of irradiation is sufficient to destroy hemopoietic tissues within the host animals completely, a total repopulation of these sites takes place. Under these conditions, a chimeric condition with donor cells of different genotype may persist indefinitely. At lower dosages of radiation, regression and disappearance of the donor cells may ultimately take place, as the regenerating native cells progressively mount a homograft reaction.

The obvious parallel between radiation chimeras and tolerant animals harboring foreign cells suggests that a graft-versus-host response should occur whenever the host's immunological defenses are completely obliterated by irradiation, while at lower doses of irradiation, a variable combination of host-versus-graft and graft-versus-host reactions may be expected. These assumptions have been borne out in extensive studies (see Koller, Davies, and Doak, 1961). The manifestations of immunological disparity in radiation chimeras are seen in a secondary wasting, which occurs when homologous spleen or bone marrow are used to prevent primary radiation death. This wasting syndrome has been variously termed "secondary disease" or "homologous disease," and develops characteristically some weeks after the initial therapy. The affected animals suffer extreme weight loss and exhibit a variety of pathological changes that do not develop within individuals injected as controls with isogenic cells. Provided the possibility of graft rejection by the irradiated host in some instances is taken into account, secondary radiation disease seems otherwise indistinguishable from runting in tolerant animals; that is, both stem from an immunological response by grafted cells, where the host is incapable of eliminating them (Trentin, 1959; Van Bekkum, Vos, and Weyzen, 1959).

As a practical matter, it should be pointed out that graft-versus-host reactions may be avoided experimentally while introducing immunologically competent cells into hosts of differing genotype. Homologous disease, either in tolerant or irradiated animals, can be prevented in principle by the use of fetal donor cells (Billingham and Brent, 1959; Koller, Davies, and Doak, 1961). These should become tolerant toward the host in which they come to reside. This ideal relationship appears to have been reached in some instances; for example, in the use of fetal liver for radiation therapy. Residual antagonism, however, has been observed with fetal spleen and bone marrow. A more clear-cut solution to the compatibility problem lies in the use of F_1 hybrid cells for transplantation, if it becomes desirable to transfer tissues between two specified strains of animals. The implanted cells by means of this stratagem possess all the antigens characteristic of the host, but are immunologically incapable of reacting to them (Billingham and Brent, 1959). Tolerance, for example, can be conferred on *CBA* mice with respect to A-strain tissues without graft-versus-host reactions, if the cells inoculated are from F_1 hybrids between the two inbred lines. This technique has been used effectively by Billingham and Silvers (1962), for example, to construct dose-response curves for the establishment of tolerance following inoculation of spleen, bone marrow, leucocytes, lymph node cells, and thymocytes.

In a continuing analysis of tolerance, the factor of host age has become increasingly significant. Originally, it appeared that tolerance was a prerogative of embryos or neonatal animals in which the capacity for immunological response had not yet matured. The concept of a "neutral period" at or shortly after birth was therefore suggested; before this period, confrontation with a foreign antigen would result in tolerance, whereas afterward an immune response should be elicited (Billingham, Brent, and Medawar, 1956a). This postulate, which seemed to accord both with theoretical and experimental considerations, has formed the cornerstone of many general discussions. It is increasingly clear, however, that the idea of a neutral period must now be abandoned as a speculative aid (Brent and Gowland, 1961). Evidence at hand shows that if sufficiently large doses of cells are administered to adult hosts, a state of immunological unresponsiveness can be established, which differs little if at all from neonatally induced tolerance. Thus, Shapiro, Martinez, Smith, and Good (1961) found that C_3H adult mice will accept $A \times C_3H$ skin grafts if injected repeatedly with large doses of hybrid spleen cells via an intravenous route.

Guttman and Aust (1961) were similarly successful with high doses of spleen cells in achieving compatibility for skin grafts from the corresponding alien donors. Lower dosages were required for combinations in which differences exist at histocompatibility loci other than the "strong" H-2 site. A comprehensive study of tolerance in adult animals has now been presented by Brent and Gowland (1963). Broad confirmation has been obtained for the finding that adult mice may be rendered immunologically unresponsive to tissues of a specific genotype if given repeated injections of spleen intravenously. These animals do not exhibit homograft responses to assay transplants of skin from the donor strain. They are, in fact, clearly chimeras, with donor cells in the spleen and lymph nodes readily demonstrable by the technique of Mitchison (1956a). The presence of these elements in host organs, however, does not signify any generalized depression of transplantation immunity. With skin grafts derived from inbred strains other than the donor line, a normal homograft reaction can be obtained. Moreover, the hosts that are specifically unresponsive to donor cells can be made to reject them if equipped by adoptive transfer with lymphoid cells from an untreated isogenic individual. In all these respects, the similarity to immunological tolerance in neonatal animals is striking, and at the cellular level, Brent and Gowland suggest that the two processes may indeed be identical.

Finally, evidence is now forthcoming that even in neonatal animals, both tolerance and transplantation immunity can be produced, with the dosage of cellular antigens as the governing factor. Using newborn mice, Howard and Michie (1962) found that very small doses of homologous spleen will definitely confer a state of resistance toward subsequent challenge with the same material. If larger numbers of spleen cells are employed for preliminary injection, the usual state of tolerance sets in. This demonstration that neonatal animals can become either immune or tolerant toward cells of another genotype has been confirmed by Billingham and Silvers (1962). With homotransplants of skin as an assay system, they likewise observed that low dosages of tolerance-inducing antigens (for example, spleen or lymph node cells) actually sensitized the recipients to test grafts made subsequently. These experiments suggest that the only distinction that can be made between tolerance and immunity in young animals is an operational one. Contrary to earlier beliefs, the neonatal organism does not become tolerant because of any inability to develop an immune response to specific cellular antigens. Either modality of response can in fact be evoked by quantitative manipulation in the strength of stimulus.

Whatever the inception of tolerance, it is important to know whether this phenomenon depends for its continuity on the presence of specific antigen. The assumption has frequently been made that tolerance is established by an inductive or selective process, and a number of cogent arguments can be marshaled to support the concept that committed cells no longer require persistence of the initial stimulus (Billingham and Silvers, 1959). As the experimental evidence accumulates, however, it is apparent that the continuing presence of antigen is a feature of most, if not all, systems in which tolerance is found (Brent and Gowland, 1963; Medawar, 1961a). A causal relation between these factors is difficult to ascertain in animals that are cellular chimeras, because of the stability of donor-host associations, once tolerance is fully established (Billingham, 1958). In at least one system, however, the limited survival of donor cells makes it possible to evaluate their persistence as a basis for continuity of the tolerant state. The cells in question are chicken erythrocytes, which, although nucleated, are short-lived even when reinjected into the original donor (Mitchison, 1959a, 1962a, 1962b). While in vitro, the red cells may be conveniently labeled with ^{51}Cr, and disappearance of this marker from injected animals serves to measure the elimination of erythrocytes experimentally. Mitchison has shown that immunity to homologous red cells or to turkey erythrocytes can be placed in being by inoculating the corresponding red cells into chickens. This state is then made evident by an accelerated removal of the foreign erythrocytes. On the other hand, tolerance to either of these foreign antigens may be induced by introducing blood into the chorioallantoic circulation of chick embryos. A modified host response can be carried over into these chicks after hatching, and is manifest in the attenuated elimination of erythrocytes that are administered as a challenge dose.

Tolerance acquired in this way is transient, but can be stabilized indefinitely by the periodic administration of antigen. If the periodic inoculation of erythrocytes is discontinued, however, tolerance dies away (Figure 8.8). The tolerant state can also be eliminated more abruptly by injecting specific antiserum to remove the foreign red cells from circulation. Interestingly, birds given this treatment are not immediately immune to the corresponding erythrocytes, but they are capable of developing a typical immune response if again confronted with the same antigen.

The concept that tolerance depends on the continued presence of specific antigen is supported even more strongly by the extensive literature on host responses to nonliving antigens (Chase, 1959; Smith, 1961). In essence, these studies have shown that a state closely resembling tolerance of foreign cells can be obtained by inoculating young animals with purified proteins or with other specific agents having antigenic properties. Loss of reactivity can also be observed in adult animals under appropriate conditions. These various manifestations of unresponsiveness usually follow large or repeated doses of nonliving antigens; maintenance injections may be required to stabilize the reaction pattern. Where the antigen is eliminated slowly, however, nonreactivity can be long lasting even after a single injection. Such is the case when adult

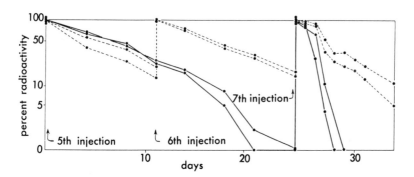

FIG. 8.8. Tolerance in young fowls to turkey erythrocytes. A state of tolerance can be readily established if chickens are given repeated transfusions of foreign red cells, beginning in embryonic stages. The rate of elimination of ^{51}Cr-labeled red cells, which is retarded in these animals, serves as an index of tolerance. The diagram illustrates the loss of tolerance if periodic transfusions are discontinued. Four chickens are tolerant after receiving their fifth injection of turkey red cells; of these, only two (*dotted lines*) receive the sixth injection. When all four birds are transfused at the seventh occasion, only those that had received the sixth inoculation remain tolerant. (From Mitchison, 1962b.)

mice are inoculated with pneumococcal capsular polysaccharide (Felton and Ottinger, 1942; Felton, 1949). A small amount of this material induces type-specific immunity, but larger doses give rise instead to a selectively unresponsive state, which may persist for a year or more. Felton described the phenomenon in question as "immunological paralysis." He showed that pneumococcal polysaccharides are remarkably inert in mouse tissues; an excess of the specific antigen can be demonstrated in various organs for many months after injection. This fact has given rise to speculations that unresponsiveness to polysaccharide is based on peripheral neutralization of specific antibody as soon as it is formed, that is, a "treadmill" effect (Mitchison, 1959b). However, through the application of immunofluorescent techniques to this problem, it has been possible to show that an inhibition of antibody formation actually occurs. By this means, Sercarz and Coons (1959) could readily detect the presence of antibody in the spleen cells of mice given small doses of pneumococcal polysaccharide, but after large doses, the cell picture was consistently negative. A similar suppression after massive administration of antigen was observed with bovine serum albumin. Thus it appears that Felton's original characterization of this phenomenon as immunological paralysis is substantially correct. No real distinction can be drawn between paralysis and tolerance in an immunological sense; both seem to reflect a central inhibition of immune response to specific antigens (Medawar, 1961b; Mitchison, 1961; Dresser, 1962; Howard and Michie, 1962).

The fundamental nature of tolerance has been the subject of much discussion ever since the original demonstration of this event within transplant systems (Billingham, Brent, and Medawar, 1955, 1956a; Medawar, 1958b, 1960, 1961a, 1961b; Lederberg, 1959; Chase, 1959; Burnet, 1959, 1961; Mitchison, 1961; Hašek, Lengerová, and Hraba, 1961; Brent and Gowland, 1963; Billingham and Silvers, 1962). Many of the provisional interpretations made earlier are now outmoded by the facts outlined in the preceding sections. Thus, purely developmental concepts have failed to account for the observation that tolerance, or a closely similar condition, can be induced in adults as well as neonatal animals. Explantations based on genetic changes, on the other hand, are difficult to reconcile with the need for maintenance levels of antigens. In recent discussions, a stem cell theory has found considerable favor (Medawar, 1960; Mitchison, 1961; Brent and Gowland, 1963; Billingham and Silvers, 1962). According to this concept, the precursors of mature lymphoid elements, if exposed to antigen, do not make the final transition to immunological competence with respect to this stimulus, and thus remain tolerant. It follows that tolerance should be more readily elicited in embryos or neonatal animals because of the predominance of immature stem cells within immunologically reactive centers. The need for massive or long-continued administration of antigen to induce tolerance in adults is also reasonable, if the more numerous immunologically competent elements in this case must first be eliminated. Specific deletion of the latter might occur if these cells had a limited life span or were subject to an allergic type of destruction in the presence of antigen excess. Such suggestions at present rest only on a speculative basis, but they have the virtue of potential test in appropriate experimental systems. It is generally recognized, however, that the alternative hypothesis of a homogenous reaction system cannot yet be ruled out. In that case, tolerance may be achieved by overloading or "paralysis" in adult as well as neonatal cells, the governing difference being the ease with which conversion can be implemented from a quantitative standpoint.

To round out the foregoing discussion, one variant of the homograft response may be mentioned that does not appear to stem from the suppression of immune reactions by antigen as such. This is the phenomenon of enhancement (Snell, 1954), usually seen as the facilitated growth of tumors in a foreign host following pretreatment with extracts or nonviable preparations of the corresponding cells. Indications of such an effect were observed as early as 1907, when Flexner and Jobling found that a transplantable rat sarcoma grew more readily if the hosts were given an injection of the corresponding heat-killed cells. Later, Casey and his associates discovered that the growth of certain neoplasms in mice and rabbits was similarly promoted if the hosts were given a preliminary inoculation of frozen tumor material. This phenomenon they termed the "XYZ effect" (Casey, Ross, and Langston, 1949). It was the experiments of Snell and Kaliss, however, that first led to a systematic analysis of tumor enhancement (Snell, 1954, 1957a, 1957b; Kaliss, 1957, 1958). Sarcoma I in A-strain mice has been a favorite object for these studies. The growth of this tumor in alien strains can be selectively promoted if the hosts are given previous injections of lyophilized tissues from the donor strain. Both normal and neoplastic cells may be employed for the purpose. In a series of genetic studies, Snell showed that the lyophilized preparations used to initiate enhancement need not even necessarily be derived from the donor cell type as such. The essential prerequisite is merely the presence of one or more antigens in common with the tumor to be used, but which are lacking in the corresponding host. A continuation of these studies has made clear that the specific factors in lyophilized preparations which lead toward enhancing effects in mice are actually H-2 isoantigens (Snell, 1963).

The most distinctive features of enhancement, however, became evident only through the important experiments of Kaliss and Molomut (1952). These showed that a promotion can be obtained by injecting specific antiserum that matches the isoantigens of frozen or lyophilized material. When, for example, isoantiserum produced against Sarcoma I is administered to untreated animals bearing this tumor, increased growth occurs instead of the inhibition or lack of effect that might have been anticipated. Other experiments show that enhancement can be transferred passively by injecting serum from enhanced mice into untreated animals bearing the same tumor. These results suggested that lyophilized preparations lead to enhancement by stimulating the production of humoral antibody, which is actually the mediating agent (Kaliss, 1957, 1958). This explanation has now been generally accepted as the best interpretation of the facts available. As a result, enhancement can be more specifically defined as the facilitated growth of a foreign graft, following introduction of the corresponding immune serum.

The existence of enhancement as an immunological phenomenon is particularly easy to demonstrate with tumors such as Sarcoma I, but it can be seen to a varying degree with other neoplasms as well. Similar events have also been detected in less conspicuous form with grafts of normal tissues. Billingham, Brent, and Medawar (1956b) found that the survival of skin homografts in mice could be considerably extended, although not indefinitely, by several prior inoculations of the host animals with lyophilized donor kidney, spleen, or liver. Attempts to enhance the survival of skin grafts in mice by passive transfer of isoantisera have been less successful, but a weak effect has been reported by Brent and Medawar (1961). Nelson (1962) has reported that skin homografts in guinea pigs remain viable for a longer time if the animals are given a preliminary inoculation of spleen homogenate; serum from these animals was effective in transmitting enhancement to secondary hosts. Also worthy of mention is the work of Parkes (1958) on ovarian grafts in rats, where enhancement in some instances may succeed in prolonging the life of interstrain grafts indefinitely.

In considering various possible explanations for enhancing effects, Billingham, Brent, and Medawar (1956b) pointed out that immune responses to foreign cells may conceivably be prevented by afferent, efferent, or central inhibition. The latter presupposes a suppression in antibody production per se. For inhibition of the afferent type, a neutralization of antigen produced by the implant can be visualized; that is, a "walling off of the graft," in the sense of Snell (1957b). In this case, an effective antigenic stimulus would not reach the reaction centers of the host. If an efferent inhibition takes place, some interference with effector mechanisms must be assumed. For example, coating of the graft by antiserum might be postulated, making these elements less easily recognized by cellular reaction systems of the host. Alternatively, a change might be induced within the transplant cells, rendering them less susceptible to an established host response. Billingham and his collaborators preferred the concept of afferent inhibition, but Kaliss (1957) later showed that enhancement of tumor growth can be initiated many days after the time of transplantation, even after a state of immunity is in being, making it unlikely that donor antigens in such systems are being deprived of access to reaction centers in the host. In the opinion of Kaliss (1958), enhancement may stem from some physiological change in target cells and may be produced as a consequence of contact with specific antiserum. This becomes manifest through increased survival in the face of homograft responses.

An experimental choice between these alternatives has been attempted by Snell, Winn, Stimpfling, and Parker (1960). No evidence could be found to support the concept of induced change in tumor cells as a basis for enhancement. When tumor grafts are transplanted from stock animals to enhanced mice and back to mice of the same strain, the degree of success is identical with direct transfers made without this variation. To examine the possibility of afferent or central inhibition, Snell and his co-workers inoculated antiserum into animals bearing transplants of Sarcoma I and assayed the host lymph nodes for immunity by means of adoptive transfers. The results showed that cellular immunity that had been previously established in these lymphoid cells was greatly reduced by injections of antiserum, although not by the presence of the tumor graft alone. Whether this suppression was the result of a central inhibition of antibody production as such, or was merely the cut-off of antigenic stimulus by peripheral neutralization, could not be immediately determined.

If in fact the cellular immune response can be directly suppressed by feedback from externally applied antibody, the phenomena of enhancement and humoral damage to the target homograft may conceivably represent possible alternatives. Which of the two, if any, occurs in any given instance might then be determined by the relative thresholds of antibody required to initiate cellular damage in the transplant, as compared to central inhibition of immune response in the host. By analogy to the phenomenon of tolerance, it might be easier to secure a suppression by external antibody in neonatal than in adult hosts and, under appropriate circumstances, thereby to demonstrate humoral damage and enhancement with one and the same graft. This prediction seems to be confirmed by the experiments of Steinmuller (1962), who found that skin homografts in baby rats can be enhanced with immune serum, whereas the same procedure in adult hosts produced definite evidence of damage to the skin transplants. Conversely, it is to be expected that enhancement should be secured readily with cells of high resistance to cytotoxic antibodies (for example, sarcoma I), whereas leukemias and other sensitive types ought to be enhanced with difficulty, if at all.

Experimental findings are in line with this assumption (Snell, Winn, Stimpfling, and Parker, 1960). The limiting variables are seen with an illustration from the work of Boyse, Old, and Stockert (1962). These investigators have worked with mouse lymphoma EL-4, which, as previously mentioned, offers a classic example of susceptibility to humoral antibody. Interestingly, this neoplasm can also be strikingly enhanced by specific antiserum. To demonstrate an effect, Boyse and his colleagues have shown that it is necessary merely to lower the ratio of antiserum to the tumor cells present within assay hosts, either by reducing the amount of serum injected or preferably by increasing the size of the tumor cell population. The simplest interpretation of this finding lies in assuming that the concentration of antibody falls below the minimum required for cytotoxic damage of the EL-4 cells, but still is sufficient to repress an immune response. On the whole, a convincing case can thus be made for the concept that enhancement, like tolerance, depends on a phenomenon of central inhibition. The two processes may differ primarily in the direction from which repressors impinge upon a common reaction system.

IMMUNOLOGICAL PROGRESSION IN TUMORS

The modulations of histocompatibility described in the preceding section emphasize the complexity of host-graft associations at a purely physiological level. Regulatory mechanisms can account for a surprising array of adjustments tending to minimize or reduce the effects of antigenic differences. Even so, the tacit assumption in most, if not all, of these studies is one of genotypic uniformity, at least as far as the transplanted tissues are concerned. Thus immunity, tolerance, and enhancement make up a backdrop against which one further degree of freedom can be considered for transplant systems, namely the occurrence of variation and selection within target cell populations. From this standpoint, the host organism becomes primarily a means of assay, a screen for the precise detection of antigenic differences.

Little is known of the potential which may be inherent within normal somatic cells for antigenic variation, although eventually a combination of cell culture and transplantation techniques may serve to fill this gap. However, the capacity of tumors for immunologic change in serial passage has become clear-cut, along with the tendency for progressions in morphology, karyotype, drug resistance, and other unit characters that have been detailed in preceding chapters. Both simplification and increased complexity in antigenic pattern can occur within experimental tumor systems. Much of the work on these topics is still in course of development, but there are a number of reviews on tumor transplantation that establish a useful frame of reference (Snell, 1959; G. Klein, 1959; Southam, 1960; Kaliss, 1961). The extensive monograph of G. Klein (1963) contains a particularly incisive treatment.

Reduction in Histocompatibility Requirements Although tumors in general grow progressively only in hosts of similar genotype, there are a number of exceptions in which the histocompatibility barrier becomes diminished or altered. Analysis of these phenomena has been rewarding because of the extensive background of genetic and serological information that can be applied to the problem. Among the neoplasms that do show departures from the usual laws of transplantation, two distinctive patterns can be found. In some cases, the acquisition of ability to grow in hosts of another genetic constitution is specific for a particular genotype, without any increased tendency for proliferation within alien animals in general. Other tumors in the course of serial transplantation may come to be comparatively nonspecific in host range, and can be propagated to some degree within any strain of the corresponding species.

The most conspicuous examples of the latter phenomenon are to be seen among old, long-established tumors that have been maintained for extensive periods by serial transfer. These neoplasms have sometimes been referred to as "universal tumors" because, over the course of time, the specificity of host range commonly becomes blurred or obliterated (Hauschka and Amos, 1957; G. Klein, 1959; Kaliss, 1961). Included in this category are such well-known experimental materials as the Jensen rat sarcoma, the Brown-Pearce rabbit carcinoma, and the various lines of Ehrlich and Krebs mouse tumors. All these venerable neoplasms originated many years ago in mongrel lines of uncertain ancestry. Even at the outset, the ability to grow progressively in noninbred hosts was prerequisite to propagation in the animal stocks then available. Continuous selection may thus account for the emergence of cell lineages that can now produce lethal results in a substantial fraction of homologous hosts, regardless of exact genotype. It should be emphasized, however, that loss of transplantation specificity in this sense is variable among different tumors and is not an all-or-none phenomenon. Nor is it necessary that nonspecific neoplasms originate in hosts of mixed genetic constitution. The same tendency can occasionally be observed as a progression within tumors arising from inbred lines. Strain specificity may be clear-cut initially for such neoplasms, but in serial passage, implants are found which grow progressively in hosts of other genetic constitutions, and eventually proliferation may occur more or less regularly in a variety of alien strains.

The exact basis for the generalized ability of these nonspecific tumors to grow within alien strains is not yet clear. Conceivably, a multiplicity of factors may prove limiting for particular neoplasms (G. Klein, 1959, 1963). A number of mechanisms have been suggested, but none of these has been demonstrated to be of general validity. The idea of antigenic simplification has been an attractive one (Gorer, 1948, 1956). According to this concept, genetic changes within tumor cells during serial propagation may be reflected in losses of certain antigens and changes in relative amounts of others. In a foreign environment, processes of immunoselection (Hauschka and Levan, 1953) would thus favor the establishment of sublines characterized by a diminished antigenicity and consequent extension of host range. This theory has been put in a more explicit form by Hauschka and his co-workers, on the basis of cytological and serological studies with mouse ascites tumors. Using a broad spectrum of ascitic neoplasms, Hauschka and Levan (1953) and Hauschka (1953) carried out investigations in which correlations were sought between transplantation behavior and karyotypic pattern. For this purpose, tumors were examined with modal chromosome numbers ranging from diploid to tetraploid levels. All the neoplasms that displayed diploid modes and lacked obvious karyotypic modifications proved to be strain-specific. Implants of these cells failed to grow, or regressed in hosts of unlike genetic constitution. Other tumors grew progressively in spite of isoantigenic barriers, and these were invariably aneuploid, with structurally modified chromosome complements. The modal chromosome numbers in such cases were occasionally hyperdiploid or, more frequently, subtetraploid. Nonspecific tumors with modes at the true tetraploid level were not observed. Aneuploidy thus seemed to be a consistent correlate of the ability to transgress histocompatibility differentials.

Hauschka has advocated an explanation for these findings in terms of genic imbalance. There is no obvious basis for antigenic simplification in conversion to polyploidy as such, which need not alter the effective dosage of histocompatibility factors. But as aneuploidy develops, loss or gain of individual chromosomes or their parts clearly takes place, together with structural remodeling that may alter the functional relations between remaining loci (Chapter 4). If the synthesis of isoantigens depends on the interaction of multiple determinants within a balanced genome, aneuploid cells might display a diminished antigenic output or even the loss of certain factors (Hauschka and Schultz, 1954; Hauschka, Kvedar, Grinnell, and Amos, 1956). A number of serological studies have been performed in order to assess these predictions more directly. Hoecker and Hauschka (1956) compared two mouse lymphomas of diploid and near-tetraploid constitution, respectively. The former grew only in A-strain mice and showed antigens *CDEK*, appropriate to this inbred line. Cells of the near-tetraploid neoplasm grew also in *DBA/2* mice, which possess *CD* but not *EK*. Significantly, *E* and probably *K* appeared to be lacking in the tumor cells as well. The more extensive investigations of Amos (1956) and Hauschka and Amos (1957) have provided serological data for a number of other tumors; in general these suggested a weakening or disappearance of isoantigens in cells of aneuploid karyotype, as compared to diploids. On three so-called "universal tumors," Hauschka and Amos were unable to detect any known *H*-2 products.

Despite these initial indications, there are now a number of facts that, taken together, seem to preclude any simple causal relation between antigenicity, karyotype, and transplantation specificity. The correlation between aneuploidy and homotransplantability appears at best to be only a partial one. Tumors have now been reported that are strain-specific although markedly aneuploid in pattern, while conversely, some diploid or near-diploid neoplasms grow widely in unrelated strains (G. Klein and E. Klein, 1958; G. Klein, 1959). The generalized disappearance of isoantigens from tumors may also have been overemphasized. Although some long-established tumors may appear to have suffered a comprehensive loss of histocompatibility antigens, these cells are invariably inhibited or rejected by preimmunized hosts, indicating that the antigens and presumably their controlling genetic factors are still present, with the reduction being one of degree only (G. Klein, 1959; Snell, 1963). Even a lowered output of antigens is not a necessary attribute of nonspecific tumors. Feldman and Sachs (1957) observed, in fact, that the degree of homotransplantability seemed to be in proportion to the immune response evoked by the transplant. They were inclined to attribute the ability of tumors for growth in foreign hosts to the production of excess antigen, which could then neutralize antibodies and prevent damage to the graft. The basis for this assertion is questionable, however, since the differences in mass between progressively growing tumors and those that remain static or regress would invalidate any quantitative comparisons of antigen output (E. Klein, 1959). The inadequacy of explanations based purely on antigen emission is emphasized by the last-mentioned experiments of E. Klein. In that work, the immunizing abilities of two mouse tumors were compared, one of which was strain-specific, and the other grew freely in isogenic resistant lines containing a variety of foregin H-2 alleles. The two neoplasms had originated from animals of identical genetic background, and both were predominantly diploid. In order to eliminate differences resulting from the tendency of the nonspecific tumor to proliferate in alien hosts, cell suspensions were subjected to intensive X irradiation. This procedure did not prevent either of the tumor preparations from inducing an active immunity when inoculated into mice of other genotypes. Interestingly, however, the two neoplasms under these conditions proved to be essentially identical in capacity to evoke hemagglutinins and in ability to immunize the hosts against a subsequent challenge with unirradiated cells. In this material there is thus no evidence that the loss of strain specificity results from either an increase or decrease of antigenic output. If the phenomenon depends instead on a heightened resistance to immune responses, conceivably an explanation may be found in terms of differences in surface density of isoantigenic receptors (Möller and Möller, 1962a, 1962b). Since cell surface, volume, and gene dosage are altered to a different degree in the transition from diploid to polyploid or aneuploid states, Hauschka's earlier correlations may bear re-examination with this possibility in mind. As Klein points out, however, causal factors of a quite different type may be involved in nonspecific tumor growth; for example, differences in the tempo of vascularization in a foreign host.

Turning now to specific alterations that may take place in histocompatibility, at least one type of adaptive shift can be induced in tumors without the occurrence of variation and selection in the corresponding cell population. This is the Barrett-Deringer effect, in which the ability of a strain-specific tumor to grow in backcross animals with a resistant strain can be greatly increased by intermediate passage in F_1 hybrids between the two inbred lines (Barrett and Deringer, 1950; Barrett, Deringer, and Hansen, 1953). The tumor employed originally was a transplantable mammary carcinoma, which grows in 100 percent of C_3H mice but not in animals of differing genotype (for example, $BALB/c$ or $DBA/2$). As do other similar tumors, this neoplasm grows uniformly in F_1 hybrids with alien strains and in a small percentage of mice obtained by backcrossing F_1 animals to the corresponding resistant line. Barrett and Deringer found, however, that the incidence of takes in these backcross animals rose markedly if the tumor was carried first for one passage in the F_1 hybrids. Prolonged residence in F_1 mice did not increase this effect. The change appeared to be a stable one, and was not reversed by returning the tumor from F_1 animals to the parent strain before assay in the backcross mice. Facilitated growth in resistant backcross animals could be induced regularly in this way, and the effect was highly specific; that is, there was no general acquisition of ability to grow in animals of foreign genotype. The authors were unable to derive from the experimental data a definite explanation for this phenomenon.

A detailed analysis of the Barrett-Deringer effect was subsequently reported (E. Klein and G. Klein, 1956; G. Klein and E. Klein, 1957). Critical experiments were designed to choose between a variation-selection hypothesis and the alternative of host-induced adaptation. The investigators reasoned that if facilitated growth of tumors after hybrid passage depends on immunoselection, the variant cell types must be present in low frequency in the stock tumor; direct inoculation of the backcross animals would otherwise have revealed their presence. But if the pre-existing variants are relatively rare, they should be absent in small samples of the cell population. In this case, the use of small inocula for treatment in F_1 hybrids should diminish or abolish the Barrett-Deringer phenomenon. However, even when tumors in the F_1 hosts were initiated with as few as 70 cells, the facilitation of subsequent growth in backcross animals occurred uniformly.

The pattern of progressive growth in such assays coincided closely with that of control series, in which the tumors used arose from mass inocula in the F_1 hosts. There was still the remote possibility that variants with increased growth potential existed within the stock tumor at 1:70 or higher proportions, but could not be demonstrated without additional immunoselection by F_1 passage. As a check, synthetic mixtures in this ratio were prepared from F_1-passed and stock tumor cells, and were inoculated directly into backcross mice. The resulting tumors behaved as if composed solely of F_1-passed cells. The inference drawn from these findings is that the Barrett-Deringer effect represents a direct adaptation at the cellular level, induced as a stable change within the tumor as a whole by factors within the hybrid host. This does not seem to necessitate any direct contact between the tumor and cells of the F_1 animal, since adaptation can be induced in tumors confined within diffusion chambers. A humoral factor is thus suggested, but the mechanism of action and nature of the cellular changes induced are not yet known. Interestingly, the adaptation that follows hybrid passage seems to relate only to weak histocompatibility barriers. No shifts of this type in the presence of H-2 differentials have yet been observed (G. Klein, 1963).

Induced adaptations may on occasion play a minor role in tumor transplantation, but the majority of selective changes that occur in host specificity appear to have a genetic basis. The unraveling of these phenomena within the last few years has produced some of the most elegant and persuasive examples of immunological progression. The possibility that genetic alterations leading to isoantigenic variation might occur in tumor cell populations has long been recognized, but it was not until recently that experimental designs were devised which could effectively reveal such changes. A clear statement of appropriate methods was made by Lederberg (1956), who advocated a close examination of heterozygous tumors arising within F_1 hybrids, the latter being derived from two isogenic resistant strains differing only at a single histocompatibility locus. Tumors of this type, if strain-specific, would grow ordinarily only in the hybrid hosts of origin, whereas if variants appeared that were selectively compatible with either parental line, the presumption of a genetic change would be a good one. Efforts to demonstrate such a thesis experimentally began at about the same time in two laboratories, and the results of Mitchison (1956b, 1958) were the first to be reported. In this work, F_1 hybrid mice of genotype H-$2^b/H$-2^d were used, derived by an outcross between the coisogenic strains $C_{57}BL$ and $C_{57}BL.DBA/2$. By injecting methylcholanthrene into these hybrid animals, a carcinoma was obtained and grew initially to some extent in both parental lines. On serial passage, however, derivatives appeared that were entirely restricted to one of the parental strains. Although these tumors appeared to represent stable variations, the mechanism of change was not immediately ascertained.

A more comprehensive picture of variant formation from heterozygous tumors soon emerged from the experiments of G. Klein and E. Klein (1956), E. Klein, G. Klein, and Révész (1957), and Bayreuther and E. Klein (1958). Several isogenic resistant lines were employed from the group that had been derived by Snell against an A-strain background. The original strain in this case has the genotype H-$2^a/H$-2^a, and coisogenic derivatives resulting from crosses with other strains include $A.SW$ (H-$2^s/H$-2^s), $A.BY$ (H-$2^b/H$-2^b), and $A.CA$ (H-$2^f/H$-2^f). For experimental study, sarcomas were produced by methylcholanthrene in F_1 hybrids between the A strain and its $A.SW$ subline. These tumors, of genotype H-$2^a/H$-2^s, were then examined for variant formation by transfer to other isogenic resistant strains. Since the demonstration of variants depends on the efficiency of host selection, model experiments were performed first to see whether cells specifically compatible with a given host could be detected when present at low frequency within a population of noncompatible cells. Tests showed that homozygous $H\text{-}2^a/H\text{-}2^a$ cells from a tumor originating in A-strain mice could in fact selectively multiply in these animals, even when diluted to as low a proportion as 4×10^{-7} with hybrid elements, which were simultaneously rejected in an intense homograft reaction. A high degree of selectivity thus characterizes the segregation of compatible from noncompatible cells in tumor transplant systems.

In these initial experiments by the Kleins and their collaborators, the tumor $MSWB$ illustrates a transplantation pattern that has since been found typical of numerous other heterozygous neoplasms. The $MSWB$ sarcoma arose within $A \times A.SW$ F_1 hybrids, and in general, it was specific for animals of this genetic constitution, failing to grow progressively in alien strains. A conspicuous exception to this rule, however, was the fact that tumors developed from $MSWB$ implants in about one-quarter of the $A.SW$ parental strain mice. Neoplasms that came up in this way could then be propagated uniformly in serial passage with the $A.SW$ line. They failed completely to grow in the opposite parental strain (A), or in other coisogenic lines and hybrids with foreign $H\text{-}2$ alleles. Several lines of evidence indicated that these $MSWB$ derivatives could be regarded as true variants that had acquired specific compatibility with animals of $A.SW$ genotype by a stable and apparently irreversible change. The variants, for example, were unaffected in their growth when placed in $A.SW$ mice that had been preimmunized with stock $MSWB$ cells. The latter elicit antibodies because they contain $H\text{-}2^a$, as well as the $H\text{-}2^s$, which is characteristic of the $A.SW$ genotype. When cells from a variant tumor, on the other hand, were injected into mice of a foreign strain (for example, $A.BY$ or $A.CA$), cytotoxins or hemagglutinins against $H\text{-}2^s$ could be demonstrated, but not against $H\text{-}2^a$.

Such distinctions can be more fully appreciated if translated into the isoantigens actually present. Although a number of antigenic factors are determined in common by the two alleles, $H\text{-}2^a$ cells produce components D and K, and $H\text{-}2^s$ cells do not. Mice of $A.SW$ genotype accordingly lack the D and K isoantigens, and thus they exhibit an immune response when inoculated with stock $MSWB$ cells. Significantly, neither D nor K antigens could be demonstrated serologically in the variants that had acquired compatibility with the $A.SW$ line. Interestingly, tumors lacking only K can be obtained by using a different schedule for selection. $MSWB$ cells can be inoculated, for example, into $A.SW \times DBA/2$ F_1 hybrids, which contain antigen D, but not K. Variants derived from these hosts usually possess D, but never K.

These productive approaches to isoantigenic variation have in later work been expanded on a broad front. The main presentations are to be found in reviews by G. Klein and E. Klein (1958, 1959), E. Klein and G. Klein (1959), and G. Klein (1963), to which reference may be made for data and detailed discussions. A number of generalizations gradually emerged. Even at the outset, patterns of transplantation behavior other than that described for the $MSWB$ sarcoma had been observed, and the necessity for an appreciation of these differences became increasingly apparent. Thus, some sarcomas induced with methylcholanthrene in F_1 hybrids between coisogenic lines are entirely specific, and no variants can be obtained in either of the parental strains. Others show a nonspecific transplantation pattern, growing to some extent in a variety of strains with foreign H-2 alleles, either immediately or after a number of serial passages. In such cases, however, proliferation in alien strains takes place indiscriminately, and can invariably be inhibited or eliminated by the use of preimmunized mice, showing that no true loss of antigens has occurred. A more subtle difficulty is posed by what Snell (1952, 1953) has termed "false positives"; that is, the occasional tendency of strain-specific tumors to take in a host of unrelated genetic background. In such cases, however, the initial growths do not "breed true"; that is, they die out when passaged serially within the animals in question. False positives can also be diagnosed by preimmunization, which effectively blocks growth of such a tumor. These irregularities in transplantation pattern can presumably be attributed to random fluctuations in the strength of homograft reactions.

When these complicating factors are appropriately discounted, there remain a number of heterozygous tumors that can give rise to host-specific variants within one of or both the parental strains. The frequency of variant formation is individually distinctive for each tumor and is not ordinarily the same in the two parental lines; some neoplasms, like the $MSWB$ sarcoma, may show a predilection for one parental type. A stepwise sequence in the establishment of specific variants can sometimes be observed, as well as direct takes in the parental lines. In such cases, growth occurs at first in a limited proportion of the parental animals only; nonhost antigens can still be demonstrated serologically. Such tumors either die out in serial passage or eventually give rise to true variants fully compatible with animals of the parental strain. Conversely, hybrid tumors that grow selectively in one parental line can in some instances be converted into nonspecific neoplasms. The presumed mechanism here is an additional change that increases resistance to immune responses; for example, the appearance of tumor elements with a lesser number of antigenic receptor sites on the cell surface (E. Klein and Möller, 1963).

In general, these studies by the Kleins and their collaborators emphasize the specificity and permanence of change in isoantigenic variants from heterozygous tumors. Variants established in one parental strain can never be "switched" to the opposite parental line, even when ample opportunity for selection is presented by passage through newborn mice. Similarly, variants can be obtained from heterozygous tumors by implantation into hybrids derived by crossing one parental line with a third inbred strain, but in such cases, the derivative neoplasms are always found to be specific for the parental line entering into the outcross and not for the assay hybrid as such. There seems to be nothing unique in the particular tumors used for experimental study. Isoantigenic variants have been obtained from spontaneous mammary carcinomas of hybrid mice as well as from spontaneous or estrogen-induced lymphomas and interstitial cell tumors of the testis in these animals (Hellström, 1960; E. Klein, G. Klein, and Hellström, 1960; G. Klein and Hellström, 1962). In all such materials, the stability of established isoantigenic variants is remarkable. No reversions to the precursor hybrid genotype have ever been observed, nor transformations to H-2 alleles that are not found in the parental lines. Repeated attempts have been made to establish isoantigenic variants from tumors originating within inbred lines; these have consistently met with failure. Such homozygous neoplasms either grow selectively in the strain of origin or proliferate to a varying degree as nonspecific tumors in a variety of alien hosts. When the homozygous tumors are strain-specific, "false positives" can be occasionally observed in animals of different genetic constitution, but these do not give rise to sublines with sustained ability to proliferate in mice of a particular genotype.

The basic mechanism of isoantigenic variation has been a topic of continuous interest and discussion throughout this work. Epigenetic as well as genetic concepts can be considered, but as information has accumulated, an explanation based on the latter has become increasingly probable. The exact mode of genetic change has not been conclusively established, but several possibilities seem for practical purposes to be ruled out. The concept of point mutation is difficult to reconcile with the fact that variations in this system are uniformly in the direction of antigenic loss, whereas new or modified antigenic patterns would be expected. The application of mutagenic agents to heterozygous tumors has yielded conflicting results, but in no case have unique H-2 alleles emerged by this artifice, and no effect can be demonstrated on homozygous tumors (Dhaliwal, 1961; G. Klein, 1963). The failure to induce or find spontaneous changes in homozygous tumors is particularly impressive, since the codominant nature of known H-2 factors suggests that no bar exists to the direct expression of mutant alleles. Alternatively, gross karyotypic changes might be invoked to explain the observation that isoantigens may to some extent be lost *en bloc* (for example, antigens *D* and *K*). This hypothesis drew initial support from the fact that most, if not all, variants isolated from tumors originating from small numbers of *MSWB* cells were found to exhibit individual and distinctive karyotypic patterns (Bayreuther and E. Klein, 1958). Karyotypic changes cannot be generally implicated, however, since Hellström (1960) found with near-diploid lymphomas that variants and precursor tumor were identical in chromosomal configurations.

The most convincing explanation for the origin of isoantigenic variants from hybrid tumors is the concept of somatic crossing over (E. Klein, 1961; Hellström, 1961; G. Klein, 1963). Although this process has not heretofore been documented in mammalian cells (Chapter 1), the observations of one-way, irreversible loss of antigens corresponding to one of the parental alleles are clearly consistent with such a proposal. That conversion from the heterozygous to the homozygous state actually occurs at the *H-2* locus, rather than mere deletion, is suggested by the data of Hellström (1960). He showed that homozygous mouse lymphomas and isoantigenic variants were slightly more susceptible to cytotoxic *H-2* antibodies than were the heterozygous lymphomas from which the variants had been derived. These observations appear to reflect differences in gene dosage for the respective cell types concerned. In more recent work, attention has been focused on the relative loss of antigens *D* and *K* when isoantigenic variants are isolated in hosts of differing selective background (E. Klein, 1961; Hellström, 1961). Significantly, *K* can be lost individually or in combination with *D*, but *D* is never lost alone. This fact is particularly striking when hosts that have *K*, but lack *D*, are used for selection (for example, A.SW × C_3H F_1 mice). Thus the loss of *K* in hosts containing this factor cannot be the result of a host-induced change. These results are understandable, however, if it is assumed that the genetic determinant for *K* lies distal to that for *D*, with respect to the centromere. In this case, crossing over between the *D* and *K* regions ought to give variants containing *D* only, while if crossovers occurred between the centromere and *D* region, both antigens would be lost (E. Klein, 1961).

Chromosomal rearrangements may thus be operative in segregating the *H-2* alleles or their individual components within heterozygous tumor cells, but this need not imply a restriction of mechanisms for variation in other systems. Variation and selection may conceivably stem from a number of facets of the immunological differentials between tumor cells and homologous hosts. A broader probing of this field can perhaps be achieved by the use of isolated cell populations, and pioneer studies with cell cultures have been reported by Herzenberg (1962) and by Cann and Herzenberg (1963a, 1963b). In this work, P-388 mouse cells were employed, a permanent strain derived originally from $DBA/2$ mice (H-$2^d/H$-2^d). Even after extended serial culture, these cells were found to possess the isoantigens appropriate to this genotype, and were killed for the most part by exposure to H-2^d antiserum. A small fraction of cells survives without cytotoxic destruction, however, and these can be regrown in standard medium and recycled through antiserum in similar fashion. After 12 such cycles, clones were isolated from P-388 populations that were partially or completely refractory to cytotoxic damage. Interestingly, these variants still contain demonstrable H-2^d antigens, but appear to be less susceptible to the effects of antiserum. Quantitative studies showed that the variants absorbed less antibody than did parental cells, but an even more significant difference may lie in the distinctive morphological alterations found to accompany resistance. The variants were fusiform and spread out, with a surface area nearly twice that of the precursor cell type. Considering that cytotoxicity depends on the surface concentration of isoantigenic receptors (Möller and Möller, 1962a, 1962b), this enlargement of cell surface may have a direct selective value. Cell cultures may thus be used to assess variations that confer resistance to isoantibodies, and also those that involve a remodeling of antigenic structure. Whether either can be produced by mutation per se in isolated systems is still unknown, but the variety of selective factors that can be imposed on cells of known serotype offer a number of promising experimental designs.

Appearance of New Antigens The possibility that tumors may acquire antigens not shared by normal cells and tissues has intrigued investigators in cancer research for many years (see Zilber, 1958; Kidd, 1961). Until recently, however, this question has been regarded for the most part as settled in the negative. Immunity to tumors in serial passage can be effected by a variety of procedures, and a large literature on this topic accumulated during the early period of experimental investigation. But interest declined gradually as it became apparent that the processes under study had been largely, if not entirely, related to transplantation immunity rather than tumor-specific immunity per se. Thus there is little to be gained from a detailed discussion of the past work in which this distinction was not clearly made. A very general opinion developed that tumors do not possess antigens not shared by normal cells of the same genetic background, and that primary neoplasms have an antigenic pattern defined by the host of origin.

Several discoveries within recent years, however, suggest that these conclusions may have been premature. Studies with viruses as well as with chemical carcinogens point toward the appearance, in some instances at least, of novel antigens within tumor cells. The exact nature, significance, and origin of these factors remain to be worked out. Evidently the appearance of new antigens is not of decisive importance for the natural history of cancer within a primary (that is, autochthonous) host, since the regression of malignant tumors within such individuals is an exceedingly rare event. But this need not imply that antigenic differentials are lacking. If such differences do arise between neoplasms and their primary hosts of origin, the promotion of immunity to autografts or isografts of the tumor may reveal their existence. The most critical evidence for the production of antigenic novelty beyond the framework of isoantigenic differences rests on experiments of this type.

Definite support for the concept of tumor-specific antigens can be drawn from several sources, of which the investigations by Gorer and his co-workers on the EL-4 lymphoma may be mentioned first. As previously noted, this neoplasm grows uniformly in the $C_{57}BL$ strain of origin and is particularly susceptible to cytotoxic antibodies. In seeking to determine the spectrum of cytotoxic sensitivity, Gorer and Amos (1956) absorbed antisera to EL-4 cells with various normal tissues. Unexpectedly, $C_{57}BL$ cells from normal tissues were found incapable of abolishing cytotoxic activity. This phenomenon was particularly striking if the antisera were simply injected into $C_{57}BL$ mice bearing EL-4 cells. In this case, all hemagglutinating activity was removed by exposure to the host tissues, but a considerable degree of protection against the tumor was nevertheless conferred. Gorer and Amos concluded, therefore, that EL-4 cells possess a unique X component; that is, an antigen not found in the isoantigenic spectrum of $C_{57}BL$ cells in general.

A continuation of this work has shown that X factors can be demonstrated by similar methods in a number of other mouse lymphomas, both spontaneous and chemically induced (Amos and Day, 1957; Gorer, 1961). Some individuality is apparent in the fact that components from the different tumors vary in their antigenicity within a foreign host. Serological cross-reactions are found between some, but not all, of these X antigens (Gorer, Tuffrey, and Batchelor, 1962). None of them reacts with antisera prepared against normal cells of otherwise identical genetic constitution. The origin of the factors in question is unknown, but certain obvious explanations are deemed unlikely. The possibility of genetic drift in host or tumor background, for example, does not account for the regularity with which X components can be found, even in lymphomas transferred only a few times beyond the primary host.

Gorer and his associates were unable to establish an active immunity by inoculating $C_{57}BL$ mice with heavily irradiated EL-4 cells or through experiments in which other lymphomas were irradiated and injected into isogenic hosts. Conceivably, this negative result may represent a threshold phenomenon, however, since Howard and Michie (1962) report that the antigenicity of cell suspensions declines greatly after extensive irradiation. Of more immediate interest is the demonstration that active immunity can be induced directly against certain other lymphomas within isogenic hosts (G. Klein, Sjögren, and E. Klein, 1962; Sjögren, 1963a, 1963b). The tumors in question were all induced by inoculation of the Gross virus (Chapter 1) in strains of mice that appear to be genetically homozygous when tested by mutual skin transfers. Each neoplasm appears to contain an antigen foreign to any of the inbred lines used, but shared in common by the other tumors arising from the Gross agent. Resistance to the growth of any particular tumor can be demonstrated (1) by a preliminary inoculation of the same cells at a level too low to produce progressive growth, or (2) by a homograft of Gross-induced lymphoma cells from an alien strain. The latter procedure does not confer any resistance to isografts of normal cells within the assay host strain or to native tumors of different type, including lymphomas that are derived by some other means than administration of the Gross agent. The specificity of these immune responses can also be demonstrated by serological reactions. Klein and his collaborators have shown that resistance to Gross virus-induced lymphomas is accompanied by cytotoxins that can be demonstrated *in vitro*. These antibodies show cross-reactions with the various Gross virus-induced lymphomas, but are without effect on normal lymphoid cells (Slettenmark and Klein, 1962). Still other examples of novel antigens in leukemic cells can now be cited (Old, Boyse, and Stockert, 1963; Boyse, Old, and Luell, 1963), and the phenomenon appears to be a general one.

As mentioned previously (Chapter 7), the emergence of unique antigens in tumors is seen even more explicitly in neoplasms induced with polyoma virus or SV_{40}. The nature of this phenomenon has been examined chiefly through studies with the polyoma agent, and some of the most interesting evidence is indirect. It is significant, for example, that the appearance of tumors in mice treated with the polyoma agent can be correlated closely with host age. Newborn animals respond with a variety of neoplastic growths, but adult mice injected with polyoma virus do not give rise to tumors. Interestingly enough, adults that have been treated with virus actually become resistant to the growth of transplantable polyoma tumors originating in the same or a different strain of animals (Sjögren, Hellström, and Klein, 1961a, 1961b; Sjögren, 1963a, 1963b; Habel, 1961, 1962a, 1963). A state of partial or complete resistance is observed when such tumors are implanted, whether the neoplasms are homografts or isogenic to the assay host. The refractory state in virus-treated animals is one of degree; with massive inocula, the resistance barrier can be broken to yield progressively growing tumors. Resistance is specific, however, for polyoma-induced tumors in this system. Other types of neoplasms grow equally well in virus-treated and normal adult hosts, respectively. The phenomenon in question does not seem to be confined to a particular species. Although the majority of studies have been carried out with mice, adult hamsters can acquire resistance in the same way.

These observations may be explained by assuming that polyoma tumors contain a cellular antigen not shared by unrelated tumors or by normal cells. To establish the validity of this view, however, it has been necessary to eliminate first a number of more obvious possibilities. The inoculation of polyoma virus into adults is known to evoke circulating antiviral antibodies, and at least some polyoma tumors contain demonstrable virus. At first sight, it would seem that a direct interaction between these components would offer the simplest explanation for host resistance. Several types of experiments make this interpretation improbable. Resistance is observed whether or not the challenge tumor contains demonstrable polyoma virus, and it occurs even in animals without detectable humoral antiviral antibodies. The latter observation stems from the experiments of Sjögren (1961), who induced resistance to polyoma tumors in adult mice by homografts of polyoma-induced neoplasms rather than by direct inoculation of polyoma virus as such. In most of these animals, antiviral antibodies could not be demonstrated by the usual hemagglutination-inhibition test. Nevertheless, growth inhibition with polyoma tumors occurred as consistently as in virus-treated mice with high titres of antibody. Habel (1962a, 1963) likewise has been unable to demonstrate any correlation between resistance to polyoma tumor transplants and humoral antiviral antibodies. No resistance could be conferred in adult mice by the passive transfer of anti-polyoma hyperimmune serum produced in rabbits. Habel showed further that newborn mice, which had received antipolyoma antibodies transplacentally from the mother, were not protected against polyoma tumor implants. In his experiments, resistance to polyoma tumors could only be transmitted by the adoptive transfer of lymphoid cells from immune animals.

Sjögren, Hellström, and Klein (1961b) considered the possibility that resistance to transplants of polyoma tumors might represent merely a homograft reaction to specific isoantigens found in cell cultures used to propagate the polyoma virus, but lacking in the assay hosts. But such an explanation does not account for the specificity of resistance to polyoma tumors as such, and can be ruled out on other grounds. In particular, resistance as described is observed even when tumors, assay hosts, and cells used to produce virus are all derived from the same inbred strain of mice. Isoantigenic differences thus do not seem to enter this picture, a conclusion also reached by Habel (1962a, 1963). The latter has shown that both uninfected culture fluids and polyoma-containing media inactivated by ultraviolet light are incapable of inducing resistance to polyoma tumors in adult mice.

These observations support the view that neoplastic conversion with the polyoma agent does lead to the appearance of a characteristic new antigen, one that is a product of a virus-cell interaction rather than part of the virus as such (Sjögren, 1963a, 1963b; Habel, 1962b, 1963). Speculation about the possible mechanisms that may underlie this process have taken various forms (Sjögren, Hellström, and G. Klein, 1961b). The integration of viral specificities in the cell surface by some means could explain the unique transplantation behavior of polyoma tumor cells. Such a change would have to be stable and heritable, since the antigenic properties of polyoma tumors in mice, at least, seem to persist indefinitely without reversion and can be demonstrated in all clonal derivatives. In hamster tumor cells, there is evidence that polyoma-induced antigens may be secondarily lost in some instances (Habel, 1962b). As an alternative concept, the presence of virus or viral derivatives can be viewed as channeling the synthesis of cellular antigens in a new direction. This possibility, which is favored by Sjögren and his colleagues, has already been discussed in Chapter 7 along with the proposed analogies to virogenic conversion in microbial systems (Luria, 1959). Whether polyoma tumor antigens bear any relation to interferons that arise through cell-virus interaction remains to be seen. At present, the exact characterization of virus-induced antigens is limited by the necessity of transplantation as a means of assay.

Immunological changes in polyoma-treated cells have been invoked more broadly by Habel (1962a, 1963) to account for the differences that exist in the susceptibility of newborn and adult mouse hosts to overt neoplastic transformation. According to this concept, contact with polyoma virus in both cases elicits the conversion of normal to tumor cells. Owing to the appearance of foreign antigen, however, the presumptive neoplasms in adult mice are effectively eliminated by immunologically competent cells, leaving such hosts refractory to subsequent challenge by the same stimulus. In neonatal animals, the quantitative difference in immunological response permits the emerging tumor to attain a critical mass, beyond which immune responses are incapable of preventing progressive growth. Several aspects of this interpretation are subject to experimental verification. It should be possible, for example, to cause the appearance of tumors in adult mice treated with polyoma merely by depressing the immune response, and this is reported to occur (Habel, 1963). Other experiments show that there is, as expected, a correlation between the acquisition of immunological competence and the ability to develop resistance to polyoma tumors after exposure to this agent. Whether this interesting response pattern can be extended to other virus-induced tumors remains to be seen.

Viewed against such a background, the individuation of antigens within chemically induced tumors becomes particularly interesting. Information about this topic has accumulated gradually, beginning with the experiments of Foley (1953). While working with transplantable sarcomas that had been induced by 3-methylcholanthrene, he attempted to establish an immune state in isogenic mice by ligation and atrophy of established tumors. Success by this method was achieved for several of the chemically induced neoplasms, such that growth of the same tumor in subsequent implants was regularly prevented. Significantly, however, no immunity could be established against transplantable mammary carcinomas that had originated spontaneously in mice of the same strain. Genetic drift thus seemed an unlikely interpretation of Foley's results, although this concept had been assumed by previous workers to account for occasional instances of tumor immunity in isologous animals.

In 1957, Prehn and Main conducted a series of experiments designed to confirm and extend the observations of Foley. Twelve fibrosarcomas induced with 3-methylcholanthrene were obtained, and all proved capable of eliciting immunity within isogenic mice of the same inbred strain. Seven spontaneous sarcomas, however, failed to do so. In contrast to the antigens of polyoma tumors, those of methylcholanthrene-induced sarcomas showed only partial cross-reactions, if any. Some clearly failed to react with antisera of any other tumors. Prehn and Main demonstrated that the immunity in these cases was tumor-specific. Mice resistant to methylcholanthrene tumors accepted isografts of skin without any sign of an immune reaction. Conversely, it did not prove possible to bring about immunity to methylcholanthrene tumors by injections of normal tissues. These facts point toward the appearance of new specificities as a result of carcinogen treatment, and antigenicity persists through many serial passages. It is evident, therefore, that complexing or binding of carcinogens with cell constituents does not in itself provide a satisfactory explanation for the stimulation of immune responses.

The basic picture of antigenicity in methylcholanthrene tumors, as outlined above, has been confirmed and extended by the Kleins and their collaborators. Heavily irradiated cell suspensions were employed by Révész (1960) to assess the immunizing ability of various tumors and normal tissues in isologous mice. In this system, protection from a secondary challenge was consistently observed if the same individual sarcomas induced by methylcholanthrene were used for both inoculations. These neoplasms were quite unaffected by pretreating the assay hosts with irradiated normal cells. Interestingly, spontaneous lymphomas and carcinomas of recent origin did not give rise to immunity when tested by repeated inoculation. Several tumors that had been maintained for long periods in serial passage did, however, evoke a host response. Incompatibility in this case seemed to represent a simple homograft reaction elicited by a genetic divergence that had developed over a period of time between the tumors and strain of origin.

The induction of novel antigens within tumor cells does not seem to be the property of a single chemical agent. Prehn (1960) found that tumor-specific immunity can be established with neoplasms arising from the administration of dibenz[a,h]anthracene as well as with those caused by methylcholanthrene. Similarly, Old, Boyse, Clarke, and Carswell (1962) were successful in demonstrating antigenicity with transplants of tumors elicited with dibenzyprene, dibenzanthracene, and methylcholanthrene. The individual neoplasms obtained with each agent varied greatly in their ability to immunize isologous mice, but in general, dibenzyprene-induced tumors were less effective. Interestingly, new antigens can even be detected in mouse sarcomas produced by the implantation of cellophane films, if the corresponding tumors are injected into isogenic hosts (Klein, Sjögren, and Klein, 1963). On the other hand, Prehn (1962) could establish a tumor-specific immunity with only one out of eight urethane-induced mouse lung adenomas. A comprehensive survey of antigenicity produced by various chemical and physical agents and in different cell types is obviously needed, but has yet to be made.

Although the various experiments described here assume for practical purposes that animals of an inbred strain are equivalent in genetic background, they do not prove directly that an animal can be immunized against its own tumor cells. Perhaps the closest approach to this problem is that of G. Klein, Sjögren, E. Klein, and Hellström, (1960). By an ingenious experimental design, these workers have obtained evidence that methylcholanthrene-induced sarcomas can, in fact, induce a state of resistance within primary autochthonous hosts (Figure 8.9). For this purpose, tumors were induced by injecting carcinogen into the leg muscles of mice. When these neoplasms were of appropriate size, the entire limb was amputated and the tumor suspended in saline. Part of

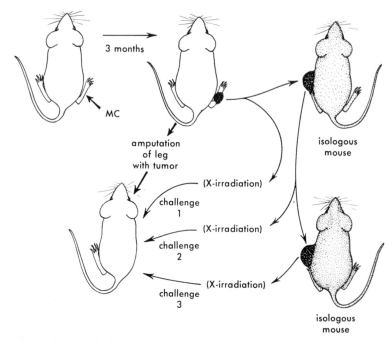

FIG. 8.9. Method for inducing resistance in an autochthonous primary host to its own tumor. A sarcoma is induced by injecting methylcholanthrene into the hind limb of a mouse, and the tumor is later removed by amputation of the limb. A lethally irradiated suspension from the tumor is administered to the primary host as an immunizing dose, and untreated cells from the tumor are passaged in isologous mice. The challenge procedure is repeated twice with these neoplasms. (After Klein, Sjögren, Klein, and Hellström, 1960. Copyright, University of Chicago Press.)

the suspension was passaged in isologous mice and part was irradiated and inoculated as an immunizing dose into the original host animal. The immunizing treatment was repeated on two subsequent occasions with irradiated cells derived from first and second passages of the tumors in isologous animals. In 12 of 16 cases in which tests were made by challenge with unirradiated cells of the original neoplasm, resistance to some degree could be detected in the primary autochthonous host. The degree of immunity is apparently conditional on the size of the challenge dose, and can usually be overriden by administering massive numbers of cells. At least two mice in the experiments in question, however, were refractory even to large inocula. Cross-reactions were not observed between the various methylcholanthrene tumors used; each neoplasm appeared to be distinct antigenically.

Although there are several discussions of tumor-specific immunity with chemically induced neoplasms (G. Klein, 1962; Sjögren, 1963a; Prehn, 1963a), it is obvious that the guidelines in this field have yet to be established. In comparison to the unique antigens of polyoma tumors that are shared in common by the group, those of chemically induced neoplasms seem to be individualized. If new antigenic specificities in the latter stem from interaction with some extrinsic agent, few common elements can be assumed for the process in different tumors. Conceivably, methylcholanthrene and similar chemical carcinogens may simply increase the incidence of cellular change in random fashion, as the induction of variants by these agents *in vitro* (Chapter 7) would suggest. However, the actual appearance of antigenic novelty within the intact organism ought to require a depression of immunological mechanisms, since otherwise the variants would tend to be eliminated as alien cells. In confirmation of this thesis, Miller, Grant, and Roe (1963) showed that thymectomy at three days of age greatly increases the incidence of tumors in mice that are treated with benzpyrene. Similarly, Prehn (1963b) has marshalled evidence that one aspect, at least, of carcinogenesis with 3-methylcholanthrene is an interference with immune responses. This agent, for example, serves to block the rejection of male skin grafts if administered to female mice, and can promote the growth of chemically induced tumors as transplants in isologous hosts. These observations emphasize the need for broad study of the antigenic alterations that may be induced by carcinogens within cell populations *in vitro*. Here, presumably, variation should be free from the restrictions of immunological selection. As one more model of unit change in somatic systems, the results promise to be of continuing interest.

■ References

ALBERT, F., and MEDAWAR, P. B. 1959. Biological problems of grafting. A symposium. Springfield: Charles C Thomas, Publisher. 453 pp.
ALGIRE, G. H., WEAVER, J. M., and PREHN, R. T. 1954. Growth of cells *in vivo* in diffusion chambers. I. Survival of homografts in immunized mice. J. Natl. Cancer Inst., 15: 493–508.
ALGIRE, G. H., WEAVER, J. M., and PREHN, R. T. 1957. Studies on tissue homo-transplantation in mice, using diffusion-chamber methods. Ann. N. Y. Acad. Sci., 64: 1009–1013.
ALLEN, S. L. 1955. Linkage relations of the genes histocompatibility-2 and fused tail, brachyury, and kinky tail in the mouse, as determined by tumor transplantation. Genetics, 40: 627–650.

AMOS, D. B. 1956. Serological differences between comparable diploid and tetraploid lines of three mouse ascites tumors. Ann. N. Y. Acad. Sci., **63**: 706–710.

AMOS, D. B., and DAY, E. D. 1957. Passive immunity against four mouse leukoses by means of isoimmune sera. Ann. N. Y. Acad. Sci., **64**: 851–858.

AMOS, D. B., GORER, P. A., and MIKULSKA, Z. B. 1955. An analysis of an antigenic system in the mouse (the H-2 system). Proc. Roy Soc. (London) Ser. B., **144**: 369–380.

AMOS, D. B., GORER, P. A., MIKULSKA, B. M., BILLINGHAM, R. E., and SPARROW, E. M. 1954. An antibody response to skin homografts in mice. Brit. J. Exptl. Pathol., **35**: 203–208.

BARNES, A. D., and KROHN, P. L. 1957. The estimation of the number of histocompatibility genes controlling the successful transplantation of normal skin in mice. Proc. Roy. Soc. (London) Ser. B., **146**: 505–526.

BARRETT, M. K. 1958. The erythrocyte-borne antigen in tumor immunity. Ann. N. Y. Acad. Sci., **73**: 767–771.

BARRETT, M. K., and DERINGER, M. K. 1950. An induced adaptation in a transplantable tumor of mice. J. Natl. Cancer Inst., **11**: 51–59.

BARRETT, M. K., DERINGER, M. K., and HANSEN, W. H. 1953. Induced adaptation in a tumor: specificity of the change. J. Natl. Cancer Inst., **14**: 381–394.

BAYREUTHER, K., and KLEIN, E. 1958. Cytogenetic, serologic and transplantation studies on a heterozygous tumor and its derived variant sublines. J. Natl. Cancer Inst., **21**: 885–923.

BERRIAN, J. H., and BRENT, L. 1958. Cell-bound antibodies in transplantation immunity. Ann. N. Y. Acad. Sci., **73**: 654–662.

BERRIAN, J. H., and McKHANN, C. F. 1960. Strength of histocompatibility genes. Ann. N. Y. Acad. Sci., **87**: 106–111.

BIGGS, P. M., and PAYNE, L. N. 1959. Cytological identification of proliferating donor cells in chick embryos injected with adult chicken blood. Nature, **184**: 1594.

BILLINGHAM, R. E. 1958. Studies on the reaction of injected homologous lymphoid tissue cells against the host. Ann. N. Y. Acad. Sci., **73**: 782–788.

BILLINGHAM, R. E., and BOSWELL, T. 1953. Studies on the problem of corneal homografts. Proc. Roy. Soc. (London), Ser. B., **141**: 392–406.

BILLINGHAM, R. E., and BRENT, L. 1956. Further attempts to transfer transplantation immunity by means of serum. Brit. J. Exptl. Pathol., **37**: 566–569.

BILLINGHAM, R. E., and BRENT, L. 1957a. Acquired tolerance of foreign cells in newborn animals. Proc. Roy. Soc. (London), Ser. B., **146**: 78–90.

BILLINGHAM, R. E., and BRENT, L. 1957b. A simple method for inducing tolerance of skin homografts in mice. Transpl. Bull., **4**: 67–71.

BILLINGHAM, R. E., and BRENT, L. 1959. Quantitative studies on tissue transplantation immunity. IV. Induction of tolerance in newborn mice and studies on the phenomenon of runt disease. Phil. Trans. Roy. Soc. London, Ser. B., **242**: 439–477.

BILLINGHAM, R. E., BRENT, L., and MEDAWAR, P. B. 1953. "Actively acquired tolerance" of foreign cells. Nature, 172: 603–606.

BILLINGHAM, R. E., BRENT, L., and MEDAWAR, P. B. 1954. Quantitative studies on tissue transplantation immunity. II. The origin, strength and duration of actively and adoptively acquired immunity. Proc. Roy. Soc. (London), Ser. B., 143: 58–80.

BILLINGHAM, R. E., BRENT, L., and MEDAWAR, P. B. 1955. Acquired tolerance of skin homografts. Ann. N. Y. Acad. Sci., 59: 409–416.

BILLINGHAM, R. E., BRENT, L., and MEDAWAR, P. B. 1956a. Quantitative studies on tissue transplantation immunity. III. Actively acquired tolerance. Phil. Trans. Roy. Soc. London, Ser. B., 239: 357–414.

BILLINGHAM, R. E., BRENT, L., and MEDAWAR, P. B. 1956b. "Enhancement" in normal homografts, with a note on its possible mechanism. Transpl. Bull., 3: 84–88.

BILLINGHAM, R. E., BRENT, L., and MEDAWAR, P. B. 1956c. The antigenic stimulus in transplantation immunity. Nature, 178: 514–519.

BILLINGHAM, R. E., BRENT, L., and MEDAWAR, P. B. 1958. Extraction of antigens causing transplantation immunity. Transpl. Bull., 5: 377–381.

BILLINGHAM, R. E., BRENT, L., MEDAWAR, P. B., and SPARROW, E. M. 1954. Quantitative studies on tissue transplantation immunity. I. The survival times of skin homografts exchanged between members of different inbred strains of mice. Proc. Roy. Soc. (London), Ser. B., 143: 43–58.

BILLINGHAM, R. E., FERRIGAN, L. W., and SILVERS, W. K. 1960. Cheek pouch of the Syrian hamster and tissue transplantation immunity. Science, 132: 1488.

BILLINGHAM, R. E., HODGE, B. A., and SILVERS, W. K. 1962. An estimate of the number of histocompatibility loci in the rat. Proc. Natl. Acad. Sci., 48: 138–147.

BILLINGHAM, R. E., KROHN, P. L., and MEDAWAR, P. B. 1951. Effect of cortisone on survival of skin homografts in rabbits. Brit. Med. J., 1: 1157–1163.

BILLINGHAM, R. E., LAMPKIN, G. H., MEDAWAR, P. B., and WILLIAMS, H. L. 1952. Tolerance to homografts, twin diagnosis, and the freemartin condition in cattle. Heredity, 6: 201–212.

BILLINGHAM, R. E., and PARKES, A. S. 1955. Studies on the survival of homografts of skin and ovarian tissue in rats. Proc. Roy. Soc. (London), Ser. B., 143: 550–560.

BILLINGHAM, R. E., SAWCHUCK, G. H., and SILVERS, W. K. 1960. Studies on the histocompatibility genes of the Syrian hamster. Proc. Natl. Acad. Sci., 46: 1079–1090.

BILLINGHAM, R. E., and SILVERS, W. K. 1959. Studies on tolerance of the Y chromosome antigen in mice. J. Immunol., 85: 14–26.

BILLINGHAM, R. E., and SILVERS, W. K. 1961. Transplantation of tissues and cells. Philadelphia: Wistar Institute Press. 149 pp.

BILLINGHAM, R. E., and SILVERS, W. K. 1962. Some factors that determine the ability of cellular inocula to induce tolerance of tissue homografts. J. Cellular Comp. Physiol., 60(Suppl. 1): 183–200.

BILLINGHAM, R. E., and SILVERS, W. K. 1963. Sensitivity to homografts of normal tissues and cells. Ann. Rev. Microbiol., 71: 531–564.

BILLINGHAM, R. E., SILVERS, W. K., and WILSON, D. B. 1962. Adoptive transfer of transplantation immunity by means of blood-bourne cells. Lancet, 1: 512–515.

BILLINGHAM, R. E., and SPARROW, E. M. 1954. Studies on the nature of immunity to homologous grafted skin, with special reference to the use of pure epidermal grafts. J. Exptl. Biol., 31: 16–39.

BOYSE, E. A., OLD, L. J., and LUELL, S. 1963. Antigenic properties of experimental leukemias. II. Immunological studies in vivo with C57BL/6 radiation-induced leukemias. J. Natl. Cancer Inst., 31: 987–995.

BOYSE, E. A., OLD, L. J., and STOCKERT, E. 1962. Immunological enhancement of a leukaemia. Nature, 194: 1142–1144.

BRENT, L., BROWN, J. B., and MEDAWAR, P. B. 1959. Skin transplantation immunity in relation to hypersensitivity reactions of the delayed type. In: Biological Problems of Grafting, pp. 64–82. F. Albert and P. B. Medawar, eds. Springfield: Charles C Thomas, Publisher.

BRENT, L., and GOWLAND, G. 1961. Cellular dose and age of host in the induction to tolerance. Nature, 192: 1265–1267.

BRENT, L., and GOWLAND, G. 1963. On the mechanism of immunological tolerance. In: Conceptual Advances in Immunology and Oncology, pp. 355–387. New York: Hoeber-Harper, Inc.

BRENT, L., and MEDAWAR, P. B. 1961. Quantitative studies on tissue transplantation immunity. V. The role of antiserum in enhancement and sensitization. Proc. Roy. Soc. (London), Ser. B., 155: 392–416.

BRENT, L., MEDAWAR, P. B., and RUSKIEWICZ, M. 1961. Serological methods in the study of transplantation antigens. Brit. J. Exptl. Pathol., 42: 464–477.

BURNET, F. M. 1959. The clonal selection theory of acquired immunity. Nashville: Vanderbilt University Press. 209 pp.

BURNET, F. M. 1961. Immunological recognition of self. Science, 133: 307–311.

BURNET, F. M., and FENNER, F. 1949. The production of antibodies. Second edition. Melbourne: McMillan. 142 pp.

CANN, H. M., and HERZENBERG, L. A. 1963a. In vitro studies of mammalian somatic cell variation. I. Detection of H-2 phenotype in cultured mouse cell lines. J. Exptl. Med., 117: 259–265.

CANN, H. M., and HERZENBERG, L. A. 1963b. In vitro studies of mammalian somatic cell variation. II. Isoimmune cytotoxicity with a cultured mouse lymphoma and selection of resistant variants. J. Exptl. Med., 117: 267–284.

CASEY, A. E., ROSS, G. L., and LANGSTON, R. R. 1949. Selective XYZ factor in C57 black mammary carcinoma EO771. Proc. Soc. Exptl. Biol. Med., 72: 83–89.

CASTERMANS, A. 1961. Nucleic acids as transplantation antigens. Nature, 189: 504–505.

CELADA, F., and WELSHONS, W. J. 1962. Demonstration of F_1 hybrid anti-parent immunological reaction. Proc. Natl. Acad. Sci., **48:** 326–331.

CELADA, F., and WELSHONS, W. J. 1963. An immunogenetic analysis of the male antigen in mice utilizing animals with an exceptional chromosome constitution. Genetics, **48:** 139–151.

CHASE, M. W. 1959. Immunologic tolerance. Ann. Rev. Microbiol., **13:** 349–376.

CHRISTOFFANINI, A. P. 1962. Transplantation of bone marrow: current problems. Progr. in Hematol., **3:** 360–376.

CHRISTOFFANINI, A., and HOECKER, G. (eds.), 1962. Proceedings of the International Symposium on Tissue Transplantation. Santiago, Viña del Mar, and Valparaiso, Chile, August 31–September 2, 1961. Santiago: Ediciones de la Universidad de Chile. 269 pp.

CONGDON, C. C. 1962. Radiation injury: bone marrow transplantation. Ann. Rev. Med., **13:** 203–212.

CONVERSE, J. M. (ed.) 1957. Second tissue homotransplantation conference. Ann. N. Y. Acad. Sci., **64:** 735–1073.

CONVERSE, J. M. (ed.) 1960. Fourth tissue homotransplantation conference. Ann. N. Y. Acad. Sci., **87:** 1–607.

COUNCE, S., SMITH, P., BARTH, R., and SNELL, G. D. 1956. Strong and weak histocompatibility gene differences in mice and their role in the rejection of homografts of tumors and skin. Ann. Surg., **144:** 198–204.

CRAIGMYLE, M. B. L. 1958. An autoradiographic and histochemical study of long-term cartilage grafts in the rabbit. J. Anat., **92:** 467–472.

DAVIES, D. A. L. 1962a. Chemical nature of mouse histocompatibility antigens. Nature, **193:** 34–36.

DAVIES, D. A. L. 1962b. H-2 histocompatibility antigens of the mouse. In: Transplantation, pp. 45–71. G. E. W. Wolstenholme and M. P. Cameron, eds. Boston: Little, Brown & Company.

DHALIWAL, S. S. 1961. Studies on histocompatibility mutations in mouse tumor cells using isogenic strains of mice. Genet. Res., **2:** 309–332.

DRESSER, D. W. 1962. Specific inhibition of antibody production. II. Paralysis induced in adult mice by small quantities of protein antigen. Immunology, **5:** 378–388.

EBERT, J. D. 1959. The acquisition of biological specificity. In: The Cell. Biochemistry, Physiology, Morphology, Vol. 1, pp. 619–693. J. Brachet and A. E. Mirsky, eds. New York: Academic Press, Inc.

EICHWALD, E. J., and SILMSER, C. R. 1955. (No title). Transpl. Bull., **2:** 148–149.

EICHWALD, E. J., SILMSER, C. R., and WEISSMAN, I. 1958. Sex-linked rejection of normal and neoplastic tissue. I. Distribution and specificity. J. Natl. Cancer Inst., **20:** 563–575.

FELDMAN, M., and SACHS, L. 1957. The antibody response to successful tumor homografts. J. Natl. Cancer Inst., **18:** 529–553.

FELTON, L. D. 1949. The significance of antigen in animal tissues. J. Immunol., **61:** 107–117.

FELTON, L. D., and OTTINGER, B. 1942. Pneumococcus polysaccharide as a paralyzing agent on the mechanism of immunity in white mice. J. Bacteriol., **43**: 94–95.

FLEXNER, S., and JOBLING, J. W. 1907. On the promoting influence of heated tumor emulsions on tumor growth. Proc. Soc. Exptl. Biol. Med., **4**: 156–157.

FOLEY, E. J. 1953. Antigenic properties of methylcholanthrene-induced tumors in mice of the strain of origin. Cancer Res., **13**: 835–837.

FORD, C. E., HAMERTON, J. L., BARNES, D. W. H., and LOUTIT, J. F. 1956. Cytological identification of radiation-chimaeras. Nature, **177**: 452–454.

FORD, C. E., ILBERY, P. L. T., and LOUTIT, J. F. 1957. Further cytological observations on radiation chimeras. J. Cellular Comp. Physiol., **50** (Suppl. 1): 109–121.

GIBSON, T., and MEDAWAR, P. B. 1943. The fate of skin homografts in man. J. Anat., **77**: 299–310.

GORER, P. A. 1937. The genetic and antigenic basis of tumor transplantation. J. Pathol. Bacteriol., **44**: 691–697.

GORER, P. A. 1948. The significance of studies with transplanted tumors. Brit. J. Cancer, **2**: 103–107.

GORER, P. A. 1955. The antibody response to skin homografts in mice. Ann. N. Y. Acad. Sci., **59**: 365–373.

GORER, P. A. 1956. Some recent work on tumor immunity. Advan. Cancer Res., **4**: 149–186.

GORER, P. A. 1958. Some reactions of H-2 antibodies *in vitro* and *in vivo*. Ann. N. Y. Acad. Sci., **73**: 707–721.

GORER, P. A. 1959. Some recent data on the H-2 system of mice. In: *Biological Problems of Grafting*, pp. 25–33. F. Albert and P. B. Medawar, eds. Springfield: Charles C Thomas, Publisher.

GORER, P. A. 1961. The antigenic structure of tumors. Advan. Immunol., **1**: 345–393.

GORER, P. A., and AMOS, D. B. 1956. Passive immunity in mice against C57BL leukosis E.L.4 by means of isoimmune serum. Cancer Res., **16**: 338–343.

GORER, P. A., and KALISS, N. 1959. The effect of isoantibodies *in vivo* on three different transplantable neoplasms in mice. Cancer Res., **19**: 824–830.

GORER, P. A., LOUTIT, J. F., and MICKLEM, H. S. 1961. Proposed revisions of "transplantese." Nature, **189**: 1024–1025.

GORER, P. A., LYMAN, S., and SNELL, G. D. 1948. Studies on the genetic and antigenic basis of tumour transplantation. Linkage between a histocompatibility gene and "fused" in mice. Proc. Roy. Soc. (London), Ser. B., **135**: 499–505.

GORER, P. A., and MIKULSKA, Z. B. 1954. The antibody response to tumor inoculation. Improved methods of antibody detection. Cancer Res., **14**: 651–655.

GORER, P. A., and MIKULSKA, Z. B. 1959. Some further data on the H-2 system of antigens. Proc. Roy. Soc. (London), Ser. B., **151**: 57–69.

GORER, P. A., MIKULSKA, Z. B., and O'GORMAN, P. 1959. The time of appearance of isoantibodies during the homograft response to mouse tumors. Immunol., **2**: 211–218.

GORER, P. A., TUFFREY, M. A., and BATCHELOR, J. R. 1962. Serological studies on the X antigens. Ann. N. Y. Acad. Sci., **101**: 5–11.

GREENE, H. S. N. 1942. The participation of the anterior chamber of the eye in resistance phenomena related to tumor growth. Cancer Res., **2**: 669–674.

GREENE, H. S. N. 1955. Compatibility and noncompatibility. Ann. N. Y. Acad. Sci., **59**: 311–325.

GUTTMAN, R. D., and AUST, J. B. 1961. Acquired tolerance to homografts produced by homologous spleen cell injection in adult mice. Nature, **192**: 564–565.

HABEL, K. 1961. Resistance of polyoma virus immune animals to transplanted polyoma tumors. Proc. Soc. Exptl. Biol. Med., **106**: 722–725.

HABEL, K. 1962a. Immunological determinants of polyoma virus oncogenesis. J. Exptl. Med., **115**: 181–193.

HABEL, J. 1962b. Antigenic properties of cells transformed by polyoma virus. Cold Spring Harbor Symp. Quant. Biol., **27**: 433–439.

HABEL, K. 1963. Immunological aspects of oncogenesis by polyoma virus. In: Conceptual Advances in Immunology and Oncology, pp. 486–502. New York: Hoeber-Harper, Inc.

HAENEN-SEVERYNS, A. M., VRANCKEN-PARIS, M., LEJEUNE, G., CASTERMANS, A., and DIEU, H. 1962. Separation of a transplantation antigen. Bioch. Pharmacol., **11**: 398–399.

HARRIS, M. 1942. Differentiation and growth of gastrular anlagen implanted homoplastically into tadpoles of Hyla regilla. Univ. Calif. Publ. Zoöl., **51**: 41–86.

HARRIS, M. 1943. The compatibility of rat and mouse cells in mixed tissue cultures. Anat. Record, **87**: 107–117.

HARRIS, M., and EAKIN, R. M. 1949. Survival of transplanted ovaries in rats. J. Exptl. Zool., **112**: 131–164.

HAŠEK, M. 1953a. Parabiosa ptáků embryonálním vývoji. Československ. Biol., **2**: 25–26.

HAŠEK, M. 1953b. Vegetativní hydridisace živočichů spojením krevních oběhů v embryonálním vývoji. Československ. Biol., **2**: 265–277.

HAŠEK, M., LENGEROVÁ, A., and HRABA, T. 1961. Transplantation immunity and tolerance. Advan. Immunol., **1**: 1–66.

HAŠKOVÁ, V., HRUBEŠOVÁ, M., and MEDAWAR, P. B. 1958. Part played by deoxyribonucleic acid in transplantation immunity. Nature, **182**: 61–62.

HAUSCHKA, T. S. 1953. Cell population studies on mouse ascites tumors. Trans. N. Y. Acad. Sci., Ser II, **16**: 64–73.

HAUSCHKA, T. S., and AMOS, D. B. 1957. Cytogenetic aspects of compatibility. Ann. N. Y. Acad. Sci., **69**: 561–579.

HAUSCHKA, T. S., GRINNELL, S. T., MEAGHER, M., and AMOS, D. B. 1959. Sex-linked incompatibility of male skin and primary tumors transplanted to isologous female mice. *In: Genetics and Cancer*, pp. 271–294. Austin: Univ. Texas Press.

HAUSCHKA, T. S., KVEDAR, B. J., GRINNELL, S. T., and AMOS, D. B. 1956. Immuno-selection of polyploids from predominantly diploid populations. Ann. N. Y. Acad. Sci., **63:** 683–705.

HAUSCHKA, T. S., and LEVAN, A. 1953. Inverse relationship between chromosome ploidy and host specificity of sixteen transplantable tumors. Exptl. Cell Res., **4:** 457–467.

HAUSCHKA, T. S., and SCHULTZ, J. 1954. Cytologic aspects of immunogenetic specificity. Transpl. Bull., **1:** 203–206.

HELLSTRÖM, K. E. 1960. Studies on isoantigenic variation in mouse lymphomas. J. Natl. Cancer Inst., **25:** 237–269.

HELLSTRÖM, K. E. 1961. Studies on the mechanism of isoantigenic variant formation in heterozygous mouse tumors. II. Behavior of H-2 antigens D and K: Cytotoxic tests on mouse lymphomas. J. Natl. Cancer Inst., **27:** 1095–1105.

HERZENBERG, L. A. 1962. I. Steps toward a genetics of somatic cells in culture. II. Maternal isoimmunization as a result of breeding in the mouse. J. Cellular Comp. Physiol., **60** (Suppl. 1): 145–157.

HILDEMANN, W. H., and MEDAWAR, P. B. 1959. Relationship between skin transplantation immunity and the formation of humoral isoantibodies in mice. Immunology, **2:** 44–52.

HITCHINGS, G. H., and ELION, G. B. 1963. Chemical suppression of the immune response. Pharmacol. Revs., **15:** 365–405.

HOECKER, G. 1956. Genetic mechanisms in tissue transplantation in the mouse. Cold Spring Harbor Symp. Quant. Biol., **21:** 355–362.

HOECKER, G., COUNCE, S., and SMITH, P, 1954. The antigens determined by the H-2 locus: a Rhesus-like system in the mouse. Proc. Natl. Acad. Sci., **40:** 1040–1051.

HOECKER, G., and HAUSCHKA, T. S. 1956. Apparent loss of specific isoantigens in heteroploid transplanted tumor cells. Transpl. Bull., **3:** 134–136.

HOWARD, J. G., and MICHIE, D. 1962. Induction of transplantation immunity in the newborn mouse. Transpl. Bull., **29:** 1–6.

HOWARD, J. G., MICHIE, D., and SIMONSEN, M. 1961. Splenomegaly as a host response in graft-versus-host disease. Brit. J. Exptl. Pathol., **42:** 478–485.

JENSEN, E., and STETSON, C. A. 1961. Humoral aspects of the immune response to homografts. II. Relationship between the hemagglutinating and cytotoxic activities of certain isoimmune sera. J. Exptl. Med., **113:** 785–794.

JUTILA, J. W., and WEISER, R. S. 1962. Studies on homologous disease. I. Factors concerned in the production of homologous disease of mice. J. Immunol., **88:** 621–635.

KALISS, N. 1957. The survival of homografts in mice pretreated with antisera to mouse tissue. Ann. N. Y. Acad. Sci., **64:** 977–993.

KALISS, N. 1958. Immunological enhancement of tumor homografts in mice. A review. Cancer Res., **18:** 992–1003.

KALISS, N. 1961. The transplanted tumor as a research tool in cancer immunology. Cancer Res., 21: 1203–1208.

KALISS, N., and MOLOMUT, N. 1952. The effect of prior injections of tissue antiserum on the survival of cancer homografts in mice. Cancer Res., 12: 110–112.

KANDUTSCH, A. A., and STIMPFLING, J. H. 1963. Partial purification of tissue isoantigens from a mouse sarcoma. Transplantation, 1: 201–216.

KARUSH, F., and EISEN, H. N. 1962. A theory of delayed hypersensitivity. Science, 136: 1032–1039.

KIDD, J. G. 1961. Does the host react against his own cancer cells? Cancer Res., 21: 1170–1183.

KLEIN, E. 1959. Isoantigenicity of X-ray-inactivated implants of a homotransplantable and a non-homotransplantable mouse sarcoma. Transpl. Bull., 6: 420–424.

KLEIN, E. 1961. Studies on the mechanism of isoantigenic variant formation in heterozygous mouse tumors. I. Behavior of H-2 antigens D and K: Quantitative absorption tests on mouse sarcomas. J. Natl. Cancer Inst., 27: 1069–1093.

KLEIN, E., and KLEIN, G. 1956. Mechanism of induced change in transplantation specificity of a mouse tumor passed through hybrid hosts. Transpl. Bull., 3: 136–142.

KLEIN, E., and KLEIN, G. 1959. The use of histocompatibility genes as markers for the study of isoantigenic variation in populations of tumor cells. In: Biological Problems of Grafting, pp. 380–399. F. Albert and P. B. Medawar, eds. Springfield: Charles C Thomas, Publisher.

KLEIN, E., KLEIN, G., and HELLSTRÖM, K. E. 1960. Further studies on isoantigenic variation in mouse carcinomas and sarcomas. J. Natl. Cancer Inst., 25: 271–294.

KLEIN, E., KLEIN, G., and RÉVÉSZ, L. 1957. Permanent modification (mutation?) of a histocompatibility gene in a heterozygous tumor. J. Natl. Cancer Inst., 19: 95–114.

KLEIN, E., and MÖLLER, E. 1963. Relationship between host range and isoantigenic properties in different sublines of the same sarcoma. J. Natl. Cancer Inst., 31: 347–364.

KLEIN, G. 1959. The usefulness and limitations of tumor transplantation in cancer research. A review. Cancer Res., 19: 343–358.

KLEIN, G. 1962. Some features of tumor-specific antigens: a general discussion. Ann. N. Y. Acad. Sci., 101: 170–172.

KLEIN, G. 1963. Genetics of somatic cells. In: Methodology in Mammalian Genetics, pp. 407–468. W. J. Burdette, ed. San Francisco: Holden-Day, Inc.

KLEIN, G., and HELLSTRÖM, K. E. 1962. Transplantation studies on estrogen-induced interstitial-cell tumors of testis in mice. J. Natl. Cancer Inst., 28: 99–115.

KLEIN, G., and KLEIN, E. 1956. Detection of an allelic difference at a simple gene locus in a small fraction of a large tumor-cell population. Nature, 178: 1389–1391.

KLEIN, G., and KLEIN, E. 1957. The evolution of independence from specific growth stimulation and inhibition in mammalian tumour-cell populations. Symp. Soc. Exptl. Biol., 11: 305–328.

KLEIN, G., and KLEIN, E. 1958. Histocompatibility changes in tumors. J. Cellular Comp. Physiol., 52 (Suppl. 1): 125–168.

KLEIN, G., and KLEIN, E. 1959. Cytogenetics of experimental tumors. In: Genetics and Cancer, pp. 241–270. Austin: Univ. Texas Press.

KLEIN, G., SJÖGREN, H. O., and KLEIN, E. 1962. Demonstration of host resistance against isotransplantation of lymphomas induced by the Gross agent. Cancer Res., 22: 955–961.

KLEIN, G., SJÖGREN, H. O., and KLEIN, E. 1963. Demonstration of host resistance against sarcomas induced by implantation of cellophane films in isologous (syngeneic) recipients. Cancer Res., 23: 84–92.

KLEIN, G., SJÖGREN, H. O., KLEIN, E., and HELLSTRÖM, K. E. 1960. Demonstration of resistance against methylcholanthrene-induced sarcomas in the primary autochthonous host. Cancer Res., 20: 1561–1572.

KOLLER, P. C., DAVIES, A. J. S., and DOAK, S. M. A. 1961. Radiation chimeras. Advan. Cancer Res., 6: 181–289.

KRETSCHMER, R. R., and PÉREZ-TAMAYO, R. 1961. The role of humoral antibodies in rejection of skin homografts in rabbits. I. Passive transfer of isoimmune serum to conditioned hosts. J. Exptl Med., 114: 509–520.

KRETSCHMER, R. R., and PÉREZ-TAMAYO, R. 1962. The role of humoral antibodies in rejection of skin homografts in rabbits. J. Exptl. Med., 116: 879–896.

KROHN, P. L. 1959. Transplantation of endocrine glands. In: Transplantation of Tissues, Vol. 2, pp. 401–469. L. A. Peer, ed. Baltimore: the Williams & Wilkins Company.

LAWRENCE, H. S. 1959a. Homograft sensitivity. Physiol. Revs., 39: 811–859.

LAWRENCE, H. S. (ed.). 1959b. Cellular and humoral aspects of the hypersensitive states. New York: Hoeber-Harper, Inc. 667 pp.

LEDERBERG, J. 1956. Prospects for a genetics of somatic and tumor cells. Ann. N. Y. Acad. Sci., 63: 662–665.

LEDERBERG, J. 1959. Genes and antibodies. Science, 129: 1649–1653.

LINDER, O. E. A. 1961. Comparisons between survival of grafted skin, ovaries, and tumors in mice across histocompatibility barriers of different strength. J. Natl. Cancer Inst., 27: 351–374.

LITTLE, C. C. 1941. The genetics of tumor transplantation. In: Biology of the Laboratory Mouse, pp. 279–309. G. D. Snell, ed. New York: McGraw-Hill Book Company, Inc.

LOEB, L. 1926. Autotransplantation and homoiotransplantation of cartilage in the guinea pig. Am. J. Pathol., 2: 111–122.

LOEB, L. 1930. Transplantation and individuality. Physiol. Revs., 10: 547–616.

LOEB, L. 1945. The biological basis of individuality. Springfield: Charles C Thomas, Publisher. 711 pp.

LURIA, S. E. 1959. Viruses as determinants of cellular functions. Can. Cancer Conf., **3:** 261–270.

MANSON, L. A., FOSCHI, G. V., and PALM, J. 1963. An association of transplantation antigens with microsomal lipoproteins of normal and malignant mouse tissues. J. Cellular Comp. Physiol., **61:** 109–118.

MEDAWAR, P. B. 1944. The behavior and fate of skin autografts and skin homografts in rabbits. J. Anat., **78:** 176–199.

MEDAWAR, P. B. 1945. A second study of the behavior and fate of skin homografts in rabbits. J. Anat., **79:** 157–176.

MEDAWAR, P. B. 1946a. Immunity to homologous grafted skin. I. The suppression of cell division in grafts transplanted to immunized animals. Brit. J. Exptl. Pathol., **27:** 9–14.

MEDAWAR, P. B. 1946b. Immunity to homologous grafted skin. II. The relationship between the antigens of blood and skin. Brit. J. Exptl. Pathol., **27:** 15–24.

MEDAWAR, P. B. 1948. Immunity to homologous grafted skin. III. The fate of skin homografts transplanted to the brain, to subcutaneous tissue, and to the anterior chamber of the eye. Brit. J. Exptl. Pathol., **29:** 58–69.

MEDAWAR, P. B. 1958a. The homograft reaction. Proc. Roy. Soc. (London), Ser. B., **148:** 145–166.

MEDAWAR, P. B. 1958b. The immunology of transplantation. Harvey Lectures, **52:** 144–176. New York: Academic Press Inc.

MEDAWAR, P. B. 1959a. Reactions to homologous tissue antigens in relation to hypersensitivity. In: *Cellular and Humoral Aspects of the Hypersensitive States*, pp. 504–534. H. S. Lawrence, ed. New York: Hoeber-Harper, Inc.

MEDAWAR, P. B. 1959b. Iso-antigens. In: *Biological Problems of Grafting*, pp. 6–24. F. Albert and P. B. Medawar, eds. Springfield: Charles C Thomas, Publisher.

MEDAWAR, P. B. 1960. Theories of immunological tolerance. In: *Cellular Aspects of Immunity*, pp. 134–156. G. E. W. Wolstenholme and M. O'Connor, eds. Boston: Little, Brown & Company.

MEDAWAR, P. B. 1961a. Immunologic tolerance. Science, **133:** 303–306.

MEDAWAR, P. B. 1961b. Theories of immunological tolerance. Folia Biol. (Prague), **7:** 1–10.

MERRILL, J. P. 1959. Transplantation of normal tissue. Physiol. Revs., **39:** 860–884.

MILLER, J. F. A. P. 1962. Role of the thymus in transplantation immunity. Ann. N. Y. Acad. Sci., **99:** 340–354.

MILLER, J. F. A. P., GRANT, G. A., and ROE, F. J. C. 1963. Effect of thymectomy on the induction of skin tumours by 3,4-benzpyrene. Nature, **199:** 920–922.

MILLER, J. F. A. P., MARSHALL, A. H. E., and WHITE, R. G. 1962. The immunological significance of the thymus. Advan. Immunol., **2:** 111–162.

MITCHISON, N. A. 1954. Passive transfer of transplantation immunity. Proc. Roy. Soc. (London), Ser. B., **142:** 72–87.

MITCHISON, N. A. 1955. Studies on the immunological response to foreign tumor transplants in the mouse. I. The role of lymph node cells in conferring immunity by adoptive transfer. J. Exptl. Med., 102: 157–177.

MITCHISON, N. A. 1956a. The colonisation of irradiated tissue by transplanted spleen cells. Brit. J. Exptl. Pathol., 37: 239–247.

MITCHISON, N. A. 1956b. Antigens of heterozygous tumours as material for the study of cell heredity. Proc. Roy. Phys. Soc. Edinburgh, 25: 45–48.

MITCHISON, N. A. 1958. Tissue transplantation and cellular heredity. Symp. Soc. Exptl. Biol., 12: 225–241.

MITCHISON, N. A. 1959a. Blood transfusion in fowl: an example of immunological tolerance requiring the persistence of antigen. In: Biological Problems of Grafting, pp. 239–259. F. Albert and P. B. Medawar, eds. Springfield: Charles C Thomas, Publisher.

MITCHISON, N. A. 1959b. Cells as tolerance antigens. In: Negende Jaarboek van Kankeronderzoek en Kankerbestrijding in Nederland, pp. 65–71. Amsterdam: Vereeniging Het Nederlandsch Kankerinstituut.

MITCHISON, N. A. 1961. Immunological tolerance and immunological paralysis. Brit. Med. Bull., 17: 102–106.

MITCHISON, N. A. 1962a. Tolerance of erythrocytes in poultry: induction and specificity. Immunol., 5: 341–358.

MITCHISON, N. A. 1962b. Tolerance of erythrocytes in poultry: loss and abolition. Immunol., 5: 359–369.

MITCHISON, N. A., and DUBE, O. L. 1955. Studies on the immunological response to foreign tumor transplants in the mouse. II. The relation between hemagglutinating antibody and graft resistance in the normal mouse and mice pretreated with tissue preparations. J. Exptl. Med., 102: 179–197.

MÖLLER, G. 1961. Demonstration of mouse isoantigens at the cellular level by the fluorescent antibody technique. J. Exptl. Med., 114: 415–434.

MÖLLER, E., and MÖLLER, G. 1962a. Quantitative studies of the sensitivity of normal and neoplastic mouse cells to the cytotoxic action of isoantibodies. J. Exptl. Med., 115: 527–553.

MÖLLER, G., and MÖLLER, E. 1962b. Phenotypic expression of mouse isoantigens. J. Cellular Comp. Physiol., 60 (Suppl. 1): 107–128.

NAJARIAN, J. S., and FELDMAN, J. D. 1961. Passive transfer of tuberculin sensitivity by tritiated thymidine-labeled lymphoid cells. J. Exptl. Med., 114: 779–790.

NAJARIAN, J. S., and FELDMAN, J. D. 1962a. Passive transfer of transplantation immunity. I. Tritiated lymphoid cells. II. Lymphoid cells in Millipore chambers. J. Exptl. Med., 115: 1083–1093.

NAJARIAN, J. S., and FELDMAN, J. D. 1962b. Induction of runt disease in adult mice by presensitized homologous lymphoid cells. Proc. Soc. Exptl. Biol. Med., 110: 16–21.

NAJARIAN, J. S., and FELDMAN, J. D. 1963. Passive transfer of transplantation immunity. III. Inbred guinea pigs. J. Exptl. Med., 117: 449–456.

NELSON, D. S. 1962. Immunological enhancement of skin homografts in guinea pigs. Brit. J. Exptl. Pathol., 43: 1–11.

OLD, L. J., BOYSE, E. A., CLARKE, D. A., and CARSWELL, E. A. 1962. Antigenic properties of chemically induced tumors. Ann. N. Y. Acad. Sci., **101**: 80–106.

OLD, L. J., BOYSE, E. A., and STOCKERT, E. 1963. Antigenic properties of experimental leukemias. I. Serological studies *in vitro* with spontaneous and radiation-induced leukemias. J. Natl. Cancer Inst., **31**: 977–986.

OSABA, D., and MILLER, J. F. A. P. 1964. The lymphoid tissues and immune responses of neonatally thymectomized mice bearing thymus tissue in Millipore diffusion chambers. J. Exptl. Med., **119**: 177–194.

OWEN, R. D. 1945. Immunogenetic consequences of vascular anastomoses between bovine twins. Science, **102**: 400–401.

OWEN, R. D. 1959. Genetic aspects of tissue transplantation and tolerance. J. Med. Educ., **34**: 366–383.

OWEN, R. D. 1960. Current status of mammalian immunogenetics. J. Cellular Comp. Physiol., **56** (Suppl. 1): 73–87.

PARKES, A. S. 1958. Enhancement of the survival of interstrain ovarian homografts in rats. Transpl. Bull., **5**: 45–47.

PEER, L. A. 1955. Transplantation of tissues. Vol. 1. Cartilage, bone, fascia, tendon, and muscle. Baltimore: The Williams & Wilkins Company. 421 pp.

PEER, L. A. (ed.). 1959. Transplantation of tissues. Vol. 2. Skin, cornea, fat, nerves, teeth, blood vessels, endocrine glands, organs, peritoneum, cancer cells. Baltimore: The Williams & Wilkins Company. 690 pp.

PIZARRO, O., HOECKER, G., RUBINSTEIN, P., and RAMOS, A. 1961. The distribution in the tissues and the development of H-2 antigens of the mouse. Proc. Natl. Acad. Sci., **47**: 1900–1907.

PONTECORVO, G. 1958. Trends in genetic analysis. New York: Columbia Univ. Press. 145 pp.

PREHN, R. T. 1960. Tumor-specific immunity to transplanted dibenz[*a,h*]-anthracene-induced sarcomas. Cancer Res., **20**: 1614–1617.

PREHN, R. T. 1962. Specific isoantigenicities among chemically induced tumors. Ann. N. Y. Acad. Sci., **101**: 107–113.

PREHN, R. T. 1963a. Tumor-specific immunity to nonviral tumors. Can. Cancer Conf., **5**: 387–395.

PREHN, R. T. 1963b. Function of depressed immunologic reactivity during carcinogenesis. J. Natl. Cancer Inst., **31**: 791–805.

PREHN, R. T., and MAIN, J. M. 1957. Immunity to methylcholanthrene-induced sarcomas. J. Natl. Cancer Inst., **18**: 769–778.

PREHN, R. T., WEAVER, J. M., and ALGIRE, G. H. 1954. The diffusion-chamber technique applied to a study of the nature of homograft resistance. J. Natl. Cancer Inst., **15**: 509–518.

RÉVÉSZ, L. 1960. Detection of antigenic differences in isologous host-tumor systems by pretreatment with heavily irradiated tumor cells. Cancer Res., **20**: 443–451.

ROGERS, B. O. (ed.). 1955. The relation of immunology to tissue homo-transplantation. Ann. N. Y. Acad. Sci., **59**: 277–466.

ROGERS, B. O. (ed.). 1958. Third tissue homotransplantation conference. Ann. N. Y. Acad. Sci., 73: 539–868.

ROGERS, B. O. (ed.). 1962. Fifth tissue homotransplantation conference. Ann. N. Y. Acad. Sci., 99: 335–942.

RUSSELL, P. S. 1961. Endocrine grafting techniques. In: Transplantation of Tissues and Cells, pp. 35–48. R. E. Billingham and W. K. Silvers, eds. Philadelphia: The Wistar Institute Press.

SCHÖNE, G. 1912. Die heteroplastische und homöoplastische Transplantation. Berlin: Springer-Verlag. 161 pp.

SCHWARTZ, R. S. 1963. Alteration of immunity by antimetabolites. In: Conceptual Advances in Immunology and Oncology, pp. 137–164. New York: Hoeber-Harper, Inc.

SERCARZ, E., and COONS, A. H. 1959. Specific inhibition of antibody formation during immunological paralysis and unresponsiveness. Nature, 184: 1080–1082.

SHAPIRO, F., MARTINEZ, C., SMITH, J. M., and GOOD, R. A. 1961. Tolerance of skin homografts induced in adult mice by multiple injections of homologous spleen cells. Proc. Soc. Exptl. Biol. Med., 106: 472–475.

SIMONSEN, M. 1953. Biological incompatibility in kidney transplantation in dogs. II. Serological investigations. Acta Pathol. Microbiol. Scand., 32: 36–84.

SIMONSEN, M. 1957. The impact on the developing embryo and newborn animal of adult homologous cells. Acta Pathol. Microbiol. Scand., 40: 480–500.

SIMONSEN, M. 1962. Graft versus host reactions. Their natural history and applicability as tools of research. Progr. in Allergy, 6: 349–467.

SJÖGREN, H. O. 1961. Further studies on the induced resistance against iso-transplantation of polyoma tumors. Virology, 15: 214–219.

SJÖGREN, H. O. 1963a. Experimental immunization against carcinogen-induced and virus-induced mouse tumors in isologous or autologous systems. In: Conceptual Advances in Immunology and Oncology, pp. 459–474. New York: Hoeber-Harper, Inc.

SJÖGREN, H. O. 1963b. Immunity to virus-induced tumors. Can. Cancer Conf., 5: 377–386.

SJÖGREN, H. O., HELLSTRÖM, I., and KLEIN, G. 1961a. Resistance of polyoma virus immunized mice against transplantation of established polyoma tumors. Exptl. Cell Res., 23: 204–208.

SJÖGREN, H. O., HELLSTRÖM, I., and KLEIN, G. 1961b. Transplantation of polyoma virus-induced tumors in mice. Cancer Res., 21: 329–337.

SLETTENMARK, B., and KLEIN, E. 1962. Cytotoxic and neutralization tests with serum and lymph node cells of isologous mice with induced resistance against Gross lymphomas. Cancer Res., 22: 947–954.

SMITH, R. T. 1961. Immunological tolerance of nonliving antigens. Advan. Immunol., 1: 67–129.

SNELL, G. D. 1948. Methods for the study of histocompatibility genes. J. Genet., 49: 87–108.

SNELL, G. D. 1952. Preliminary data on crossing over between H-2 and *Fu, Ki* and *T* in the mouse. Heredity, **6:** 247–254.

SNELL, G. D. 1953. The genetics of transplantation. J. Natl. Cancer Inst., **14:** 691–704.

SNELL, G. D. 1954. The enhancing effect (or actively acquired tolerance) and the histocompatibility-2 locus in the mouse. J. Natl. Cancer Inst., **15:** 665–675.

SNELL, G. D. 1957a. Incompatibility reactions to tumor homotransplants with particular reference to the role of the tumor. A review. Cancer Res., **17:** 2–10.

SNELL, G. D. 1957b. The homograft reaction. Ann. Rev. Microbiol., **11:** 439–458.

SNELL, G. D. 1957c. The genetics of transplantation. Ann. N. Y. Acad. Sci., **69:** 555–560.

SNELL, G. D. 1958a. Histocompatibility genes of the mouse. I. Demonstration of weak histocompatibility differences by immunization and controlled tumor dosage. J. Natl. Cancer Inst., **20:** 787–824.

SNELL, G. D. 1958b. Histocompatibility genes of the mouse. II. Production and analysis of isogenic resistant lines. J. Natl. Cancer Inst., **21:** 843–877.

SNELL, G. D. 1959. Transplantable tumors. In: *The Physiopathology of Cancer,* Second edition, pp. 293–345. F. Homburger, ed. New York: Hoeber-Harper, Inc.

SNELL, G. D. 1963. The immunology of tissue transplantation. In: *Conceptual Advances in Immunology and Oncology,* pp. 323–354. New York: Hoeber-Harper, Inc.

SNELL, G. D., SMITH, P., and GABRIELSON, F. 1953. Analysis of the histocompatibility-2 locus in the mouse. J. Natl. Cancer Inst., **14:** 457–480.

SNELL, G. D., and STEVENS, L. C. 1961. Histocompatibility genes of mice. III. H-1 and H-4, two histocompatibility loci in the first linkage group. Immunology, **4:** 366–379.

SNELL, G. D., WINN, H. J., STIMPFLING, J. H., and PARKER, S. J. 1960. Depression by antibody of the immune response to homografts and its role in immunological enhancement. J. Exptl. Med., **112:** 293–314.

SOUTHAM, C. M. 1960. Relationships of immunology to cancer: A review. Cancer Res., **20:** 271–291.

STEINMULLER, D. 1962. Passive transfer of immunity to skin homografts in rats. Ann. N. Y. Acad. Sci., **99:** 629–644.

STETSON, C. A. 1963. The role of humoral antibody in the homograft reaction. Advan. Immunol., **3:** 97–130.

TERASAKI, P. I. 1959. Identification of the type of blood-cell responsible for the graft-versus-host reaction in chicks. J. Embryol. Exptl. Morphol., **7:** 394–408.

TERASAKI, P. I., McCLELLAND, J. D., CANNON, J. A., and LONGMIRE, W. P., JR. 1961. Antibody response to homografts. VII. The role of complement in cytotoxicity of serum from homografted rabbits. J. Immunol., **87:** 39–45.

TRENTIN, J. J. 1959. Tolerance and homologous disease in unirradiated F_1 hybrid mice receiving parental lymphoid tissue. *In: Biological Problems of Grafting*, pp. 207–213. F. Albert and P. B. Medawar, eds. Springfield: Charles C Thomas, Publisher.

VAN BEKKUM, D. W., Vos, O., and WEYZEN, W. W. H. 1959. The pathogenesis of the secondary disease following foreign bone marrow transplantation in irradiated mice. *In: Biological Problems of Grafting*, pp. 292–305. F. Albert, and P. B. Medawar, eds. Springfield: Charles C Thomas, Publisher.

WEAVER, J. M., ALGIRE, G. H., and PREHN, R. T. 1955. The growth of cells *in vivo* in diffusion chambers. II. The role of cells in the destruction of homografts in mice. J. Natl. Cancer Inst., 15: 1737–1767.

WINN, H. J. 1960a. Immune mechanisms in homotransplantation. I. The role of serum antibody and complement in the neutralization of lymphoma cells. J. Immunol., 84: 530–538.

WINN, H. J. 1960b. The immune response and the homograft reaction. Natl. Cancer Inst. Monogr., 2: 113–138.

WINN, H. J. 1962. The participation of complement in isoimmune reactions. Ann. N. Y. Acad. Sci., 101: 23–44.

WOLSTENHOLME, G. E. W., and CAMERON, M. P. (eds.). 1962. Transplantation. Boston: Little, Brown & Company. 426 pp.

WOLSTENHOLME, G. E. W., and O'CONNOR, M. (eds.). 1960. Cellular aspects of immunity. Boston: Little, Brown & Company. 495 pp.

WOODRUFF, M. F. A. 1960. The transplantation of tissues and organs. Springfield: Charles C Thomas, Publisher. 777 pp.

WOODRUFF, M. F. A., and SIMPSON, L. O. 1955. Induction of tolerance to skin homografts in rats by injection of cells from the prospective donor soon after birth. Brit. J. Exptl. Pathol., 36: 494–499.

ZILBER, L. A. 1958. Specific tumor antigens. Advan. Cancer Res., 5: 291–329.

Author Index

Bold-face page references refer to bibliographic citations.

Del Vecchio, P. R., 213, **243**
de Margerie-Hottinguer, H., 102, **116**
DeMars, R., 159, 184, 253, **297**
Demerec, M., 23, **59**, 74, 75, 87, **115**, 308, 309, 310, 363, **364**
Demerec, Z. E., 87, **115**
Denis, H., 424, **434**
de Oca, H. M., 139, **185**
DeOme, K. B., 41, **59**, **65**
Deringer, M. K., 488, **504**
de Serres, F. J., 356, **364**
Deutsch, H. F., 274, **297**
Devlin, T. M., 268, **305**
Dewey, V. C., 317, **368**
DeWitt, S. H., 213, **243**
Dhaliwal, S. S., 493, **507**
Diamond, L. K., 318, **365**
Di Berardino, M. A., 17, **58**, 427, **435**
Dieu, H., 461, **509**
DiMayorca, G. A., 412, **435**
Dingle, J. T., 338, **364**
DiPaolo, J. A., 204, **243**
Dixon, F. J., Jr., 431, **441**
Djordjevic, B., 349, 357, **364**
Doak, S. M. A., 475, 476, **512**
Dokos, J. M., 164, **186**
Doljanski, L., 156, **184**, 401, 402, **438**, **444**
Donohue, D. R., 332, **361**
Dorstewitz, E. L., 152, 176, **183**
Dougherty, R. M., 139, **185**
Dougherty, T. F., 335, 338, **366**
Drabble, W. T., 308, **365**
Dresser, D. W., 480, **507**
Driesch, H., 3, 5, **59**
Drolet, B. P., 164, **186**
Dubbs, D. R., 350, **368**
Dube, O. L., 465, 467, **514**
Dubos, R. J., 397, **435**
Duchesne, E. M., 380, 382, 383, 417, **442**
Dulbecco, R., 129, 134, **185**, 189, 221, 230, **250**, 359, 374, 400, 402, 407, 411, 412, 413, 416, 417, 418, 419, 420, 422, **435**, **444**, **445**
Dunn, L. C., 22, **59**
Dunn, T. B., 33, 39, 45, 46, **59**, **61**, 327, 369, 413, **442**
Dunnebacke, T. H., 173, **195**
Dupree, L. T., 133, **192**, 289, **297**, **304**, 399, 413, **442**, **443**
Duran-Reynals, F., 40, 43, **59**
Duryee, W. R., 426, **435**
Duschinsky, R., 318, **365**
Dwight, S. A., 388, 389, **434**

Eagle, H., 124, 131, 150, 171, **184**, **185**, **188**, 252, 253, 255, 256, 257, 258, 259, 260, 261, 262, 263, 265, 266, 267, 272, 273, 278, 279, 280, 281, 284, 289, 294, 295, 296, **297**, **298**, **302**, **303**, **304**
Eakin, R. M., 450, 452, **509**
Earle, W. R., 127, 128, 130, 132, 133, 134, 150, 169, **185**, 188, 192, 194, 206, 215, 229, **242**, **249**, 287, 288, 289, 290, **296**, **297**, **299**, **302**, **304**, 376, 377, 378, 379, 380, 381, 382, 383, 384, 386, 392, 393, 394, 395, 396, 397, 398, 399, 403, 413, 417, **433**, **435**, **436**, **440**, **442**, **443**, **445**
Easton, J. M., 272, 273, **298**
Easty, D. M., 275, **299**
Easty, G. C., 275, **299**
Ebeling, A. H., 156, 162, 163, **183**, **185**
Ebert, J. D., 447, **507**
Ebner, K. E., 153, 154, **185**
Eddy, B. E., 42, 43, **66**, 220, **243**, 401, 411, 412, 421, **435**, **436**, **438**, **444**
Edwards, G. A., 173, **186**
Ehrensvärd, G., 258, **299**
Ehrlich, P., 307, **365**
Eichwald, E. J., 457, 458, **507**
Eirich, F. R., 36, **64**
Eisen, H. N., 463, **511**
Elion, G. B., 317, 328, **363**, **365**, 469, **510**
Elkind, M. M., 237, **247**
Ellis, D. B., 328, **365**
Ellison, S. A., 220, **244**
Elsdale, T. R., 13, 14, 16, **59**, **61**
Ely, J. O., 204, **243**
Enders, J. F., 221, **249**, 401, 420, **443**
Englesberg, E., 88, **116**
Ephrussi, B., 100, 101, 102, 103, 104, 105, 106, **114**, **116**, **120**, 162, **185**, 230, **243**, **249**, 353, **365**
Ephrussi-Taylor, H., 85, 86, **116**
Erikson, R. L., 357, **365**
Escher, G. C., 318, **370**
Evans, H. J., 208, **243**
Evans, V. J., 128, 130, 139, 150, 169, **185**, 192, 194, 287, 288, 289, 290, **296**, **297**, **299**, **302**, **304**, 381, 383, 386, 397, 399, **436**, **440**, **443**, **445**

Fankhauser, G., 5, **59**, 217, **243**
Fanshier, L., 405, 406, **442**
Farber, S., 318, **365**
Fardon, J., 43, **59**
Fargie, B., 94, **117**
Fawcett, D. W., 426, **436**
Featherstone, R. M., 157, **183**
Febvre, H. L., 412, **433**

Subject Index

Ac-Ds model, maize, 30–31, 83–84
Acatalasia, 181
Acetabularia, 424
Actinomycin D, 423–424
Activator element (Ac), 31
Adoptively acquired immunity, 454–455, 467
Alkaline phosphatase
  clonal differences in activity, 158
  induction in cell cultures, 158
  in resistance to deoxyglucose, 333
Amino acids (see Cell nutrition)
Amoeba
  nuclear transplantation, 110–113
  streptomycin sensitivity, 315
Analogues (see Resistance)
Anaplasia
  definition, 45
  evolution of enzyme patterns, 47–49
  morphological changes, 45–46
Aneuploidy
  definition, 198–199
  development of, 173–176, 216–217
  induced by viruses, 220–222
  in permanent cell strains, 201–202
  and transplantability, tumors, 486–487
  in tumors, 200–201
  See also Chromosome changes
Antigenic changes in tumors
  Barrett-Deringer effect, 488–490
  chromosomal variation and, 486–487, 494
  immunity to primary neoplasms and, 501–502
  from increased gene dosage, 494
  induced by polyoma virus, 497–500
  isoantigenic variation, 486–487, 490–495
  in leukemic cells, 496–497
  loss of host specificity, 485–488
  mutagens and, 493–494
  produced by chemical carcinogens, 500–503
  selection for, 490–491
  from somatic crossing over, 494
  variation in antigenic output, 487–488

  See also Isoantigens
Antimetabolites (see Drug resistance; Resistance)
Antipurines, 317–318
Antipyrimidines, 318
Ascites tumors
  chromosome patterns, 200–202
  clones of, 224
  differing in ploidy, 235
  drug resistance, 330–331, 336
  growth characteristics, 50–51
  transformations of, 51–56
Aspergillus, 25, 28
Autografts, 448
Auxotrophic bacteria, 86, 89
Azaserine, 318, 320, 325

ß-galactosidase (see Enzyme induction in bacteria)
Bacteriophage
  characteristics of, 70
  lysogeny and, 95–99
  resistance to, 70–72
  RNA-containing, 408
  temperate, 88, 95–99
  transduction by, 86–89
Bar eye, 28
Barrett-Deringer effect, 488–490
Benzpyrene
  as carcinogen, 34, 501
  cellular transformations by, 384–385
  formula, 35
Binucleate cells, 215
Bromodeoxyuridine, 346, 349–350, 357

C-mitosis, 215
Carbohydrates (see Cell nutrition)
Carcinogenesis in animals
  by chemical agents, 34–37: aromatic amines, 35–36; azo dyes, 35; coal tar, 34; polycyclic hydrocarbons, 34–35
  cocarcinogens, 38
  depression of immune responses, 503
  epigenetic concepts, 422–432
  genetic factors, 38–39

535

humoral damage and, 483–484
mechanisms of, 482–484
Enzymatic patterns
clonal variation, 399–400
dedifferentiation *in vitro*, 152–154
of drug-resistant cells, 328–337
as genetic markers, 181
in permanent cell strains, 153
of petites, yeast, 101–102
of primary cultures, 152–153
of tumors, 47–49, 327–337
Enzyme induction in bacteria, 78–84
cytoplasmic repressors, 78, 82–83
following conjugation, 95
formation of ß-galactosidase, 78–84
genetic control of, 82–83
kinetics of, 79–80
model resembling mutation, 81
modification by fluorouracil, 353
of penicillinase, 78–79
by substrate analogues, 79–81
Enzyme induction in cell cultures
alkaline phosphatase, 158, 333
arginase, 157–158
cholinesterase, 156–157
drug resistance and, 308, 333
Epigenetic variation
basis for chromosome changes, 221–223
in carcinogenesis, 422–432
concept of, 1–2
dedifferentiation and, 161–162
in drug resistance, 353–354
in microorganisms, 100–113
in morphogenesis, 2–10
phenocopies, 20–21
See also Modulation; Mutation
Episomes
in bacteria, 95–99
colicinogenic factor, 98
concept of, 95, 98–99
controlling elements as, 99
in morphogenesis, 99
and multiple drug resistance, 311–312
sex (*F*) factor, 90–95, 98
temperate phages, 88, 95–99
See also Lysogeny
Epithelium, in culture, 126
Escherichia coli
colicins, 98
conjugation, 89–95
drug resistance, 308–311, 330
enzyme induction, 78–84
episomes, 95–99
fluctuation test, 70–72
galactose mutants, 80–81

and lysogeny, 96
periodic selection, 75–77
phage resistance, 70–72
streptomycin dependence, 311
transduction, 88
Established strains, 177
See also Permanent cell strains; Primary cell strains
Euchromatin, 29
Euploid cells, 198–199
Explant cultures, 123–127
Extracellular material (ECM), 147–148
Extrachromosomal inheritance (*see* Nonchromosomal inheritance)

Feeder systems
carbon dioxide and, 138
for clonal isolations, 134–135
mechanism of action, 137–138
for monolayers, 134–138
of mouse embryo cells, 137–138, 173–176
in suspension cultures, 280, 295
F factor (*see* Sex factor)
Ferritin, 272–273
Fetuin, 274–275
Fibroblasts, characteristics of, 125–127
Fluctuation test
in bacteria, 70–72
in cell cultures, 340
and drug resistance: *Chlamydomonas*, 313–314; tumors, 322–324
Fluorescent antibodies (*see* Immunofluorescence)
Fluorinated pyrimidines, 318, 353
Folic acid analogues, 318–319
Folic acid reductase, 331–333, 349
Fraudulent nucleotides, 328
Freezing of cells, 138–140
glycerol pretreatment, 138–139
by liquid nitrogen, 139
mechanisms of injury, 140
protection by additives, 139–140
techniques for, 139

Galactosemia, 181
Genetic drift, 394, 500
Genetic particulates
bacteriophage, 70–72, 86–89, 95–99
controlling elements, 30–31, 83–84
cytoplasmic: *Chlamydomonas*, 313–315; in yeast, 103–106
episomes, 95–99
heterochromatin, 29–31
kappa factor, *Paramecium*, 100, 162, 424
metagons, *Paramecium*, 424

M